GREAT BOOKS OF THE WESTERN WORLD

GREAT BOOKS
OF THE WESTERN WORLD

ROBERT MAYNARD HUTCHINS, *EDITOR IN CHIEF*

33.

PASCAL

THE PROVINCIAL LETTERS
PENSÉES
SCIENTIFIC TREATISES

BY BLAISE PASCAL

WILLIAM BENTON, *Publisher*

ENCYCLOPÆDIA BRITANNICA, INC.

CHICAGO · LONDON · TORONTO

The text and annotations of *Pensées*, translated
by W. F. Trotter, in this edition are derived from the edition in
Everyman's Library by permission of J. M. DENT & SONS LTD., London,
and E. P. DUTTON & CO., INC., New York.

THE UNIVERSITY OF CHICAGO

The Great Books
is published with the editorial advice of the faculties
of The University of Chicago

BIOGRAPHICAL NOTE
BLAISE PASCAL, 1623–1662

PASCAL was born at Clermont Ferrand in Auvergne, June 19, 1623. His father, Étienne Pascal, had been trained as a lawyer in Paris and held the post of President of the Court of Aids at Clermont. His mother, the pious Antoinette Bégon, died in 1626, leaving her husband to care for Gilberte, Blaise, and the baby, Jacqueline.

In 1631 Étienne Pascal sold his post, moved to Paris, and set about the education of his son. His method, according to Gilberte, "was to keep the child always in advance of his work." The boy was first to learn to think for himself, stimulated by the observations, questions, and conversation of his father. Later, after he had mastered Greek and Latin, he was to be allowed to study geometry. But at the age of twelve the boy began geometry by himself and is supposed to have achieved the equivalent of Euclid's first thirty-two theorems before his father noticed his precocity.

The elder Pascal always associated with men of eminence in science and the arts, and in his company the young Pascal was introduced to Father Mersenne's circle and became acquainted with Desargues, Fermat, and Roberval. Following a geometrical method of Desargues, Pascal completed before he was sixteen a work on conic sections that was widely circulated, though never published, which, according to his own account, embraced the work of Apollonius. Though his health was seriously affected by the intensity of his intellectual work, a few years later he achieved a still greater reputation by his invention of the first calculating machine.

Although the Pascal family had been regular and respectful in their religious practice, religion was not especially important in their lives until 1646 when they became acquainted with Jansenism. Pascal, then only twenty-three, had his attention directed to religious and theological questions, and he seems to have been influential in converting his whole family to the Jansenist version of Catholicism. His sister, Jacqueline, decided to renounce the world, and on the death of her father in 1651 she entered the Jansenist convent of Port Royal.

Pascal himself continued his scientific and mathematical researches. The same year that he began to think about Jansenism he performed his variations on Torricelli's experiment, which resulted in his *New Experiments concerning the Vacuum* (1647). This in turn led to his investigation of the action of fluids under pressure of air which established his reputation as one of the founders of hydrodynamics. By 1651 he had apparently completed most of the work for his *Great Experiment concerning the Equilibrium of Fluids*, although it was not published until 1663. Upon the death of his father, he laid aside to some extent his scientific researches, frequented polite society with his friends, the young Duc de Roannez and the Chevalier de Méré, shared their interests, and read Epictetus and Montaigne. Puzzling over a problem posed by De Méré concerning the division of stakes in a game of chance, he began to investigate the theory of probability. His results appeared in 1654 in the correspondence with Fermat and in the *Treatise on the Arithmetical Triangle*.

By 1654 Pascal felt "an extreme aversion for the beguilements of the world." The contrast between his life and that of Jacqueline, whom he visited the same year at Port Royal, intensified his dissatisfaction. His growing decision to retire from the world was confirmed on November 23, 1654, when he experienced what is known as his "second conversion." The written memorial of that experience, which he wore thereafter as a kind of amulet, records that from ten-thirty until twelve-thirty that night he knew "the God of Abraham, God of Isaac, God of Jacob, not of philosophers and scientists," and that he resolved "total submission to Jesus Christ and to my director." The following January he went on retreat at Port Royal, and, although he did not actually become one of its famous solitaries, he was henceforth identified with its interests.

Pascal's talents were soon employed by the Jansenists. In 1655 Antoine Arnauld, the official theologian of Port Royal, was condemned by the Sorbonne, and it was considered expedient to enlist public opinion for the Jansenists against their Jesuit adversaries. Perhaps at the suggestion of Arnauld himself, Pascal began his *Provincial Letters*, which, from January, 1656 to April, 1657, captivated Paris by their style as well as their polemic. He was also asked to work upon a manual of geometry for use in the Port Royal schools, and it is probably in connection with this that he wrote his essay *On Geometrical Demonstration*.

Afflicted with ill-health since infancy, Pascal's suffering had become so acute in 1658 that any sustained effort became increasingly difficult. In one attempt to distract his mind from a persistent toothache, he turned to the problem of the cycloid, which had occupied his friend, Roberval, as well as many other mathematicians of the time. Before publishing his results, he proposed his theorems for public competition. Wallis and Lalouère among others accepted the challenge, but only Pascal was able to provide the complete solution.

Although he considered geometry the "highest exercise of the mind," as he wrote Fermat, "it is only a trade, . . . and I am steeped in studies so far from that mentality, that scarcely do I remember that there is any such." After the cure of his niece at Port Royal in 1656, which was known as the Miracle of the Holy Thorn, Pascal began reading and collecting material for what he planned to be an *Apology for the Christian Religion*. He put down his thoughts "upon the first scrap of paper that came to hand . . . a few words and very often parts of words only." These fragments, found after his death, compose what has come to be known as his *Pensées*, which were first edited by the Jansenists in 1670 and constantly re-edited thereafter.

As death approached, Pascal's life became more austere. He gave his possessions to the poor and continually strove for complete detachment from those he loved. "It is unjust that anyone should attach himself to me . . . for I am not an end and aim of anyone," he wrote on a paper he kept always about him to fix his resolve. In June, 1662, he gave shelter to a poor family which developed small-pox. Rather than dispossess them, he moved to the house of Gilberte, where he was seized with a violent illness which lingered for two months. He died August 19, at the age of thirty-nine.

GENERAL CONTENTS

CONTENTS
THE PROVINCIAL LETTERS

THE PROVINCIAL LETTERS

LETTER I

Paris, *January* 23, 1656

Sir,

We were entirely mistaken. It was only yesterday that I was undeceived. Until that time I had laboured under the impression that the disputes in the Sorbonne were vastly important, and deeply affected the interests of religion. The frequent convocations of an assembly so illustrious as that of the Theological Faculty of Paris, attended by so many extraordinary and unprecedented circumstances, led one to form such high expectations that it was impossible to help coming to the conclusion that the subject was most extraordinary. You will be greatly surprised, however, when you learn from the following account the issue of this grand demonstration, which, having made myself perfectly master of the subject, I shall be able to tell you in very few words.

Two questions, then, were brought under examination; the one a question of fact, the other a question of right.

The question of fact consisted in ascertaining whether M. Arnauld was guilty of presumption, for having asserted in his second letter that he had carefully perused the book of Jansenius, and that he had not discovered the propositions condemned by the late pope; but that, nevertheless, as he condemned these propositions wherever they might occur, he condemned them in Jansenius, if they were really contained in that work.

The question here was, if he could, without presumption, entertain a doubt that these propositions were in Jansenius, after the bishops had declared that they were.

The matter having been brought before the Sorbonne, seventy-one doctors undertook his defence, maintaining that the only reply he could possibly give to the demands made upon him in so many publications, calling on him to say if he held that these propositions were in that book, was that he had not been able to find them, but that if they were in the book, he condemned them in the book.

Some even went a step farther and protested that, after all the search they had made into the book, they had never stumbled upon these propositions, and that they had, on the contrary, found sentiments entirely at variance with them. They then earnestly begged that, if any doctor present had discovered them, he would have the goodness to point them out; adding that what was so easy could not reasonably be refused, as this would be the surest way to silence the whole of them, M. Arnauld included; but this proposal has been uniformly declined. So much for the one side.

1

On the other side are eighty secular doctors and some forty mendicant friars, who have condemned M. Arnauld's proposition, without choosing to examine whether he has spoken truly or falsely—who, in fact, have declared that they have nothing to do with the veracity of his proposition, but simply with its temerity.

Besides these, there were fifteen who were not in favor of the censure, and who are called Neutrals.

Such was the issue of the question of fact, regarding which, I must say, I give myself very little concern. It does not affect my conscience in the least whether M. Arnauld is presumptuous or the reverse; and should I be tempted, from curiosity, to ascertain whether these propositions are contained in Jansenius, his book is neither so very rare nor so very large as to hinder me from reading it over from beginning to end, for my own satisfaction, without consulting the Sorbonne on the matter.

Were it not, however, for the dread of being presumptuous myself, I really think that I would be disposed to adopt the opinion which has been formed by the most of my acquaintances, who, though they have believed hitherto on common report that the propositions were in Jansenius, begin now to suspect the contrary, owing to this strange refusal to point them out—a refusal the more extraordinary to me as I have not yet met with a single individual who can say that he has discovered them in that work. I am afraid, therefore, that this censure will do more harm than good, and that the impression which it will leave on the minds of all who know its history will be just the reverse of the conclusion that has been come to. The truth is the world has become sceptical of late and will not believe things till it sees them. But, as I said before, this point is of very little moment, as it has no concern with religion.

The question of right, from its affecting the faith, appears much more important, and, accordingly, I took particular pains in examining it. You will be relieved, however, to find that it is of as little consequence as the former.

The point of dispute here was an assertion of M. Arnauld's in the same letter, to the effect "that the grace, without which we can do nothing, was wanting to St. Peter at his fall." You and I supposed that the controversy here would turn upon the great principles of grace; such as whether grace is given to all men? Or if it is efficacious of itself? But we were quite mistaken. You must know I have become a great theologian within this short time; and now for the proofs of it!

To ascertain the matter with certainty, I repaired to my neighbor, M. N——, doctor of Navarre, who, as you are aware, is one of the keenest opponents of the Jansenists, and, my curiosity having made me almost as keen as himself, I asked him if they would not formally decide at once that "grace is given to all men," and thus set the question at rest. But he gave me a sore rebuff and told me that that was not the point; that there were some of his party who held that grace was not given to all; that the examiners themselves had declared, in a full assembly of the Sorbonne, that that opinion was *problematical;* and that he himself held the same sentiment, which he confirmed by quoting to me what he called that celebrated passage of St. Augustine: "We know that grace is not given to all men."

I apologized for having misapprehended his sentiment and requested him to say if they would not at least condemn that other opinion of the Jansenists which is making so much noise: "That grace is efficacious of itself, and invincibly determines our will to what is good." But in this second query I was equally unfortunate. "You know nothing about the matter," he said; "that is not a heresy—it is an orthodox opinion; all the Thomists maintain it; and I myself have defended it in my Sorbonic thesis."

I did not venture again to propose my doubts, and yet I was as far as ever from understanding where the difficulty lay; so, at last, in order to get at it, I begged him to tell me where, then, lay the heresy of M. Arnauld's proposition. "It lies here," said he, "that he does not acknowledge that the righteous have the power of obeying the commandments of God, in the manner in which we understand it."

On receiving this piece of information, I took my leave of him; and, quite proud at having discovered the knot of the question, I sought M. N——, who is gradually getting better and was sufficiently recovered to conduct me to the house of his brother-in-law, who is a Jansenist, if ever there was one, but a very good man notwithstanding. Thinking to insure myself a better reception, I pretended to be very high on what I took to be his side, and said: "Is it possible that the Sorbonne has introduced into the Church such an error as this, 'that all the righteous have always the power of obeying the commandments of God?'"

"What say you?" replied the doctor. "Call you that an error—a sentiment so Catholic that none but Lutherans and Calvinists impugn it?"

"Indeed!" said I, surprised in my turn; "so you are not of their opinion?"

"No," he replied; "we anathematize it as heretical and impious."

Confounded by this reply, I soon discovered that I had overacted the Jansenist, as I had formerly overdone the Molinist. But, not being sure if I had rightly understood him, I requested him to tell me frankly if he held "that the righteous have always a real power to observe the divine precepts?" Upon this, the good man got warm (but it was with a holy zeal) and protested that he would not disguise his sentiments on any consideration—that such was, indeed, his belief, and that he and all his party would defend it to the death, as the pure doctrine of St. Thomas, and of St. Augustine their master.

This was spoken so seriously as to leave me no room for doubt; and under this impression I returned to my first doctor and said to him, with an air of great satisfaction, that I was sure there would be peace in the Sorbonne very soon; that the Jansenists were quite at one with them in reference to the power of the righteous to obey the commandments of God; that I could pledge my word for them and could make them seal it with their blood.

"Hold there!" said he. "One must be a theologian to see the point of this question. The difference between us is so subtle that it is with some difficulty we can discern it ourselves—you will find it rather too much for your powers of comprehension. Content yourself, then, with knowing that it is very true the Jansenists will tell you that all the righteous have always the power of obeying the commandments; that is not the point in dispute between us; but mark you, they will not tell you that that power is *proximate*. That is the point."

This was a new and unknown word to me. Up to this moment I had managed to understand matters, but that term involved me in obscurity; and I verily believe that it has been invented for no other purpose than to mystify. I requested him to give me an explanation of it, but he made a mystery of it, and sent me back, without any further satisfaction, to demand of the Jansenists if they would admit this *proximate power*. Having charged my memory with the phrase (as to my understanding, that was out of the question), I hastened with all possible expedition, fearing that I might forget it, to my Jansenist friend and accosted him, immediately after our first salutations, with: "Tell me, pray, if you admit *the proximate power?*" He smiled, and replied, coldly: "Tell me yourself in what sense you understand it, and I may then inform you what I think of it." As my knowledge did not extend quite so far, I was at a loss what reply to make; and yet, rather than lose the object of my visit, I said at random: "Why, I understand it in the sense of the Molinists." "To which of the Molinists do you refer me?" replied he, with the utmost coolness. I referred him to the whole of them together, as forming one body, and animated by one spirit.

"You know very little about the matter," returned he. "So far are they from being united in sentiment that some of them are diametrically opposed to each other. But, being all united in the design to ruin M. Arnauld, they have resolved to agree on this term *proximate*, which both parties might use indiscriminately, though they understand it diversely, that thus, by a similarity of language and an apparent conformity, they may form a large body and get up a majority to crush him with the greater certainty."

This reply filled me with amazement; but, without imbibing these impressions of the malicious designs of the Molinists, which I am unwilling to believe on his word, and with which I have no concern, I set myself simply to ascertain the various senses which they give to that mysterious word *proximate*. "I would enlighten you on the subject with all my heart," he said; "but you would discover in it such a mass of contrariety and contradiction that you would hardly believe me. You would suspect me. To make sure of the matter, you had better learn it from some of themselves; and I shall give you some of their addresses. You have only to make a separate visit to one called M. le Moine and to Father Nicolai."

"I have no acquaintance with any of these persons," said I.

"Let me see, then," he replied, "if you know any of those whom I shall name to you; they all agree in sentiment with M. le Moine."

I happened, in fact, to know some of them.

"Well, let us see if you are acquainted with any of the Dominicans whom they call the 'New Thomists,' for they are all the same with Father Nicolai."

I knew some of them also whom he named; and, resolved to profit by this council and to investigate the matter, I took my leave of him and went immediately to one of the disciples of M. le Moine. I begged him to inform me what it was to have the *proximate power* of doing a thing.

"It is easy to tell you that," he replied; "it is merely to have all that is necessary for doing it in such a manner that nothing is wanting to performance."

"And so," said I, "to have the proximate power of crossing a river, for example, is to have a boat, boatmen, oars, and all the rest, so that nothing is wanting?"

"Exactly so," said the monk.

"And to have the proximate power of *seeing*," continued I, "must be to have good eyes and the light of day; for a person with good sight in the dark would not have the proximate power of seeing, according to you, as he would want the light, without which one cannot see?"

"Precisely," said he.

"And consequently," returned I, "when you say that all the righteous have the proximate power of observing the commandments of God, you mean that they have always all the grace necessary for observing them, so that nothing is wanting to them on the part of God."

"Stay there," he replied; "they have always all that is necessary for observing the commandments, or at least for asking it of God."

"I understand you," said I; "they have all that is necessary for praying to God to assist them, without requiring any new grace from God to enable them to pray."

"You have it now," he rejoined.

"But is it not necessary that they have an efficacious grace, in order to pray to God?"

"No," said he; "not according to M. le Moine."

To lose no time, I went to the Jacobins, and requested an interview with some whom I knew to be New Thomists, and I begged them to tell me what *proximate power* was. "Is it not," said I, "that power to which nothing is wanting in order to act?"

"No," said they.

"Indeed! fathers," said I; "if anything is wanting to that power, do you call it *proximate?* Would you say, for instance, that a man in the night-time, and without any light, had the proximate power of seeing?"

"Yes, indeed, he would have it, in our opinion, if he is not blind."

"I grant that," said I; "but M. le Moine understands it in a different manner."

"Very true," they replied; "but so it is that we understand it."

"I have no objections to that," I said; "for I never quarrel about a name, provided I am apprised of the sense in which it is understood. But I perceive from this that, when you speak of the righteous having always the proximate power of praying to God, you understand that they require another supply for praying, without which they will never pray."

"Most excellent!" exclaimed the good fathers, embracing me; "exactly the thing; for they must have, besides, an efficacious grace bestowed upon all, and which determines their wills to pray; and it is heresy to deny the necessity of that efficacious grace in order to pray."

"Most excellent!" cried I, in return; "but, according to you, the Jansenists are Catholics, and M. le Moine a heretic; for the Jansenists maintain that, while the righteous have power to pray, they require nevertheless an efficacious grace; and this is what you approve. M. le Moine, again, maintains that the righteous may pray without efficacious grace; and this is what you condemn."

"Ay," said they; "but M. le Moine calls that power *proximate power.*"

"How now! fathers," I exclaimed; "this is merely playing with words, to say that you are agreed as to the common terms which you employ, while you differ with them as to the sense of these terms."

The fathers made no reply; and at this juncture, who should come in but my old friend, the disciple of M. le Moine! I regarded this at the time as an extraordinary piece of good fortune; but I have discovered since then that such meetings are not rare—that, in fact, they are constantly mixing in each other's society.

"I know a man," said I, addressing myself to M. le Moine's disciple, "who holds that all the righteous have always the power of praying to God, but that, notwithstanding this, they will never pray without an efficacious grace which determines them, and which God does not always give to all the righteous. Is he a heretic?"

"Stay," said the doctor; "you might take me by surprise. Let us go cautiously to work. *Distinguo*. If he call that power *proximate power*, he will be a Thomist, and therefore a Catholic; if not, he will be a Jansenist and, therefore, a heretic."

"He calls it neither *proximate* nor *non-proximate*," said I.

"Then he is a heretic," quoth he; "I refer you to these good fathers if he is not."

I did not appeal to them as judges, for they had already nodded assent; but I said to them: "He refuses to admit that word *proximate*, because he can meet with nobody who will explain it to him."

Upon this one of the fathers was on the point of offering his definition of the term, when he was interrupted by M. le Moine's disciple, who said to him: "Do you mean, then, to renew our broils? Have we not agreed not to explain that word *proximate*, but to use it on both sides without saying what it signifies?" To this the Jacobin gave his assent.

I was thus let into the whole secret of their plot; and, rising to take my leave of them, I remarked: "Indeed, fathers, I am much afraid this is nothing better than pure chicanery; and, whatever may be the result of your convocations, I venture to predict that, though the censure should pass, peace will not be established. For though it should be decided that the syllables of that word *proximate* should be pronounced, who does not see that, the meaning not being explained, each of you will be disposed to claim the victory? The Jacobins will contend that the word is to be understood in their sense; M. le Moine will insist that it must be taken in his; and thus there will be more wrangling about the explanation of the word than about its introduction. For, after all, there would be no great danger in adopting it without any sense, seeing it is through the sense only that it can do any harm. But it would be unworthy of the Sorbonne and of theology to employ equivocal and captious terms without giving any explanation of them. In short, fathers, tell me, I entreat you, for the last time, what is necessary to be believed in order to be a good Catholic?"

"You must say," they all vociferated simultaneously, "that all the righteous have the *proximate power*, abstracting from it all sense—from the sense of the Thomists and the sense of other divines."

"That is to say," I replied, in taking leave of them, "that I must pronounce that word to avoid being the heretic of a name. For, pray, is this a Scripture word?" "No," said they. "Is it a word of the Fathers, the Councils, or the Popes?" "No." "Is the word, then, used by St. Thomas?" "No." "What necessity, therefore, is there for using it since it has neither the authority of others nor any sense of itself?" "You are an opinionative fellow," said they; "but you shall say it, or you shall be a heretic, and M. Arnauld into the bargain; for we are the majority, and, should it be necessary, we can bring a sufficient number of Cordeliers into the field to carry the day."

On hearing this solid argument, I took my leave of them, to write you the foregoing account of my interview, from which you will perceive that the following points remain undisputed and uncondemned by either party. *First*, That grace is not given to all men. *Second*, That all the righteous have always the power of obeying the divine commandments. *Third*, That they require, nevertheless, in order to obey them, and even to pray, an efficacious grace, which invincibly determines their will. *Fourth*, That this efficacious grace is not always granted to all the righteous, and that it depends on the pure mercy of God. So that, after all, the truth is safe, and nothing runs any risk but that word without the sense, *proximate*.

Happy the people who are ignorant of its existence! happy those who lived before it was born! for I see no help for it, unless the gentlemen of the Acadamy, by an act of absolute authority, banish that barbarous term, which causes so many divisions, from beyond the precincts of the Sorbonne. Unless this be done, the censure appears certain; but I can easily see that it will do no other harm than diminish the credit of the Sorbonne, and deprive it of that authority which is so necessary to it on other occasions.

Meanwhile, I leave you at perfect liberty to hold by the word *proximate* or not, just as you please; for I love you too much to persecute you under that pretext. If this account is not displeasing to you, I shall continue to apprise you of all that happens. I am, &c.

LETTER II

Paris, *January* 29, 1656

SIR,

Just as I had sealed up my last letter, I received a visit from our old friend M. N——. Nothing could have happened more luckily for my curiosity; for he is thoroughly informed in the questions of the day and is completely in the secret of the Jesuits, at whose houses, including those of their leading men, he is a constant visitor. After having talked over the business which brought him to my house, I asked him to state, in a few words, what were the points in dispute between the two parties.

He immediately complied, and informed me that the principal points were two —the *first* about the *proximate power*, and the *second* about *sufficient grace*. I have enlightened you on the first of these points in my former letter and shall now speak of the second.

In one word, then, I found that their difference about sufficient grace may be defined thus: The Jesuits maintain that there is a grace given generally to all men, subject in such a way to free-will that the will renders it efficacious or inefficacious at its pleasure, without any additional aid from God and without wanting anything on his part in order to act effectively; and hence they term this grace *sufficient*, because it suffices of itself for action. The Jansenists, on the other hand, will not allow that any grace is actually sufficient which is not also efficacious; that is, that all those kinds of grace which do not determine the will to act effectively are insufficient for action; for they hold that a man can never act without *efficacious grace*.

Such are the points in debate between the Jesuits and the Jansenists; and my next object was to ascertain the doctrine of the New Thomists. "It is rather an odd one," he said; "they agree with the Jesuits in admitting a *sufficient grace* given to all men; but they maintain, at the same time, that no man can act with this grace alone, but that, in order to do this, he must receive from God an efficacious grace which really determines his will to the action, and which God does not grant to all men." "So that, according to this doctrine," said I, "this grace is *sufficient* without being sufficient." "Exactly so," he replied; "for if it suffices, there is no need of anything more for acting; and if it does not suffice, why—it is not sufficient."

"But," asked I, "where, then, is the difference between them and the Jansenists?" "They differ in this," he replied, "that the Dominicans have this good qualification, that they do not refuse to say that all men have the *sufficient grace*." "I understand you," returned I; "but they say it without thinking it; for they add that, in order to act, we must have an *efficacious grace which is not given to all;* consequently, if they agree with the Jesuits in the use of a term which has no sense, they differ from them and coincide with the Jansenists in the substance of the thing." "That is very true," said he. "How, then," said I, "are the Jesuits united with them? and why do they not combat them as well as the Jansenists, since they will always find powerful antagonists in these men, who, by maintaining the necessity of the efficacious grace which determines the will, will prevent them from establishing that grace which they hold to be of itself sufficient?"

"The Dominicans are too powerful," he replied, "and the Jesuits are too politic, to come to an open rupture with them. The Society is content with having prevailed on them so far as to admit the name of *sufficient grace*, though they understand it in another sense; by which manœuvre they gain this advantage, that they will make their opinion appear untenable, as soon as they judge it proper to do so. And this will be no difficult matter; for, let it be once granted that all men have the sufficient graces, nothing can be more natural than to conclude that the efficacious grace is not necessary to action—the sufficiency of the general grace precluding the necessity of all others. By saying *sufficient* we express all that is necessary for action; and it will serve little purpose for the Dominicans to exclaim that they attach another sense to the expression; the people, accustomed to the common acceptation of that term, would not even listen to their explanation. Thus the Society gains a sufficient advantage from the expression which has been adopted by the Dominicans, without pressing them any further; and were you but acquainted with what passed under Popes Clement VIII and Paul V, and knew how the Society was thwarted by the Dominicans in the establishment of the sufficient grace, you would not be surprised to find that it avoids embroiling itself in quarrels with them and allows them to hold their own opinion, provided that of the Society is left untouched; and more especially, when the Dominicans countenance its doctrine, by agreeing to employ, on all public occasions, the term *sufficient grace*.

"The Society," he continued, "is quite satisfied with their complaisance. It does not insist on their denying the necessity of efficacious grace, this would be urging them too far. People should not tyrannize over their friends; and the Jesuits have gained quite enough. The world is content with words; few think of searching into the nature of things; and thus the name of *sufficient grace* being adopted on both sides, though in different senses, there is nobody, except the most subtle theologians, who ever dreams of doubting that the thing signified by that word is held by the Jacobins as well as by the Jesuits; and the result will show that these last are not the greatest dupes."

I acknowledged that they were a shrewd class of people, these Jesuits; and, availing myself of his advice, I went straight to the Jacobins, at whose gate I found one of my good friends, a staunch Jansenist (for you must know I have got friends among all parties), who was calling for another monk, different from him whom

I was in search of. I prevailed on him, however, after much entreaty, to accompany me, and asked for one of my New Thomists. He was delighted to see me again. "How now! my dear father," I began, "it seems it is not enough that all men have a *proximate power*, with which they can never act with effect; they must have besides this a *sufficient grace*, with which they can act as little. Is not that the doctrine of your school?" "It is," said the worthy monk; "and I was upholding it this very morning in the Sorbonne. I spoke on the point during my whole half-hour; and, but for the *sand-glass*, I bade fair to have reversed that wicked proverb, now so current in Paris: 'He votes without speaking, like a monk in the Sorbonne.' " "What do you mean by your *half-hour* and your *sand-glass*?" I asked; "do they cut your speeches by a certain measure?" "Yes," said he, "they have done so for some days past." "And do they oblige you to speak for half an hour?" "No; we may speak as little as we please." "But not as much as you please," said I. "O what a capital regulation for the boobies! what a blessed excuse for those who have nothing worth the saying! But, to return to the point, father; this grace given to all men is *sufficient*, is it not?" "Yes," said he. "And yet it has no effect without *efficacious grace*?" "None whatever," he replied. "And all men have the sufficient," continued I, "and all have not the efficacious?" "Exactly," said he. "That is," returned I, "all have enough of grace, and all have not enough of it— that is, this grace suffices, though it does not suffice—that is, it is sufficient in name and insufficient in effect! In good sooth, father, this is particularly subtle doctrine! Have you forgotten, since you retired to the cloister, the meaning attached, in the world you have quitted, to the word *sufficient*? don't you remember that it includes all that is necessary for acting? But no, you cannot have lost all recollection of it; for, to avail myself of an illustration which will come home more vividly to your feelings, let us suppose that you were supplied with no more than two ounces of bread and a glass of water daily, would you be quite pleased with your prior were he to tell you that this would be sufficient to support you, under the pretext that, along with something else, which however, he would not give you, you would have all that would be necessary to support you? How, then can you allow yourselves to say that all men have sufficient grace for acting, while you admit that there is another grace absolutely necessary to acting which all men have not? Is it because this is an unimportant article of belief, and you leave all men at liberty to believe that efficacious grace is necessary or not, as they choose? Is it a matter of indifference to say, that with sufficient grace a man may really act?" "How!" cried the good man; "indifference! it is heresy—formal heresy. The necessity of *efficacious grace* for acting effectively, is a point of *faith*—it is heresy to deny it."

"Where are we now?" I exclaimed; "and which side am I to take here? If I deny the sufficient grace, I am a Jansenist. If I admit it, as the Jesuits do, in the way of denying that efficacious grace is necessary, I shall be a heretic, say you. And if I admit it, as you do, in the way of maintaining the necessity of efficacious grace, I sin against common sense, and am a blockhead, say the Jesuits. What must I do, thus reduced to the inevitable necessity of being a blockhead, a heretic, or a Jansenist? And what a sad pass are matters come to, if there are none but the Jansenists who avoid coming into collision either with the faith or with reason, and who save themselves at once from absurdity and from error!"

My Jansenist friend took this speech as a good omen and already looked upon me as a convert. He said nothing to me, however; but, addressing the monk: "Pray, father," inquired he, "what is the point on which you agree with the Jesuits?" "We agree in this," he replied, "that the Jesuits and we acknowledge the sufficient grace given to all." "But," said the Jansenist, "there are two things in this expression *sufficient grace*—there is the sound, which is only so much breath; and there is the thing which it signifies, which is real and effectual. And, therefore, as you are agreed with the Jesuits in regard to the word *sufficient* and opposed to them as to the sense, it is apparent that you are opposed to them in regard to the substance of that term, and that you only agree with them as to the sound. Is this what you call acting sincerely and cordially?"

"But," said the good man, "what cause have you to complain, since we deceive nobody by this mode of speaking? In our schools we openly teach that we understand it in a manner different from the Jesuits."

"What I complain of," returned my friend, "is, that you do not proclaim it everywhere, that by sufficient grace you understand the grace which is *not* sufficient. You are bound in conscience, by thus altering the sense of the ordinary terms of theology, to tell that, when you admit a sufficient grace in all men, you understand that they have not sufficient grace in effect. All classes of persons in the world understand the word *sufficient* in one and the same sense; the New Thomists alone understand it in another sense. All the women, who form one-half of the world, all courtiers, all military men, all magistrates, all lawyers, merchants, artisans, the whole populace—in short, all sorts of men, except the Dominicans, understand the word *sufficient* to express all that is necessary. Scarcely any one is aware of this singular exception. It is reported over the whole earth, simply that the Dominicans hold that all men have the *sufficient graces*. What other conclusion can be drawn from this, than that they hold that all men have all the graces necessary for action; especially when they are seen joined in interest and intrigue with the Jesuits, who understand the thing in that sense? Is not the uniformity of your expressions, viewed in connection with this union of party, a manifest indication and confirmation of the uniformity of your sentiments?

"The multitude of the faithful inquire of theologians: What is the real condition of human nature since its corruption? St. Augustine and his disciples reply that it has no sufficient grace until God is pleased to bestow it. Next come the Jesuits, and they say that all have the effectually sufficient graces. The Dominicans are consulted on this contrariety of opinion; and what course do they pursue? They unite with the Jesuits; by this coalition they make up a majority; they secede from those who deny these sufficient graces; they declare that all men possess them. Who, on hearing this, would imagine anything else than that they gave their sanction to the opinion of the Jesuits? And then they add that, nevertheless, these said sufficient graces are perfectly useless without the efficacious, which are not given to all!

"Shall I present you with a picture of the Church amidst these conflicting sentiments? I consider her very like a man who, leaving his native country on a journey, is encountered by robbers, who inflict many wounds on him and leave him half dead. He sends for three physicians resident in the neighboring towns. The first, on probing his wounds, pronounces them mortal and assures him that none but God can restore to him his lost powers. The second, coming after the other, chooses to flatter the man—tells him that he has still sufficient strength to reach his home; and, abusing the first physician who opposed his advice, determines upon his ruin. In this dilemma, the poor patient, observing the third medical gentleman at a distance, stretches out his hands to him as the person who should determine the controversy. This practitioner, on examining his wounds, and ascertaining the opinions of the first two doctors, embraces that of the second, and uniting with him, the two combine against the first, and being the stronger party in number drive him from the field in disgrace. From this proceeding, the patient naturally concludes that the last comer is of the same opinion with the second; and, on putting the question to him, he assures him most positively that his strength is sufficient for prosecuting his journey. The wounded man, however, sensible of his own weakness, begs him to explain to him how he considered him sufficient for the journey. 'Because,' replies his adviser, 'you are still in possession of your legs, and legs are the organs which naturally suffice for walking.' 'But,' says the patient, 'have I all the strength necessary to make use of my legs? for, in my present weak condition, it humbly appears to me that they are wholly useless.' 'Certainly you have not,' replies the doctor; 'you will never walk *effectively*, unless God vouchsafes some extraordinary assistance to sustain and conduct you.' 'What!' exclaims the poor man, 'do you not mean to say that I have sufficient strength in me, so as to want for nothing to walk effectively?' 'Very far from it,' returns the physician. 'You must, then,' says the patient, 'be of a different opinion from your companion there about my real condition.' 'I must admit that I am,' replies the other.

"What do you suppose the patient said to this? Why, he complained of the strange conduct and ambiguous terms of this third physician. He censured him for taking part with the second, to whom he was opposed in sentiment, and with whom he had only the semblance of agreement, and for having driven away the first doctor, with whom he in reality agreed; and, after making a trial of his strength, and finding by experience his actual weakness, he sent them both about their business, recalled his first adviser, put himself under his care, and having, by his advice, implored from God the strength of which he confessed his need, obtained the mercy he sought, and, through divine help, reached his house in peace."

The worthy monk was so confounded with this parable that he could not find words to reply. To cheer him up a little, I said to him, in a mild tone: "But after all, my dear father, what made you think of giving the name of *sufficient* to a grace which you say it is a point of faith to believe is, in fact, insufficient?" "It is very easy for you to talk about it," said he. "You are an independent and private man; I am a monk and in a community—cannot you estimate the difference between the two cases? We depend on superiors; they depend on others. They have promised our votes—what would you have to become of me?" We understood the hint; and this brought to our recollection the case of his brother monk, who, for a similar piece of indiscretion, has been exiled to Abbeville.

"But," I resumed, "how comes it about that your community is bound to admit this grace?" "That is another question," he replied. "All that I can tell you is, in one word, that our order has defended, to the utmost of its ability, the doctrine of St. Thomas on efficacious grace. With what ardor did it oppose, from the very commencement, the doctrine of Molina? How did it labor to establish the necessity of the efficacious grace of Jesus Christ? Don't you know what happened under Clement VIII and Paul V, and how, the former having been prevented by death, and the latter hindered by some Italian affairs from publishing his bull, our arms still sleep in the Vatican? But the Jesuits, availing themselves, since the introduction of the heresy of Luther and Calvin, of the scanty light which the people possess for discriminating between the error of these men and the truth of the doctrine of St. Thomas, disseminated their principles with such rapidity and success that they became, ere long, masters of the popular belief; while we, on our part, found ourselves in the predicament of being denounced as Calvinists and treated as the Jansenists are at present, unless we qualified the efficacious grace with, at least, the apparent avowal of a *sufficient*. In this extremity, what better course could we have taken for saving the truth, without losing our own credit, than by admitting the name of sufficient grace, while we denied that it was such in effect? Such is the real history of the case."

This was spoken in such a melancholy tone that I really began to pity the man; not so, however, my companion. "Flatter not yourselves," said he to the monk, "with having saved the truth; had she not found other defenders, in your feeble hands she must have perished. By admitting into the Church the name of her enemy, you have admitted the enemy himself. Names are inseparable from things. If the term *sufficient grace* be once established, it will be vain for you to protest that you understand by it a grace which is *not* sufficient. Your protest will be held inadmissible. Your explanation would be scouted as odious in the world, where men speak more ingenuously about matters of infinitely less moment. The Jesuits will gain a triumph—it will be their grace, which is sufficient in fact, and not yours, which is only so in name, that will pass as established; and the converse of your creed will become an article of faith."

"We will all suffer martyrdom first," cried the father, "rather than consent to the establishment of *sufficient grace in the sense of the Jesuits*. St. Thomas, whom we have sworn to follow even to the death, is diametrically opposed to such doctrine."

To this my friend, who took up the matter more seriously than I did, replied: "Come now, father, your fraternity has received an honor which it sadly abuses. It abandons that grace which was confided to its care, and which has never been abandoned since the creation of the world. That victorious grace, which was waited for by the patriarchs, predicted by the prophets, introduced by Jesus Christ, preached by St. Paul, explained by St. Augustine, the greatest of the fathers, embraced by his followers, confirmed by St. Bernard, the last of the fathers, supported by St. Thomas, the angel of the schools, transmitted by him to your order, maintained by so many of your fathers, and so nobly defended by your monks under Popes Clement and Paul—that efficacious grace, which had been committed as a sacred deposit into your hands, that it might find, in a sacred and everlasting order, a succession of preachers, who might proclaim it to the end of time —is discarded and deserted for interests the most contemptible. It is high time for other hands to arm in its quarrel. It is time for God to raise up intrepid disciples of the Doctor of grace, who, strangers to the entanglements of the world, will serve God for God's sake. Grace may not, indeed, number the Dominicans among her champions, but champions she shall never want; for, by her own almighty energy, she creates them for herself. She demands hearts pure and disengaged; nay, she herself purifies and disengages them from worldly interests, incompatible with the truths of the Gospel. Reflect seriously on this, father; and take care that God does not remove this candlestick from its place, leaving you in darkness and without the crown, as a punishment for the coldness which you manifest to a cause so important to his Church."

He might have gone on in this strain much longer, for he was kindling as he advanced, but I interrupted him by rising to take my leave and said: "Indeed, my dear father, had I any influence in France, I should have it proclaimed, by sound of trumpet: 'BE IT KNOWN TO ALL MEN, *that when the Jacobins* SAY *that sufficient grace is given to all, they* MEAN *that all have not the grace which actually suffices!*' After which, you might say it as often as you please, but not otherwise." And thus ended our visit.

You will perceive, therefore, that we have here a *politic sufficiency* somewhat similar to *proximate power*. Meanwhile I may tell you that it appears to me that both the proximate power and this same sufficient grace may be safely doubted by anybody, provided he is not a Jacobin.

I have just come to learn, when closing my letter, that the censure has passed. But as I do not yet know in what terms it is worded, and as it will not be published till the 15th of February, I shall delay writing you about it till the next post. I am, &c.

REPLY OF THE "PROVINCIAL" TO THE FIRST TWO LETTERS OF HIS FRIEND

February 2, 1656

SIR,

Your two letters have not been confined to me. Everybody has seen them, everybody understands them, and everybody believes them. They are not only in high repute among theologians—they have proved agreeable to men of the world, and intelligible even to the ladies.

In a communication which I lately received from one of the gentlemen of the Academy—one of the most illustrious names in a society of men who are all illustrious—who had seen only your first letter, he writes me as follows: "I only wish that the Sorbonne, which owes so much to the memory of the late cardinal, would acknowledge the jurisdiction of his French Academy. The author of the letter would be satisfied; for, in the capacity of an academician, I would authoritatively condemn, I would banish, I would proscribe—I had almost said exterminate—to the extent of my power, this *proximate power*, which makes so much noise about nothing and without knowing what it would have. The misfortune is that our academic *power* is a very limited and *remote* power. I am sorry for it; and still more sorry that my small power cannot discharge me from my obligations to you," &c.

My next extract is from the pen of a lady, whom I shall not indicate in any way whatever. She writes thus to a female friend who had transmitted to her the first of your letters: "You can have no idea how much I am obliged to you for the letter you sent me—it is so very ingenious, and so nicely written. It narrates, and yet it is not a narrative; it clears up the most intricate and involved of all possible matters; its raillery is exquisite; it enlightens those who know little about the subject and imparts double delight to those who understand it. It is an admirable apology; and, if they would so take it, a delicate and innocent censure. In short, that letter displays so much art, so much spirit, and so much judgment, that I burn with curiosity to know who wrote it," &c.

You too, perhaps, would like to know who the lady is that writes in this style; but you must be content to esteem without knowing her; when you come to know her, your esteem will be greatly enhanced.

Take my word for it, then, and continue your letters; and let the censure come when it may, we are quite prepared for receiving it. These words *proximate power* and *sufficient grace*, with which we are threatened, will frighten us no longer. We have learned from the Jesuits, the Jacobins, and M. le Moine, in how many different ways they may be turned, and how little solidity there is in these new-fangled terms, to give ourselves any trouble about them. Meanwhile, I remain, &c.

LETTER III

Paris, *February* 9, 1658

SIR,

I have just received your letter; and, at the same time, there was brought me a copy of the censure in manuscript. I find that I am as well treated in the former as M. Arnauld is ill treated in the latter. I am afraid there is some extravagance in both cases and that neither of us is sufficiently well known by our judges. Sure I am that, were we better known, M. Arnauld would merit the approval of the Sorbonne, and I the censure of the Academy. Thus our interests are quite at variance with each other. It is his interest to make himself known, to vindicate his innocence; whereas it is mine to remain in the dark, for fear of forfeiting my reputation. Prevented, therefore, from showing my face, I must devolve on you the task of making my acknowledgments to my illustrious admirers, while I undertake that of furnishing you with the news of the censure.

I assure you, sir, it has filled me with astonishment. I expected to find it condemning the most shocking heresy in the world, but your wonder will equal mine, when informed that these alarming preparations, when on the point of producing the grand effect anticipated, have all ended in smoke.

To understand the whole affair in a pleasant way, only recollect, I beseech you, the strange impressions which, for a long time past, we have been taught to form of the Jansenists. Recall to mind the cabals, the factions, the errors, the schisms, the outrages, with which they have been so long charged; the manner in which they have been denounced and vilified from the pulpit and the press; and the degree to which this torrent of abuse, so remarkable for its violence and duration, has swollen of late years, when they have been openly and publicly accused of being not only heretics and schismatics, but apostates and infidels—with "denying the mystery of transubstantiation, and renouncing Jesus Christ and the Gospel."

After having published these startling accusations, it was resolved to examine their writings, in order to pronounce judgement on them. For this purpose the second letter of M. Arnauld, which was reported to be full of the greatest errors, is selected. The examiners appointed are his most open and avowed enemies. They employ all their learning to discover something that they might lay hold upon, and at length they produce one proposition of a doctrinal character, which they exhibit for censure.

What else could any one infer from such proceedings than that this proposition, selected under such remarkable circumstances, would contain the essence of the blackest heresies imaginable. And yet the proposition so entirely agrees with what is clearly and formally expressed in the passages from the fathers quoted by M. Arnauld that I have not met with a single individual who could comprehend the difference between them. Still, however, it might be imagined that there was a very great difference; for the passages from the fathers being unquestionably Catholic, the proposition of M. Arnauld, if heretical, must be widely opposed to them.

Such was the difficulty which the Sorbonne was expected to clear up. All Christendom waited, with wide-opened eyes, to discover, in the censure of these learned doctors, the point of difference which had proved imperceptible to ordinary mortals. Meanwhile M. Arnauld gave in his defences, placing his own proposition and the passages of the fathers from which he had drawn it in parallel columns, so as to make the agreement between them apparent to the most obtuse understandings.

He shows, for example, that St. Augustine says in one passage that "Jesus Christ points out to us, in the person of St. Peter, a righteous man warning us by his fall to avoid presumption." He cites another passage from the same father, in which he says "that God, in order to show us that without grace we can do nothing, left St. Peter without grace." He produces a third, from St. Chrysostom, who says, "that the fall of St. Peter happened, not through any coldness towards Jesus Christ, but because grace failed him; and that he fell, not so much through his own negligence as through the withdrawment of God, as a lesson to the whole Church, that without God we can do nothing." He then gives his own accused proposition, which is as follows: "The fathers point out to us, in the person of St. Peter, a righteous man to whom that grace without which we can do nothing was wanting."

In vain did people attempt to discover how it could possibly be that M. Arnauld's expression differed from those of the fathers as much as the truth from error and faith from heresy. For where was the difference to be found? Could it be in these words: "that the fathers point out to us, in the person of St. Peter, a righteous man"? St. Augustine has said the same thing in so many words. Is it because he says "that grace had failed him"? The same St. Augustine who had said that "St. Peter was a righteous man," says "that he had not had grace on that occasion." Is it, then, for his having said "that without grace we can do nothing"? Why, is not this just what St. Augustine says in the same place, and what St. Chrysostom had said before him, with this difference only, that he expresses it in much stronger language, as when he says "that his fall did not happen through his own coldness or negligence, but through the failure of grace, and the withdrawment of God"?

Such considerations as these kept everybody in a state of breathless suspense to learn in what this diversity could consist, when at length, after a great many meetings, this famous and long-looked-for censure made its appearance. But, alas! it has sadly baulked our expectation. Whether it be that the Molinist doctors would not condescend so far as to enlighten us on the point, or for some other mysterious reason, the fact is they have done nothing more than pronounce these words: "This proposition is rash, impious, blasphemous, accursed, and heretical!"

Would you believe it, sir, that most people, finding themselves deceived in their expectations, have got into bad humor, and begin to fall foul upon the censors themselves? They are drawing strange inferences from their conduct in favour of M. Arnauld's innocence. "What!" they are saying, "is this all that could be achieved, during all this time, by so many doctors joining in a furious attack on one individual? Can they find nothing in all his works worthy of reprehension, but three lines, and these extracted, word for word, from the greatest doctors of the Greek and Latin Churches? Is there any author whatever whose writings, were it intended to ruin him, would not furnish a more specious pretext for the purpose? And what higher proof could be furnished of the orthodoxy of this illustrious accused?

"How comes it to pass," they add, "that so many denunciations are launched in this censure, into which they have crowded such terms as 'poison, pestilence, horror, rashness, impiety, blasphemy, abomination, execration, anathema, heresy' —the most dreadful epithets that could be used against Arius, or Antichrist himself; and all to combat an imperceptible heresy, and that, moreover, without telling us what it is? If it be against the words of the fathers that they inveigh in this style, where is the faith and tradition? If against M. Arnauld's proposition, let them point out the difference between the two; for we can see nothing but the most perfect harmony between them. As soon as we have discovered the evil of the proposition, we shall hold it in abhorrence; but so long as we do not see it, or rather see nothing in the statement but the sentiments of the holy fathers, conceived and expressed in their own terms, how can we possibly regard it with any other feelings than those of holy veneration?"

Such is the specimen of the way in which they are giving vent to their feelings. But these are by far too deep-thinking people. You and I, who make no pretensions to such extraordinary penetration, may keep ourselves quite easy about the whole affair. What! would we be wiser than our masters? No: let us take example from them, and not undertake what they have not ventured upon. We would be sure to get boggled in such an attempt. Why it would be the easiest thing imaginable, to render this censure itself heretical. Truth, we know, is so delicate that, if we make the slightest deviation from it, we fall into error; but this alleged error is so extremely finespun that, if we diverge from it in the slightest degree, we fall back upon the truth. There is positively nothing between this obnoxious proposition and the truth but an imperceptible point. The distance between them is so impalpable that I was in terror lest, from pure inability to perceive it, I might, in my over-anxiety to agree with the doctors of the Sorbonne, place myself in opposition to the doctors of the Church. Under this apprehension, I judged it expedient to consult one of those who, through policy, was neutral on the first question, that from him I might learn the real state of the matter. I have accordingly had an interview with one of the most intelligent of that party, whom I requested to point out to me the difference between the two things, at the same time frankly owning to him that I could see none.

He appeared to be amused at my simplicity and replied, with a smile: "How simple it is in you to believe that there is any difference! Why, where could it be? Do you imagine that, if they could have found out any discrepancy between M. Arnauld and the fathers, they would not have boldly pointed it out and been delighted with the opportunity of exposing it before the public, in whose eyes they are so anxious to depreciate that gentleman?"

I could easily perceive, from these few words, that those who had been neutral on the first question would not all prove so on the second; but, anxious to hear his reasons, I asked: "Why, then, have they attacked this unfortunate proposition?"

"Is it possible," he replied, "you can be ignorant of these two things, which I thought had been known to the veriest tyro in these matters? that, on the one hand, M. Arnauld has uniformly avoided advancing a single tenet which is not powerfully supported by the tradition of the Church; and that, on the other hand, his enemies have determined, cost what it may, to cut that ground from under him; and, accordingly, that as the writings of the former afforded no handle to the designs of the latter, they have been obliged, in order to satiate their revenge, to seize on some proposition, it mattered not what, and to condemn it without telling why or wherefore. Do not you know how the Jansenists keep them in check, and annoy them so desperately that they cannot drop the slightest word against the principles of the fathers without being incontinently overwhelmed with whole volumes, under the pressure of which they are forced to succumb? So that, after a great many proofs of their weakness, they have judged it more to the purpose, and much less troublesome, to censure than to reply—it being a much easier matter with them to find monks than reasons."

"Why then," said I, "if this be the case, their censure is not worth a straw; for who will pay any regard to it, when they see it to be without foundation, and refuted, as it no doubt will be, by the answers given to it?"

"If you knew the temper of people," replied my friend the doctor, "you would talk in another sort of way. Their censure, censurable as it is, will produce nearly all its designed effect for a time; and although, by the force of demonstration, it is certain that, in course of time, its invalidity will be made apparent, it is equally true that, at first, it will tell as effectually on the minds of most people as if it had been the most righteous sentence in the world. Let it only be cried about the streets: 'Here you have the censure of M. Arnauld!—here you have the condemnation of the Jansenists!' and the Jesuits will find their account in it. How few will ever read it! How few, of them who do read, will understand it! How few will observe that it answers no objections! How few will take the matter to heart, or attempt to sift it to the bottom! Mark, then, how much advantage this gives to the enemies of the Jansenists. They are sure to make a triumph of it, though a vain one, as usual, for some months at least— and that is a great matter for them— they will look out afterwards for some new means of subsistence. They live from hand to mouth, sir. It is in this way they have contrived to maintain themselves down to the present day. Sometimes it is by a catechism in which a child is made to condemn their opponents; then it is by a procession, in which sufficient grace leads the efficacious in triumph; again it is by a comedy, in which Jansenius is represented as carried off by devils; at another time it is by an almanac; and now it is by this censure."

"In good sooth," said I "I was on the point of finding fault with the conduct of the Molinists; but after what you have told me, I must say I admire their prudence and their policy. I see perfectly well that they could not have followed a safer or more judicious course."

"You are right," returned he; "their safest policy has always been to keep silent;

and this led a certain learned divine to remark, 'that the cleverest among them are those who intrigue much, speak little, and write nothing.'

"It is on this principle that, from the commencement of the meetings, they prudently ordained that, if M. Arnauld came into the Sorbonne, it must be simply to explain what he believed, and not to enter the lists of controversy with any one. The examiners, having ventured to depart a little from this prudent arrangement, suffered for their temerity. They found themselves rather too vigourously refuted by his second apology.

"On the same principle, they had recourse to that rare and very novel device of the half-hour and the sand-glass. By this means they rid themselves of the importunity of those troublesome doctors, who might undertake to refute all their arguments, to produce books which might convict them of forgery, to insist on a reply, and reduce them to the predicament of having none to give.

"It is not that they were so blind as not to see that this encroachment on liberty, which has induced so many doctors to withdraw from the meetings, would do no good to their censure; and that the protest of nullity, taken on this ground by M. Arnauld before it was concluded, would be a bad preamble for securing it a favourable reception. They know very well that unprejudiced persons place fully as much weight on the judgement of seventy doctors, who had nothing to gain by defending M. Arnauld, as on that of a hundred others who had nothing to lose by condemning him. But, upon the whole, they considered that it would be of vast importance to have a censure, although it should be the act of a party only in the Sorbonne, and not of the whole body; although it should be carried with little or no freedom of debate and obtained by a great many small manœuvres not exactly according to order; although it should give no explanation of the matter in dispute; although it should not point out in what this heresy consists, and should say as little as possible about it, for fear of committing a mistake. This very silence is a mystery in the eyes of the simple; and the censure will reap this singular advantage from it, that they may defy the most critical and subtle theologians to find in it a single weak argument.

"Keep yourself easy, then, and do not be afraid of being set down as a heretic, though you should make use of the condemned proposition. It is bad, I assure you, only as occurring in the second letter of M. Arnauld. If you will not believe this statement on my word, I refer you to M. le Moine, the most zealous of the examiners, who, in the course of conversation with a doctor of my acquaintance this very morning, on being asked by him where lay the point of difference in dispute, and if one would no longer be allowed to say what the fathers had said before him, made the following exquisite reply: 'This proposition would be orthodox in the mouth of any other—it is only as coming from M. Arnauld that the Sorbonne has condemned it!' You must now be prepared to admire the machinery of Molinism, which can produce such prodigious overturnings in the Church —that what is Catholic in the fathers becomes heretical in M. Arnauld—that what is heretical in the Semi-Pelagians becomes orthodox in the writings of the Jesuits; the ancient doctrine of St. Augustine becomes an intolerable innovation, and new inventions, daily fabricated before our eyes, pass for the ancient faith of the Church." So saying, he took his leave of me.

This information has satisfied my purpose. I gather from it that this same heresy is one of an entirely new species. It is not the sentiments of M. Arnauld that are heretical; it is only his person. This is a personal heresy. He is not a heretic for anything he has said or written, but simply because he is M. Arnauld. This is all they have to say against him. Do what he may, unless he cease to be, he will never be a good Catholic. The grace of St. Augustine will never be the true grace, so long as he continues to defend it. It would become so at once, were he to take it into his head to impugn it. That would be a sure stroke, and almost the only plan for establishing the truth and demolishing Molinism; such is the fatality attending all the opinions which he embraces.

Let us leave them, then, to settle their own differences. These are the disputes of theologians, not of theology. We, who are no doctors, have nothing to do with their quarrels. Tell our friends the news of the censure, and love me while I am, &c.

LETTER IV

Paris, *February* 25, 1656

SIR,

Nothing can come up to the Jesuits. I have seen Jacobins, doctors, and all sorts of people in my day, but such an interview as I have just had was wanting to complete my knowledge of mankind. Other men are merely copies of them. As things are always found best at the fountainhead, I paid a visit to one of the ablest among them, in company with my trusty Jansenist—the same who accompanied me to the Dominicans. Being particularly anxious to learn something of a dispute which they have with the Jansenists about what they call *actual grace*, I said to the worthy father that I would be much obliged to him if he would instruct me on this point—that I did not even know what the term meant and would thank him to explain it. "With all my heart," the Jesuit replied; "for I dearly love inquisitive people. Actual grace, according to our definition, 'is an inspiration of God, whereby He makes us to know His will and excites within us a desire to perform it.'"

"And where," said I, "lies your difference with the Jansenists on this subject?"

"The difference lies here," he replied; "we hold that God bestows actual grace *on all men in every case of temptation;* for we maintain that unless a person have, whenever tempted, actual grace to keep him from sinning, his sin, whatever it may be, can never be imputed to him. The Jansenists, on the other hand, affirm that sins, though committed without actual grace, are, nevertheless, imputed; but they are a pack of fools." I got a glimpse of his meaning; but, to obtain from him a fuller explanation, I observed: "My dear father, it is that phrase *actual grace* that puzzles me; I am quite a stranger to it, and if you would have the goodness to tell me the same thing over again, without employing that term, you would infinitely oblige me."

"Very good," returned the father; "that is to say, you want me to substitute the definition in place of the thing defined; that makes no alteration of the sense; I have no objections. We maintain it, then, as an undeniable principle, *that an action cannot be imputed as a sin, unless God bestow on us, before committing it, the knowledge of the evil that is in the action, and an inspiration inciting us to avoid it.* Do you understand me now?"

Astonished at such a declaration, according to which, no sins of surprise, nor any of those committed in entire forgetfulness of God, could be imputed, I turned round to my friend the Jansenist and easily discovered from his looks that he was of a different way of thinking. But as he did not utter a word, I said to the monk, "I would fain wish, my dear father, to think that what you have now said is true, and that you have good proofs for it."

"Proofs, say you!" he instantly exclaimed: "I shall furnish you with these very soon, and the very best sort too; let me alone for that."

So saying, he went in search of his books, and I took this opportunity of asking my friend if there was any other person who talked in this manner? "Is this so strange to you?" he replied. "You may depend upon it that neither the fathers, nor the popes, nor councils, nor Scripture, nor any book of devotion employ such language; but, if you wish casuists and modern schoolmen, he will bring you a goodly number of them on his side." "O! but I care not a fig about these authors, if they are contrary to tradition," I said. "You are right," he replied.

As he spoke, the good father entered the room, laden with books; and presenting to me the first that came to hand. "Read that," he said; "this is *The Summary of Sins*, by Father Bauny—the fifth edition too, you see, which shows that it is a good book."

"It is a pity, however," whispered the Jansenist in my ear, "that this same book has been condemned at Rome, and by the bishops of France."

"Look at page 906," said the father. I did so and read as follows: "In order to sin and become culpable in the sight of God, it is necessary to know that the thing we wish to do is not good, or at least to doubt that it is—to fear or to judge that God takes no pleasure in the action which we contemplate, but forbids it; and in spite of this, to commit the deed, leap the fence, and transgress."

"This is a good commencement," I remarked. "And yet," said he, "mark how far envy will carry some people. It was on that very passage that M. Hallier, before he became one of our friends, bantered Father Bauny, by applying to him these words: *Ecce qui tollit peccata mundi*—'Behold the man that taketh away the sins of the world!'"

"Certainly," said I, "according to Father Bauny, we may be said to behold a redemption of an entirely new description."

"Would you have a more authentic witness on the point?" added he. "Here is the book of Father Annat. It is the last that he wrote against M. Arnauld. Turn up to page 34, where there is a dog's ear, and read the lines which I have marked with pencil—they ought to be written in letters of gold." I then read these words: "He that has no thought of God, nor of his sins, nor any apprehension (that is, as he explained it, any knowledge) of his obligation to exercise the acts of love to God or contrition, has no actual grace for exercising those acts; but it is equally true that he is guilty of no sin in omitting them, and that, if he is damned, it will not be as a punishment for that omission." And a few lines below, he adds: "The same thing may be said of a culpable commission."

"You see," said the monk, "how he speaks of sins of *omission* and of *commission*. Nothing escapes him. What say you to that?"

"Say!" I exclaimed. "I am delighted! What a charming train of consequences do I discover flowing from this doctrine! I can see the whole results already; and such mysteries present themselves before me! Why, I see more people, beyond all comparison, justified by this ignorance and forgetfulness of God, than by grace and the sacraments! But, my dear father, are you not inspiring me with a delusive joy? Are you sure there is nothing here like that *sufficiency which suffices not?* I am terribly afraid of the *Distinguo;* I was taken in with that once already! Are you quite in earnest?"

"How now!" cried the monk, beginning to get angry, "here is no matter for jesting. I assure you there is no such thing as equivocation here."

"I am not making a jest of it," said I; "but that is what I really dread, from pure anxiety to find it true."

"Well then," he said, "to assure yourself still more of it, here are the writings of M. le Moine, who taught the doctrine in a full meeting of the Sorbonne. He learned it from us, to be sure; but he has the merit of having cleared it up most admirably. O how circumstantially he goes to work! He shows that, in order to make out an action to be *a sin*, all these things must have passed through the mind. Read, and weigh every word." I then read what I now give you in a translation from the original Latin: "1. On the one hand, God sheds abroad on the soul some measure of love, which gives it a bias toward the thing commanded; and on the other, a rebellious concupiscence solicits it in the opposite direction. 2. God inspires the soul with a knowledge of its own weakness. 3. God reveals the knowledge of the physician who can heal it. 4. God inspires it with a desire to be healed. 5. God inspires a desire to pray and solicit his assistance."

"And unless all these things occur and pass through the soul," added the monk, "the action is not properly a sin, and cannot be imputed, as M. le Moine shows in the same place and in what follows. Would you wish to have other authorities for this? Here they are."

"All modern ones, however," whispered my Jansenist friend.

"So I perceive," said I to him aside; and then, turning to the monk: "O my dear sir," cried I, "what a blessing this will be to some persons of my acquaintance! I must positively introduce them to you. You have never, perhaps, met with people who had fewer sins to account for all your life. For, in the first place, they never think of God at all; their vices have got the better of their reason; they have never known either their weakness or the physician who can cure it; they have never thought of 'desiring the health of their soul,' and still less of 'praying to God to bestow it'; so that, according to M. le Moine, they are still in the state of baptismal innocence. They have 'never had a thought of loving God or of being contrite for their sins'; so that, according to Father Annat, they have never committed sin through the want of charity and penitence. Their life is spent in a perpetual round of all sorts of pleasures, in the course of which they have not been interrupted by the slightest remorse. These excesses had led me to imagine that their perdition was inevitable; but you, father, inform me that these same excesses secure their salvation. Blessings on you, my good father, for this way of justifying people! Others prescribe painful austerities for healing the soul; but you show that souls which may be thought desperately distempered are in quite good health. What an excellent device for being happy both in this world and in the next! I had always supposed that the less a man thought of God, the more he sinned; but, from what I see now, if one could only succeed in bringing himself not to think upon God at all, everything would be pure with him in all time coming. Away with your half-and-half sinners, who retain some sneaking affection for virtue! They will be damned every one of them, these semi-sinners. But commend me to your arrant sinners—hardened, unalloyed, out-and-out, thorough-bred sinners. Hell is no place for them; they have cheated the devil, purely by virtue of their devotion to his service!"

The good father, who saw very well the connection between these consequences and his principle, dexterously evaded them; and, maintaining his temper, either from good nature or policy, he merely replied: "To let you understand how we avoid these inconveniences, you must know that, while we affirm that these reprobates to whom you refer would be without sin if they had no thoughts of conversion and no desires to devote themselves to God, we maintain that they all actually *have* such thoughts and desires, and that God never permitted a man to sin without giving him previously a view of the evil which he contemplated, and a desire, either to avoid the offence, or at all events to implore his aid to enable him to avoid it; and none but Jansenists will assert the contrary."

"Strange! father," returned I; "is this, then, the heresy of the Jansenists, to deny that every time a man commits a sin he is troubled with a remorse of conscience, in spite of which, he 'leaps the fence and transgresses,' as Father Bauny has it? It is rather too good a joke to be made a heretic for that. I can easily believe that a man may be damned for not having good thoughts; but it never would have entered my head to imagine that any man could be subjected to that doom for not believing that all mankind must have good thoughts! But, father, I hold myself bound in conscience to disabuse you and to inform you that there are thousands of people who have no such desires— who sin without regret—who sin with delight—who make a boast of sinning. And who ought to know better about these things than yourself? You cannot have failed to have confessed some of those to whom I allude; for it is among persons of high rank that they are most generally to be met with. But mark, father, the dangerous consequences of your maxim. Do you not perceive what effect it may have on those libertines who like nothing better than to find out matter of doubt in religion? What a handle do you give them, when you assure them, as an article of faith, that, on every occasion when they commit a sin, they feel an inward presentiment of the evil and a desire to avoid it? Is it not obvious that, feeling convinced by their own experience of the falsity of your doctrine on this point, which you say is a matter of faith, they will extend the inference drawn from this to all the other points? They will argue that, since you are not trustworthy in one article, you are to be suspected in them all; and thus you shut them up to conclude either that religion is false or that you must know very little about it."

Here my friend the Jansenist, following up my remarks, said to him: "You would do well, father, if you wish to preserve your doctrine, not to explain so precisely as you have done to us what you mean by *actual grace*. For, how could you, without forfeiting all credit in the estimation of men, openly declare that *nobody sins without having previously the knowledge of his weakness, and of a physician, or the desire of a cure, and of asking it of God?* Will it be believed, on your word, that those who are immersed in avarice, impurity, blasphemy, duelling, revenge, robbery and sacrilege, have really a desire to embrace chastity, humility, and the other Christian virtues? Can it be conceived that those philosophers who boasted so loudly of the powers of nature, knew its infirmity and its physician? Will you maintain that those who held it as a settled maxim that 'it is not God that bestows virtue, and that no one ever asked it from him,' would think of asking it for themselves? Who can believe that the Epicureans, who denied a divine providence, ever felt any inclination to pray to God? men who said that 'it would be an insult to invoke the Deity in our necessities, as if he were capable of wasting a thought on beings like us'? In a word, how can it be imagined that idolaters and atheists, every time they are tempted to the commission of sin, in other words, infinitely often during their lives, have a desire to pray to the true God, of whom they are ignorant, that he would bestow on them virtues of which they have no conception?"

"Yes," said the worthy monk, in a resolute tone, "we will affirm it: and sooner than allow that any one sins without having the consciousness that he is doing evil, and the desire of the opposite virtue, we will maintain that the whole world, reprobates and infidels included, have these inspirations and desires in every case of temptation. You cannot show me, from the Scripture at least, that this is not the truth."

On this remark I struck in, by exclaiming: "What! father, must we have recourse to the Scripture to demonstrate a thing so clear as this? This is not a point of faith, nor even of reason. It is a matter of fact: we see it—we know it—we feel it."

But the Jansenist, keeping the monk to his own terms, addressed him as follows: "If you are willing, father, to stand or fall by Scripture, I am ready to meet you there; only you must promise to yield to its authority; and, since it is written that 'God has not revealed his judgements to the Heathen, but left them to wander in their own ways,' you must not say that God has enlightened those whom the Sacred Writings assure us 'he has left in darkness and in the shadow of death.' Is it not enough to show the erroneousness of your principle, to find that St. Paul calls himself 'the chief of sinners,' for a sin which he committed 'ignorantly, and with zeal'? Is it not enough, to and from the Gospel, that those who crucified Jesus Christ had need of the pardon which he asked for them, although they knew not the malice of their action, and would never have committed it, according to St. Paul, if they had known it? Is it not enough that Jesus Christ apprises us that there will be persecutors of the Church, who, while making every effort to ruin her, will 'think that they are doing God service'; teaching us that this sin, which in the judgement of the apostle, is the greatest of all sins, may be committed by persons who, so far from knowing that they were sinning, would think that they sinned by not committing it? In fine, it is not enough that Jesus Christ himself has taught us that there are two kinds of sinners, the one of whom sin with 'knowledge of their Master's will,' and the other without knowledge; and that both of them will be 'chastised,' although, indeed, in a different manner?"

Sorely pressed by so many testimonies from Scripture, to which he had appealed, the worthy monk began to give way; and, leaving the wicked to sin without inspiration, he said: "You will not deny that *good men*, at least, never sin unless God give them"—"You are flinching," said I, interrupting him; "you are flinching now, my good father; you abandon the general principle, and, finding that it will not hold good in regard to the wicked, you would compound the matter, by making it apply at least to the righteous. But in this point of view the application of it is, I conceive, so circumscribed that it will hardly apply to anybody, and it is scarcely worth while to dispute the point."

My friend, however, who was so ready on the whole question, that I am inclined to think he had studied it all that very morning, replied: "This, father, is the last entrenchment to which those of your party who are willing to reason at all are sure to retreat; but you are far from being safe even here. The example of the saints is not a whit more in your favour. Who doubts that they often fall into sins of surprise, without being conscious of them? Do we not learn from the saints themselves how often concupiscence lays hidden snares for them; and how generally it happens, as St. Augustine complains of himself in his *Confessions*, that, with all their discretion, they 'give to pleasure what they mean only to give to necessity'?

"How usual is it to see the more zealous friends of truth betrayed by the heat of controversy into sallies of bitter passion for their personal interests, while their consciences, at the time, bear them no other testimony than that they are acting in this manner purely for the interests of truth, and they do not discover their mistake till long afterwards!

"What, again, shall we say of those who, as we learn from examples in ecclesiastical history, eagerly involve themselves in affairs which are really bad, because they believe them to be really good; and yet this does not hinder the fathers from condemning such persons as having sinned on these occasions?

"And were this not the case, how could the saints have their secret faults? How could it be true that God alone knows the magnitude and the number of our offences; that no one knows whether he is worthy of hatred or love; and that the best of saints, though unconscious of any culpability, ought always, as St. Paul says of himself, to remain in 'fear and trembling'?

"You perceive, then, father, that this knowledge of the evil and love of the opposite virtue, which you imagine to be essential to constitute sin, are equally disproved by the examples of the righteous and of the wicked. In the case of the wicked, their passion for vice sufficiently testifies that they have no desire for virtue; and in regard to the righteous, the love which they bear to virtue plainly shows that they are not always conscious of those sins which, as the Scripture teaches, they are daily committing.

"So true is it, indeed, that the righteous often sin through ignorance, that the greatest saints rarely sin otherwise. For how can it be supposed that souls so pure, who avoid with so much care and zeal the least things that can be displeasing to God as soon as they discover them, and who yet sin many times every day, could possibly have, every time before they fell into sin, 'the knowledge of their infirmity on that occasion, and of their physician, and the desire of their souls' health, and of praying to God for assistance,' and that, in spite of these inspirations, these devoted souls 'nevertheless transgress,' and commit the sin?

"You must conclude then, father, that neither sinners nor yet saints have always that knowledge, or those desires and inspirations, every time they offend; that is, to use your own terms, they have not always *actual grace*. Say no longer, with your modern authors, that it is impossible for those to sin who do not know righteousness; but rather join with St. Augustine and the ancient fathers in saying that it is impossible *not* to sin, when we do not know righteousness: *Necesse est ut peccet, a quo ignoratur justitia.*"

The good father, though thus driven from both of his positions, did not lose courage, but after ruminating a little, "Ha!" he exclaimed, "I shall convince you immediately." And again taking up Father Bauny, he pointed to the same place he had before quoted, exclaiming, "Look now—see the ground on which he establishes his opinion! I was sure he would not be deficient in good proofs. Read what he quotes from Aristotle, and you will see that, after so express an authority, you must either burn the books of this prince of philosophers or adopt our opinion. Hear, then, the principles which support Father Bauny: Aristotle states first, '*that an action cannot be imputed as blameworthy, if it be involuntary.*'"

"I grant that," said my friend.

"This is the first time you have agreed together," said I. "Take my advice, father, and proceed no further."

"That would be doing nothing," he replied; "we must know what are the conditions necessary to constitute an action voluntary."

"I am much afraid," returned I, "that you will get at loggerheads on that point."

"No fear of that," said he; "this is sure ground—Aristotle is on my side. Hear now, what Father Bauny says: 'In order that an action be voluntary, it must proceed from a man who perceives, knows, and comprehends what is good and what is evil in it. *Voluntarium est*—that is a voluntary action, as we commonly say with the philosopher' (that is Aristotle, you know, said the monk, squeezing my hand); '*quod fit a principio cognoscente singula in quibus est actio*—which is done by a person knowing the particulars of the action; so that when the will is led inconsiderately, and without mature reflection, to embrace or reject, to do or omit to do anything, before the understanding has been able to see whether it would be right or wrong, such an action is neither good nor evil; because previous to this mental inquisition, view, and reflection on the good or bad qualities of the matter in question, the act by which it is done is not voluntary.' Are you satisfied now?" said the father.

"It appears," returned I, "that Aristotle agrees with Father Bauny; but that does not prevent me from feeling surprised at this statement. What, sir! is it not enough to make an action voluntary that the man knows what he is doing, and does it just because he chooses to do it? Must we suppose, besides this, that he 'perceives, knows, and comprehends what is good and evil in the action'? Why, on this supposition there would be hardly such a thing in nature as voluntary actions, for no one scarcely thinks about all this. How many oaths in gambling, how many excesses in debauchery, how many riotous extravagances in the carnival, must, on this principle, be excluded from the list of voluntary actions, and consequently neither good nor bad, because not accompanied by those 'mental reflections on the good and evil qualities' of the action? But is it possible, father, that Aristotle held such a sentiment? I have always understood that he was a sensible man."

"I shall soon convince you of that," said the Jansenist, and requesting a sight of Aristotle's *Ethics*, he opened it at the beginning of the third book, from which Father Bauny had taken the passage quoted, and said to the monk: "I excuse you, my dear sir, for having believed, on the word of Father Bauny, that Aristotle held such a sentiment; but you would have changed your mind had you read him for yourself. It is true that he teaches, that 'in order to make an action voluntary, we must know the particulars of that action'—*singula in quibus est actio*. But what else does he means by that, than the *particular circumstances* of the action? The examples which he adduces clearly show this to be his meaning, for they are exclusively confined to cases in which the persons were ignorant of some of the circumstances; such as that of 'a person who, wishing to exhibit a machine, discharges a dart which wounds a bystander; and that of Merope, who killed her own son instead of her enemy,' and such like.

"Thus you see what is the kind of ignorance that renders actions involuntary; namely, that of the particular circumstances, which is termed by divines, as you must know, *ignorance of the fact*. But with respect to *ignorance of the right*—ignorance of the good or evil in an action—which is the only point in question, let us see if Aristotle agrees with Father Bauny. Here are the words of the philosopher: 'All wicked men are ignorant of what they ought to do, and what they ought to avoid; and it is this very ignorance which makes them wicked and vicious. Accordingly, a man cannot be said to act involuntarily merely because he is ignorant of what it is proper for him to do in order to fulfil his duty. This ignorance in the choice of good and evil does not make the action involuntary; it only makes it vicious. The same thing may be affirmed of the man who is ignorant generally of the rules of his duty; such ignorance is worthy of blame, not of excuse. And consequently, the ignorance which renders actions involuntary and excusable is simply that which relates to the fact and its particular circumstances. In this case the person is excused and forgiven, being considered as having acted contrary to his inclination.'

"After this, father, will you maintain that Aristotle is of your opinion? And who can help being astonished to find that a Pagan philosopher had more enlightened views than your doctors, in a matter so deeply affecting morals, and the direction of conscience, too, as the knowledge of those conditions which render actions voluntary or involuntary, and which, accordingly, charge or discharge them as sinful? Look for no more support, then, father, from the prince of philosophers, and no longer oppose yourselves to the prince of theologians, who has thus decided the point in the first book of his *Retractations*, chapter xv: 'Those who sin through ignorance, though they sin without meaning to sin, commit the deed only because they *will* commit it. And, therefore, even this sin of ignorance cannot be committed except by the will of him who commits it, though by a will which incites him to the action merely, and not to the sin; and yet the action itself is nevertheless sinful, for it is enough to constitute it such that he has done what he was bound not to do.'"

The Jesuit seemed to be confounded more with the passage from Aristotle, I thought, than that from St. Augustine; but while he was thinking on what he could reply, a messenger came to inform him that Madame la Maréchale of ——, and Madame the Marchioness of ——, requested his attendance. So, taking a hasty leave of us, he said: "I shall speak about it to our fathers. They will find an answer to it, I warrant you; we have got some long heads among us."

We understood him perfectly well; and, on our being left alone, I expressed to my friend my astonishment at the subversion which this doctrine threatened to the whole system of morals. To this he replied that he was quite astonished at my astonishment. "Are you not yet aware," he said, "that they have gone to far greater excess in morals than in any other matter?" He gave me some strange illustrations of this, promising me more at some future time. The information which I may receive on this point will, I hope, furnish the topic of my next communication. I am, &c.

LETTER V

Paris, *March* 20, 1656

SIR,

According to my promise, I now send you the first outlines of the morals taught by those good fathers the Jesuits, "those men distinguished for learning and sagacity, who are all under the guidance of divine wisdom—a surer guide than all philosophy." You imagine, perhaps, that I am in jest, but I am perfectly serious; or rather, they are so when they speak thus of themselves in their book entitled *The Image of the First Century.* I am only copying their own words, and may now give you the rest of the eulogy: "They are a society of men, or rather let us call them angels, predicted by Isaiah in these words, 'Go, ye swift and ready angels.'" The prediction is as clear as day, is it not? "They have the spirit of eagles they are a flock of phœnixes (a late author having demonstrated that there are a great many of these birds); they have changed the face of Christendom!" Of course, we must believe all this, since they have said it; and in one sense you will find the account amply verified by the sequel of this communication, in which I propose to treat of their maxims.

Determined to obtain the best possible information, I did not trust to the representations of our friend the Jansenist, but sought an interview with some of themselves. I found however, that he told me nothing but the bare truth, and I am persuaded he is an honest man. Of this you may judge from the following account of these conferences.

In the conversation I had with the Jansenist, he told me so many strange things about these fathers that I could with difficulty believe them, till he pointed them out to me in their writings; after which he left me nothing more to say in their defence than that these might be the sentiments of some individuals only, which it was not fair to impute to the whole fraternity. And, indeed, I assured him that I knew some of them who were as severe as those whom he quoted to me were lax. This led him to explain to me the spirit of the Society, which is not known to every one; and you will perhaps have no objections to learning something about it.

"You imagine," he began, "that it would tell considerably in their favour to show that some of their fathers are as friendly to Evangelical maxims as others are opposed to them; and you would conclude from that circumstance, that these loose opinions do not belong to the whole Society. That I grant you; for had such been the case, they would not have suffered persons among them holding sentiments so diametrically opposed to licentiousness. But, as it is equally true that there are among them those who hold these licentious doctrines, you are bound also to conclude that the holy Spirit of the Society is not that of Christian severity, for had such been the case, they would not have suffered persons among them holding sentiments so diametrically opposed to that severity."

"And what, then," I asked, "can be the design of the whole as a body? Perhaps they have no fixed principle, and every one is left to speak out at random whatever he thinks."

"That cannot be," returned my friend; "such an immense body could not subsist in such a haphazard sort of way, or without a soul to govern and regulate its movements; besides, it is one of their express regulations that none shall print a page without the approval of their superiors."

"But," said I, "how can these same superiors give their consent to maxims so contradictory?"

"That is what you have yet to learn," he replied. "Know then that their object is not the corruption of manners—that is not their design. But as little is it their sole aim to reform them—that would be bad policy. Their idea is briefly this: They have such a good opinion of themselves as to believe that it is useful, and in some sort essentially necessary to the good of religion, that their influence should extend everywhere, and that they should govern all consciences. And the Evangelical or severe maxims being best fitted for managing some sorts of people, they avail themselves of these when they find them favourable to their purpose. But as these maxims do not suit the views of the great bulk of the people, they waive them in the case of such persons, in order to keep on good terms with all the world. Accordingly, having to deal with persons of all classes and of all different nations, they find it necessary to have casuists assorted to match this diversity.

"On this principle, you will easily see that, if they had none but the looser sort of casuists, they would defeat their main design, which is to embrace all; for those that are truly pious are fond of a stricter discipline. But as there are not many of that stamp, they do not require many severe directors to guide them. They have a few for the select few; while whole multitudes of lax casuists are provided for the multitudes that prefer laxity.

"It is in virtue of this 'obliging and accommodating, conduct,' as Father Petau calls it, that they may be said to stretch out a helping hand to all mankind. Should any person present himself before them, for example, fully resolved to make restitution of some ill-gotten gains, do not suppose that they would dissuade him from it. By no means; on the contrary, they would applaud and confirm him in such a holy resolution. But suppose another should come who wishes to be absolved without restitution, and it will be a particularly hard case indeed, if they cannot furnish him with means of evading the duty, of one kind or another, the lawfulness of which they will be ready to guarantee.

"By this policy they keep all their friends, and defend themselves against all their foes; for, when charged with extreme laxity, they have nothing more to do than produce their austere directors, with some books which they have written on the severity of the Christian code of morals; and simple people, or those who never look below the surface of things, are quite satisfied with these proofs of the falsity of the accusation.

"Thus are they prepared for all sorts of persons, and so ready are they to suit the supply to the demand that, when they happen to be in any part of the world where the doctrine of a crucified God is accounted foolishness, they suppress the offence of the cross and preach only a glorious and not a suffering Jesus Christ. This plan they followed in the Indies and in China, where they permitted Christians to practise idolatry itself, with the aid of the following ingenious contrivance: they made their converts conceal under their clothes an image of Jesus Christ, to which they taught them to transfer mentally those adorations which they rendered ostensibly to the idol of Cachinchoam and Keum-fucum. This charge is brought against them by Gravina, a Dominican, and is fully established by the Spanish memorial presented to Philip IV, king of Spain, by the Cordeliers of the Philippine Islands, quoted by Thomas Hurtado, in his *Martyrdom of the Faith*, page 427. To such a length did this practice go that the Congregation *De Propaganda* were obliged expressly to forbid the Jesuits, on pain of excommunication, to permit the worship of idols on any pretext whatever, or to conceal the mystery of the cross from their catechumens; strictly enjoining them to admit none to baptism who were not thus instructed, and ordering them to expose the image of the crucifix in their churches: all of which is amply detailed in the decree of that Congregation, dated the 9th of July, 1646, and signed by Cardinal Capponi.

"Such is the manner in which they have spread themselves over the whole earth, aided by *the doctrine of probable opinions*, which is at once the source and the basis of all this licentiousness. You must get some of themselves to explain this doctrine to you. They make no secret of it, any more than of what you have already learned; with this difference only, that they conceal their carnal and worldly policy under the garb of divine and Christian prudence; as if the faith, and tradition, its ally, were not always one and the same at all times and in all places; as if it were the part of the rule to bend in conformity to the subject which it was meant to regulate; and as if souls, to be purified from their pollutions, had only to corrupt the law of the Lord, in place of the law of the Lord, which is clean and pure, converting the soul which lieth in sin,' and bringing it into conformity with its salutary lessons!

"Go and see some of these worthy fathers, I beseech you, and I am confident that you will soon discover, in the laxity of their moral system, the explanation of their doctrine about grace. You will then see the Christian virtues exhibited in such a strange aspect, so completely stripped of the charity which is the life and soul of them, you will see so many crimes palliated and irregularities tolerated that you will no longer be surprised at their maintaining that 'all men have always enough of grace' to lead a pious life, in the sense of which they understand piety. Their morality being entirely Pagan, nature is quite competent to its observance. When we maintain the necessity of efficacious grace, we assign it another sort of virtue for its object. Its office is not to cure one vice by means of another; it is not merely to induce men to practise the external duties of religion: it aims at a virtue higher than that propounded by Pharisees, or the greatest sages of Heathenism. The law and reason are 'sufficient graces' for these purposes. But to disenthral the soul from the love of the world—to tear it from what it holds most dear—to make it die to itself—to lift it up and bind it wholly, only, and forever, to God—can be the work of none but an all-powerful hand. And it would be as absurd to affirm that we have the full power of achieving such objects, as it would be to allege that those virtues, devoid of the love of God, which these fathers confound with the virtues of Christianity, are beyond our power."

Such was the strain of my friend's discourse, which was delivered with much feeling; for he takes these sad disorders very much to heart. For my own part, I began to entertain a high admiration for these fathers, simply on account of the ingenuity of their policy; and, following his advice, I waited on a good casuist of the Society, one of my old acquaintances, with whom I now resolved purposely to renew my former intimacy. Having my instructions how to manage them, I had no great difficulty in getting him afloat. Retaining his old attachment, he received me immediately with a profusion of kindness; and, after talking over some indifferent matters, I took occasion from the present season to learn something from him about fasting and, thus, slip insensibly into the main subject. I told him, therefore, that I had difficulty in supporting the fast. He exhorted me to do violence to my inclinations; but, as I continued to murmur, he took pity on me and began to search out some ground for a dispensation. In fact he suggested a number of excuses for me, none of which happened to suit my case, till at length he bethought himself of asking me whether I did not find it difficult to sleep without taking supper. "Yes, my good father," said I; "and for that reason I am obliged often to take a refreshment at mid-day and supper at night."

"I am extremely happy," he replied, "to have found out a way of relieving you without sin: go in peace—you are under no obligation to fast. However, I would not have you depend on my word: step this way to the library."

On going thither with me he took up a book, exclaiming with great rapture, "Here is the authority for you: and, by my conscience, such an authority! It is *Escobar*!"

"Who is Escobar?" I inquired.

"What! not know Escobar!" cried the monk; "the member of our Society who compiled this *Moral Theology* from twenty-four of our fathers, and on this founds an analogy, in his preface, between his book and 'that in the Apocalypse which was sealed with seven seals,' and states that 'Jesus presents it thus sealed to the four living creatures, Suarez, Vasquez, Molina, and Valencia, in presence of the four-and-twenty Jesuits who represent the four-and-twenty elders.'"

He read me, in fact, the whole of that allegory, which he pronounced to be admirably appropriate, and which conveyed to my mind a sublime idea of the excellence of the work. At length, having sought out the passage of fasting, "Oh, here it is!" he said; "treatise 1, example 13, no. 67: 'If a man cannot sleep without taking supper, is he bound to fast? Answer: *By no means!*' Will that not satisfy you?"

"Not exactly," replied I; "for I might sustain the fast by taking my refreshment in the morning, and supping at night."

"Listen, then, to what follows; they have provided for all that: 'And what is to be said, if the person might make a shift with a refreshment in the morning and supping at night?'"

"That's my case exactly."

"'Answer: Still he is not obliged to fast; because no person is obliged to change the order of his meals.'"

"A most excellent reason!" I exclaimed.

"But tell me, pray," continued the monk, "do you take much wine?"

"No, my dear father," I answered; "I cannot endure it."

"I merely put the question," returned he, "to apprise you that you might, without breaking the fast, take a glass or so in the morning, or whenever you felt inclined for a drop; and that is always something in the way of supporting nature. Here is the decision at the same place, no. 57: 'May one, without breaking the fast, drink wine at any hour he pleases, and even in a large quantity? Yes, he may: and a dram of hippocrass too.' I had no recollection of the hippocrass," said the monk; "I must take a note of that in my memorandum-book."

"He must be a nice man, this Escobar," observed I.

"Oh! everybody likes him," rejoined the father; "he has such delightful questions! Only observe this one in the same place, no. 38: 'If a man doubt whether he is twenty-one years old, is he obliged to fast? No. But suppose I were to be twenty-one to-night an hour after midnight, and to-morrow were the fast, would I be obliged to fast to-morrow? No; for you were at liberty to eat as much as you pleased for an hour after midnight, not being till then fully twenty-one; and therefore having a right to break the fast day, you are not obliged to keep it.'"

"Well, that is vastly entertaining!" cried I.

"Oh," rejoined the father, "it is impossible to tear one's self away from the book: I spend whole days and nights in reading it; in fact, I do nothing else."

The worthy monk, perceiving that I was interested, was quite delighted, and went on with his quotations. "Now," said he, "for a taste of Filiutius, one of the four-and-twenty Jesuits: 'Is a man who has exhausted himself any way—by profligacy, for example—obliged to fast? By no means. But if he has exhausted himself expressly to procure a dispensation from fasting, will he be held obliged? He will not, even though he should have had that design.' There now! would you have believed that?"

"Indeed, good father, I do not believe it yet," said I. "What! is it no sin for a man not to fast when he has it in his power? And is it allowable to court occasions of committing sin, or rather, are we not bound to shun them? That would be easy enough, surely."

"Not always so," he replied; "that is just as it may happen."

"Happen, how?" cried I.

"Oh!" rejoined the monk, "so you think that if a person experience some inconvenience in avoiding the occasions of sin, he is still bound to do so? Not so thinks Father Bauny. 'Absolution,' says he, 'is not to be refused to such as continue in the proximate occasions of sin, if they are so situated that they cannot give them up without becoming the common talk of the world, or subjecting themselves to personal inconvenience.'"

"I am glad to hear it, father," I remarked; "and now that we are not obliged to avoid the occasions of sin, nothing more remains but to say that we may deliberately court them."

"Even that is occasionally permitted," added he; "the celebrated casuist, Basil Ponce, has said so, and Father Bauny quotes his sentiment with approbation in his *Treatise on Penance*, as follows: 'We may seek an occasion of sin directly and designedly—*primo et per se*—when our own or our neighbour's spiritual or temporal advantage induces us to do so.'"

"Truly," said I, "it appears to be all a dream to me, when I hear grave divines talking in this manner! Come now, my dear father, tell me conscientiously, do *you* hold such a sentiment as that?"

"No, indeed," said he, "I do not."

"You are speaking, then, against your conscience," continued I.

"Not at all," he replied; "I was speaking on that point not according to my own conscience, but according to that of Ponce and Father Bauny, and them you may follow with the utmost safety, for I assure you that they are able men."

"What, father! because they have put down these three lines in their books, will it therefore become allowable to court the occasions of sin? I always thought that we were bound to take the Scripture and the tradition of the Church as our only rule, and not your cauists."

"Goodness!" cried the monk, "I declare you put me in mind of these Jansenists. Think you that Father Bauny and Basil Ponce are not able to render their opinion *probable?*"

"*Probable* won't do for me," said I; "I must have certainty."

"I can easily see," replied the good father, "that you know nothing about our doctrine of *probable opinions*. If you did, you would speak in another strain. Ah! my dear sir, I must really give you some instructions on this point; without knowing this, positively you can understand nothing at all. It is the foundation—the very A, B, C, of our whole moral philosophy."

Glad to see him come to the point to which I had been drawing him on, I expressed my satisfaction and requested him to explain what was meant by a *probable opinion?*

"That," he replied, "our authors will answer better than I can do. The generality of them, and, among others, our four-and-twenty elders, describe it thus: 'An opinion is called *probable* when it is founded upon reasons of some consideration. Hence it may sometimes happen that a single *very grave doctor* may render an opinion probable.' The reason is added: 'For a man particularly given to study would not adhere to an opinion unless he was drawn to it by a good and sufficient reason.'"

"So it would appear," I observed, with a smile, "that a single doctor may turn consciences round about and upside down as he pleases, and yet always land them in a safe position."

"You must not laugh at it, sir," returned the monk; "nor need you attempt to combat the doctrine. The Jansenists tried this; but they might have saved themselves the trouble—it is too firmly established. Hear Sanchez, one of the most famous of our fathers: 'You may doubt, perhaps, whether the authority of a single good and learned doctor renders an opinion probable. I answer that it does; and this is confirmed by Angelus, Sylvester, Navarre, Emanuel Sa, &c. It is proved thus: A probable opinion is one that has a considerable foundation. Now the authority of a learned and pious man is entitled to very great consideration; because (mark the reason), if the testimony of such a man has great influence in convincing us that such and such an event occurred, say at Rome, for example, why should it not have the same weight in the case of a question in morals?'"

"An odd comparison this," interrupted I, "between the concerns of the world and those of conscience!"

"Have a little patience," rejoined the monk; "Sanchez answers that in the very next sentence: 'Nor can I assent to the qualification made here by some writers, namely, that the authority of such a doctor, though sufficient in matters of human right, is not so in those of divine right. It is of vast weight in both cases.'"

"Well, father," said I, frankly, "I really cannot admire that rule. Who can assure me, considering the freedom your doctors claim to examine everything by reason, that what appears safe to one may seem so to all the rest? The diversity of judgements is so great"—

"You don't understand it," said he, interrupting me; "no doubt they are often of different sentiments, but what signifies that? Each renders his own opinion probable and safe. We all know well enough that they are far from being of the same mind; what is more, there is hardly an instance in which they ever agree. There are very few questions, indeed, in which you do not find the one saying *yes* and the other saying *no*. Still, in all these cases, each of the contrary opinions is probable. And hence Diana says on a certain subject: 'Ponce and Sanchez hold opposite views of it; but, as they are both learned men, each renders his own opinion probable.'"

"But, father," I remarked, "a person must be sadly embarrassed in choosing between them!" "Not at all," he rejoined; "he has only to follow the opinion which suits him best." "What! if the other is more probable?" "It does not signify," "And if the other is the safer?" "It does not signify," repeated the monk; "this is made quite plain by Emanuel Sa, of our Society, in his *Aphorisms:* 'A person may do what he considers allowable according to a probable opinion, though the contrary may be the safer one. The opinion of a single grave doctor is all that is requisite.'"

"And if an opinion be at once the less probable and the less safe, it is allowable to follow it," I asked, "even in the way of rejecting one which we believe to be more probable and safe?"

"Once more, I say yes," replied the monk. "Hear what Filiutius, that great Jesuit of Rome, says: 'It is allowable to follow the less probable opinion, even though it be the less safe one. That is the common judgement of modern authors.' Is not that quite clear?"

"Well, reverend father," said I, "you have given *us* elbowroom, at all events! Thanks to your probable opinions, we have got liberty of conscience with a witness! And are you casuists allowed the same latitude in giving your responses?"

"Oh, yes," said he, "we answer just as we please; or rather, I should say, just as it may please those who ask our advice. Here are our rules, taken from Fathers Layman, Vasquez, Sanchez, and the four-and-twenty worthies, in the words of Layman: 'A doctor, on being consulted, may give an advice, not only probable according to his own opinion, but contrary to his own opinion, provided this judgement happens to be more favourable or more agreeable to the person that consults him—*si forte hæc favorabilior seu exoptatior sit.* Nay, I go further and say that there would be nothing unreasonable in his giving those who consult him a judgement held to be probable by some learned person, even though he should be satisfied in his own mind that it is absolutely false.'"

"Well, seriously, father," I said, "your doctrine is a most uncommonly comfortable one! Only think of being allowed to answer *yes* or *no*, just as you please! It is impossible to prize such a privilege too highly. I see now the advantage of the contrary opinions of your doctors. One of them always serves your turn, and the other never gives you any annoyance. If you do not find your account on the one side, you fall back on the other and always land in perfect safety."

"That is quite true," he replied; "and, accordingly, we may always say with Diana, on his finding that Father Bauny was on his side, while Father Lugo was against him: *Sæpe premente deo, fert deus alter opem.*"[1]

"I understand you," resumed I; "but a practical difficulty has just occurred to me, which is this, that supposing a person to have consulted one of your doctors and obtained from him a pretty liberal opinion, there is some danger of his getting into a scrape by meeting a confessor who takes a different view of the matter and refuses him absolution unless he recant the sentiment of the casuist. Have you not provided for such a case as that, father?"

[1] Ovid, *Appendice*, xiii. "If pressed by any god, we will be delivered by another."

"Can you doubt it?" he replied, "We have bound them, sir, to absolve their penitents who act according to probable opinions, under the pain of mortal sin, to secure their compliance. 'When the penitent,' says Father Bauny, 'follows a probable opinion, the confessor is bound to absolve him, though his opinion should differ from that of his penitent.'"

"But he does not say it would be a mortal sin not to absolve him" said I.

"How hasty you are!" rejoined the monk; "listen to what follows; he has expressly decided that, 'to refuse absolution to a penitent who acts according to a probable opinion is a sin which is in its nature mortal.' And, to settle that point, he cites the most illustrious of our fathers—Suarez, Vasquez, and Sanchez."

"My dear sir," said I, "that is a most prudent regulation. I see nothing to fear now. No confessor can dare to be refractory after this. Indeed, I was not aware that you had the power of issuing your orders on pain of damnation. I thought that your skill had been confined to the taking away of sins; I had no idea that it extended to the introduction of new ones. But, from what I now see, you are omnipotent."

"That is not a correct way of speaking," rejoined the father. "We do not introduce sins; we only pay attention to them. I have had occasion to remark, two or three times during our conversation, that you are no great scholastic."

"Be that as it may, father, you have at least answered my difficulty. But I have another to suggest. How do you manage when the Fathers of the Church happen to differ from any of your casuists?"

"You really know very little of the subject," he replied. "The Fathers were good enough for the morality of their own times; but they lived too far back for that of the present age, which is no longer regulated by them, but by the modern casuists. On this Father Cellot, following the famous Reginald, remarks: 'In questions of morals, the modern casuists are to be preferred to the ancient fathers, though those lived nearer to the times of the apostles.' And following out this maxim, Diana thus decides: 'Are beneficiaries bound to restore their revenue when guilty of mal-appropriation of it? The ancients would say *yes*, but the moderns say *no*; let us, therefore, adhere to the latter opinion, which relieves from the obligation of restitution.'"

"Delightful words these, and most comfortable they must be to a great many people!" I observed.

"We leave the fathers," resumed the monk, "to those who deal with positive divinity. As for us, who are the directors of conscience, we read very little of them and quote only the modern casuists. There is Diana, for instance, a most voluminous writer; he has prefixed to his works a list of his authorities, which amount to two hundred and ninety-six, and the most ancient of them is only about eighty years old."

"It would appear, then," I remarked, "that all these have come into the world since the date of your Society?"

"Thereabouts," he replied.

"That is to say, dear father, on your advent, St. Augustine, St. Chrysostom, St. Ambrose, St. Jerome, and all the rest, in so far as morals are concerned, disappeared from the stage. Would you be so kind as let me know the names, at least, of those modern authors who have succeeded them?"

"A most able and renowned class of men they are," replied the monk. "Their names are: Villalobos, Conink, Llamas, Achokier, Dealkozer, Dellacruz, Veracruz, Ugolin, Tambourin, Fernandez, Martinez, Suarez, Henriquez, Vasquez, Lopez, Gomez, Sanchez, De Vechis, De Grassis, De Grassalis, De Pitigianis, De Graphæis, Squilanti, Bizozeri, Barcola, De Bobadilla, Simanacha, Perez de Lara, Aldretta, Lorca, De Scarcia, Quaranta, Scophra, Pedrezza, Cabrezza, Bisbe, Dias, De Clavasio, Villagut, Adam à Manden, Iribarne, Binsfeld, Volfangi à Vorberg, Vosthery, Strevesdorf."

"O my dear father!" cried I, quite alarmed, "were all these people Christians?"

"How! Christians!" returned the casuist; "did I not tell you that these are the only writers by whom we now govern Christendom?"

Deeply affected as I was by this announcement, I concealed my emotion from the monk and only asked him if all these authors were Jesuits?

"No," said he; "but that is of little consequence; they have said a number of good things for all that. It is true the greater part of these same good things are extracted or copied from our authors, but we do not stand on ceremony with them on that score, more especially as they are in the constant habit of quoting our authors with applause. When Diana, for example, who does not belong to our Society, speaks of Vasquez, he calls him 'that phœnix of genius'; and he declares more than once 'that Vasquez alone is to him worth all the rest of men put together'—*instar omnium*. Accordingly, our fathers often make use of this good Diana; and, if you understand our doctrine of probability, you will see that this is no small help in its way. In fact, we are anxious that others besides the Jesuits would render their opinions probable, to prevent people from ascribing them all to us; for you will observe that, when any author, whoever he may be, advances a probable opinion, we are entitled, by the doctrine of probability, to adopt it if we please; and yet, if the author does not belong to our fraternity, we are not responsible for its soundness."

"I understand all that," said I. "It is easy to see that all are welcome that come your way, except the ancient fathers; you are masters of the field, and have only to walk the course. But I foresee three or four serious difficulties and powerful barriers which will oppose your career."

"And what are these?" cried the monk, looking quite alarmed.

"They are the Holy Scriptures," I replied, "the popes, and the councils, whom you cannot gainsay, and who are all in the way of the Gospel."

"Is that all?" he exclaimed; "I declare you put me in a fright. Do you imagine that we would overlook such an obvious scruple as that, or that we have not provided against it? A good idea, forsooth, to suppose that we would contradict Scripture, popes, and councils! I must convince you of your mistake; for I should be sorry you should go away with an impression that we are deficient in our respect to these authorities. You have doubtless taken up this notion from some of the opinions of our fathers, which are apparently at variance with their decisions, though in reality they are not. But to illustrate the harmony between them would require more leisure than we have at present; and, as I would not like you to retain a bad impression of us, if you agree to meet with me to-morrow, I shall clear it all up then."

Thus ended our interview, and thus shall end my present communication, which has been long enough, besides, for one letter. I am sure you will be satisfied with it, in the prospect of what is forthcoming. I am, &c.

LETTER VI

Paris, *April* 10, 1656

SIR,

I mentioned, at the close of my last letter, that my good friend, the Jesuit, had promised to show me how the casuists reconcile the contrarieties between their opinions and the decisions of the popes, the councils, and the Scripture. This promise he fulfilled at our last interview, of which I shall now give you an account.

"One of the methods," resumed the monk, "in which we reconcile these apparent contradictions, is by the interpretation of some phrase. Thus, Pope Gregory XIV decided that assassins are not worthy to enjoy the benefit of sanctuary in churches and ought to be dragged out of them; and yet our four-and-twenty elders affirm that 'the penalty of this bull is not incurred by all those that kill in treachery.' This may appear to you a contradiction; but we get over this by interpreting the word *assassin* as follows: 'Are assassins unworthy of sanctuary in churches? Yes, by the bull of Gregory XIV they are. But by the word *assassins* we understand those that have received money to murder one; and, accordingly, such as kill without taking any reward for the deed, but merely *to oblige their friends*, do not come under the category of assassins.'"

"Take another instance: It is said in the Gospel, 'Give alms of your superfluity.' Several casuists, however, have contrived to discharge the wealthiest from the obligation of alms-giving. This may appear another paradox, but the matter is easily put to rights by giving such an interpretation to the word *superfluity* that it will seldom or never happen that any one is troubled with such an article. This feat has been accomplished by the learned Vasquez, in his *Treatise on Alms*, c. 4: 'What men of the world lay up to improve their circumstances, or those of their relatives, cannot be termed *superfluity;* and accordingly, such a thing as superfluity is seldom to be found among men of the world, not even excepting kings.' Diana, too, who generally founds on our fathers, having quoted these words of Vasquez, justly concludes, 'that as to the question whether the rich are bound to give alms of their superfluity, even though the affirmative were true, it will seldom or never happen to be obligatory in practice.'"

"I see very well how that follows from the doctrine of Vasquez," said I. "But how would you answer this objection, that, in working out one's salvation, it would be as safe, according to Vasquez, to give no alms, provided one can muster as much ambition as to have no superfluity; as it is safe, according to the Gospel, to have no ambition at all, in order to have some superfluity for the purpose of alms-giving?"

"Why," returned he, "the answer would be that both of these ways are safe according to the Gospel; the one according to the Gospel in its more literal and obvious sense, and the other according to the same Gospel as interpreted by Vasquez. There you see the utility of interpretations. When the terms are so clear, however," he continued, "as not to admit of an interpretation, we have recourse to the observation of favourable circumstances. A single example will illustrate this. The popes have denounced excommunication on monks who lay aside their canonicals; our casuists, notwithstanding, put it as a question, 'On what occasions may a monk lay aside his religious habits without incurring excommunication?' They mention a number of cases in which they may, and among others the following: 'If he has laid it aside for an infamous purpose, such as to pick pockets or to go *incognito* into haunts of profligacy, meaning shortly after to resume it.' It is evident the bulls have no reference to cases of that description.''

I could hardly believe that and begged the father to show me the passage in the original. He did so, and under the chapter headed ''Practice according to the School of the Society of Jesus''—*Praxis ex Societatis Jesu Schola*—I read these very words: *Si habitum dimittat ut furetur occulte, vel fornicetur*. He showed me the same thing in Diana, in these terms: *Ut eat incognitus ad lupanar*. ''And why, father,'' I asked, ''are they discharged from excommunication on such occasions?''

''Don't you understand it?'' he replied. ''Only think what a scandal it would be, were a monk surprised in such a predicament with his canonicals on! And have you never heard,'' he continued, ''how they answer the first bull *contra sollicitantes* and how our four-and-twenty, in another chapter of the Practice according to the School of our Society, explain the bull of Pius V *contra clericos*, &c.?''

''I know nothing about all that,'' said I.

''Then it is a sign you have not read much of Escobar,'' returned the monk.

''I got him only yesterday, father,'' said I; ''and I had no small difficulty, too, in procuring a copy. I don't know how it is, but everybody of late has been in search of him.''

''The passage to which I referred,'' returned the monk, ''may be found in treatise 1, example 8, no. 102. Consult it at your leisure when you go home.''

I did so that very night; but it is so shockingly bad that I dare not transcribe it.

The good father then went on to say: ''You now understand what use we make of favourable circumstances. Sometimes, however, obstinate cases will occur, which will not admit of this mode of adjustment; so much so, indeed, that you would almost suppose they involved flat contradictions. For example, three popes have decided that monks who are bound by a particular vow to a Lenten life cannot be absolved from it even though they should become bishops. And yet Diana avers that notwithstanding this decision they *are* absolved.''

''And how does he reconcile that?'' said I.

''By the most subtle of all the modern methods, and by the nicest possible application of probability,'' replied the monk. ''You may recollect you were told the other day that the affirmative and negative of most opinions have each, according to our doctors, some probability—enough, at least, to be followed with a safe conscience. Not that the *pro* and *con* are both true in the same sense—that is impossible—but only they are both probable and, therefore, safe, as a matter of course. On this principle our worthy friend Diana remarks: 'To the decision of these three popes, which is contrary to my opinion, I answer that they spoke in this way by adhering to the affirmative side—which, in fact, even in my judgement, is probable; but it does not follow from this that the negative may not have its probability too.' And in the same treatise, speaking of another subject on which he again differs from a pope, he says: 'The pope, I grant, has said it as the head of the Church; but his decision does not extend beyond the sphere of the probability of his own opinion.' Now you perceive this is not doing any harm to the opinions of the popes; such a thing would never be tolerated at Rome, where Diana is in high repute. For he does not say that what the popes have decided is not probable; but leaving their opinion within the sphere of probability, he merely says that the contrary is also probable."

"That is very respectful," said I.

"Yes," added the monk, "and rather more ingenious than the reply made by Father Bauny, when his books were censured at Rome; for, when pushed very hard on this point by M. Hallier, he made bold to write: 'What has the censure of Rome to do with that of France?' You now see how, either by the interpretation of terms, by the observation of favourable circumstances, or by the aid of the double probability of *pro* and *con*, we always contrive to reconcile those seeming contradictions which occasioned you so much surprise, without ever touching on the decisions of Scripture, councils, or popes."

"Reverend father," said I, "how happy the world is in having such men as you for its masters! And what blessings are these probabilities! I never knew the reason why you took such pains to establish that a single doctor, *if a grave one*, might render an opinion probable, and that the contrary might be so too, and that one may choose any side one pleases, even though he does not believe it to be the right side, and all with such a safe conscience, that the confessor who should refuse him absolution on the faith of the casuists would be in a state of damnation. But I see now that a single casuist may make new rules of morality at his discretion and dispose, according to his fancy, of everything pertaining to the regulation of manners."

"What you have now said," rejoined the father, "would require to be modified a little. Pay attention now, while I explain our method, and you will observe the progress of a new opinion, from its birth to its maturity. First, the grave doctor who invented it exhibits it to the world, casting it abroad like seed, that it may take root. In this state it is very feeble; it requires time gradually to ripen. This accounts for Diana, who has introduced a great many of these opinions, saying: 'I advance this opinion; but as it is new, I give it time to come to maturity—*relinquo tempori maturandum.*' Thus in a few years it becomes insensibly consolidated; and, after a considerable time, it is sanctioned by the tacit approbation of the Church, according to the grand maxim of Father Bauny, 'that if an opinion has been advanced by some casuist, and has not been impugned by the Church, it is a sign that she approves of it.' And, in fact, on this principle he authenticates one of his own principles in his sixth treatise, p. 312."

"Indeed, father!" cried I, "why, on this principle the Church would approve of all the abuses which she tolerates, and all the errors in all the books which she does not censure!"

"Dispute the point with Father Bauny," he replied. "I am merely quoting his words, and you begin to quarrel with *me*. There is no disputing with facts, sir. Well, as I was saying, when time has thus matured an opinion, it thenceforth becomes completely probable and safe. Hence the learned Caramuel, in dedicating his *Fundamental Theology* to Diana, declares that this great Diana has rendered many opinions probable which were not so before—*quæ antea non erant;* and that, therefore, in following them, persons do not sin now, though they would have sinned formerly—*jam non peccant, licet ante peccaverint.*"

"Truly, father," I observed, "it must be worth one's while living in the neighbourhood of your doctors. Why, of two individuals who do the same actions, he that knows nothing about their doctrine sins, while he that knows it does no sin.

It seems, then, that their doctrine possesses at once an edifying and a justifying virtue! The law of God, according to St. Paul, made transgressors; but this law of yours makes nearly all of us innocent. I beseech you, my dear sir, let me know all about it. I will not leave you till you have told me all the maxims which your casuists have established."

"Alas!" the monk exclaimed, "our main object, no doubt, should have been to establish no other maxims than those of the Gospel in all their strictness: and it is easy to see, from the Rules for the regulation of our manners, that, if we tolerate some degree of relaxation in others, it is rather out of complaisance than through design. The truth is, sir, we are forced to it. Men have arrived at such a pitch of corruption nowadays that, unable to make them come to us, we must e'en go to them, otherwise they would cast us off altogether; and, what is worse, they would become perfect castaways. It is to retain such characters as these that our casuists have taken under consideration the vices to which people of various conditions are most addicted, with the view of laying down maxims which, while they cannot be said to violate the truth, are so gentle that he must be a very impracticable subject indeed who is not pleased with them. The grand project of our Society, for the good of religion, is never to repulse any one, let him be what he may, and so avoid driving people to despair.

"They have got maxims, therefore, for all sorts of persons; for beneficiaries, for priests, for monks; for gentlemen, for servants; for rich men, for commercial men; for people in embarrassed or indigent circumstances; for devout women, and women that are not devout; for married people, and irregular people. In short, nothing has escaped their foresight."

"In other words," said I, "they have got maxims for the clergy, the nobility, and the commons. Well, I am quite impatient to hear them."

"Let us commence," resumed the father, 'with the beneficiaries. You are aware of the traffic with benefices that is now carried on, and that, were the matter referred to St. Thomas and the ancients who had written on it, there might chance to be some simoniacs in the Church. This rendered it highly necessary for our fathers to exercise their prudence in finding out a palliative. With what success they have done so will appear from the following words of Valencia, who is one of Escobar's 'four living creatures.' At the end of a long discourse, in which he suggests various expedients, he propounds the following at page 2039, vol. iii, which, to my mind, is the best: 'If a person gives a temporal in exchange for a spiritual good'—that is, if he gives money for a benefice—'and gives the money as the price of the benefice, it is manifest simony. But if he gives it merely as the motive which inclines the will of the patron to confer on him the living, it is not simony, even though the person who confers it considers and expects the money as the principal object.' Tanner, who is also a member of our Society, affirms the same thing, vol. iii, p.1519, although he 'grants that St. Thomas is opposed to it; for he expressly teaches that it is always simony to give a spiritual for a temporal good, if the temporal is the end in view.' By this means we prevent an immense number of simoniacal transactions; for who would be so desperately wicked as to refuse, when giving money for a benefice, to take the simple precaution of so directing his intentions as to give it as *a motive* to induce the beneficiary to part with it, instead of giving it as *the price* of the benefice? No man, surely, can be so far left to himself as that would come to."

"I agree with you there," I replied; "all men, I should think, have *sufficient grace* to make a bargain of that sort."

"There can be no doubt of it," returned the monk. "Such, then, is the way in which we soften matters in regard to the beneficiaries. And now for the priests—we have maxims pretty favourable to them also. Take the following, for example, from our four-and-twenty elders: 'Can a priest, who has received money to say a mass, take an additional sum upon the same mass? Yes, says Filiutius, he may, by applying that part of the sacrifice which belongs to himself as a priest to the person who paid him last; provided he does not take a sum equivalent to a whole mass, but only a part, such as the third of a mass.'"

"Surely, father," said I, "this must be one of those cases in which the *pro* and the *con* have both their share of probability. What you have now stated cannot fail, of course, to be probable, having the authority of such men as Filiutius and Escobar; and yet, leaving that within the sphere of probability, it strikes me that the contrary opinion might be made out to be probable too, and might be supported by such reasons as the following: That, while the Church allows priests who are in poor circumstances to take money for their masses, seeing it is but right that those who serve at the altar should live by the altar, she never intended that they should barter the sacrifice for money, and, still less, that they should deprive themselves of those benefits which they ought themselves, in the first place, to draw from it; to which I might add that, according to St. Paul, the priests are to offer sacrifice first for themselves and then for the people; and that, accordingly, while permitted to participate with others in the benefit of the sacrifice, they are not at liberty to forego their share by transferring it to another for a third of a mass, or, in other words, for the matter of fourpence or fivepence. Verily, father, little as I pretend to be a *grave* man, I might contrive to make this opinion probable."

"It would cost you no great pains to do that," replied the monk; "it is visibly probable already. The difficulty lies in discovering probability in the converse of opinions manifestly good; and this is a feat which none but great men can achieve. Father Bauny shines in this department. It is really delightful to see that learned casuist examining with characteristic ingenuity and subtlety the negative and affirmative of the same question, and proving both of them to be right! Thus in the matter of priests, he says in one place: 'No law can be made to oblige the curates to say mass every day; for such a law would unquestionably (*haud dubie*) expose them to the danger of saying it sometimes in mortal sin.' And yet, in another part of the same treatise, he says, 'that priests who have received money for saying mass every day ought to say it every day, and that they cannot excuse themselves on the ground that they are not always in a fit state for the service; because it is in their power at all times to do penance, and if they neglect this they have themselves to blame for it and not the person who made them say mass.' And to relieve their minds from all scruples on the subject, he thus resolves the question: 'May a priest say mass on the same day in which he has committed a mortal sin of the worst kind, in the way of confessing himself beforehand?' Villalobos says no, because of his impurity; but Sancius says: 'He may without any sin; and I hold his opinion to be safe, and one which may be followed in practice—*et tuta et sequenda in praxi.*'"

"Follow this opinion in practice!" cried I. "Will any priest who has fallen into such irregularities have the assurance on the same day to approach the altar, on the mere word of Father Bauny? Is he not bound to submit to the ancient laws of the Church, which debarred from the sacrifice forever, or at least for a long time, priests who had committed sins of that description—instead of following the modern opinions of casuists, who would admit him to it on the very day that witnessed his fall?"

"You have a very short memory," returned the monk. "Did I not inform you a little ago that, according to our fathers Cellot and Reginald, 'in matters of morality we are to follow, not the ancient fathers, but the modern casuists?'"

"I remember it perfectly," said I; "but we have something more here: we have the laws of the Church."

"True," he replied; "but this shows you do not know another capital maxim of our fathers, 'that the laws of the Church lose their authority when they have gone into desuetude—*cum jam desuetudine abierunt*—as Filiutius says. We know the present exigencies of the Church much better than the ancients could do. Were we to be so strict in excluding priests from the altar, you can understand there would not be such a great number of masses. Now a multitude of masses brings such a revenue of glory to God and of good to souls that I may venture to say, with Father Cellot, that there would not be too many priests, 'though not only all men and women, were that possible, but even inanimate bodies, and even brute beasts—*bruta animalia*—were transformed into priests to celebrate mass.'"

I was so astounded at the extravagance of this imagination that I could not utter a word and allowed him to go on with his discourse. "Enough, however, about priests; I am afraid of getting tedious: let us come to the *monks*. The grand difficulty with them is the obedience they owe to their superiors; now observe the palliative which our fathers apply in this case. Castro Palao of our Society has said: 'Beyond all dispute, a monk who has a probable opinion of his own, is not bound to obey his superior, though the opinion of the latter is the more probable. For the monk is at liberty to adopt the opinion which is more agreeable to himself—*quæ sibi gratior fuerit*—as Sanchez says. And though the order of his superior be just, that does not oblige you to obey him, for it is not just at all points or in every respect—*non undequaque juste præcepit*—but only probably so; and, consequently, you are only probably bound to obey him, and probably not bound—*probabiliter obligatus, et probabiliter deobligatus.*'"

"Certainly, father," said I, "it is impossible too highly to estimate this precious fruit of the double probability."

"It is of great use indeed," he replied; "but we must be brief. Let me only give you the following specimen of our famous Molina in favour of monks who are expelled from their convents for irregularities. Escobar quotes him thus: 'Molina asserts that a monk expelled from his monastery is not obliged to reform in order to get back again, and that he is no longer bound by his vow of obedience.'"

"Well, father," cried I, "this is all very comfortable for the clergy. Your casuists, I perceive, have been very indulgent to them, and no wonder—they were legislating, so to speak, for themselves. I am afraid people of other conditions are not so liberally treated. Every one for himself in this world."

"There you do us wrong," returned the monk; "they could not have been kinder to themselves than we have been to them. We treat all, from the highest to the lowest, with an even-handed charity, sir. And to prove this, you tempt me to

tell you our maxims for servants. In reference to this class, we have taken into consideration the difficulty they must experience, when they are men of conscience,
in serving profligate masters. For, if they refuse to perform all the errands in which
they are employed, they lose their places; and if they yield obedience, they have
their scruples. To relieve them from these, our four-and-twenty fathers have specified the services which they may render with a safe conscience; such as 'carrying
letters and presents, opening doors and windows, helping their master to reach
the window, holding the ladder which he is mounting. All this,' say they, 'is allowable and indifferent; it is true that, as to holding the ladder, they must be
threatened, more than usually, with being punished for refusing; for it is doing an
injury to the master of a house to enter it by the window.' You perceive the judi-
ciousness of that observation, of course?"

"I expected nothing less," said I, "from a book edited by four-and-twenty Jesuits."

"But," added the monk, "Father Bauny has gone beyond this; he has taught
valets how to perform these sorts of offices for their masters quite innocently, by
making them direct their intention, not to the sins to which they are accessary,
but to the gain which is to accrue from them. In his *Summary of Sins*, p. 710, first
edition, he thus states the matter: 'Let confessors observe,' says he, 'that they cannot absolve valets who perform base errands, if they consent to the sins of their
masters; but the reverse holds true, if they have done the thing merely from a regard to their temporal emolument.' And that, I should conceive, is no difficult
matter to do; for why should they insist on consenting to sins of which they taste
nothing but the trouble? The same Father Bauny has established a prime maxim
in favour of those who are not content with their wages: 'May servants who are
dissatisfied with their wages use means to raise them by laying their hands on as
much of the property of their masters as they may consider necessary to make the
said wages equivalent to their trouble? They may, in certain circumstances; as
when they are so poor that, in looking for a situation, they have been obliged to
accept the offer made to them, and when other servants of the same class are
gaining more than they, elsewhere.'"

"Ha, father!" cried I, "that is John d'Alba's passage, I declare."

"What John d'Alba?" inquired the father: "what do you mean?"

"Strange, father!" returned I: "do you not remember what happened in this
city in the year 1647? Where in the world were you living at that time?"

"I was teaching cases of conscience in one of our colleges far from Paris," he
replied.

"I see you don't know the story, father: I must tell it to you. I heard it related the
other day by a man of honour, whom I met in company. He told us that this John
d'Alba, who was in the service of your fathers in the College of Clermont, in the
Rue St. Jacques, being dissatisfied with his wages, had purloined something to
make himself amends; and that your fathers, on discovering the theft, had thrown
him into prison on the charge of larceny. The case was reported to the court, if I
recollect right, on the 16th of April, 1647; for he was very minute in his statements, and indeed they would hardly have been credible otherwise. The poor fellow, on being questioned, confessed to having taken some pewter plates, but
maintained that for all that he had not *stolen* them; pleading in his defence this
very doctrine of Father Bauny, which he produced before the judges, along with a

pamphlet by one of your fathers, under whom he had studied cases of conscience, and who had taught him the same thing. Whereupon M. de Montrouge, one of the most respected members of the court, said, in giving his opinion, 'that he did not see how, on the ground of the writings of these fathers—writings containing a doctrine so illegal, pernicious, and contrary to all laws, natural, divine, and human, and calculated to ruin all families, and sanction all sorts of household robbery—they could discharge the accused. But his opinion was that this too faithful disciple should be whipped before the college gate, by the hand of the common hangman; and that, at the same time, this functionary should burn the writings of these fathers which treated of larceny, with certification that they were prohibited from teaching such doctrine in future, upon pain of death.'

"The result of this judgement, which was heartily approved of, was waited for with much curiosity, when some incident occurred which made them delay procedure. But in the meantime the prisoner disappeared, nobody knew how, and nothing more was heard about the affair; so that John d'Alba got off, pewter plates and all. Such was the account he gave us, to which he added, that the judgement of M. de Montrouge was entered on the records of the court, where any one may consult it. We were highly amused at the story."

"What are you trifling about now?" cried the monk. "What does all that signify? I was explaining the maxims of our casuists, and was just going to speak of those relating to gentlemen, when you interrupt me with impertinent stories."

"It was only something put in by the way, father," I observed; "and besides, I was anxious to apprise you of an important circumstance, which I find you have overlooked in establishing your doctrine of probability."

"Ay, indeed!" exclaimed the monk, "what defect can this be that has escaped the notice of so many ingenious men?"

"You have certainly," continued I, "contrived to place your disciples in perfect safety so far as God and the conscience are concerned; for they are quite safe in that quarter, according to you, by following in the wake of a grave doctor. You have also secured them on the part of the confessors, by obliging priests, on the pain of mortal sin, to absolve all who follow a probable opinion. But you have neglected to secure them on the part of the judges; so that, in following your probabilities, they are in danger of coming into contact with the whip and the gallows. This is a sad oversight."

"You are right," said the monk; "I am glad you mentioned it. But the reason is we have no such power over magistrates as over the confessors, who are obliged to refer to us in cases of conscience, in which we are the sovereign judges."

"So I understand," returned I; "but if, on the one hand, you are the judges of the confessors, are you not, on the other hand, the confessors of the judges? Your power is very extensive. Oblige them, on pain of being debarred from the sacraments, to acquit all criminals who act on a probable opinion; otherwise it may happen, to the great contempt and scandal of probability, that those whom you render innocent in theory may be whipped or hanged in practice. Without something of this kind, how can you expect to get disciples?"

"The matter deserves consideration," said he; "it will never do to neglect it. I shall suggest it to our father Provincial. You might, however, have reserved this advice to some other time, without interrupting the account I was about to give you of the maxims which we have established in favour of gentlemen; and I shall not give you any more information, except on condition that you do not tell me any more stories."

This is all you shall have from me at present; for it would require more than the limits of one letter to acquaint you with all that I learned in a single conversation. Meanwhile I am, &c.

LETTER VII

Paris, *April* 25, 1656

Sir,

Having succeeded in pacifying the good father, who had been rather disconcerted by the story of John d'Alba, he resumed the conversation, on my assuring him that I would avoid all such interruptions in future, and spoke of the maxims of his casuists with regard to gentlemen, nearly in the following terms:

"You know," he said, "that the ruling passion of persons in that rank of life is 'the point of honor,' which is perpetually driving them into acts of violence apparently quite at variance with Christian piety; so that, in fact, they would be almost all of them excluded from our confessionals, had not our fathers relaxed a little from the strictness of religion, to accommodate themselves to the weakness of humanity. Anxious to keep on good terms both with the Gospel, by doing their duty to God, and with the men of the world, by showing charity to their neighbour, they needed all the wisdom they possessed to devise expedients for so nicely adjusting matters as to permit these gentlemen to adopt the methods usually resorted to for vindicating their honour, without wounding their consciences, and thus reconcile two things apparently so opposite to each other as piety and the point of honour. But, sir, in proportion to the utility of the design, was the difficulty of the execution. You cannot fail, I should think, to realize the magnitude and arduousness of such an enterprise?"

"It astonishes me, certainly," said I, rather coldly.

"It astonishes you, forsooth!" cried the monk. "I can well believe that; many besides you might be astonished at it. Why, don't you know that, on the one hand, the Gospel commands us 'not to render evil for evil, but to leave vengeance to God'; and that, on the other hand, the laws of the world forbid our enduring an affront without demanding satisfaction from the offender, and that often at the expense of his life? You have never, I am sure, met with anything to all appearance more diametrically opposed than these two codes of morals; and yet, when told that our fathers have reconciled them, you have nothing more to say than simply that this astonishes you!"

"I did not sufficiently explain myself, father. I should certainly have considered the thing perfectly impracticable, if I had not known, from what I have seen of your fathers, that they are capable of doing with ease what is impossible to other men. This led me to anticipate that they must have discovered some method for meeting the difficulty—a method which I admire even before knowing it, and which I pray you to explain to me."

"Since that is your view of the matter," replied the monk, "I cannot refuse you. Know then, that this marvellous principle is our grand method of *directing the in-*

tention—the importance of which, in our moral system, is such that I might almost venture to compare it with the doctrine of probability. You have had some glimpses of it in passing, from certain maxims which I mentioned to you. For example, when I was showing you how servants might execute certain troublesome jobs with a safe conscience, did you not remark that it was simply by diverting their intention from the evil to which they were accessary to the profit which they might reap from the transaction? Now that is what we call *directing the intention*. You saw, too, that, were it not for a similar divergence of the mind, those who give money for benefices might be downright simoniacs. But I will now show you this grand method in all its glory, as it applies to the subject of homicide—a crime which it justifies in a thousand instances; in order that, from this startling result, you may form an idea of all that it is calculated to effect."

"I foresee already," said I, "that, according to this mode, everything will be permitted; it will stick at nothing."

"You always fly from the one extreme to the other," replied the monk: "prithee avoid that habit. For, just to show you that we are far from permitting everything, let me tell you that we never suffer such a thing as a formal intention to sin, with the sole design of sinning; and if any person whatever should persist in having no other end but evil in the evil that he does, we break with him at once: such conduct is diabolical. This holds true, without exception of age, sex, or rank. But when the person is not of such a wretched disposition as this, we try to put in practice our method of *directing the intention*, which simply consists in his proposing to himself, as the end of his actions, some allowable object. Not that we do not endeavour, as far as we can, to dissuade men from doing things forbidden; but when we cannot prevent the action, we at least purify the motive, and thus correct the viciousness of the means by the goodness of the end. Such is the way in which our fathers have contrived to permit those acts of violence to which men usually resort in vindication of their honour. They have no more to do than to turn off their intention from the desire of vengeance, which is criminal, and direct it to a desire to defend their honour, which, according to us, is quite warrantable. And in this way our doctors discharge all their duty towards God and towards man. By permitting the action, they gratify the world; and by purifying the intention, they give satisfaction to the Gospel. This is a secret, sir, which was entirely unknown to the ancients; the world is indebted for the discovery entirely to our doctors. You understand it now, I hope?"

"Perfectly well," was my reply. "To men you grant the outward material effect of the action; and to God you give the inward and spiritual movement of the intention; and by this equitable partition, you form an alliance between the laws of God and the laws of men. But, my dear sir, to be frank with you, I can hardly trust your premises, and I suspect that your authors will tell another tale."

"You do me injustice," rejoined the monk; "I advance nothing but what I am ready to prove, and that by such a rich array of passages that altogether their number, their authority, and their reasonings, will fill you with admiration. To show you, for example, the alliance which our fathers have formed between the maxims of the Gospel and those of the world, by thus regulating the intention, let me refer you to Reginald: 'Private persons are forbidden to avenge themselves; for St. Paul says to the Romans (12), "Recompense to no man evil for evil"; and Ecclesiasticus says (28), "He that taketh vengeance shall draw on himself the vengeance of God, and his sins will not be forgotten." Besides all that is said in the Gospel about forgiving offences, as in chapters 6 and 18 of St. Matthew.'"

"Well, father, if after that he says anything contrary to the Scripture, it will not be from lack of scriptural knowledge, at any rate. Pray, how does he conclude?"

"You shall hear," he said. "From all this it appears that a military man may demand satisfaction on the spot from the person who has injured him—not, indeed, with the intention of rendering evil for evil, but with that of preserving his honour—'*non ut malum pro malo reddat, sed ut conservet honorem.*' See you how carefully they guard against the intention of rendering evil for evil, because the Scripture condemns it? This is what they will tolerate on no account. Thus Lessius observes, that 'if a man has received a blow on the face, he must on no account have an intention to avenge himself; but he may lawfully have an intention to avert infamy, and may, with that view, repel the insult immediately, even at the point of the sword—*etiam cum gladio!*' So far are we from permitting any one to cherish the design of taking vengeance on his enemies that our fathers will not allow any even to *wish their death*—by a movement of hatred. 'If your enemy is disposed to injure you,' says Escobar, 'you have no right to wish his death, by a movement of hatred; though you may, with a view to save yourself from harm.' So legitimate, indeed, is this wish, with such an intention, that our great Hurtado de Mendoza says that 'we may *pray God* to visit with speedy death those who are bent on persecuting us, if there is no other way of escaping from it.'"

"May it please your reverence," said I, "the Church has forgotten to insert a petition to that effect among her prayers."

"They have not put in everything into the prayers that one may lawfully ask of God," answered the monk. "Besides, in the present case, the thing was impossible, for this same opinion is of more recent standing than the Breviary. You are not a good chronologist, friend. But, not to wander from the point, let me request your attention to the following passage, cited by Diana from Gaspar Hurtado, one of Escobar's four-and-twenty fathers: 'An incumbent may, without any mortal sin, desire the decease of a life-renter on his benefice, and a son that of his father, and rejoice when it happens; provided always it is for the sake of the profit that is to accrue from the event, and not from personal aversion.'"

"Good!" cried I. "That is certainly a very happy hit; and I can easily see that the doctrine admits of a wide application. But yet there are certain cases, the solution of which, though of great importance for gentlemen, might present still greater difficulties."

"Propose them, if you please, that we may see," said the monk.

"Show me, with all your directing of the intention," returned I, "that it is allowable to fight a duel."

"Our great Hurtado de Mendoza," said the father, "will satisfy you on that point in a twinkling. 'If a gentleman,' says he, in a passage cited by Diana, 'who is challenged to fight a duel, is well known to have no religion, and if the vices to which he is openly and unscrupulously addicted are such as would lead people to conclude, in the event of his refusing to fight, that he is actuated, not by the fear of God, but by cowardice, and induce them to say of him that he was a *hen*, and not a man, *gallina, et non vir;* in that case he may, to save his honour, appear at the appointed spot—not, indeed, with the express intention of fighting a duel, but merely with that of defending himself, should the person who challenged him come there unjustly to attack him. His action in this case, viewed by itself, will be perfectly indifferent; for what moral evil is there in one stepping into a field, taking a stroll in expectation of meeting a person, and defending one's self in the event of being attacked? And thus the gentleman is guilty of no sin whatever; for in fact it cannot be called *accepting a challenge* at all, his intention being directed to other circumstances, and the acceptance of a challenge consisting in an express intention to fight, which we are supposing the gentleman never had.'"

"You have not kept your word with me, sir," said I. "This is not, properly speaking, to permit duelling; on the contrary, the casuist is so persuaded that this practice is forbidden that, in licensing the action in question, he carefully avoids calling it a duel."

"Ah!" cried the monk, "you begin to get knowing on my hand, I am glad to see. I might reply that the author I have quoted grants all that duellists are disposed to ask. But since you must have a categorical answer, I shall allow our Father Layman to give it for me. He permits duelling in so many words, provided that, in accepting the challenge, the person directs his intention solely to the preservation of his honour or his property: 'If a soldier or a courtier is in such a predicament that he must lose either his honour or his fortune unless he accepts a challenge, I see nothing to hinder him from doing so in self-defence.' The same thing is said by Peter Hurtado, as quoted by our famous Escobar; his words are: 'One may fight a duel even to defend one's property, should that be necessary; because every man has a right to defend his property, though at the expense of his enemy's life!'"

I was struck, on hearing these passages, with the reflection that, while the piety of the king appears in his exerting all his power to prohibit and abolish the practice of duelling in the State, the piety of the Jesuits is shown in their employing all their ingenuity to tolerate and sanction it in the Church. But the good father was in such an excellent key for talking that it would have been cruel to have interrupted him; so he went on with his discourse.

"In short," said he, "Sanchez (mark, now, what great names I am quoting to you!) Sanchez, sir, goes a step further; for he shows how, simply by managing the intention rightly, a person may not only receive a challenge, but give one. And our Escobar follows him."

"Prove that, father," said I, "and I shall give up the point: but I will not believe that he has written it, unless I see it in print."

"Read it yourself, then," he replied: and, to be sure, I read the following extract from the *Moral Theology* of Sanchez: "It is perfectly reasonable to hold that a man may fight a duel to save his life, his honour, or any considerable portion of his property, when it is apparent that there is a design to deprive him of these unjustly, by law-suits and chicanery, and when there is no other way of preserving them. Navarre justly observes that, in such cases, it is lawful either to accept or to send a challenge—*licet acceptare et offerre duellum*. The same author adds that there is nothing to prevent one from despatching one's adversary in a private way. Indeed, in the circumstances referred to, it is advisable to avoid employing the method of the duel, if it is possible to settle the affair by privately killing our enemy; for, by this means, we escape at once from exposing our life in the combat, and from participating in the sin which our opponent would have committed by fighting the duel!"

"A most pious assassination!" said I. "Still, however, pious though it be, it is assassination, if a man is permitted to kill his enemy in a treacherous manner."

"Did I say that he might kill him treacherously?" cried the monk. "God forbid! I said he might kill him *privately*, and you conclude that he may kill him *treacherously*, as if that were the same thing! Attend, sir, to Escobar's definition before allowing yourself to speak again on this subject: 'We call it *killing in treachery* when the person who is slain had no reason to suspect such a fate. He, therefore, that slays his *enemy* cannot be said to kill him in treachery, even although the blow should be given insidiously and behind his back—*licet per insidias aut a tergo percutiat.*' And again: 'He that kills his enemy, with whom he was reconciled under a promise of never again attempting his life, cannot be *absolutely* said to kill in treachery, unless there was between them all the stricter friendship—*arctior amicitia.*' You see now you do not even understand what the terms signify, and yet you pretend to talk like a doctor."

"I grant you this is something quite new to me," I replied; "and I should gather from that definition that few, if any, were ever killed in treachery; for people seldom take it into their heads to assassinate any but their enemies. Be this as it may, however, it seems that, according to Sanchez, a man may freely slay (I do not say *treacherously*, but only insidiously and behind his back) a calumniator, for example, who prosecutes us at law?"

"Certainly he may," returned the monk, "always, however, in the way of giving a right direction to the intention: you constantly forget the main point. Molina supports the same doctrine; and what is more, our learned brother Reginald maintains that we may despatch the false witnesses whom he summons against us. And, to crown the whole, according to our great and famous fathers Tanner and Emanuel Sa, it is lawful to kill both the false witnesses and *the judge himself*, if he has had any collusion with them. Here are Tanner's very words: 'Sotus and Lessius think that it is not lawful to kill the false witnesses and the magistrate who conspire together to put an innocent person to death; but Emanuel Sa and other authors with good reason impugn that sentiment, at least so far as the conscience is concerned.' And he goes on to show that it is quite lawful to kill both the witnesses and the judge."

"Well, father," said I, "I think I now understand pretty well your principle regarding the direction of the intention: but I should like to know something of its consequences, and all the cases in which this method of yours arms a man with the power of life and death. Let us go over them again, for fear of mistake, for equivocation here might be attended with dangerous results. Killing is a matter which requires to be well-timed, and to be backed with a good probable opinion. You have assured me, then, that by giving a proper turn to the intention, it is lawful, according to your fathers, for the preservation of one's honour, or even property, to accept a challenge to a duel, to give one sometimes, to kill in a private way a false accuser, and his witnesses along with him, and even the judge who has been bribed to favour them; and you have also told me that he who has got a blow may, without avenging himself, retaliate with the sword. But you have not told me, father, to what length he may go."

"He can hardly mistake there," replied the father, "for he may go all the length of killing his man. This is satisfactorily proved by the learned Henriquez, and others of our fathers quoted by Escobar, as follows: 'It is perfectly right to kill a person who has given us a box on the ear, although he should run away, provided it is not done through hatred or revenge, and there is no danger of giving occasion thereby to murders of a gross kind and hurtful to society. And the reason is that it is as lawful to pursue the thief that has stolen our honour, as him that has run away with our property. For, although your honour cannot be said to be in the hands of your enemy in the same sense as your goods and chattels are in the hands of the thief, still it may be recovered in the same way—by showing proofs of greatness and authority, and thus acquiring the esteem of men. And, in point of fact, is it not certain that the man who has received a buffet on the ear is held to be under disgrace, until he has wiped off the insult with the blood of his enemy?'"

I was so shocked on hearing this that it was with great difficulty I could contain myself; but, in my anxiety to hear the rest, I allowed him to proceed.

"Nay," he continued, "it is allowable to prevent a buffet, by killing him that meant to give it, if there be no other way to escape the insult. This opinion is quite common with our fathers. For example, Azor, one of the four-and-twenty elders, proposing the question, 'Is it lawful for a man of honour to kill another who threatens to give him a slap on the face, or strike him with a stick?' replies, 'Some say he may not; alleging that the life of our neighbour is more precious than our honour, and that it would be an act of cruelty to kill a man merely to avoid a blow. Others, however, think that it is allowable; and I certainly consider it probable, when there is no other way of warding off the insult; for, otherwise, the honour of the innocent would be constantly exposed to the malice of the insolent.' The same opinion is given by our great Filiutius; by Father Hereau, in his *Treatise on Homicide;* by Hurtado de Mendoza, in his *Disputations;* by Becan, in his *Summary;* by our Fathers Flahaut and Lecourt, in those writings which the University, in their third petition, quoted at length, in order to bring them into disgrace (though in this they failed); and by Escobar. In short, this opinion is so general that Lessius lays it down as a point which no casuist has contested; he quotes a great many that uphold, and none that deny it; and particularly Peter Navarre, who, speaking of affronts in general (and there is none more provoking than a box on the ear), declares that 'by the universal consent of the casuists, it is lawful to kill the calumniator, if there be no other way of averting the affront—*ex sententia omnium, licet contumeliosum occidere, si aliter ea injuria arceri nequit.*' Do you wish any more authorities?" asked the monk.

I declared I was much obliged to him; I had heard rather more than enough of them already. But, just to see how far this damnable doctrine would go, I said, "But, father, may not one be allowed to kill for something still less? Might not a person so direct his intention as lawfully to kill another for telling a lie, for example?"

"He may," returned the monk; "and according to Father Baldelle, quoted by Escobar, 'you may lawfully take the life of another for saying, "You have told a lie"; if there is no other way of shutting his mouth.' The same thing may be done in the case of slanders. Our Fathers Lessius and Hereau agree in the following sentiments: 'If you attempt to ruin my character by telling stories against me in the presence of men of honour, and I have no other way of preventing this than by putting you to death, may I be permitted to do so? According to the modern authors, I may, and that even though I have been really guilty of the crime which you divulge, provided it is a secret one, which you could not establish by legal evidence. And I prove it thus: If you mean to rob me of my honour by giving me a box on the ear, I may prevent it by force of arms; and the same mode of defence is lawful when you would do me the same injury with the tongue. Besides, we may lawfully obviate affronts and, therefore, slanders. In fine, honour is dearer than life; and as it is lawful to kill in defence of life, it must be so to kill in defence of honour.' There, you see, are arguments in due form; this is demonstration, sir— not mere discussion. And, to conclude, this great man Lessius shows, in the same place, that it is lawful to kill even for a simple gesture, or a sign of contempt. 'A man's honour,' he remarks, 'may be attacked or filched away in various ways—in all of which vindication appears very reasonable; as, for instance, when one offers to strike us with a stick, or give us a slap on the face, or affront us either by words or signs—*sive per signa.*'"

"Well, father," said I, "it must be owned that you have made every possible provision to secure the safety of reputation; but it strikes me that human life is greatly in danger, if any one may be conscientiously put to death simply for a defamatory speech or a saucy gesture."

"That is true," he replied; "but, as our fathers are very circumspect, they have thought it proper to forbid putting this doctrine into practice on such trifling occasions. They say, at least, 'that it ought *hardly* to be reduced to practice—*practice vix probari potest.*' And they have a good reason for that, as you shall see."

"Oh, I know what it will be," interrupted I; "because the law of God forbids us to kill, of course."

"They do not exactly take that ground," said the father; "as a matter of conscience, and viewing the thing abstractly, they hold it allowable."

"And why then, do they forbid it?"

"I shall tell you that, sir. It is because, were we to kill all the defamers among us, we should very shortly depopulate the country. 'Although,' says Reginald, 'the opinion that we may kill a man for calumny is not without its probability in theory, the contrary one ought to be followed in practice; for, in our mode of defending ourselves, we should always avoid doing injury to the commonwealth; and it is evident that by killing people in this way there would be too many murders.' 'We should be on our guard,' says Lessius, 'lest the practice of this maxim prove hurtful to the State; for in this case it ought not to be permitted—*tunc enim non est permittendus.*'"

"What, father! is it forbidden only as a point of policy, and not of religion? Few people, I am afraid, will pay any regard to such a prohibition, particularly when in a passion. Very probably they might think they were doing no harm to the State, by ridding it of an unworthy member."

"And accordingly," replied the monk, "our Filiutius has fortified that argument with another, which is of no slender importance, namely, 'that for killing people after this manner, one might be punished in a court of justice.'"

"There now, father; I told you before, that you will never be able to do anything worth the while, unless you get the magistrates to go along with you."

"The magistrates," said the father, "as they do not penetrate into the conscience, judge merely of the outside of the action, while we look principally to the intention; and hence it occasionally happens that our maxims are a little different from theirs."

"Be that as it may, father; from yours, at least, one thing may be fairly inferred—

that, by taking care not to injure the commonwealth, we may kill defamers with a safe conscience, provided we can do it with a sound skin. But, sir, after having seen so well to the protection of honour, have you done nothing for property? I am aware it is of inferior importance, but that does not signify; I should think one might direct one's intention to kill for its preservation also."

"Yes," replied the monk; "and I gave you a hint to that effect already, which may have suggested the idea to you. All our casuists agree in that opinion; and they even extend the permission to those cases 'where no further violence is appre-hended from those that steal our property; as, for example, where the thief runs away.' Azor, one of our Society, proves that point."

"But, sir, how much must the article be worth, to justify our proceeding to that extremity?"

"According to Reginald and Tanner, 'the article must be of great value in the estimation of a judicious man.' And so think Layman and Filiutius."

"But, father, that is saying nothing to the purpose; where am I to find 'a judi-cious man' (a rare person to meet with at any time), in order to make this estima-tion? Why do they not settle upon an exact sum at once?"

"Ay, indeed!" retorted the monk; "and was it so easy, think you, to adjust the comparative value between the life of a man, and a Christian man, too, and money? It is here I would have you feel the need of our casuists. Show me any of your ancient fathers who will tell for how much money we may be allowed to kill a man. What will they say, but 'Non occides—Thou shalt not kill?'"

"And who, then, has ventured to fix that sum?" I inquired.

"Our great and incomparable Molina," he replied—"the glory of our Society— who has, in his inimitable wisdom, estimated the life of a man 'at six or seven ducats; for which sum he assures us it is warrantable to kill a thief, even though he should run off'; and he adds, 'that he would not venture to condemn that man as guilty of any sin who should kill another for taking away an article worth a crown, or even less—unius aurei, vel minoris adhuc valoris'; which has led Escobar to lay it down, as a general rule, 'that a man may be killed quite regularly, according to Molina, for the value of a crownpiece.'"

"O father," cried I; "where can Molina have got all this wisdom to enable him to determine a matter of such importance, without any aid from Scripture, the councils, or the fathers? It is quite evident that he has obtained an illumination peculiar to himself, and is far beyond St. Augustine in the matter of homicide, as well as of grace. Well, now, I suppose I may consider myself master of this chap-ter of morals; and I see perfectly that, with the exception of ecclesiastics, nobody need refrain from killing those who injure them in their property or reputation."

"What say you?" exclaimed the monk. "Do you, then, suppose that it would be reasonable that those, who ought of all men to be most respected, should alone be exposed to the insolence of the wicked? Our fathers have provided against that disorder; for Tanner declares that 'Churchmen, and even monks, are permit-ted to kill, for the purpose of defending not only their lives, but their property, and that of their community.' Molina, Escobar, Becan, Reginald, Layman, Les-sius, and others, hold the same language. Nay, according to our celebrated Father Lamy, priests and monks may lawfully prevent those who would injure them by calumnies from carrying their ill designs into effect, by putting them to death. Care, however, must always be taken to direct the intention properly. His words are: 'An ecclesiastic or a monk may warrantably kill a defamer who threatens to publish the scandalous crimes of his community, or his own crimes, when there is no other way of stopping him; if, for instance, he is prepared to circulate his defamations unless promptly despatched. For, in these circumstances, as the monk would be allowed to kill one who threatened to take his life, he is also warranted to kill him who would deprive him of his reputation or his property, in the same way as the men of the world.'"

"I was not aware of that," said I; "in fact, I have been accustomed simply enough to believe the very reverse, without reflecting on the matter, in consequence of having heard that the Church had such an abhorrence of bloodshed as not even to permit ecclesiastical judges to attend in criminal cases."

"Never mind that," he replied; "our Father Lamy has completely proved the doctrine I have laid down, although, with a humility which sits uncommonly well on so great a man, he submits it to the judgement of his judicious readers. Caramuel, too, our famous champion, quoting it in his *Fundamental Theology*, p. 543, thinks it so certain, that he declares the contrary opinion to be destitute of probability, and draws some admirable conclusions from it, such as the following, which he calls 'the conclusion of conclusions—*conclusionum conclusio*': 'That a priest not only may kill a slanderer, but there are certain circumstances in which it may be his *duty* to do so—*etiam aliquando debet occidere*.' He examines a great many new questions on this principle, such as the following, for instance: '*May the Jesuits kill the Jansenists?*'"

"A curious point of divinity that, father!" cried I. "I hold the Jansenists to be as good as dead men, according to Father Lamy's doctrine."

"There, now, you are in the wrong," said the monk: "Caramuel infers the very reverse from the same principles."

"And how so, father?"

"Because," he replied, "it is not in the power of the Jansenists to injure our reputation. 'The Jansenists,' says he, 'call the Jesuits *Pelagians;* may they not be killed for that? No; inasmuch as the Jansenists can no more obscure the glory of the Society than an owl can eclipse that of the sun; on the contrary, they have, though against their intention, enhanced it—*occidi non possunt, quia nocere non potuerunt.*'"

"Ha, father! do the lives of the Jansenists, then, depend on the contingency of their injuring your reputation? If so, I reckon them far from being in a safe position; for supposing it should be thought in the slightest degree *probable* that they might do you some mischief, why, they are *killable* at once! You have only to draw up a syllogism in due form, and, with a direction of the intention, you may despatch your man at once with a safe conscience. Thrice happy must those hot spirits be who cannot bear with injuries, to be instructed in this doctrine! But woe to the poor people who have offended them! Indeed, father, it would be better to have to do with persons who have no religion at all than with those who have been taught on this system. For, after all, the intention of the wounder conveys no comfort to the wounded. The poor man sees nothing of that secret direction of which you speak; he is only sensible of the direction of the blow that is dealt him. And I am by no means sure but a person would feel much less sorry to see himself brutally killed by an infuriated villain than to find himself conscientiously stilettoed by a devotee. To be plain with you, father, I am somewhat staggered at all this;

and these questions of Father Lamy and Caramuel do not please me at all."

"How so?" cried the monk. "Are you a Jansenist?"

"I have another reason for it," I replied. "You must know I am in the habit of writing from time to time, to a friend of mine in the country, all that I can learn of the maxims of your doctors. Now, although I do no more than simply report and faithfully quote their own words, yet I am apprehensive lest my letter should fall into the hands of some stray genius who may take into his head that I have done you injury, and may draw some mischievous conclusion from your premises."

"Away!" cried the monk; "no fear of danger from that quarter, I'll give you my word for it. Know that what our fathers have themselves printed, with the approbation of our superiors, it cannot be wrong to read nor dangerous to publish."

I write you, therefore, on the faith of this worthy father's word of honour. But, in the meantime, I must stop for want of paper—not of passages; for I have got as many more in reserve, and good ones too, as would require volumes to contain them. I am, &c.

LETTER VIII

Paris, *May* 28, 1656

SIR,

You did not suppose that anybody would have the curiosity to know who we were; but it seems there are people who are trying to make it out, though they are not very happy in their conjectures. Some take me for a doctor of the Sorbonne; others ascribe my letters to four or five persons, who, like me, are neither priests nor Churchmen. All these false surmises convince me that I have succeeded pretty well in my object, which was to conceal myself from all but yourself and the worthy monk, who still continues to bear with my visits, while I still contrive, though with considerable difficulty, to bear with his conversations. I am obliged, however, to restrain myself; for, were he to discover how much I am shocked at his communications, he would discontinue them and thus put it out of my power to fulfil the promise I gave you, of making you acquainted with their morality. You ought to think a great deal of the violence which I thus do to my own feelings. It is no easy matter, I can assure you, to stand still and see the whole system of Christian ethics undermined by such a set of monstrous principles, without daring to put in a word of flat contradiction against them. But, after having borne so much for your satisfaction, I am resolved I shall burst out for my own satisfaction in the end, when his stock of information has been exhausted. Meanwhile, I shall repress my feelings as much as I possibly can for I find that the more I hold my tongue, he is the more communicative. The last time I saw him, he told me so many things that I shall have some difficulty in repeating them all. On the point of restitution you will find they have some most convenient principles. For, however the good monk palliates his maxims, those which I am about to lay before you really go to sanction corrupt judges, usurers, bankrupts, thieves, prostitutes and sorcerers—all of whom are most liberally absolved from the obligation of restoring their ill-gotten gains. It was thus the monk resumed the conversation:

"At the commencement of our interviews, I engaged to explain to you the maxims of our authors for all ranks and classes; and you have already seen those that relate to beneficiaries, to priests, to monks, to domestics, and to gentlemen. Let us now take a cursory glance at the remaining, and begin with the judges.

"Now I am going to tell you one of the most important and advantageous maxims which our fathers have laid down in their favour. Its author is the learned Castro Palao, one of our four-and-twenty elders. His words are: 'May a judge, in a question of right and wrong, pronounce according to a probable opinion, in preference to the more probable opinion? He may, even though it should be contrary to his own judgement—*imo contra propriam opinionem.*'"

"Well, father," cried I, "that is a very fair commencement! The judges, surely, are greatly obliged to you; and I am surprised that they should be so hostile, as we have sometimes observed, to your probabilities, seeing these are so favourable to them. For it would appear from this that you give them the same power over men's fortunes as you have given to yourselves over their consciences."

"You perceive we are far from being actuated by self-interest," returned he; "we have had no other end in view than the repose of their consciences; and to the same useful purpose has our great Molina devoted his attention, in regard to the presents which may be made them. To remove any scruples which they might entertain in accepting of these on certain occasions, he has been at the pains to draw out a list of all those cases in which bribes may be taken with a good conscience, provided, at least, there be no special law forbidding them. He says: 'Judges may receive presents from parties when they are given them either for friendship's sake, or in gratitude for some former act of justice, or to induce them to give justice in future, or to oblige them to pay particular attention to their case, or to engage them to despatch it promptly.' The learned Escobar delivers himself to the same effect: 'If there be a number of persons, none of whom have more right than another to have their causes disposed of, will the judge who accepts of something from one of them, on condition—*ex pacto*—of taking up his cause first, be guilty of sin? Certainly not, according to Layman; for, in common equity, he does no injury to the rest by granting to one, in consideration of his present, what he was at liberty to grant to any of them he pleased; and besides, being under an equal obligation to them all in respect of their right, he becomes more obliged to the individual who furnished the donation, who thereby acquired for himself a preference above the rest—a preference which seems capable of a pecuniary valuation—*quae obligatio videtur pretio æstimabilis.*'"

"May it please your reverence," said I, "after such a permission, I am surprised that the first magistrates of the kingdom should know no better. For the first president has actually carried an order in Parliament to prevent certain clerks of court from taking money for that very sort of preference—a sign that he is far from thinking it allowable in judges; and everybody has applauded this as a reform of great benefit to all parties."

The worthy monk was surprised at this piece of intelligence, and replied: "Are you sure of that? I heard nothing about it. Our opinion, recollect, is only probable; the contrary is probable also."

"To tell you the truth, father," said I, "people think that the first president has acted more than probably well, and that he has thus put a stop to a course of public corruption which has been too long winked at."

"I am not far from being of the same mind," returned he; "but let us waive that point, and say no more about the judges."

"You are quite right, sir," said I; "indeed, they are not half thankful enough for all you have done for them."

"That is not my reason," said the father; "but there is so much to be said on all the different classes that we must study brevity on each of them. Let us now say a word or two about men of business. You are aware that our great difficulty with these gentlemen is to keep them from usury—an object to accomplish which our fathers have been at particular pains; for they hold this vice in such abhorrence that Escobar declares 'it is heresy to say that usury is no sin'; and Father Bauny has filled several pages of his *Summary of Sins* with the pains and penalties due to usurers. He declares them 'infamous during their life, and unworthy of sepulture after their death.'"

"O dear!" cried I, "I had no idea he was so severe."

"He can be severe enough when there is occasion for it," said the monk; "but then this learned casuist, having observed that some are allured into usury merely from the love of gain, remarks in the same place that 'he would confer no small obligation on society, who, while he guarded it against the evil effects of usury, and of the sin which gives birth to it, would suggest a method by which one's money might secure as large, if not a larger profit, in some honest and lawful employment than he could derive from usurious dealings.'"

"Undoubtedly, father, there would be no more usurers after that."

"Accordingly," continued he, "our casuist has suggested 'a general method for all sorts of persons—gentlemen, presidents, councillors,' &c.; and a very simple process it is, consisting only in the use of certain words which must be pronounced by the person in the act of lending his money; after which he may take his interest for it without fear of being a usurer, which he certainly would be on any other plan."

"And pray what may those mysterious words be, father?"

"I will give you them exactly in his own words," said the father; "for he has written his *Summary* in French, you know, 'that it may be understood by everybody,' as he says in the preface: 'The person from whom the loan is asked must answer, then, in this manner: I have got no money to *lend;* I have got a little, however, to lay out for an honest and lawful profit. If you are anxious to have the sum you mention in order to make something of it by your industry, dividing the profit and loss between us, I may perhaps be able to accommodate you. But now I think of it, as it may be a matter of difficulty to agree about the profit, if you will secure me a certain portion of it, and give me so much for my principal, so that it incur no risk, we may come to terms much sooner, and you shall touch the cash immediately.' Is not that an easy plan for gaining money without sin? And has not Father Bauny good reason for concluding with these words: 'Such, in my opinion, is an excellent plan by which a great many people, who now provoke the just indignation of God by their usuries, extortions, and illicit bargains, might save themselves, in the way of making good, honest, and legitimate profits'?"

"O sir!" I exclaimed, "what potent words these must be! Doubtless they must possess some latent virtue to chase away the demon of usury which I know nothing of, for, in my poor judgement, I always thought that that vice consisted in recovering more money that what was lent."

"You know little about it indeed," he replied. "Usury, according to our fathers, consists in little more than the intention of taking the interest as usurious. Escobar, accordingly, shows you how you may avoid usury by a simple shift of the intention. 'It would be downright usury,' says he 'to take interest from the borrower, if we should exact it as due in point of justice; but if only exacted as due in point of gratitude, it is not usury. Again, it is not lawful to have directly the intention of profiting by the money lent; but to claim it through the medium of the benevolence of the borrower—*media benevolentia*—is not usury.' These are subtle methods; but, to my mind, the best of them all (for we have a great choice of them) is that of the Mohatra bargain."

"The Mohatra, father!"

"You are not acquainted with it, I see," returned he. "The name is the only strange thing about it. Escobar will explain it to you: 'The Mohatra bargain is effected by the needy person purchasing some goods at a high price and on credit, in order to sell them over again, at the same time and to the same merchant, for ready money and at a cheap rate.' This is what we call the Mohatra—a sort of bargain, you perceive, by which a person receives a certain sum of ready money by becoming bound to pay more."

"But, sir, I really think nobody but Escobar has employed such a term as that; is it to be found in any other book?"

"How little you do know of what is going on, to be sure!" cried the father. "Why, the last work on theological morality, printed at Paris this very year, speaks of the Mohatra, and learnedly, too. It is called *Epilogus Summarum*, and is an abridgment of all the summaries of divinity—extracted from Suarez, Sanchez, Lessius, Fagundez, Hurtado, and other celebrated casuists, as the title bears. There you will find it said, on p.54, that 'the Mohatra bargain takes place when a man who has occasion for twenty pistoles purchases from a merchant goods to the amount of thirty pistoles, payable within a year, and sells them back to him on the spot for twenty pistoles ready money.' This shows you that the Mohatra is not such an unheard-of term as you supposed."

"But, father, is that sort of bargain lawful?"

"Escobar," replied he, "tells us in the same place that there are laws which prohibit it under very severe penalties."

"It is useless, then, I suppose?"

"Not at all; Escobar, in the same passage, suggests expedients for making it lawful: 'It is so, even though the principal intention both of the buyer and seller is to make money by the transaction, provided the seller, in disposing of the goods, does not exceed their highest price, and in re-purchasing them does not go below their lowest price, and that no previous bargain has been made, expressly or otherwise.' Lessius, however, maintains that 'even though the merchant has sold his goods, with the intention of re-purchasing them at the lowest price, he is not bound to make restitution of the profit thus acquired, unless, perhaps, as an act of charity, in the case of the person from whom it had been exacted being in poor circumstances, and not even then, if he cannot do it without inconvenience—*si commode non potest*.' This is the utmost length to which they could go."

"Indeed, sir," said I, "any further indulgence would, I should think, be rather too much."

"Oh, our fathers know very well when it is time for them to stop!" cried the monk. "So much, then, for the utility of the Mohatra. I might have mentioned several other methods, but these may suffice; and I have now to say a little in regard to those who are in embarrassed circumstances. Our casuists have sought to relieve them, according to their condition of life. For, if they have not enough of property for a decent maintenance, and at the same time for paying their debts, they permit them to secure a portion by making a bankruptcy with their creditors. This has been decided by Lessius, and confirmed by Escobar, as follows: 'May a person who turns bankrupt, with a good conscience keep back as much of his personal estate as may be necessary to maintain his family in a respectable way— *ne indecore vivat?* I hold, with Lessius, that he may, even though he may have acquired his wealth unjustly and by notorious crimes—*ex injustitia et notorio delicto;* only, in this case, he is not at liberty to retain so large an amount as he otherwise might.'"

"Indeed, father! what a strange sort of charity is this, to allow property to remain in the hands of the man who has acquired it by rapine, to support him in his extravagance rather than go into the hands of his creditors, to whom it legitimately belongs!"

"It is impossible to please everybody," replied the father; "and we have made it our particular study to relieve these unfortunate people. This partiality to the poor has induced our great Vasquez, cited by Castro Palao, to say that 'if one saw a thief going to rob a poor man, it would be lawful to divert him from his purpose by pointing out to him some rich individual, whom he might rob in place of the other.' If you have not access to Vasquez or Castro Palao, you will find the same thing in your copy of Escobar; for, as you are aware, his work is little more than a compilation from twenty-four of the most celebrated of our fathers. You will find it in his treatise, entitled *The Practice of our Society, in the Matter of Charity towards our Neighbours.*"

"A very singular kind of charity this," I observed, "to save one man from suffering loss, by inflicting it upon another! But I suppose that, to complete the charity, the charitable adviser would be bound in conscience to restore to the rich man the sum which he had made him lose?"

"Not at all, sir," returned the monk; "for he did not rob the man—he only advised the other to do it. But only attend to this notable decision of Father Bauny, on a case which will still more astonish you, and in which you would suppose there was a much stronger obligation to make restitution. Here are his identical words: 'A person asks a soldier to beat his neighbour, or to set fire to the barn of a man that has injured him. The question is whether, in the essence of the soldier, the person who employed him to commit these outrages is bound to make reparation out of his own pocket for the damage that has followed? My opinion is that he is not. For none can be held bound to restitution, where there has been no violation of justice; and is justice violated by asking another to do us a favour? As to the nature of the request which he made, he is at liberty either to acknowledge or deny it; to whatever side he may incline, it is a matter of mere choice; nothing obliges him to it, unless it may be the goodness, gentleness, and easiness of his disposition. If the soldier, therefore, makes no reparation for the mischief he has done, it ought not to be exacted from him at whose request he injured the innocent.'"

This sentence had very nearly broken up the whole conversation, for I was on the point of bursting into a laugh at the idea of the *goodness and gentleness* of a burner of barns, and at these strange sophisms which would exempt from the duty of restitution the principal and real incendiary, whom the civil magistrate would not exempt from the halter. But, had I not restrained myself, the worthy monk, who was perfectly serious, would have been displeased; he proceeded, therefore, without any alteration of countenance, in his observations.

"From such a mass of evidence, you ought to be satisfied now of the futility of your objections; but we are losing sight of our subject. To revert, then, to the succour which our fathers apply to persons in straitened circumstances, Lessius, among others, maintains that 'it is lawful to steal, not only in a case of extreme necessity, but even where the necessity is *grave*, though not extreme.'"

"This is somewhat startling, father," said I. "There are very few people in this world who do not consider their cases of necessity to be *grave* ones, and to whom, accordingly, you would not give the right of stealing with a good conscience. And, though you should restrict the permission to those only who are really and truly in that condition, you open the door to an infinite number of petty larcenies which the magistrates would punish in spite of your *grave necessity*, and which you ought to repress on a higher principle—you who are bound by your office to be the conservators, not of justice only, but of charity between man and man, a grace which this permission would destroy. For after all, now, is it not a violation of the law of charity, and of our duty to our neighbour, to deprive a man of his property in order to turn it to our own advantage? Such, at least, is the way I have been taught to think hitherto."

"That will not always hold true," replied the monk; "for our great Molina has taught us that 'the rule of charity does not bind us to deprive ourselves of a profit, in order thereby to save our neighbour from a corresponding loss.' He advances this in corroboration of what he had undertaken to prove— 'that one is not bound in conscience to restore the goods which another had put into his hands in order to cheat his creditors.' Lessius holds the same opinion, on the same ground. Allow me to say, sir, that you have too little compassion for people in distress. Our fathers have had more charity than that comes to: they render ample justice to the poor, as well as the rich; and, I may add, to sinners as well as saints. For, though far from having any predilection for criminals, they do not scruple to teach that the property gained by crime may be lawfully retained. 'No person,' says Lessius, speaking generally, 'is bound, either by the law of nature or by positive laws (that is, *by any law*), to make restitution of what has been gained by committing a criminal action, such as adultery, even though that action is contrary to justice.' For, as Escobar comments on this writer, 'though the property which a woman acquires by adultery is certainly gained in an illicit way, yet once acquired, the possession of it is lawful—*quamvis mulier illicite acquisat, licite tamen retinet acquisita.*' It is on this principle that the most celebrated of our writers have formally decided that the bribe received by a judge from one of the parties who has a bad case, in order to procure an unjust decision in his favour, the money got by a soldier for killing a man, or the emoluments gained by infamous crimes, may be legitimately retained. Escobar, who has collected this from a number of our authors, lays down this general rule on the point that 'the means acquired by infamous courses, such as murder, unjust decisions, profligacy, &c., are legitimately possessed, and none are obliged to restore them.' And, further, 'they may dispose of what they have received for homicide, profligacy, &c., as they please; for the possession is just, and they have acquired a propriety in the fruits of their iniquity.'"

"My dear father," cried I, "this is a mode of acquisition which I never heard of before; and I question much if the law will hold it good, or if it will consider assassination, injustice, and adultery, as giving valid titles to property."

"I do not know what your law-books may say on the point," returned the monk; "but I know well that our books, which are the genuine rules for conscience, bear me out in what I say. It is true they make one exception, in which restitution is positively enjoined; that is, in the case of any receiving money from those who have no right to dispose of their property such as *minors and monks*. 'Unless,' says the great Molina, 'a woman has received money from one who cannot dispose of it, such as a monk or a minor—*nisi mulier accepisset ab eo qui alienare non potest, ut a religioso et filio familias*. In this case she must give back the money.' And so says Escobar."

"May it please your reverence," said I, "the monks, I see, are more highly favoured in this way than other people."

"By no means," he replied; "have they not done as much generally for all minors, in which class monks may be viewed as continuing all their lives? It is barely an act of justice to make them an exception; but with regard to all other people, there is no obligation whatever to refund to them the money received from them for a criminal action. For, as has been amply shown by Lessius, 'a wicked action may have its price fixed in money, by calculating the advantage received by the person who orders it to be done and the trouble taken by him who carries it into execution; on which account the latter is not bound to restore the money he got for the deed, whatever that may have been—homicide, injustice, or a foul act' (for such are the illustrations which he uniformly employs in this question); 'unless he obtained the money from those having no right to dispose of their property. You may object, perhaps, that he who has obtained money for a piece of wickedness is sinning and, therefore, ought neither to receive nor retain it. But I reply that, after the thing is done, there can be no sin either in giving or in receiving payment for it.' The great Filiutius enters still more minutely into details, remarking 'that a man is *bound in conscience* to vary his payments for actions of this sort, according to the different conditions of the individuals who commit them, and some may bring a higher price than others.' This he confirms by very solid arguments."

He then pointed out to me, in his authors, some things of this nature so indelicate that I should be ashamed to repeat them; and indeed the monk himself, who is a good man, would have been horrified at them himself, were it not for the profound respect which he entertains for his fathers, and which makes him receive with veneration everything that proceeds from them. Meanwhile, I held my tongue, not so much with the view of allowing him to enlarge on this matter as from pure astonishment at finding the books of men in holy orders stuffed with sentiments at once so horrible, so iniquitous, and so silly. He went on, therefore, without interruption in his discourse, concluding as follows:

"From these premises, our illustrious Molina decides the following question (and after this, I think you will have got enough: 'If one has received money to perpetrate a wicked action, is he obliged to restore it? We must distinguish here,' says this great man; 'if he has not done the deed, he must give back the cash; if he has, he is under no such obligation!' Such are some of our principles touching restitution. You have got a great deal of instruction to-day; and I should like, now, to see what proficiency you have made. Come, then, answer me this question: 'Is a judge, who has received a sum of money from one of the parties before him, in order to pronounce a judgement in his favour, obliged to make restitution?'"

"You were just telling me a little ago, father, that he was not."

"I told you no such thing," replied the father; "did I express myself so generally? I told you he was not bound to make restitution, provided he succeeded in gaining the cause for the party who had the wrong side of the question. But if a man has justice on his side, would you have him to purchase the success of his cause, which is his legitimate right? You are very unconscionable. Justice, look you, is a debt which the judge owes, and therefore he cannot sell it; but he cannot be said to owe injustice, and therefore he may lawfully receive money for it. All our leading authors, accordingly, agree in teaching 'that though a judge is bound to restore the money he had received for doing an act of justice, unless it was given him out of mere generosity, he is not obliged to restore what he has received from a man in whose favour he has pronounced an unjust decision.'"

This preposterous decision fairly dumbfounded me, and, while I was musing on its pernicious tendencies, the monk had prepared another question for me. "Answer me again," said he, "with a little more circumspection. Tell me now, 'if a man who deals in divination is obliged to make restitution of the money he has acquired in the exercise of his art?'"

"Just as you please, your reverence," said I.

"Eh! what!— just as I please! Indeed, but you are a pretty scholar! It would seem, according to your way of talking, that the truth depended on our will and pleasure. I see that, in the present case, you would never find it out yourself: so I must send you to Sanchez for a solution of the problem—no less a man than Sanchez. In the first place, he makes a distinction between 'the case of the diviner who has recourse to astrology and other natural means, and that of another who employs the diabolical art. In the one case, he says, the diviner is bound to make restitution; in the other he is not.' Now, guess which of them is the party bound?"

"It is not difficult to find out that," said I.

"I see what you mean to say," he replied. "You think that he ought to make restitution in the case of his having employed the agency of demons. But you know nothing about it; it is just the reverse. 'If,' says Sanchez, 'the sorcerer has not taken care and pains to discover, by means of the devil, what he could not have known otherwise, he must make restitution—*si nullam operam apposuit ut arte diaboli id sciret;* but if he has been at that trouble, he is not obliged.'"

"And why so, father?"

"Don't you see?" returned he. "It is because men may truly divine by the aid of the devil, whereas astrology is a mere sham."

"But, sir, should the devil happen not to tell the truth (and he is not much more to be trusted than astrology), the magician must, I should think, for the same reason, be obliged to make restitution?"

"Not always," replied the monk: "*Distinguo,* as Sanchez says, here. If the magician be ignorant of the diabolic art—*si sit artis diabolicæ ignarus*—he is bound to restore: but if he is an expert sorcerer, and has done all in his power to arrive at the truth, the obligation ceases; for the industry of such a magician may be estimated at a certain sum of money.'"

"There is some sense in that," I said; "for this is an excellent plan to induce sorcerers to aim at proficiency in their art, in the hope of making an honest livelihood, as you would say, by faithfully serving the public."

"You are making a jest of it, I suspect," said the father: "that is very wrong. If you were to talk in that way in places where you were not known, some people might take it amiss and charge you with turning sacred subjects into ridicule."

"That, father, is a charge from which I could very easily vindicate myself; for certain I am that whoever will be at the trouble to examine the true meaning of my words will find my object to be precisely the reverse; and perhaps, sir, before our conversations are ended, I may find an opportunity of making this very amply apparent."

"Ho, ho," cried the monk, "there is no laughing in your head now."

"I confess," said I, "that the suspicion that I intended to laugh at things sacred would be as painful for me to incur as it would be unjust in any to entertain it."

"I did not say it in earnest," returned the father; "but let us speak more seriously."

"I am quite disposed to do so, if you prefer it; that depends upon you, father. But I must say, that I have been astonished to see your friends carrying their attentions to all sorts and conditions of men so far as even to regulate the legitimate gains of sorcerers."

"One cannot write for too many people," said the monk, "nor be too minute in particularising cases, nor repeat the same things too often in different books. You may be convinced of this by the following anecdote, which is related by one of the gravest of our fathers, as you may well suppose, seeing he is our present Provincial—the reverend Father Cellot: 'We know a person,' says he, 'who was carrying a large sum of money in his pocket to restore it, in obedience to the orders of his confessor, and who, stepping into a bookseller's shop by the way, inquired if there was anything new?—*numquid novi?*—when the bookseller showed him a book on moral theology, recently published; and turning over the leaves carelessly, and without reflection, he lighted upon a passage describing his own case, and saw that he was under no obligation to make restitution: upon which, relieved from the burden of his scruples, he returned home with a purse no less heavy, and a heart much lighter, than when he left it—*abjecta scrupuli sarcina, retento auri pondere, levior domum repetiit.*'

"Say, after hearing that, if it is useful or not to know our maxims? Will you laugh at them now? or rather, are you not prepared to join with Father Cellot in the pious reflection which he makes on the blessedness of that incident? 'Accidents of that kind,' he remarks, 'are, with God, the effect of his providence; with the guardian angel, the effect of his good guidance; with the individuals to whom they happen, the effect of their predestination. From all eternity, God decided that the golden chain of their salvation should depend on such and such an author, and not upon a hundred others who say the same thing, because they never happen to meet with them. Had that man not written, this man would not have been saved. All, therefore, who find fault with the multitude of our authors, we would beseech, in the bowels of Jesus Christ, to beware of envying others those books which the eternal election of God and the blood of Jesus Christ have purchased for them!' Such are the eloquent terms in which this learned man proves so successfully the proposition which he had advanced, namely, 'How useful it must be to have a great many writers on moral theology—*quam utile sit de theologia morali multos scribere!*'"

"Father," said I, "I shall defer giving you my opinion of that passage to another opportunity; in the meantime, I shall only say that as your maxims are so useful, and as it is so important to publish them, you ought to continue to give me further instruction in them. For I can assure you that the person to whom I send them shows my letters to a great many people. Not that we intend to avail ourselves of them in our own case; but, indeed, we think it will be useful for the world to be informed about them."

"Very well," rejoined the monk, "you see I do not conceal them; and, in continuation, I am ready to furnish you, at our next interview, with an account of the comforts and indulgences which our fathers allow, with the view of rendering salvation easy, and devotion agreeable; so that, in addition to what you have hitherto learned as to particular conditions of men, you may learn what applies in general to all classes, and thus you will have gone through a complete course of instruction." So saying, the monk took his leave of me. I am, &c.

P. S. I have always forgot to tell you that there are different editions of Escobar. Should you think of purchasing him, I would advise you to choose the Lyons edition, having on the title page the device of a lamb lying on a book sealed with seven seals; or the Brussels edition of 1651. Both of these are better and larger than the previous editions published at Lyons in the years 1644 and 1646.

LETTER IX

Paris, *July* 3, 1656

SIR,

I shall use as little ceremony with you as the worthy monk did with me when I saw him last. The moment he perceived me, he came forward, with his eyes fixed on a book which he held in his hand, and accosted me thus: "'Would you not be infinitely obliged to any one who should open to you the gates of paradise? Would you not give millions of gold to have a key by which you might gain admittance whenever you thought proper? You need not be at such expense; here is one—here are a hundred for much less money.'"

At first I was at a loss to know whether the good father was reading, or talking to me, but he soon put the matter beyond doubt by adding:

"These, sir, are the opening words of a fine book, written by Father Barry of our Society; for I never give you anything of my own."

"What book is it?" asked I.

"Here is its title," he replied: "*Paradise opened to Philagio, in a Hundred Devotions to the Mother of God, easily practised.*"

"Indeed, father! and is each of these easy devotions a sufficient passport to heaven?"

"It is," returned he. "Listen to what follows: 'The devotions to the Mother of God, which you will find in this book, are so many celestial keys, which will open wide to you the gates of paradise, provided you practise them'; and, accordingly, he says at the conclusion, 'that he is satisfied if you practise only one of them.' "

"Pray, then, father, do teach me one of the easiest of them."

"They are all easy," he replied, "for example—'Saluting the Holy Virgin when you happen to meet her image—saying the little chaplet of the pleasures of the Virgin—fervently pronouncing the name of Mary—commissioning the angels to bow to her for us—wishing to build her as many churches as all the monarchs on earth have done—bidding her good morrow every morning, and good night in the evening—saying the *Ave Maria* every day, in honour of the heart of Mary'— which last devotion, he says, possesses the additional virtue of securing us the heart of the Virgin."

"But, father," said I, "only provided we give her our own in return, I presume?"

"That," he replied, "is not absolutely necessary, when a person is too much attached to the world. Hear Father Barry: 'Heart for heart would, no doubt, be highly proper; but yours is rather too much attached to the world, too much bound up in the creature, so that I dare not advise you to offer, at present, that *poor little slave* which you call your heart.' And so he contents himself with the *Ave Maria* which he had prescribed."

"Why, this is extremely easy work," said I, "and I should really think that no-body will be damned after that."

"Alas!" said the monk, "I see you have no idea of the hardness of some people's hearts. There are some, sir, who would never engage to repeat, every day, even these simple words, *Good day, Good evening*, just because such a practice would re-quire some exertion of memory. And, accordingly, it became necessary for Father Barry to furnish them with expedients still easier, such as wearing a chaplet night and day on the arm, in the form of a bracelet, or carrying about one's person a ro-sary, or an image of the Virgin. 'And, tell me now,' as Father Barry says, 'if I have not provided you with easy devotions to obtain the good graces of Mary?' "

"Extremely easy indeed, father," I observed.

"Yes," he said, "it is as much as could possibly be done, and I think should be quite satisfactory. For he must be a wretched creature indeed, who would not spare a single moment in all his lifetime to put a chaplet on his arm, or a rosary in his pocket, and thus secure his salvation; and that, too, with so much certainty that none who have tried the experiment have ever found it to fail, in whatever way they may have lived; though, let me add, we exhort people not to omit holy living. Let me refer you to the example of this, given at p. 34; it is that of a female who, while she practised daily the devotion of saluting the images of the Virgin, spent all her days in mortal sin, and yet was saved after all, by the merit of that single devotion."

"And how so?" cried I.

"Our Saviour," he replied, "raised her up again, for the very purpose of show-ing it. So certain it is that none can perish who practise any one of these devotions."

"My dear sir," I observed, "I am fully aware that the devotions to the Virgin are a powerful means of salvation, and that the least of them, if flowing from the exercise of faith and charity, as in the case of the saints who have practised them, are of great merit; but to make persons believe that, by practising these without reforming their wicked lives, they will be converted by them at the hour of death, or that God will raise them up again, does appear calculated rather to keep sinners going on in their evil courses, by deluding them with false peace and foolhardy confidence, than to draw them off from sin by that genuine conversion which grace alone can effect."

"What does it matter," replied the monk, "by what road we enter paradise, provided we do enter it? as our famous Father Binet, formerly our Provincial, remarks on a similar subject, in his excellent book, *On the Mark of Predestination*. 'Be it by hook or by crook,' as he says, 'what need we care, if we reach at last the celestial city.'"

"Granted," said I; "but the great question is if we will get there at all."

"The Virgin will be answerable for that," returned he; "so says Father Barry in the concluding lines of his book: 'If at the hour of death, the enemy should happen to put in some claim upon you, and occasion disturbance in the little commonwealth of your thoughts, you have only to say that Mary will answer for you, and that he must make his application to her.'"

"But, father, it might be possible to puzzle you, were one disposed to push the question a little further. Who, for example, has assured us that the Virgin will be answerable in this case?"

"Father Barry will be answerable for her," he replied. "'As for the profit and happiness to be derived from these devotions,' he says, 'I will be answerable for that; I will stand bail for the good Mother.'"

"But, father, who is to be answerable for Father Barry?"

"How!" cried the monk; "for Father Barry? is he not a member of our Society; and do you need to be told that our Society is answerable for all the books of its members? It is highly necessary and important for you to know about this. There is an order in our Society, by which all booksellers are prohibited from printing any work of our fathers without the approbation of our divines and the permission of our superiors. This regulation was passed by Henry III, 10th May 1583, and confirmed by Henry IV, 20th December 1603, and by Louis XIII, 14th February 1612; so that the whole of our body stands responsible for the publications of each of the brethren. This is a feature quite peculiar to our community. And, in consequence of this, not a single work emanates from us which does not breathe the spirit of the Society. That, sir, is a piece of information quite *apropos*."

"My good father," said I, "you oblige me very much, and I only regret that I did not know this sooner, as it will induce me to pay considerably more attention to your authors."

"I would have told you sooner," he replied, "had an opportunity offered; I hope, however, you will profit by the information in future, and, in the meantime, let us prosecute our subject. The methods of securing salvation which I have mentioned are, in my opinion, very easy, very sure, and sufficiently numerous; but it was the anxious wish of our doctors that people should not stop short at this first step, where they only do what is absolutely necessary for salvation and nothing more. Aspiring, as they do without ceasing, after the greater glory of God, they sought to elevate men to a higher pitch of piety; and, as men of the world are generally deterred from devotion by the strange ideas they have been led to form of it by some people, we have deemed it of the highest importance to remove this obstacle which meets us at the threshold. In this department Father Le Moine has acquired much fame, by his work entitled *Devotion Made Easy*, composed for this very purpose. The picture which he draws of devotion in this work is perfectly charming. None ever understood the subject before him. Only hear what he says in the beginning of his work: 'Virtue has never as yet been seen aright; no portrait of her, hitherto produced, has borne the least verisimilitude. It is by no means surprising that so few have attempted to scale her rocky eminence. She has been held up as a cross-tempered dame, whose only delight is in solitude; she has been associated with toil and sorrow; and, in short, represented as the foe of sports and diversions, which are, in fact, the flowers of joy and the seasoning of life.'"

"But, father, I am sure, I have heard, at least, that there have been great saints who led extremely austere lives."

"No doubt of that," he replied; "but still, to use the language of the doctor, 'there have always been a number of genteel saints, and well-bred devotees'; and this difference in their manners, mark you, arises entirely from a difference of humours. 'I am far from denying,' says my author, 'that there are devout persons to be met with, pale and melancholy in their temperament, fond of silence and retirement, with phlegm instead of blood in their veins, and with faces of clay; but there are many others of a happier complexion, and who possess that sweet and warm humour, that genial and rectified blood, which is the true stuff that joy is made of.'

"You see," resumed the monk, "that the love of silence and retirement is not common to all devout people; and that, as I was saying, this is the effect rather of their complexion than their piety. Those austere manners to which you refer are, in fact, properly the character of a savage and barbarian, and, accordingly, you will find them ranked by Father Le Moine among the ridiculous and brutal manners of a moping idiot. The following is the description he has drawn of one of these in the seventh book of his *Moral Pictures:* 'He has no eyes for the beauties of art or nature. Were he to indulge in anything that gave him pleasure, he would consider himself oppressed with a grievous load. On festival days, he retires to hold fellowship with the dead. He delights in a grotto rather than a palace, and prefers the stump of a tree to a throne. As to injuries and affronts, he is as insensible to them as if he had the eyes and ears of a statue. Honour and glory are idols with whom he has no acquaintance, and to whom he has no incense to offer. To him a beautiful woman is no better than a spectre; and those imperial and commanding looks—those charming tyrants who hold so many slaves in willing and chainless servitude—have no more influence over his optics than the sun over those of owls,' &c."

"Reverend sir," said I, "had you not told me that Father Le Moine was the author of that description, I declare I would have guessed it to be the production of some profane fellow who had drawn it expressly with the view of turning the saints into ridicule. For if that is not the picture of a man entirely denied to those feelings which the Gospel obliges us to renounce, I confess that I know nothing of the matter."

"You may now perceive, then, the extent of your ignorance," he replied; "for these are the features of a feeble, uncultivated mind, 'destitute of those virtuous and natural affections which it ought to possess,' as Father Le Moine says at the close of that description. Such is his way of teaching 'Christian virtue and philosophy,' as he announces in his advertisement; and, in truth, it cannot be denied that this method of treating devotion is much more agreeable to the taste of the world than the old way in which they went to work before our times."

"There can be no comparison between them," was my reply, "and I now begin to hope that you will be as good as your word."

"You will see that better by-and-by," returned the monk. "Hitherto I have only spoken of piety in general, but, just to show you more in detail how our fathers have disencumbered it of its toils and troubles, would it not be most consoling to the ambitious to learn that they may maintain genuine devotion along with an inordinate love of greatness?"

"What, father! even though they should run to the utmost excess of ambition?"

"Yes," he replied; "for this would be only a venial sin, unless they sought after greatness in order to offend God and injure the State more effectually. Now venial sins do not preclude a man from being devout, as the greatest saints are not exempt from them. 'Ambition,' says Escobar, 'which consists in an inordinate appetite for place and power, is of itself a venial sin; but when such dignities are coveted for the purpose of hurting the commonwealth, or having more opportunity to offend God, these adventitious circumstances render it mortal.'"

"Very savoury doctrine, indeed, father."

"And is it not still more savoury," continued the monk, "for misers to be told, by the same authority, 'that the rich are not guilty of mortal sin by refusing to give alms out of their superfluity to the poor in the hour of their greatest need?—*scio in gravi pauperum necessitate divites non dando superflua, non peccare mortaliter.*'"

"Why truly," said I, "if that be the case, I give up all pretension to skill in the science of sins."

"To make you still more sensible of this," returned he, "you have been accustomed to think, I suppose, that a good opinion of one's self, and a complacency in one's own works, is a most dangerous sin? Now, will you not be surprised if I can show you that such a good opinion, even though there should be no foundation for it, is so far from being a sin that it is, on the contrary, *the gift of God?*"

"Is it possible, father?"

"That it is," said the monk; "and our good Father Garasse shows it in his French work, entitled *Summary of the Capital Truths of Religion:* 'It is a result of commutative justice that all honest labour should find its recompense either in praise or in self-satisfaction. When men of good talents publish some excellent work, they are justly remunerated by public applause. But when a man of weak parts has wrought hard at some worthless production, and fails to obtain the praise of the public, in order that his labour may not go without its reward, God imparts to him a personal satisfaction, which it would be worse than barbarous injustice to envy him. It is thus that God, who is infinitely just, has given even to frogs a certain complacency in their own croaking.'"

"Very fine decisions in favour of vanity, ambition, and avarice!" cried I; "and envy, father, will it be more difficult to find an excuse for it?"

"That is a delicate point," he replied. "We require to make use here of Father Bauny's distinction, which he lays down in his *Summary of Sins:* 'Envy of the spiritual good of our neighbour is mortal but envy of his temporal good is only venial.'"

"And why so, father?"

"You shall hear," said he. "'For the good that consists in temporal things is so slender, and so insignificant in relation to heaven, that it is of no consideration in the eyes of God and His saints.'"

"But, father, if temporal good is so *slender*, and of so little consideration, how do you come to permit men's lives to be taken away in order to preserve it?"

"You mistake the matter entirely," returned the monk; "you were told that temporal good was of no consideration in the eyes of God, but not in the eyes of men."

"That idea never occurred to me," I replied; "and now, it is to be hoped that, in virtue of these same distinctions, the world will get rid of mortal sins altogether."

"Do not flatter yourself with that," said the father; "there are still such things as mortal sins—there is sloth, for example."

"Nay, then, father dear!" I exclaimed, "after that, farewell to all 'the joys of life!'"

"Stay," said the monk, "when you have heard Escobar's definition of that vice, you will perhaps change your tone: 'Sloth,' he observes, 'lies in grieving that spiritual things are spiritual, as if one should lament that the sacraments are the sources of grace; which would be a mortal sin.'"

"O my dear sir!" cried I, "I don't think that anybody ever took it into his head to be slothful in that way."

"And accordingly," he replied, "Escobar afterwards remarks: 'I must confess that it is very rarely that a person falls into the sin of sloth.' You see now how important it is to *define* things properly?"

"Yes, father, and this brings to my mind your other definitions about assassinations, ambuscades, and superfluities. But why have you not extended your method to all cases, and given definitions of all vices in your way, so that people may no longer sin in gratifying themselves?"

"It is not always essential," he replied, "to accomplish that purpose by changing the definitions of things. I may illustrate this by referring to the subject of good cheer, which is accounted one of the greatest pleasures of life, and which Escobar thus sanctions in his *Practice according to our Society:* 'Is it allowable for a person to eat and drink to repletion, unnecessarily, and solely for pleasure? Certainly he may, according to Sanchez, provided he does not thereby injure his health; because the natural appetite may be permitted to enjoy its proper functions.'"

"Well, father, that is certainly the most complete passage, and the most finished maxim in the whole of your moral system! What comfortable inferences may be drawn from it! Why, and is gluttony, then, not even a venial sin?"

"Not in the shape I have just referred to," he replied; "but, according to the same author, it would be a venial sin 'were a person to gorge himself, unnecessarily, with eating and drinking, to such a degree as to produce vomiting.' So much for that point. I would now say a little about the facilities we have invented for avoiding sin in worldly conversations and intrigues. One of the most embarrassing of these cases is how to avoid telling lies, particularly when one is anxious to induce a belief in what is false. In such cases, our doctrine of equivocations has been found of admirable service, according to which, as Sanchez has it, 'it is permitted to use ambiguous terms, leading people to understand them in another sense from that in which we understand them ourselves.'"

"I know that already, father," said I.

"We have published it so often," continued he, "that at length, it seems, everybody knows of it. But do you know what is to be done when no equivocal words can be got?"

"No, father."

"I thought as much," said the Jesuit; "this is something new, sir: I mean the doctrine of mental reservations. 'A man may swear,' as Sanchez says in the same place, 'that he never did such a thing (though he actually did it), meaning within himself that he did not do so on a certain day, or before he was born, or understanding any other such circumstance, while the words which he employs have no such sense as would discover his meaning. And this is very convenient in many cases, and quite innocent, when necessary or conducive to one's health, honour, or advantage.'"

"Indeed, father! is that not a lie, and perjury to boot?"

"No," said the father; "Sanchez and Filiutius prove that it is not; for, says the latter, 'it is the intention that determines the quality of the action.' And he suggests a still surer method for avoiding falsehood, which is this: After saying aloud, 'I swear that I have not done that,' to add, in a low voice, 'to-day'; or after saying aloud, 'I swear,' to interpose in a whisper, 'that I say,' and then continue aloud, 'that I have done that.' This, you perceive, is telling the truth."

"I grant it," said I; "it might possibly, however, be found to be telling the truth in a low key, and falsehood in a loud one; besides, I should be afraid that many people might not have sufficient presence of mind to avail themselves of these methods."

"Our doctors," replied the Jesuit, "have taught, in the same passage, for the benefit of such as might not be expert in the use of these reservations, that no more is required of them, to avoid lying, than simply to say that 'they have not done' what they have done, provided 'they have, in general, the intention of giving to their language the sense which an *able man* would give to it.' Be candid, now, and confess if you have not often felt yourself embarrassed, in consequence of not knowing this?"

"Sometimes," said I.

"And will you not also acknowledge," continued he, "that it would often prove very convenient to be absolved in conscience from keeping certain engagements one may have made?"

"The most convenient thing in the world!" I replied.

"Listen, then, to the general rule laid down by Escobar: 'Promises are not binding, when the person in making them had no intention to bind himself. Now, it seldom happens that any have such an intention, unless when they confirm their promises by an oath or contract; so that when one simply says, "I will do it," he means that he will do it if he does not change his mind; for he does not wish, by saying that, to deprive himself of his liberty.' He gives other rules in the same strain, which you may consult for yourself, and tells us, in conclusion, 'that all this is taken from Molina and our other authors, and is therefore settled beyond all doubt.'"

"My dear father," I observed, "I had no idea that the direction of the intention possessed the power of rendering promises null and void."

"You must perceive," returned he, "what facility this affords for prosecuting the business of life. But what has given us the most trouble has been to regulate the commerce between the sexes; our fathers being more chary in the matter of chastity. Not but that they have discussed questions of a very curious and very indulgent character, particularly in reference to married and betrothed persons."

At this stage of the conversation I was made acquainted with the most extraordinary questions you can well imagine. He gave me enough of them to fill many letters; but, as you show my communications to all sorts of persons, and as I do not choose to be the vehicle of such reading to those who would make it the subject of diversion, I must decline even giving the quotations.

The only thing to which I can venture to allude, out of all the books which he showed me, and these in French, too, is a passage which you will find in Father Bauny's *Summary*, p. 165, relating to certain little familiarities, which, provided the intention is well directed, he explains *"as passing for gallant"*; and you will be surprised to find, on p.148, a principle of morals, as to the power which daughters have to dispose of their persons without the leave of their relatives, couched in these terms: "When that is done with the consent of the daughter, although the father may have reason to complain, it does not follow that she, or the person to whom she has sacrificed her honour, has done him any wrong, or violated the rules of justice in regard to him; for the daughter has possession of her honour, as well as of her body, and can do what she pleases with them, bating death or mutilation of her members." Judge, from that specimen, of the rest. It brings to my recollection a passage from a heathen poet, a much better casuist, it would appear, than these reverend doctors; for he says, "that the person of a daughter does not belong wholly to herself, but partly to her father and partly to her mother, without whom she cannot dispose of it, even in marriage." And I am much mistaken if there is a single judge in the land who would not lay down as law the very reverse of this maxim of Father Bauny.

This is all I dare tell you of this part of our conversation, which lasted so long that I was obliged to beseech the monk to change the subject. He did so and proceeded to entertain me with their regulations about female attire.

"We shall not speak," he said, "of those who are actuated by impure intentions; but, as to others, Escobar remarks that 'if the woman adorn herself without any evil intention, but merely to gratify a natural inclination to vanity—*ob naturalem fastus inclinationem*—this is only a venial sin, or rather no sin at all.' And Father Bauny maintains, that 'even though the woman knows the bad effect which her care in adorning her person may have upon the virtue of those who may behold her, all decked out in rich and precious attire, she would not sin in so dressing.' And, among others, he cites our Father Sanchez as being of the same mind."

"But, father, what do your authors say to those passages of Scripture which so strongly denounce everything of that sort?"

"Lessius has well met that objection," said the monk, "by observing, 'that these passages of Scripture have the force of precepts only in regard to the women of that period, who were expected to exhibit, by their modest demeanour, an example of edification to the Pagans.'"

"And where did he find that, father"?

"It does not matter where he found it," replied he; "it is enough to know that the sentiments of these great men are always probable of themselves. It deserves to be noticed, however, that Father Le Moine has qualified this general permission; for he will on no account allow it to be extended to *the old ladies*. 'Youth,' he observes, 'is naturally entitled to adorn itself, nor can the use of ornament be condemned at an age which is the flower and verdure of life. But there it should be allowed to remain: it would be strangely out of season to seek for roses on the snow. The stars alone have a right to be always dancing, for they have the gift of perpetual youth. The wisest course in this matter, therefore, for old women, would be to consult good sense and a good mirror, to yield to decency and necessity, and to retire at the first approach of the shades of night.'"

"A most judicious advice," I observed.

"But," continued the monk, "just to show you how careful our fathers are about everything you can think of, I may mention that, after granting the ladies permission to gamble, and foreseeing that, in many cases, this license would be of little avail unless they had something to gamble with, they have established another maxim in their favour, which will be found in Escobar's chapter on larceny, no. 13: 'A wife,' says he, 'may gamble, and for this purpose may pilfer money from her husband.'"

"Well, father, that is capital!"

"There are many other good things besides that," said the father; "but we must waive them and say a little about those more important maxims, which facilitate the practice of holy things—the manner of attending mass, for example. On this subject, our great divines, Gaspard Hurtado and Coninck, have taught 'that it is quite sufficient to be present at mass in body, though we may be absent in spirit, provided we maintain an outwardly respectful deportment.' Vasquez goes a step further, maintaining 'that one fulfils the precept of hearing mass, even though one should go with no such intention at all.' All this is repeatedly laid down by Escobar, who, in one passage, illustrates the point by the example of those who are dragged to mass by force, and who put on a fixed resolution not to listen to it."

"Truly, sir," said I, "had any other person told me that, I would not have believed it."

"In good sooth," he replied, "it requires all the support which the authority of these great names can lend it; and so does the following maxim by the same Escobar, 'that even a wicked intention, such as that of ogling the women, joined to that of hearing mass rightly, does not hinder a man from fulfilling the service.' But another very convenient device, suggested by our learned brother Turrian, is that 'one may hear the half of a mass from one priest, and the other half from another; and that it makes no difference though he should hear first the conclusion of the one, and then the commencement of the other.' I might also mention that it has been decided by several of our doctors to be lawful 'to hear the two halves of a mass at the same time, from the lips of two different priests, one of whom is commencing the mass, while the other is at the elevation; it being quite possible to attend to both parties at once, and two halves of a mass making a whole—*duæ medietates unam missam constituunt.*' 'From all which,' says Escobar, 'I conclude, that you may hear mass in a very short period of time; if, for example, you should happen to hear four masses going on at the same time, so arranged that when the first is at the commencement, the second is at the gospel, the third at the consecration, and the last at the communion.'"

"Certainly, father, according to that plan, one may hear mass any day at Notre Dame in a twinkling."

"Well," replied he, "that just shows how admirably we have succeeded in facilitating the hearing of mass. But I am anxious now to show you how we have softened the use of the sacraments, and particularly that of penance. It is here that the benignity of our fathers shines in its truest splendour; and you will be really astonished to find that devotion, a thing which the world is so much afraid of, should have been treated by our doctors with such consummate skill that, to use the words of Father Le Moine, in his *Devotion Made Easy*, demolishing the bugbear which the devil had placed at its threshold, they have rendered it easier than vice and more agreeable than pleasure; so that, in fact, simply to live is incomparably more irksome than to live well. Is that not a marvellous change, now?"

"Indeed, father, I cannot help telling you a bit of my mind: I am sadly afraid that you have overshot the mark, and that this indulgence of yours will shock more people than it will attract. The mass, for example, is a thing so grand and so holy that, in the eyes of a great many, it would be enough to blast the credit of your doctors forever to show them how you have spoken of it."

"With a certain class," replied the monk, "I allow that may be the case; but do you not know that we accommodate ourselves to all sorts of persons? You seem to have lost all recollection of what I have repeatedly told you on this point. The first time you are at leisure, therefore, I propose that we make this the theme of our conversation, deferring till then the lenitives we have introduced into the confessional. I promise to make you understand it so well that you will never forget it."

With these words we parted, so that our next conversation, I presume, will turn on the policy of the Society. I am, &c.

P.S. Since writing the above, I have seen *Paradise Opened by a Hundred Devotions Easily Practised*, by Father Barry; and also the *Mark of Predestination*, by Father Binet; both of them pieces well worth the seeing.

LETTER X

Paris, *August* 2, 1656

SIR,

I have not come yet to the policy of the Society, but shall first introduce you to one of its leading principles. I refer to the palliatives which they have applied to confession, and which are unquestionably the best of all the schemes they have fallen upon to "attract all and repel none." It is absolutely necessary to know something of this before going any further; and, accordingly, the monk judged it expedient to give me some instructions on the point, nearly as follows:

"From what I have already stated," he observed, "you may judge of the success with which our doctors have laboured to discover, in their wisdom, that a great many things, formerly regarded as forbidden, are innocent and allowable; but as there are some sins for which one can find no excuse, and for which there is no remedy but confession, it became necessary to alleviate, by the methods I am now going to mention, the difficulties attending that practice. Thus, having shown you, in our previous conversations, how we relieve people from troublesome scruples of conscience by showing them that what they believed to be sinful was indeed quite innocent, I proceed now to illustrate our convenient plan for expiating what is really sinful, which is effected by making confession as easy a process as it was formerly a painful one."

"And how do you manage that, father?"

"Why," said he, "it is by those admirable subtleties which are peculiar to our Company, and have been styled by our fathers in Flanders, in *The Image of the First Century*, 'the pious finesse, the holy artifice of devotion—*piam et religiosam calliditatem, et pietatis solertiam.*' By the aid of these inventions, as they remark in the same place, 'crimes may be expiated nowadays *alacrius*—with more zeal and alacrity than they were committed in former days, and a great many people may be washed from their stains almost as cleverly as they contracted them—*plurimi vix citius maculas contrahunt quam eluunt.*' "

"Pray, then, father, do teach me some of these most salutary lessons of *finesse.*"

"We have a good number of them," answered the monk; "for there are a great many irksome things about confession, and for each of these we have devised a palliative. The chief difficulties connected with this ordinance are the shame of confessing certain sins, the trouble of specifying the circumstances of others, the penance exacted for them, the resolution against relapsing into them, the avoidance of the proximate occasions of sins, and the regret for having committed them. I hope to convince you to-day that it is now possible to get over all this with hardly any trouble at all; such is the care we have taken to allay the bitterness and nauseousness of this very necessary medicine. For, to begin with the difficulty of confessing certain sins, you are aware it is of importance often to keep in the good graces of one's confessor; now, must it not be extremely convenient to be permitted, as you are by our doctors, particularly Escobar and Suarez, 'to have two confessors, one for the mortal sins and another for the venial, in order to maintain a fair character with your ordinary confessor—*uti bonam famam apud ordinarium tueatur*—provided you do not take occasion from thence to indulge in mortal sin?' This is followed by another ingenious contrivance for confessing a sin, even to the ordinary confessor, without his perceiving that it was committed since the last confession, which is, 'to make a general confession, and huddle this last sin in a lump among the rest which we confess.' And I am sure you will own that the following decision of Father Bauny goes far to alleviate the shame which one must feel in confessing his relapses, namely, 'that, except in certain cases, which rarely occur, the confessor is not entitled to ask his penitent if the sin of which he accuses himself is an habitual one, nor is the latter obliged to answer such a question; because the confessor has no right to subject his penitent to the shame of disclosing his frequent relapses.' "

"Indeed, father! I might as well say that a physician has no right to ask his patient if it is long since he had the fever. Do not sins assume quite a different aspect according to circumstances? and should it not be the object of a genuine penitent to discover the whole state of his conscience to his confessor, with the same sincerity and open-heartedness as if he were speaking to Jesus Christ himself, whose place the priest occupies? If so, how far is he from realizing such a disposition who, by concealing the frequency of his relapses, conceals the aggravations of his offence!"

I saw that this puzzled the worthy monk, for he attempted to elude rather than resolve the difficulty by turning my attention to another of their rules, which only goes to establish a fresh abuse, instead of justifying in the least the decision of Father Bauny; a decision which, in my opinion, is one of the most pernicious of their maxims, and calculated to encourage profligate men to continue in their evil habits.

"I grant you," replied the father, "that habit aggravates the malignity of a sin, but it does not alter its nature; and that is the reason why we do not insist on people confessing it, according to the rule laid down by our fathers, and quoted by Escobar, 'that one is only obliged to confess the circumstances that alter the species of the sin, and not those that aggravate it.' Proceeding on this rule, Father Granados says, 'that if one has eaten flesh in Lent, all he needs to do is to confess that he has broken the fast, without specifying whether it was by eating flesh, or by taking two fish meals.' And, according to Reginald, 'a sorcerer who has employed the diabolical art is not obliged to reveal that circumstance; it is enough to say that he has dealt in magic, without expressing whether it was by palmistry or by a paction with the devil.' Fagundez, again, has decided that 'rape is not a circumstance which one is bound to reveal, if the woman give her consent.' All this is quoted by Escobar, with many other very curious decisions as to these circumstances, which you may consult at your leisure."

"These 'artifices of devotion' are vastly convenient in their way," I observed.

"And yet," said the father, "notwithstanding all that, they would go for nothing, sir, unless we had proceeded to mollify penance, which, more than anything else, deters people from confession. Now, however, the most squeamish have nothing to dread from it, after what we have advanced in our theses of the College of Clermont, where we hold that, if the confessor imposes a suitable penance, and the penitent be unwilling to submit himself to it, the latter may go home, 'waiving both the penance and the absolution.' Or, as Escobar says, in giving the Practice of our Society, 'if the penitent declare his willingness to have his penance remitted to the next world, and to suffer in purgatory all the pains due to him, the confessor may, for the honour of the sacrament, impose a very light penance on him, particularly if he has reason to believe that this penitent would object to a heavier one.'"

"I really think," said I, "that, if that is the case, we ought no longer to call confession the *sacrament of penance*."

"You are wrong," he replied; "for we always administer something in the way of penance, for the form's sake."

"But, father, do you suppose that a man is worthy of receiving absolution when he will submit to nothing painful to expiate his offences? And, in these circumstances, ought you not to retain rather than remit their sins? Are you not aware of the extent of your ministry, and that you have the power of binding and loosing? Do you imagine that you are at liberty to give absolution indifferently to all who ask it, and without ascertaining beforehand if Jesus Christ looses in heaven those whom you loose on earth?"

"What!" cried the father, "do you suppose that we do not know that 'the confessor (as one remarks) ought to sit in judgement on the disposition of his penitent, both because he is bound not to dispense the sacraments to the unworthy, Jesus Christ having enjoined him to be a faithful steward and not give that which is holy unto dogs; and because he is a judge, and it is the duty of a judge to give righteous judgement, by loosing the worthy and binding the unworthy, and he ought not to absolve those whom Jesus Christ condemns.'"

"Whose words are these, father?"

"They are the words of our father Filiutius," he replied.

"You astonish me," said I; "I took them to be a quotation from one of the fathers of the Church. At all events, sir, that passage ought to make an impression on the confessors, and render them very circumspect in the dispensation of this sacrament, to ascertain whether the regret of their penitents is sufficient, and whether their promises of future amendment are worthy of credit."

"That is not such a difficult matter," replied the father; "Filiutius had more sense than to leave confessors in that dilemma, and accordingly he suggests an easy way of getting out of it, in the words immediately following: 'The confessor may easily set his mind at rest as to the disposition of his penitent; for, if he fail to give sufficient evidence of sorrow, the confessor has only to ask him if he does not detest the sin in his heart, and, if he answers that he does, he is bound to believe it. The same thing may be said of resolutions as to the future, unless the case involves an obligation to restitution, or to avoid some proximate occasion of sin.' "

"As to that passage, father, I can easily believe that it is Filiutius' own."

"You are mistaken though," said the father, "for he has extracted it, word for word, from Suarez."

"But, father, that last passage from Filiutius overturns what he had laid down in the former. For confessors can no longer be said to sit as judges on the disposition of their penitents, if they are bound to take it simply upon their word, in the absence of all satisfying signs of contrition. Are the professions made on such occasions so infallible, that no other sign is needed? I question much if experience has taught your fathers that all who make fair promises are remarkable for keeping them; I am mistaken if they have not often found the reverse."

"No matter," replied the monk; "confessors are bound to believe them for all that; for Father Bauny, who has probed this question to the bottom, has concluded 'that at whatever time those who have fallen into frequent relapses, without giving evidence of amendment, present themselves before a confessor, expressing their regret for the past, and a good purpose for the future, he is bound to believe them on their simple averment, although there may be reason to presume that such resolution only came from the teeth outwards. Nay,' says he, 'though they should indulge subsequently to greater excess than ever in the same delinquencies, still, in my opinion, they may receive absolution.' There now! that, I am sure, should silence you."

"But, father," said I, "you impose a great hardship, I think, on the confessors, by thus obliging them to believe the very reverse of what they see."

"You don't understand it," returned he; "all that is meant is that they are obliged to act and absolve *as if* they believed that their penitents would be true to their engagements, though, in point of fact, they believe no such thing. This is explained, immediately afterwards, by Suarez and Filiutius. After having said that 'the priest is bound to believe the penitent on his word,' they add: 'It is not necessary that the confessor should be convinced that the good resolution of his penitent will be carried into effect, nor even that he should judge it probable; it is enough that he thinks the person has at the time the design in general, though he may very shortly after relapse. Such is the doctrine of all our authors—*ita docent omnes autores.*' Will you presume to doubt what has been taught by our authors?"

"But, sir, what then becomes of what Father Petau himself is obliged to own, in the preface to his *Public Penance*, 'that the holy fathers, doctors, and councils of the Church agree in holding it as a settled point that the penance preparatory to the eucharist must be genuine, constant, resolute, and not languid and sluggish, or subject to after-thoughts and relapses?' "

"Don't you observe," replied the monk, "that Father Petau is speaking of the *ancient Church?* But all that is now *so little in season*, to use a common saying of our doctors, that, according to Father Bauny, the reverse is the only true view of the matter. 'There are some,' says he, 'who maintain that absolution ought to be refused to those who fall frequently into the same sin, more especially if, after being often absolved, they evince no signs of amendment; and others hold the opposite view. But the only true opinion is that they ought not to be refused absolution; and, though they should be nothing the better of all the advice given them, though they should have broken all their promises to lead new lives, and been at no trouble to purify themselves, still it is of no consequence; whatever may be said to the contrary, the true opinion which ought to be followed is that even in all these cases, they ought to be absolved.' And again: 'Absolution ought neither to be denied nor delayed in the case of those who live in habitual sins against the law of God, of nature, and of the Church, although there should be no apparent prospect of future amendment—*etsi emendationis futuræ nulla spes appareat.*' "

"But, father, this certainty of always getting absolution may induce sinners—"

"I know what you mean," interrupted the Jesuit; "but listen to Father Bauny, Q. 15: 'Absolution may be given even to him who candidly avows that the hope of being absolved induced him to sin with more freedom than he would otherwise have done.' And Father Caussin, defending this proposition, says 'that, were this not true, confession would be interdicted to the greater part of mankind; and the only resource left poor sinners would be a branch and a rope.' "

"O father, how these maxims of yours will draw people to your confessionals!"

"Yes," he replied, "you would hardly believe what numbers are in the habit of frequenting them; 'we are absolutely oppressed and overwhelmed, so to speak, under the crowd of our penitents—*penitentium numero obruimur*'—as is said in *The Image of the First Century.*"

"I could suggest a very simple method," said I, "to escape from this inconvenient pressure. You have only to oblige sinners to avoid the proximate occasions of sin; that single expedient would afford you relief at once."

"We have no wish for such a relief," rejoined the monk; "quite the reverse; for, as is observed in the same book, 'the great end of our Society is to labor to establish the virtues, to wage war on the vices, and to save a great number of souls.' Now, as there are very few souls inclined to quit the proximate occasions of sin, we have been obliged to define what a proximate occasion is. 'That cannot be called a proximate occasion,' says Escobar, 'where one sins but rarely, or on a sudden transport—say three or four times a year'; or, as Father Bauny has it, 'once or twice in a month.' Again, asks this author, 'what is to be done in the case of masters and servants, or cousins, who, living under the same roof, are by this occasion tempted to sin?' "

"They ought to be separated," said I.

"That is what he says, too, 'if their relapses be very frequent: but if the parties offend rarely, and cannot be separated without trouble and loss, they may, according to Suarez and other authors, be absolved, provided they promise to sin no more, and are truly sorry for what is past.'"

This required no explanation, for he had already informed me with what sort of evidence of contrition the confessor was bound to rest satisfied.

"And Father Bauny," continued the monk, "permits those who are involved in the proximate occasions of sin, 'to remain as they are, when they cannot avoid them without becoming the common talk of the world, or subjecting themselves to inconvenience.' 'A priest,' he remarks in another work, 'may and ought to absolve a woman who is guilty of living with a paramour, if she cannot put him away honourably, or has some reason for keeping him—*si non potest honeste ejicere, aut habeat aliquam causam retinendi*—provided she promises to act more virtuously for the future.'"

"Well, father," cried I, "you have certainly succeeded in relaxing the obligation of avoiding the occasions of sin to a very comfortable extent, by dispensing with the duty as soon as it becomes inconvenient; but I should think your fathers will at least allow it be binding when there is no difficulty in the way of its performance?"

"Yes," said the father, "though even then the rule is not without exceptions. For Father Bauny says, in the same place, 'that any one may frequent profligate houses, with the view of converting their unfortunate inmates, though the probability should be that he fall into sin, having often experienced before that he has yielded to their fascinations. Some doctors do not approve of this opinion, and hold that no man may voluntarily put his salvation in peril to succour his neighbor; yet I decidedly embrace the opinion which they controvert.'"

"A novel sort of preachers these, father! But where does Father Bauny find any ground for investing them with such a mission?"

"It is upon one of his own principles," he replied, "which he announces in the same place after Basil Ponce. I mentioned it to you before, and I presume you have not forgotten it. It is, 'that one may seek an occasion of sin, directly and expressly—*primo et per se*—to promote the temporal or spiritual good of himself or his neighbour.'"

On hearing these passages, I felt so horrified that I was on the point of breaking out; but, being resolved to hear him to an end, I restrained myself, and merely inquired: "How, father, does this doctrine comport with that of the Gospel, which binds us to 'pluck out the right eye,' and 'cut off the right hand,' when they 'offend,' or prove prejudicial to salvation? And how can you suppose that the man who wilfully indulges in the occasions of sins, sincerely hates sin? Is it not evident, on the contrary, that he has never been properly touched with a sense of it, and that he has not yet experienced that genuine conversion of heart, which makes a man love God as much as he formerly loved the creature?"

"Indeed!" cried he, "do you call that genuine contrition? It seems you do not know that, as Father Pintereau says, 'all our fathers teach, with one accord, that it is an error, and almost a heresy, to hold that *contrition* is necessary; or that *attrition* alone, induced by the *sole* motive, the fear of the pains of hell, which excludes a disposition to offend, is not sufficient with the sacrament?'"

"What, father! do you mean to say that it is almost an article of faith that attrition, induced merely by fear of punishment, is sufficient with the sacrament? That idea, I think, is peculiar to your fathers; for those other doctors who hold that attrition is sufficient along with the sacrament, always take care to show that it must be accompanied with some love to God at least. It appears to me, more-over, that even your own authors did not always consider this doctrine of yours so certain. Your Father Suarez, for instance, speaks of it thus: 'Although it is a probable opinion that attrition is sufficient with the sacrament, yet it is not certain, and it may be false—*non est certa, et potest esse falsa*. And, if it is false, attrition is not sufficient to save a man; and he that dies knowingly in this state, wilfully exposes himself to the grave peril of eternal damnation. For this opinion is neither very ancient nor very common—*nec valde antiqua, nec multum communis.*' Sanchez was not more prepared to hold it as infallible when he said in his *Summary* that 'the sick man and his confessor, who content themselves at the hour of death with attrition and the sacrament, are both chargeable with mortal sin, on account of the great risk of damnation to which the penitent would be exposed, if the opin-ion that attrition is sufficient with the sacrament should not turn out to be true.' Comitolus, too, says that 'we should not be too sure that attrition suffices with the sacrament.'"

Here the worthy father interrupted me. "What!" he cried, "you read our au-thors then, it seems? That is all very well; but it would be still better were you never to read them without the precaution of having one of *us* beside you. Do you not see, now, that, from having read them alone, you have concluded, in your simplicity, that these passages bear hard on those who have more lately supported our doctrine of attrition? Whereas it might be shown that nothing could set them off to greater advantage. Only think what a triumph it is for our fathers of the present day to have succeeded in disseminating their opinion in such short time, and to such an extent that, with the exception of theologians, nobody almost would ever suppose but that our modern views on this subject had been the uniform belief of the faithful in all ages! So that, in fact, when you have shown, from our fathers themselves, that, a few years ago, 'this opinion was not certain,' you have only succeeded in giving our modern authors the whole merit of its establishment!

"Accordingly," he continued, "our cordial friend Diana, to gratify us, no doubt, has recounted the various steps by which the opinion reached its present position. 'In former days, the ancient schoolmen maintained that contrition was necessary as soon as one had committed a mortal sin; since then, however, it has been thought that it is not binding except on festival days; afterwards, only when some great calamity threatened the people; others, again, that it ought not to be long delayed at the approach of death. But our fathers, Hurtado and Vasquez, have ably refuted all these opinions and established that one is not bound to contrition unless he cannot be absolved in any other way, or at the point of death!' But, to continue the wonderful progress of this doctrine, I might add, what our fathers, Fagundez, Granados, and Escobar, have decided, 'that contri-tion is not necessary even at death; because,' say they, 'if attrition with the sacra-ment did not suffice at death, it would follow that attrition would not be suffi-cient with the sacrament. And the learned Hurtado, cited by Diana and Escobar, goes still further; for he asks: 'Is that sorrow for sin which flows solely from apprehension of its temporal consequences, such as having lost health or money, sufficient? We must distinguish. If the evil is not regarded as sent by the hand of God, such a sorrow does not suffice; but if the evil is viewed as sent by God, as, in fact, all evil, says Diana, except sin, comes from him, that kind of sorrow is sufficient.' Our Father Lamy holds the same doctrine."

"You surprise me, father; for I see nothing in all that attrition of which you speak but what is natural; and in this way a sinner may render himself worthy of absolution without supernatural grace at all. Now everybody knows that this is a heresy condemned by the Council."

"I should have thought with you," he replied; "and yet it seems this must not be the case, for the fathers of our College of Clermont have maintained (in their Theses of the 23rd May and 6th June 1644) 'that attrition may be holy and sufficient for the sacrament, although it may not be supernatural'; and (in that of August 1643) 'that attrition, though merely natural, is sufficient for the sacrament, provided it is honest.' I do not see what more could be said on the subject, unless we choose to subjoin an inference, which may be easily drawn from these principles, namely, that contrition, so far from being necessary to the sacrament, is rather prejudicial to it, inasmuch as, by washing away sins of itself, it would leave nothing for the sacrament to do at all. That is, indeed, exactly what the celebrated Jesuit Father Valencia remarks. (Book iv, disp. 7, q. 8, p. 4.) 'Contrition,' says he, 'is by no means necessary in order to obtain the principal benefit of the sacrament; on the contrary, it is rather an obstacle in the way of it—*imo obstat potius quominus effectus sequatur.*' Nobody could well desire more to be said in commendation of attrition."

"I believe that, father," said I; "but you must allow me to tell you my opinion, and to show you to what a dreadful length this doctrine leads. When you say that 'attrition, induced by the mere dread of punishment,' is sufficient, with the sacrament, to justify sinners, does it not follow that a person may always expiate his sins in this way, and thus be saved without ever having loved God all his lifetime? Would your fathers venture to hold that?"

"I perceive," replied the monk, "from the strain of your remarks, that you need some information on the doctrine of our fathers regarding the love of God. This is the last feature of their morality, and the most important of all. You must have learned something of it from the passages about contrition which I have quoted to you. But here are others still more definite on the point of love to God—Don't interrupt me, now; for it is of importance to notice the connection. Attend to Escobar, who reports the different opinions of our authors, in his *Practice of the Love of God according to our Society.* The question is: 'When is one obliged to have an actual affection for God?' Suarez says it is enough if one loves Him before being *articulo mortis*—at the point of death—without determining the exact time. Vasquez, that it is sufficient even at the very point of death. Others, when one has received baptism. Others, again, when one is bound to exercise contrition. And others, on festival days. But our father, Castro Palao, combats all these opinions, and with good reason—*merito.* Hurtado de Mendoza insists that we are obliged to love God once a year; and that we ought to regard it as a great favour that we are not bound to do it oftener. But our Father Coninck thinks that we are bound to it only once in three or four years; Henriquez, once in five years; and Filiutius says that it is *probable* that we are not strictly bound to it even once in five years. How often, then, do you ask? Why, he refers it to the judgement of the judicious."

I took no notice of all this badinage, in which the ingenuity of man seems to be sporting, in the height of insolence, with the love of God.

"But," pursued the monk, "our Father Antony Sirmond surpasses all on this point, in his admirable book, *The Defence of Virtue*, where, as he tells the reader, 'he speaks French in France,' as follows: 'St. Thomas says that we are obliged to love God as soon as we come to the use of reason: that is rather too soon! Scotus says every Sunday; pray, for what reason? Others say when we are sorely tempted: yes, if there be no other way of escaping the temptation. Scotus says when we have received a benefit from God: good, in the way of thanking Him for it. Others say at death: rather late! As little do I think it binding at the reception of any sacrament: attrition in such cases is quite enough, along with confession, if convenient. Suarez says that it is binding at some time or another; but at what time?—he leaves you to judge of that for yourself—he does not know; and what that doctor did not know I know not who should know.' In short, he concludes that we are not strictly bound to more than to keep the other commandments, without any affection for God, and without giving Him our hearts, provided that we do not hate Him. To prove this is the sole object of his second treatise. You will find it in every page; more especially where he says: 'God, in commanding us to love Him, is satisfied with our obeying Him in his other commandments. If God had said: "Whatever obedience thou yieldest me, if thy heart is not given to me, I will destroy thee!" would such a motive, think you, be well fitted to promote the end which God must, and only can, have in view? Hence it is said that we shall love God by doing His will, *as if* we loved Him with affection, as if the motive in this case was real charity. If that is really our motive, so much the better; if not, still we are strictly fulfilling the commandment of love, by having its works, so that (such is the goodness of God!) we are commanded, not so much to love Him, as not to hate Him.'

"Such is the way in which our doctors have discharged men from the *painful* obligation of actually loving God. And this doctrine is so advantageous that our Fathers Annat, Pintereau, Le Moine, and Antony Sirmond himself, have strenuously defended it when it has been attacked. You have only to consult their answers to the *Moral Theology*. That of Father Pintereau, in particular, will enable you to form some idea of the value of this dispensation, from the price which he tells us that it cost, which is no less than the blood of Jesus Christ. This crowns the whole. It appears, that this dispensation from the *painful* obligation to love God, is the privilege of the Evangelical law, in opposition to the Judaical. 'It was reasonable,' he says, 'that, under the law of grace in the New Testament, God should relieve us from that troublesome and arduous obligation which existed under the law of bondage, to exercise an act of perfect contrition, in order to be justified; and that the place of this should be supplied by the sacraments, instituted in aid of an easier disposition. Otherwise, indeed, Christians, who are the children, would have no greater facility in gaining the good graces of their Father than the Jews, who were the slaves, had in obtaining the mercy of their Lord and Master.'"

"O father!" cried I; "no patience can stand this any longer. It is impossible to listen without horror to the sentiments I have just heard."

"They are not my sentiments," said the monk.

"I grant it, sir," said I; "but you feel no aversion to them; and, so far from detesting the authors of these maxims, you hold them in esteem. Are you not afraid that your consent may involve you in a participation of their guilt? and are you not aware that St. Paul judges worthy of death, not only the authors of evil things, but also 'those who have pleasure in them that do them?' Was it not enough to have permitted men to indulge in so many forbidden things under the covert of your palliations? Was it necessary to go still further and hold out a bribe to them to commit even those crimes which you found it impossible to excuse, by offering them an easy and certain absolution; and for this purpose nullifying the power of the priests, and obliging them, more as slaves than as judges, to absolve the most inveterate sinners—without any amendment of life, without any sign of contrition except promises a hundred times broken, without penance 'unless they choose to accept of it', and without abandoning the occasions of their vices, 'if they should thereby be put to any inconvenience?'

"But your doctors have gone even beyond this; and the license which they have assumed to tamper with the most holy rules of Christian conduct amounts to a total subversion of the law of God. They violate 'the great commandment on which hang all the law and the prophets'; they strike at the very heart of piety; they rob it of the spirit that giveth life; they hold that to love God is not necessary to salvation; and go so far as to maintain that 'this dispensation from loving God is the privilege which Jesus Christ has introduced into the world!' This, sir, is the very climax of impiety. The price of the blood of Jesus Christ paid to obtain us a dispensation from loving Him! Before the incarnation, it seems men were obliged to love God; but since 'God has so loved the world as to give His only begotten Son,' the world, redeemed by him, is released from loving Him! Strange divinity of our days—to dare to take off the 'anathema' which St. Paul denounces on those 'that love not the Lord Jesus!' To cancel the sentence of St. John: 'He that loveth not, abideth in death!' and that of Jesus Christ himself: 'He that loveth me not keepeth not my precepts!' and thus to render those worthy of enjoying God through eternity who never loved God all their life! Behold the Mystery of Iniquity fulfilled! Open your eyes at length, my dear father, and if the other aberrations of your casuists have made no impression on you, let these last, by their very extravagance, compel you to abandon them. This is what I desire from the bottom of my heart, for your own sake and for the sake of your doctors; and my prayer to God is that He would vouchsafe to convince them how false the light must be that has guided them to such precipices; and that He would fill their hearts with that love of Himself from which they have dared to give man a dispensation!"

After some remarks of this nature, I took my leave of the monk, and I see no great likelihood of my repeating my visits to him. This, however, need not occasion you any regret; for, should it be necessary to continue these communications on their maxims, I have studied their books sufficiently to tell you as much of their morality, and more, perhaps, of their policy, than he could have done himself. I am, &c.

LETTER XI

To the Reverend Fathers, the Jesuits

August 18, 1656

REVEREND FATHERS,

I have seen the letters which you are circulating in opposition to those which I wrote to one of my friends on your morality; and I perceive that one of the principal points of your defence is that I have not spoken of your maxims with sufficient seriousness. This charge you repeat in all your productions, and carry it so far as to allege, that I have been "guilty of turning sacred things into ridicule."

Such a charge, fathers, is no less surprising than it is unfounded. Where do you find that I have turned sacred things into ridicule? You specify " the Mohatra contract, and the story of John d'Alba." But are these what you call "sacred things?" Does it really appear to you that the Mohatra is something so venerable that it would be blasphemy not to speak of it with respect? And the lessons of Father Bauny on larceny, which led John d'Alba to practise it at your expense, are they so sacred as to entitle you to stigmatize all who laugh at them as profane people?

What, fathers! must the vagaries of your doctors pass for the verities of the Christian faith, and no man be allowed to ridicule Escobar, or the fantastical and unchristian dogmas of your authors, without being stigmatized as jesting at religion? Is it possible you can have ventured to reiterate so often an idea so utterly unreasonable? Have you no fears that, in blaming me for laughing at your absurdities, you may only afford me fresh subject of merriment; that you may make the charge recoil on yourselves, by showing that I have really selected nothing from your writings as the matter of raillery but what was truly ridiculous; and that thus, in making a jest of your morality, I have been as far from jeering at holy things, as the doctrine of your casuists is far from being the holy doctrine of the Gospel?

Indeed, reverend sirs, there is a vast difference between laughing at religion and laughing at those who profane it by their extravagant opinions. It were impiety to be wanting in respect for the verities which the Spirit of God has revealed; but it were no less impiety of another sort to be wanting in contempt for the falsities which the spirit of man opposes to them.

For, fathers (since you will force me into this argument), I beseech you to consider that, just in proportion as Christian truths are worthy of love and respect, the contrary errors must deserve hatred and contempt; there being two things in the truths of our religion: a divine beauty that renders them lovely, and a sacred majesty that renders them venerable; and two things also about errors: an impiety, that makes them horrible, and an impertinence that renders them ridiculous. For these reasons, while the saints have ever cherished towards the truth the twofold sentiment of love and fear—the whole of their wisdom being comprised between fear, which is its beginning, and love, which is its end—they have, at the same time, entertained towards error the twofold feeling of hatred and contempt, and their zeal has been at once employed to repel, by force of reasoning, the malice of the wicked, and to chastise, by the aid of ridicule, their extravagance and folly.

Do not then expect, fathers, to make people believe that it is unworthy of a Christian to treat error with derision. Nothing is easier than to convince all who were not aware of it before that this practice is perfectly just—that it is common with the fathers of the Church, and that it is sanctioned by Scripture, by the example of the best of saints, and even by that of God himself.

Do we not find God at once hates and despises sinners; so that even at the hour of death, when their condition is most sad and deplorable, Divine Wisdom adds mockery to the vengeance which consigns them to eternal punishment? "*In interitu vestro ridebo et subsannabo*—I will laugh at your calamity." The saints, too, influenced by the same feeling, will join in the derision; for, according to David, when they witness the punishment of the wicked, "they shall fear, and yet laugh at it—*videbunt justi et timebunt, et super eum ridebunt.*" And Job says: "*Innocens subsannabit eos*—The innocent shall laugh at them."

It is worthy of remark here that the very first words which God addressed to man after his fall contain, in the opinion of the fathers, "bitter irony" and mockery. After Adam had disobeyed his Maker, in the hope, suggested by the devil, of being like God, it appears from Scripture that God, as a punishment, subjected him to death; and after having reduced him to this miserable condition, which was due to his sin, He taunted him in that state with the following terms of derision: "Behold, the man has become as one of us!—*Ecce Adam quasi unus ex nobis!*"—which, according to St. Jerome and the interpreters, is "a grievous and cutting piece of irony," with which God "stung him to the quick." "Adam," says Rupert, "deserved to be taunted in this manner, and he would be naturally made to feel his folly more acutely by this ironical expression than by a more serious one." St. Victor, after making the same remark, adds, "that this irony was due to his sottish credulity, and that this species of raillery is an act of justice, merited by him against whom it was directed."

Thus you see, fathers, that ridicule is, in some cases, a very appropriate means of reclaiming men from their errors, and that it is accordingly an act of justice, because, as Jeremiah says, "the actions of those that err are worthy of derision, because of their vanity—*vana sunt et risu digna.*" And so far from its being impious to laugh at them, St. Augustine holds it to be the effect of divine wisdom: "The wise laugh at the foolish, because they are wise, not after their own wisdom, but after that divine wisdom which shall laugh at the death of the wicked."

The prophets, accordingly, filled with the Spirit of God, have availed themselves of ridicule, as we find from the examples of Daniel and Elias. In short, examples of it are not wanting in the discourses of Jesus Christ himself. St. Augustine remarks that, when he would humble Nicodemus, who deemed himself so expert in his knowledge of the law, "perceiving him to be puffed up with pride, from his rank as doctor of the Jews, he first beats down his presumption by the magnitude of his demands, and, having reduced him so low that he was unable to answer, What! says he, you a master in Israel, and not know these things!—as if he had said, Proud ruler, confess that thou knowest nothing." St. Chrysostom and St. Cyril likewise observe upon this that "he deserved to be ridiculed in this manner."

You may learn from this, fathers, that should it so happen, in our day that persons who enact the part of "masters" among Christians, as Nicodemus and the Pharisees did among the Jews, show themselves so ignorant of the first principles of religion as to maintain, for example, that "a man may be saved who never loved God all his life," we only follow the example of Jesus Christ when we laugh at such a combination of ignorance and conceit.

I am sure, fathers, these sacred examples are sufficient to convince you that to deride the errors and extravagances of man is not inconsistent with the practice of the saints; otherwise we must blame that of the greatest doctors of the Church, who have been guilty of it—such as St. Jerome, in his letters and writings against Jovinian, Vigilantius, and the Pelagians; Tertullian, in his *Apology* against the follies of idolaters; St. Augustine against the monks of Africa, whom he styles "the hairy men"; St. Irenæus the Gnostics; St. Bernard and the other fathers of the Church, who, having been the imitators of the apostles, ought to be imitated by the faithful in all time coming; for, say what we will, they are the true models for Christians, even of the present day.

In following such examples, I conceived that I could not go far wrong; and, as I think I have sufficiently established this position, I shall only add, in the admirable words of Tertullian, which give the true explanation of the whole of my proceeding in this matter: "What I have now done is only a little sport before the real combat. I have rather indicated the wounds that might be given you than inflicted any. If the reader has met with passages which have excited his risibility, he must ascribe this to the subjects themselves. There are many things which deserve to be held up in this way to ridicule and mockery, lest, by a serious refutation, we should attach a weight to them which they do not deserve. Nothing is more due to vanity than laughter; and it is the Truth properly that has a right to laugh, because she is cheerful, and to make sport of her enemies, because she is sure of the victory. Care must be taken, indeed, that the raillery is not too low, and unworthy of the truth; but, keeping this in view, when ridicule may be employed with effect, it is a duty to avail ourselves of it." Do you not think fathers, that this passage is singularly applicable to our subject? The letters which I have hitherto written are "merely a little sport before a real combat." As yet, I have been only playing with the foils and "rather indicating the wounds that might be given you than inflicting any." I have merely exposed your passages to the light, without making scarcely a reflection on them. "If the reader has met with any that have excited his risibility, he must ascribe this to the subjects themselves." And, indeed, what is more fitted to raise a laugh than to see a matter so grave as that of Christian morality decked out with fancies so grotesque as those in which you have exhibited it? One is apt to form such high anticipations of these maxims, from being told that "Jesus Christ himself has revealed them to the fathers of the Society," that when one discovers among them such absurdities as "that a priest, receiving money to say a mass, may take additional sums from other persons by giving up to them his own share in the sacrifice"; "that a monk is not to be excommunicated for putting off his habit, provided it is to dance, swindle, or go incognito into infamous houses"; and "that the duty of hearing mass may be fulfilled by listening to four quarters of a mass at once from different priests"—when, I say, one listens to such decisions as these, the surprise is such that it is impossible to refrain from laughing; for nothing is more calculated to produce that emotion than a startling contrast between the thing looked for and the thing looked at. And why should the greater part of these maxims be treated in any other way? As Tertullian says, "To treat them seriously would be to sanction them."

What! is it necessary to bring up all the forces of Scripture and tradition, in order to prove that running a sword through a man's body, covertly and behind his back, is to murder him in treachery? or, that to give one money as a motive to resign a benefice, is to purchase the benefice? Yes, there are things which it is duty to despise, and which "deserve only to be laughed at." In short, the remark of that ancient author, "that nothing is more due to vanity than derision," with what follows, applies to the case before us so justly and so convincingly, as to put it beyond all question that we may laugh at errors without violating propriety.

And let me add, fathers, that this may be done without any breach of charity either, though this is another of the charges you bring against me in your publications. For, according to St. Augustine, "charity may sometimes oblige us to ridicule the errors of men, that they may be induced to laugh at them in their turn, and renounce them—*Hæc tu misericorditer irride, ut eis ridenda ac fugienda commendes.*" And the same charity may also, at other times, bind us to repel them with indignation, according to that other saying of St. Gregory of Nazianzen: "The spirit of meekness and charity hath its emotions and its heats." Indeed, as St. Augustine observes, "who would venture to say that truth ought to stand disarmed against falsehood, or that the enemies of the faith shall be at liberty to frighten the faithful with hard words, and jeer at them with lively sallies of wit; while the Catholics ought never to write except with a coldness of style enough to set the reader asleep?"

Is it not obvious that, by following such a course, a wide door would be opened for the introduction of the most extravagant and pernicious dogmas into the Church; while none would be allowed to treat them with contempt, through fear of being charged with violating propriety, or to confute them with indignation, from the dread of being taxed with want of charity?

Indeed, fathers! shall you be allowed to maintain, "that it is lawful to kill a man to avoid a box on the ear or an affront," and must nobody be permitted publicly to expose a public error of such consequence? Shall you be at liberty to say, "that a judge may in conscience retain a fee received for an act of injustice," and shall no one be at liberty to contradict you? Shall you print, with the privilege and approbation of your doctors, "that a man may be saved without ever having loved God"; and will you shut the mouth of those who defend the true faith, by telling them that they would violate brotherly love by attacking you, and Christian modesty by laughing at your maxims? I doubt, fathers, if there be any persons whom you could make believe this; if however, there be any such, who are really persuaded that, by denouncing your morality, I have been deficient in the charity which I owe to you, I would have them examine, with great jealousy, whence this feeling takes its rise within them. They may imagine that it proceeds from a holy zeal, which will not allow them to see their neighbour impeached without being scandalized at it; but I would entreat them to consider that it is not impossible that it may flow from another source, and that it is even extremely likely that it may spring from that secret, and often self-concealed dissatisfaction, which the unhappy corruption within us seldom fails to stir up against those who oppose the relaxation of morals. And, to furnish them with a rule which may enable them to ascertain the real principle from which it proceeds, I will ask them if, while they lament the way in which the religious have been treated, they lament still more the manner in which these religious have treated the truth; if they are incensed, not only against the letters, but still more against the maxims quoted in them. I shall grant it to be barely possible that their resentment proceeds from some zeal, though not of the most enlightened kind; and, in this case, the passages I have just cited from the fathers will serve to enlighten them. But if they are merely angry at the reprehension, and not at the things reprehended, truly, fathers, I shall never scruple to tell them that they are grossly mistaken, and that their zeal is miserably blind.

Strange zeal, indeed! which gets angry at those that censure public faults, and not at those that commit them! Novel charity this, which groans at seeing error confuted, but feels no grief at seeing morality subverted by that error. If these persons were in danger of being assassinated, pray, would they be offended at one advertising them of the stratagem that had been laid for them; and instead of turning out of their way to avoid it, would they trifle away their time in whining about the little charity manifested in discovering to them the criminal design of the assassins? Do they get waspish when one tells them not to eat such an article of food, because it is poisoned? or not to enter such a city, because it has the plague?

Whence comes it, then, that the same persons who set down a man as wanting in charity, for exposing maxims hurtful to religion, would, on the contrary, think him equally deficient in that grace were he not to disclose matters hurtful to health and life, unless it be from this, that their fondness for life induces them to take in good part every hint that contributes to its preservation, while their indifference to truth leads them, not only to take no share in its defence, but even to view with pain the efforts made for the extirpation of falsehood?

Let them seriously ponder, as in the sight of God, how shameful, and how prejudicial to the Church, is the morality which your casuists are in the habit of propagating; the scandalous and unmeasured license which they are introducing into public manners; the obstinate and violent hardihood with which you support them. And if they do not think it full time to rise against such disorders, their blindness is as much to be pitied as yours, fathers; and you and they have equal reason to dread that saying of St. Augustine, founded on the words of Jesus Christ, in the Gospel: "Woe to the blind leaders! woe to the blind followers!— *Væ cæcis ducentibus! væ cæcis sequentibus!*"

But, to leave you no room in future, either to create such impressions on the minds of others, or to harbour them in your own, I shall tell you, fathers (and I am ashamed I should have to teach you what I should have rather learnt from you), the marks which the fathers of the Church have given for judging when our animadversions flow from a principle of piety and charity, and when from a spirit of malice and impiety.

The first of these rules is that the spirit of piety always prompts us to speak with sincerity and truthfulness; whereas malice and envy make use of falsehood and calumny. "*Splendentia et vehementia, sed rebus veris*—Splendid and vehement in words, but true in things," as St. Augustine says. The dealer in falsehood is an agent of the devil. No direction of the intention can sanctify slander; and though the conversion of the whole earth should depend on it, no man may warrantably calumniate the innocent: because none may do the least evil, in order to accomplish the greatest good; and, as the Scripture says, "the truth of God stands in no need of our lie." St. Hilary observes that "it is the bounden duty of the advocates of truth, to advance nothing in its support but true things." Now, fathers, I can declare before God that there is nothing that I detest more than the slightest possible deviation from the truth, and that I have ever taken the greatest care, not only not to falsify (which would be horrible), but not to alter or wrest, in the slightest possible degree, the sense of a single passage. So closely have I adhered to this rule that, if I may presume to apply them to the present case, I may safely say, in the words of the same St. Hilary: "If we advance things that are false, let our statements be branded with infamy; but if we can show that they are public and notorious, it is no breach of apostolic modesty or liberty to expose them."

It is not enough, however, to tell nothing but the truth; we must not always tell everything that is true; we should publish only those things which it is useful to disclose, and not those which can only hurt, without doing any good. And, therefore, as the first rule is to speak with truth, the second is to speak with discretion. "The wicked," says St. Augustine, "in persecuting the good, blindly follow the dictates of their passion; but the good, in their prosecution of the wicked, are guided by a wise discretion, even as the surgeon warily considers where he is cutting, while the murderer cares not where he strikes." You must be sensible, fathers, that in selecting from the maxims of your authors, I have refrained from quoting those which would have galled you most, though I might have done it, and that without sinning against discretion, as others who were both learned and Catholic writers, have done before me. All who have read your authors know how far I have spared you in this respect. Besides, I have taken no notice whatever of what might be brought against individual characters among you; and I would have been extremely sorry to have said a word about secret and personal failings, whatever evidence I might have of them, being persuaded that this is the distinguishing property of malice, and a practice which ought never to be resorted to, unless where it is urgently demanded for the good of the Church. It is obvious, therefore, that, in what I have been compelled to advance against your moral maxims, I have been by no means wanting in due consideration: and that you have more reason to congratulate yourself on my moderation than to complain of my indiscretion.

The third rule, fathers, is: That when there is need to employ a little raillery, the spirit of piety will take care to employ it against error only, and not against things holy; whereas the spirit of buffoonery, impiety, and heresy, mocks at all that is most sacred. I have already vindicated myself on that score; and indeed there is no great danger of falling into that vice so long as I confine my remarks to the opinions which I have quoted from your authors.

In short, fathers, to abridge these rules, I shall only mention another, which is the essence and the end of all the rest: That the spirit of charity prompts us to cherish in the heart a desire for the salvation of those against whom we dispute, and to address our prayers to God while we direct our accusations to men. "We ought ever," says St. Augustine, "to preserve charity in the heart, even while we are obliged to pursue a line of external conduct which to man has the appearance of harshness; we ought to smite them with a sharpness, severe but kindly, remembering that their advantage is more to be studied than their gratification." I am sure, fathers, that there is nothing in my letters from which it can be inferred that I have not cherished such a desire towards you; and as you can find nothing to the contrary in them, charity obliges you to believe that I have been really actuated by it. It appears, then, that you cannot prove that I have offended against this rule, or against any of the other rules which charity inculcates; and you have no right to say, therefore, that I have violated it.

But, fathers, if you should now like to have the pleasure of seeing, within a short compass, a course of conduct directly at variance with each of these rules, and bearing the genuine stamp of the spirit of buffoonery, envy, and hatred, I shall give you a few examples of it; and, that they may be of the sort best known and most familiar to you, I shall extract them from your own writings.

To begin, then, with the unworthy manner in which your authors speak of holy things, whether in their sportive and gallant effusions, or in their more serious pieces, do you think that the parcel of ridiculous stories, which your father Binet has introduced into his *Consolation to the Sick*, are exactly suitable to his professed object, which is that of imparting Christian consolation to those whom God has chastened with affliction? Will you pretend to say that the profane, foppish style in which your Father Le Moine has talked of piety in his *Devotion made Easy* is more fitted to inspire respect than contempt for the picture that he draws of Christian virtues? What else does his whole book of *Moral Pictures* breathe, both in its prose and poetry, but a spirit full of vanity, and the follies of this world? Take, for example, that ode in his seventh book, entitled, "Eulogy on Bashfulness, showing that all beautiful things are red, or inclined to redden." Call you that a production worthy of a priest? The ode is intended to comfort a lady, called Delphina, who was sadly addicted to blushing. Each stanza is devoted to show that certain red things are the best of things, such as roses, pomegranates, the mouth, the tongue; and it is in the midst of this badinage, so disgraceful in a clergyman, that he has the effrontery to introduce those blessed spirits that minister before God, and of whom no Christian should speak without reverence:

> "*The cherubim—those glorious choirs—*
> *Composed of head and plumes,*
> *Whom God with His own Spirit inspires,*
> *And with His eyes illumes.*
> *These splendid faces, as they fly,*
> *Are ever red and burning high,*
> *With fire angelic or divine;*
> *And while their mutual flames combine,*
> *The waving of their wings supplies*
> *A fan to cool their ecstasies!*
> *But redness shines with better grace,*
> *Delphina, on thy beauteous face,*
> *Where modesty sits revelling—*
> *Arrayed in purple, like a king,*" &c.

What think you of this, fathers? Does this preference of the blushes of Delphina to the ardour of those spirits, which is neither more nor less than the ardour of divine love, and this simile of the fan applied to their mysterious wings, strike you as being very Christian-like in the lips which consecrate the adorable body of

Jesus Christ? I am quite aware that he speaks only in the character of a gallant and to raise a smile; but this is precisely what is called *laughing at things holy*. And is it not certain, that, were he to get full justice, he could not save himself from incurring a censure? although, to shield himself from this, he pleads an excuse which is hardly less censurable than the offence, "that the Sorbonne has no jurisdiction over Parnassus, and that the errors of that land are subject neither to censure nor the Inquisition"; as if one could act the blasphemer and profane fellow only in prose! There is another passage, however, in the preface, where even this excuse fails him, when he says, "that the water of the river, on whose banks he composes his verses, is so apt to make poets, that, though it were converted into *holy water*, it would not chase away the demon of poesy." To match this, I may add the following flight of your Father Garasse, in his *Summary of the Capital Truths in Religion*, where, speaking of the sacred mystery of the incarnation, he mixes up blasphemy and heresy in this fashion: "The human personality was grafted, as it were, or *set on horseback*, upon the personality of the Word!" And omitting many others, I might mention another passage from the same author, who, speaking on the subject of the name of Jesus, ordinarily written thus, ɪ. H̤. ş. observes that "some have taken away the cross from the top of it, leaving the characters barely thus, I. H. S.—which," says he, "is a stripped Jesus!"

Such is the indecency with which you treat the truths of religion, in the face of the inviolable law which binds us always to speak of them with reverence. But you have sinned no less flagrantly against the rule which obliges us to speak of them with truth and discretion. What is more common in your writings than calumny? Can those of Father Brisacier be called sincere? Does he speak with truth when he says that "the nuns of Port-Royal do not pray to the saints, and have no images in their church?" Are not these most outrageous falsehoods, when the contrary appears before the eyes of all Paris? And can he be said to speak with discretion when he stabs the fair reputation of these virgins, who lead a life so pure and austere, representing them as "impenitent, unsacramentalists, uncommunicants, foolish virgins, visionaries, Calagans, desperate creatures, and anything you please," loading them with many other slanders, which have justly incurred the censure of the late Archbishop of Paris? Or when he calumniates priests of the most irreproachable morals, by asserting "that they practise novelties in confession, to entrap handsome innocent females, and that he would be horrified to tell the abominable crimes which they commit." Is it not a piece of intolerable assurance to advance slanders so black and base, not merely without proof, but without the slightest shadow, or the most distant semblance of truth? I shall not enlarge on this topic, but defer it to a future occasion, for I have something more to say to you about it; but what I have now produced is enough to show that you have sinned at once against truth and discretion.

But it may be said, perhaps, that you have not offended against the last rule at least, which binds you to desire the salvation of those whom you denounce, and that none can charge you with this, except by unlocking the secrets of your breasts, which are only known to God. It is strange, fathers, but true, nevertheless, that we can convict you even of this offence; that while your hatred to your opponents has carried you so far as to wish their eternal perdition, your infatuation has driven you to discover the abominable wish that, so far from cherishing in secret desires for their salvation, you have offered up prayers in public for their damnation; and that, after having given utterance to that hideous vow in the city of Caen, to the scandal of the whole Church, you have since then ventured, in Paris, to vindicate, in your printed books, the diabolical transaction. After such gross offences against piety, first ridiculing and speaking lightly of things the most sacred; next falsely and scandalously calumniating priests and virgins; and lastly, forming desires and prayers for their damnation, it would be difficult to add anything worse. I cannot conceive, fathers, how you can fail to be ashamed of yourselves, or how you could have thought for an instant of charging me with a want of charity, who have acted all along with so much truth and moderation, without reflecting on your own horrid violations of charity, manifested in those deplorable exhibitions, which make the charge recoil against yourselves.

In fine, fathers, to conclude with another charge which you bring against me, I see you complain that among the vast number of your maxims which I quote, there are some which have been objected to already, and that I "say over again, what others have said before me." To this I reply that it is just because you have not profited by what has been said before that I say it over again. Tell me now what fruit has appeared from all the castigations you have received in all the books written by learned doctors and even the whole University? What more have your fathers Annat, Caussin, Pintereau, and Le Moine done, in the replies they have put forth, except loading with reproaches those who had given them salutary admonitions? Have you suppressed the books in which these nefarious maxims are taught? Have you restrained the authors of these maxims? Have you become more circumspect in regard to them? On the contrary, is it not the fact that since that time Escobar has been repeatedly reprinted in France and in the Low Countries, and that your fathers Cellot, Bagot, Bauny, Lamy, Le Moine, and others, persist in publishing daily the same maxims over again, or new ones as licentious as ever? Let us hear no more complaints, then, fathers, either because I have charged you with maxims which you have not disavowed, or because I have objected to some new ones against you, or because I have laughed equally at them all. You have only to sit down and look at them, to see at once your own confusion and my defence. Who can look without laughing at the decision of Bauny, respecting the person who employs another to set fire to his neighbour's barn; that of Cellot on restitution; the rule of Sanchez in favour of sorcerers; the plan of Hurtado for avoiding the sin of duelling by taking a walk through a field and waiting for a man; the compliments of Bauny for escaping usury; the way of avoiding simony by a detour of the intention, and keeping clear of falsehood by speaking high and low; and such other opinions of your most grave and reverend doctors? Is there anything more necessary, fathers, for my vindication? And, as Tertullian says, "can anything be more justly due to the vanity and weakness of these opinions than laughter?" But, fathers, the corruption of manners, to which your maxims lead, deserves another sort of consideration; and it becomes us to ask, with the same ancient writer: "Whether ought we to laugh at their folly, or deplore their blindness?—*Rideam vanitatem, an exprobrem cæcitatem?*" My humble opinion is that one may either laugh at them or weep over them, as one is in the humour. "*Hæc tolerabilius vel ridentur, vel flentur,*" as St. Augustine says. The Scripture tells us that "there is a time to laugh, and a time to weep"; and my hope is, fathers, that I may not find verified, in your case, these words in the Proverbs:

"If a wise man contendeth with a foolish man, whether he rage or laugh, there is no rest."

P.S.—On finishing this letter, there was put in my hands one of your publications, in which you accuse me of falsification, in the case of six of your maxims quoted by me, and also with being in correspondence with heretics. You will shortly receive, I trust, a suitable reply; after which, fathers, I rather think you will not feel very anxious to continue this species of warfare.

LETTER XII

To the Reverend Fathers, the Jesuits

September 9, 1656

Reverend Fathers,

I was prepared to write you on the subject of the abuse with which you have for some time past been assailing me in your publications, in which you salute me with such epithets as "reprobate," "buffoon," "blockhead," "merry-Andrew," "impostor," "slanderer," "cheat," "heretic," "Calvinist in disguise," "disciple of Du Moulin," "possessed with a legion of devils," and everything else you can think of. As I should be sorry to have all this believed of me, I was anxious to show the public why you treated me in this manner; and I had resolved to complain of your calumnies and falsifications, when I met with your *Answers*, in which you bring these same charges against myself. This will compel me to alter my plan; though it will not prevent me from prosecuting it in some sort, for I hope, while defending myself, to convict you of impostures more genuine than the imaginary ones which you have ascribed to me. Indeed, fathers, the suspicion of foul play is much more sure to rest on you than on me. It is not very likely, standing as I do, alone, without power or any human defence against such a large body, and having no support but truth and integrity, that I would expose myself to lose everything by laying myself open to be convicted of imposture. It is too easy to discover falsifications in matters of fact such as the present. In such a case there would have been no want of persons to accuse me, nor would justice have been denied them. With you, fathers, the case is very different; you may say as much as you please against me, while I may look in vain for any to complain to. With such a wide difference between our positions, though there had been no other consideration to restrain me, it became me to study no little caution. By treating me, however, as a common slanderer, you compel me to assume the defensive, and you must be aware that this cannot be done without entering into a fresh exposition and even into a fuller disclosure of the points of your morality. In provoking this discussion, I fear you are not acting as good politicians. The war must be waged within your own camp and at your own expense; and, although you imagine that, by embroiling the questions with scholastic terms, the answers will be so tedious, thorny, and obscure, that people will lose all relish for the controversy, this may not, perhaps, turn out to be exactly the case; I shall use my best endeavours to tax your patience as little as possible with that sort of writing. Your maxims have something diverting about them, which keeps up the good humour of people to the last. At all events, remember that it is you that oblige me to enter upon this *éclaircissement*, and let us see which of us comes off best in self-defence.

The first of your *Impostures*, as you call them, is on the opinion of Vasquez upon alms-giving. To avoid all ambiguity, then, allow me to give a simple explanation of the matter in dispute. It is well known, fathers, that, according to the mind of the Church, there are two precepts touching alms: *1st*, "To give out of our super-fluity in the case of the ordinary necessities of the poor"; and *2nd*, "To give even out of our necessaries, according to our circumstances, in cases of extreme ne-cessity." Thus says Cajetan, after St. Thomas; so that, to get at the mind of Vasquez on this subject, we must consider the rules he lays down, both in regard to necessaries and superfluities.

With regard to superfluity, which is the most common source of relief to the poor, it is entirely set aside by that single maxim which I have quoted in my *Letters:* "That what the men of the world keep with the view of improving their own condition, and that of their relatives, is not properly superfluity; so that such a thing as superfluity is rarely to be met with among men of the world, not even excepting kings." It is very easy to see, fathers, that, according to this definition, none can have superfluity, provided they have ambition; and thus, so far as the greater part of the world is concerned, alms-giving is annihilated. But even though a man should happen to have superfluity, he would be under no obligation, ac-cording to Vasquez, to give it away in the case of ordinary necessity; for he protests against those who would thus bind the rich. Here are his own words: "Corduba," says he, "teaches that when we have a superfluity we are bound to give out of it in cases of ordinary necessity; but *this does not please me—sed hoc non placet—*for we have demonstrated the contrary against Cajetan and Navarre." So, fathers, the obligation to this kind of alms is wholly set aside, according to the good pleasure of Vasquez.

With regard to necessaries, out of which we are bound to give in cases of extreme and urgent necessity, it must be obvious, from the conditions by which he has limited the obligation, the richest man in all Paris may not come within its reach one in a lifetime. I shall only refer to two of these. The first is: That "*we must know* that the poor man cannot be relieved from any other quarter—*hæc intelligo et cætera omnia, quando* scio *nullum alium opem laturum.*" What say you to this, fathers? Is it likely to happen frequently in Paris, where there are so many charitable people, that I *must know* that there is not another soul but myself to relieve the poor wretch who begs an alms from me? And yet, according to Vas-quez, if I have not ascertained that fact, I may send him away with nothing. The second condition is: That the poor man be reduced to such straits "that he is menaced with some fatal accident, or the ruin of his character"—none of them very common occurrences. But what marks still more the rarity of the cases in which one is bound to give charity, is his remark, in another passage, that the poor man must be so ill off, "that he may conscientiously rob the rich man!" This must surely be a very extraordinary case, unless he will insist that a man may be ordinarily allowed to commit robbery. And so, after having cancelled the obligation to give alms out of our superfluities, he obliges the rich to relieve the poor only in those cases when he would allow the poor to rifle the rich! Such is the doctrine of Vasquez, to whom you refer your readers for their edification!

I now come to your pretended *Impostures*. You begin by enlarging on the obligation to alms-giving which Vasquez imposes on ecclesiastics. But on this point I have said nothing; and I am prepared to take it up whenever you choose. This, then, has nothing to do with the present question. As for laymen, who are the only persons with whom we have now to do, you are apparently anxious to have it understood that, in the passage which I quoted, Vasquez is giving not his own judgement, but that of Cajetan. But as nothing could be more false than this, and as you have not said it in so many terms, I am willing to believe, for the sake of your character, that you did not intend to say it.

You next loudly complain that, after quoting that maxim of Vasquez, "Such a thing as superfluity is rarely if ever to be met with among men of the world, not excepting kings," *I have inferred* from it, "that the rich are rarely, if ever, bound to give alms out of their superfluity." But what do you mean to say, fathers? If it be true that the rich have almost never superfluity, is it not obvious that they will almost never be bound to give alms out of their superfluity? I might have put it into the form of a syllogism for you, if Diana, who has such an esteem for Vasquez that he calls him "the phœnix of genius," had not drawn the same conclusion from the same premises; for, after quoting the maxim of Vasquez, he concludes, "that, with regard to the question, whether the rich are obliged to give alms out of their superfluity, though the affirmation were true, it would seldom, or almost never, happen to be obligatory in practice." I have followed this language word for word. What, then, are we to make of this, fathers? When Diana quotes with approbation the sentiments of Vasquez, when he finds them probable, and "very convenient for rich people," as he says in the same place, he is no slanderer, no falsifier, and we hear no complaints of misrepresenting his author; whereas, when I cite the same sentiments of Vasquez, though without holding him up as a phœnix, I am a slanderer, a fabricator, a corrupter of his maxims. Truly, fathers, you have some reason to be apprehensive, lest your very different treatment of those who agree in their representation, and differ only in their estimate of your doctrine, discover the real secret of your hearts and provoke the conclusion that the main object you have in view is to maintain the credit and glory of your Company. It appears that, provided your accommodating theology is treated as judicious complaisance, you never disavow those that publish it, but laud them as contributing to your design; but let it be held forth as pernicious laxity, and the same interest of your Society prompts you to disclaim the maxims which would injure you in public estimation. And thus you recognize or renounce them, not according to the truth, which never changes, but according to the shifting exigencies of the times, acting on that motto of one of the ancients, "*Omnia pro tempore, nihil pro veritate*—Anything for the times, nothing for the truth." Beware of this, fathers; and that you may never have it in your power again to say that I drew from the principle of Vasquez a conclusion which he had disavowed, I beg to inform you that he has drawn it himself: "According to the opinion of Cajetan, and according to *my own—et secundum nostram*—(he says, chap. i., no. 27), one is hardly obliged to give alms at all when one is only obliged to give them out of one's superfluity." Confess then, fathers, on the testimony of Vasquez himself, that I have exactly copied his sentiment; and think how you could have the conscience to say that "the reader, on consulting the original, would see to his astonishment that he there teaches the very reverse!"

In fine, you insist, above all, that if Vasquez does not bind the rich to give alms out of their superfluity, he obliges them to atone for this by giving out of the necessaries of life. But you have forgotten to mention the list of conditions which he declares to be essential to constitute that obligation, which I have quoted, and which restrict it in such a way as almost entirely to annihilate it. In place of giving this honest statement of his doctrine, you tell us, in general terms, that he obliges the rich to give even what is necessary to their condition. This is proving too much, fathers; the rule of the Gospel does not go so far; and it would be an error, into which Vasquez is very far, indeed, from having fallen. To cover his laxity, you attribute to him an excess of severity which would be reprehensible; and thus you lose all credit as faithful reporters of his sentiments. But the truth is, Vasquez is quite free from any such suspicion; for he has maintained, as I have shown, that the rich are not bound, either in justice or in charity, to give of their super-fluities, and still less of their necessaries, to relieve the ordinary wants of the poor; and that they are not obliged to give of the necessaries, except in cases so rare that they almost never happen.

Having disposed of your objections against me on this head, it only remains to show the falsehood of your assertion that Vasquez is more severe than Cajetan. This will be very easily done. That cardinal teaches "that we are bound in justice to give alms out of our superfluity, even in the ordinary wants of the poor; because, according to the holy fathers, the rich are merely the dispensers of their superfluity, which they are to give to whom they please, among those who have need of it." And accordingly, unlike Diana, who says of the maxims of Vasquez that they will be "very convenient and agreeable to the rich and their confessors," the cardinal, who has no such consolation to afford them, declares that he has nothing to say to the rich but these words of Jesus Christ: "It is easier for a camel to go through the eye of a needle, than for a rich man to enter into heaven"; and to their confessors: "If the blind lead the blind, both shall fall into the ditch." So indispensable did he deem this obligation! This, too, is what the fathers and all the saints have laid down as a certain truth. "There are two cases," says St. Thomas, "in which we are bound to give alms as a matter of justice—*ex debito legali:* one, when the poor are in danger; the other, when we possess superfluous property." And again: "The three-tenths which the Jews were bound to eat with the poor, have been augmented under the new law; for Jesus Christ wills that we give to the poor, not the tenth only, but the whole of our superfluity." And yet it does not seem good to Vasquez that we should be obliged to give even a frag-ment of our superfluity; such is his complaisance to the rich, such his hardness to the poor, such his opposition to those feelings of charity which teach us to relish the truth contained in the following words of St. Gregory, harsh as it may sound to the rich of this world: "When we give the poor what is necessary to them, we are not so much bestowing on them what is our property as rendering to them what is their own; and it may be said to be an act of justice rather than a work of mercy."

It is thus that the saints recommend the rich to share with the poor the good things of this earth, if they would expect to possess with them the good things of heaven. While you make it your business to foster in the breasts of men that ambition which leaves no superfluity to dispose of, and that avarice which refuses to part with it, the saints have laboured to induce the rich to give up their superfluity, and to convince them that they would have abundance of it, provided they measured it, not by the standard of covetousness, which knows no bounds to its cravings, but by that of piety, which is ingenious in retrenchments, so as to have wherewith to diffuse itself in the exercise of charity. "We will have a great deal of superfluity," says St. Augustine, "if we keep only what is necessary: but if we seek after vanities, we will never have enough. Seek, brethren, what is sufficient for the work of God"—that is, for nature—"and not for what is sufficient for your covetousness," which is the work of the devil: "and remember that the superfluities of the rich are the necessaries of the poor."

I would fondly trust, fathers, that what I have now said to you may serve, not only for my vindication—that were a small matter—but also to make you feel and detest what is corrupt in the maxims of your casuists, and thus unite us sincerely under the sacred rules of the Gospel, according to which we must all be judged.

As to the second point, which regards simony, before proceeding to answer the charges you have advanced against me, I shall begin by illustrating your doctrine on this subject. Finding yourselves placed in an awkward dilemma, between the canons of the Church, which impose dreadful penalties upon simoniacs, on the one hand, and the avarice of many who pursue this infamous traffic on the other, you have recourse to your ordinary method, which is to yield to men what they desire, and give the Almighty only words and shows. For what else does the simoniac want but money in return for his benefice? And yet this is what you exempt from the charge of simony. And as the name of *simony* must still remain standing, and a subject to which it may be ascribed, you have substituted, in the place of this, an imaginary idea, which never yet crossed the brain of a simoniac, and would not serve him much though it did—the idea, namely, that simony lies in estimating the money considered in itself as highly as the spiritual gift or office considered in itself. Who would ever take it into his head to compare things so utterly disproportionate and heterogeneous? And yet, provided this metaphysical comparison be not drawn, any one may, according to your authors, give away a benefice, and receive money in return for it, without being guilty of simony.

Such is the way in which you sport with religion, in order to gratify the worst passions of men; and yet only see with what gravity your Father Valentia delivers his rhapsodies in the passage cited in my letters. He says: "One may give a spiritual for a temporal good in two ways—first, in the way of prizing the temporal more than the spiritual, and that would be simony; secondly, in the way of taking the temporal as the motive and end inducing one to give away the spiritual, but without prizing the temporal more than the spiritual, and then it is not simony. And the reason is that simony consists in receiving something temporal as the just price of what is spiritual. If, therefore, the temporal is sought—*si petatur temporale*—not as the *price*, but only as the *motive* determining us to part with the spiritual, it is by no means simony, even although the possession of the temporal may be principally intended and expected—*minime erit simonia, etiamsi temporale principaliter intendatur et expectetur.*" Your redoubtable Sanchez has been favoured with a similar revelation; Escobar quotes him thus: "If one give a spiritual for a temporal good, not as the *price*, but as a *motive* to induce the collator to give it, or as an *acknowledgement* if the benefice has been actually received, is that simony? Sanchez assures us that it is not." In your Caen Theses of 1644, you say: "It is a probable opinion, taught by many Catholics, that it is not simony to

exchange a temporal for a spiritual good, when the former is not given as a price."
And as to Tanner, here is his doctrine, exactly the same with that of Valentia; and
I quote it again to show you how far wrong it is in you to complain of me for
saying that it does not agree with that of St. Thomas, for he avows it himself in
the very passage which I quoted in my letter: "There is properly and truly no
simony," says he, "unless when a temporal good is taken as the price of a spiritual; but when taken merely as the motive for giving the spiritual, or as an acknowledgement for having received it, this is not simony, at least in point of
conscience." And again: "The same thing may be said, although the temporal
should be regarded as the principal end, and even preferred to the spiritual;
although St. Thomas and others appear to hold the reverse, inasmuch as they
maintain it to be downright simony to exchange a spiritual for a temporal good,
when the temporal is the end of the transaction."

Such, then, being your doctrine on simony, as taught by your best authors,
who follow each other very closely in this point, it only remains now to reply to
your charges of misrepresentation. You have taken no notice of Valentia's opinion, so that his doctrine stands as it was before. But you fix on that of Tanner,
maintaining that he has merely decided it to be no simony by divine right; and
you would have it to be believed that, in quoting the passage, I have suppressed
these words, *divine right*. This, fathers, is a most unconscionable trick; for these
words, *divine right*, never existed in that passage. You add that Tanner declares
it to be simony according to *positive right*. But you are mistaken; he does not say
that generally, but only of particular cases, or, as he expresses it, *in casibus a jure
expressis*, by which he makes an exception to the general rule he had laid down in
that passage, "that it is not simony in point of conscience," which must imply
that it is not so in point of positive right, unless you would have Tanner made so
impious as to maintain that simony, in point of positive right, is not simony in
point of conscience. But it is easy to see your drift in mustering up such terms as
"divine right, positive right, natural right, internal and external tribunal, expressed cases, outward presumption," and others equally little known; you mean
to escape under this obscurity of language, and make us lose sight of your aberrations. But, fathers, you shall not escape by these vain artifices; for I shall put
some questions to you so simple, that they will not admit of coming under your
distinguo.

I ask you, then, without speaking of "positive rights," of "outward presump-
tions," or "external tribunals"—I ask if, according to your authors, a beneficiary
would be simoniacal, were he to give a benefice worth four thousand livres of
yearly rent, and to receive ten thousand francs ready money, not as the price of
the benefice, but merely as a motive inducing him to give it? Answer me plainly,
fathers: What must we make of such a case as this according to your authors?
Will not Tanner tell us decidedly that "this is not simony in point of conscience,
seeing that the temporal good is not the price of the benefice, but only the motive
inducing to dispose of it?" Will not Valentia, will not your own Theses of Caen,
will not Sanchez and Escobar, agree in the same decision and give the same reason
for it? Is anything more necessary to exculpate that beneficiary from simony?
And, whatever might be your private opinion of the case, durst you deal with
that man as a simonist in your confessionals, when he would be entitled to stop
your mouth by telling you that he acted according to the advice of so many grave

doctors? Confess candidly, then, that, according to your views, that man would be no simonist; and, having done so, defend the doctrine as you best can.

Such, fathers, is the true mode of treating questions, in order to unravel, instead of perplexing them, either by scholastic terms, or, as you have done in your last charge against me here, by altering the state of the question. Tanner, you say, has, at any rate, declared that such an exchange is a great sin; and you blame me for having maliciously suppressed this circumstance, which, you maintain, "*completely justifies him.*" But you are wrong again, and that in more ways than one. For, first, though what you say had been true, it would be nothing to the point, the question in the passage to which I referred being, not if it was *sin*, but if it was *simony*. Now, these are two very different questions. Sin, according to your maxims, obliges only to confession—simony obliges to restitution; and there are people to whom these may appear two very different things. You have found expedients for making confession a very easy affair; but you have not fallen upon ways and means to make restitution an agreeable one. Allow me to add that the case which Tanner charges with sin is not simply that in which a spiritual good is exchanged for a temporal, the latter being the principal end in view, but that in which the party "prizes the temporal above the spiritual," which is the imaginary case already spoken of. And it must be allowed he could not go far wrong in charging such a case as that with sin, since that man must be either very wicked or very stupid who, when permitted to exchange the one thing for the other, would not avoid the sin of the transaction by such a simple process as that of abstaining from comparing the two things together. Besides, Valentia, in the place quoted, when treating the question—if it be sinful to give a spiritual good for a temporal, the latter being the main consideration—and after producing the reasons given for the affirmative, adds, "*Sed hoc non videtur mihi satis certum*—But this does not appear to my mind sufficiently certain."

Since that time, however, your father, Erade Bille, professor of cases of conscience at Caen, has decided that there is no sin at all in the case supposed; for probable opinions, you know, are always in the way of advancing to maturity. This opinion he maintains in his writings of 1644, against which M. Dupré, doctor and professor at Caen, delivered that excellent oration, since printed and well known. For though this Erade Bille confesses that Valentia's doctrine, adopted by Father Milhard and condemned by the Sorbonne, "is contrary to the common opinion, suspected of simony, and punishable at law when discovered in practice," he does not scruple to say that it is a probable opinion, and consequently sure in point of conscience, and that there is neither simony nor sin in it. "It is a probable opinion," he says, "taught by many Catholic doctors, that there is neither any simony *nor any sin* in giving money, or any other temporal thing, for a benefice, either in the way of acknowledgement, or as a motive, without which it would not be given, provided it is not given as a price equal to the benefice." This is all that could possibly be desired. In fact, according to these maxims of yours, simony would be so exceedingly rare that we might exempt from this sin even Simon Magus himself, who desired to purchase the Holy Spirit and is the emblem of those simonists that buy spiritual things; and Gehazi, who took money for a miracle and may be regarded as the prototype of the simonists that sell them. There can be no doubt that when Simon, as we read in the Acts, "offered the apostles money, saying, Give me also this power"; he said

nothing about buying or selling, or fixing the price; he did no more than offer
the money as a motive to induce them to give him that spiritual gift; which being,
according to you, no simony at all, he might, had be but been instructed in your
maxims, have escaped the anathema of St. Peter. The same unhappy ignorance
was a great loss to Gehazi, when he was struck with leprosy by Elisha; for, as he
accepted the money from the prince who had been miraculously cured, simply as
an acknowledgement, and not as a price equivalent to the divine virtue which
had effected the miracle, he might have insisted on the prophet healing him
again on pain of mortal sin; seeing, on this supposition, he would have acted
according to the advice of your grave doctors, who, in such cases, oblige confessors to absolve their penitents and to wash them from that spiritual leprosy of
which the bodily disease is the type.

Seriously, fathers, it would be extremely easy to hold you up to ridicule in this
matter, and I am at a loss to know why you expose yourselves to such treatment.
To produce this effect, I have nothing more to do than simply to quote Escobar,
in his *Practice of Simony according to the Society of Jesus;* "Is it simony when two
Churchmen become mutually pledged thus: Give me your vote for my election
as Provincial, and I shall give you mine for your election as prior? By no means."
Or take another: "It is not simony to get possession of a benefice by promising
a sum of money, when one has no intention of actually paying the money; for
this is merely making a show of simony, and is as far from being real simony as
counterfeit gold is from the genuine." By this quirk of conscience, he has contrived means, in the way of adding swindling to simony, for obtaining benefices
without simony and without money.

But I have no time to dwell longer on the subject, for I must say a word or two
in reply to your third accusation, which refers to the subject of bankrupts. Nothing can be more gross than the manner in which you have managed this charge.
You rail at me as a libeller in reference to a sentiment of Lessius, which I did not
quote myself, but took from a passage in Escobar; and, therefore, though it were
true that Lessius does not hold the opinion ascribed to him by Escobar, what can
be more unfair than to charge me with the misrepresentation? When I quote
Lessius or others of your authors myself, I am quite prepared to answer for it;
but, as Escobar has collected the opinions of twenty-four of your writers, I beg
to ask if I am bound to guarantee anything beyond the correctness of my citations
from his book? Or if I must, in addition, answer for the fidelity of all his quotations of which I may avail myself? This would be hardly reasonable; and yet this
is precisely the case in the question before us. I produced in my letter the following passage from Escobar, and you do not object to the fidelity of my translation:
"May the bankrupt, with a good conscience, retain as much of his property as is
necessary to afford him an honourable maintenance—*ne indecore vivat?* I answer,
with Lessius, that he may—*cum Lessio assero posse.*" You tell me that Lessius does
not hold that opinion. But just consider for a moment the predicament in which
you involve yourselves. If it turns out that he does hold that opinion, you will be
set down as impostors for having asserted the contrary; and if it is proved that he
does not hold it, Escobar will be the impostor; so it must now of necessity follow
that one or other of the Society will be convicted of imposture. Only think what
a scandal! You cannot, it would appear, foresee the consequences of things. You
seem to imagine that you have nothing more to do than to cast aspersions upon

people, without considering on whom they may recoil. Why did you not acquaint Escobar with your objection before venturing to publish it? He might have given you satisfaction. It is not so very troublesome to get word from Valladolid, where he is living in perfect health, and completing his grand work on *Moral Theology*, in six volumes, on the first of which I mean to say a few words by-and-by. They have sent him the first ten letters; you might as easily have sent him your objection, and I am sure he would have soon returned you an answer, for he has doubtless seen in Lessius the passage from which he took the *ne indecore vivat*. Read him yourselves, fathers, and you will find it word for word, as I have done. Here it is: "The same thing is apparent from the authorities cited, particularly in regard to that property which he acquires after his failure, out of which even the delinquent debtor may retain as much as is necessary for his honourable maintenance, according to his station of life—*ut non indecore vivat*. Do you ask if this rule applies to goods which he possessed at the time of his failure? Such seems to be the judgement of the doctors."

I shall not stop here to show how Lessius, to sanction his maxim, perverts the law that allows bankrupts nothing more than a mere livelihood, and that makes no provision for "honourable maintenance." It is enough to have vindicated Escobar from such an accusation—it is more, indeed, than what I was in duty bound to do. But you, fathers, have not done your duty. It still remains for you to answer the passage of Escobar, whose decisions, by the way, have this advantage, that, being entirely independent of the context and condensed in little articles, they are not liable to your distinctions. I quoted the whole of the passage, in which "bankrupts are permitted to keep their goods, though unjustly acquired, to provide an honourable maintenance for their families"—commenting on which in my letters, I exclaim: "Indeed, father! by what strange kind of charity would you have the ill-gotten property of a bankrupt appropriated to his own use, instead of that of his lawful creditors?" This is the question which must be answered; but it is one that involves you in a sad dilemma, and from which you in vain seek to escape by altering the state of the question, and quoting other passages from Lessius, which have no connection with the subject. I ask you, then: May this maxim of Escobar be followed by bankrupts with a safe conscience, or no? And take care what you say. If you answer, "No," what becomes of your doctor, and your doctrine of probability? If you say, "Yes," I delate you to the Parliament.

In this predicament I must now leave you, fathers; for my limits will not permit me to overtake your next accusation, which respects homicide. This will serve for my next letter, and the rest will follow.

In the meanwhile, I shall make no remarks on the advertisements which you have tagged to the end of each of your charges, filled as they are with scandalous falsehoods. I mean to answer all these in a separate letter, in which I hope to show the weight due to your calumnies. I am sorry, fathers, that you should have recourse to such desperate resources. The abusive terms which you heap on me will not clear up our disputes, nor will your manifold threats hinder me from defending myself. You think you have power and impunity on your side; and I think I have truth and innocence on mine. It is a strange and tedious war when violence attempts to vanquish truth. All the efforts of violence cannot weaken truth, and only serve to give it fresh vigour. All the lights of truth cannot arrest violence, and only serve to exasperate it. When force meets force, the weaker must succumb to the stronger; when argument is opposed to argument, the solid and the convincing triumphs over the empty and the false; but violence and verity can make no impression on each other. Let none suppose, however, that the two are, therefore, equal to each other; for there is this vast difference between them, that violence has only a certain course to run, limited by the appointment of Heaven, which overrules its effects to the glory of the truth which it assails; whereas verity endures forever and eventually triumphs over its enemies, being eternal and almighty as God himself.

LETTER XIII

To the Reverend Fathers of the Society of Jesus

September 30, 1656

REVEREND FATHERS,

I have just seen your last production, in which you have continued your list of *Impostures* up to the twentieth and intimate that you mean to conclude with this the first part of your accusations against me, and to proceed to the second, in which you are to adopt a new mode of defence, by showing that there are other casuists besides those of your Society who are as lax as yourselves. I now see the precise number of charges to which I have to reply; and as the fourth, to which we have now come, relates to homicide, it may be proper, in answering it, to include the 11th, 13th, 14th, 15th, 16th, 17th, and 18th, which refer to the same subject.

In the present letter, therefore, my object shall be to vindicate the correctness of my quotations from the charges of falsity which you bring against me. But as you have ventured, in your pamphlets, to assert that "the sentiments of your authors on murder are agreeable to the decisions of popes and ecclesiastical laws," you will compel me, in my next letter, to confute a statement at once so unfounded and so injurious to the Church. It is of some importance to show that she is innocent of your corruptions, in order that heretics may be prevented from taking advantage of your aberrations, to draw conclusions tending to her dishonour. And thus, viewing on the one hand your pernicious maxims, and on the other the canons of the Church which have uniformly condemned them, people will see, at one glance, what they should shun and what they should follow.

Your fourth charge turns on a maxim relating to murder, which you say I have falsely ascribed to Lessius. It is as follows: "That if a man has received a buffet, he may immediately pursue his enemy, and even return the blow with the sword, not to avenge himself, but to retrieve his honour." This, you say, is the opinion of the casuist Victoria. But this is nothing to the point. There is no inconsistency in saying that it is at once the opinion of Victoria and of Lessius; for Lessius himself says that it is also held by Navarre and Henriquez, who teach identically the same doctrine. The only question, then, is if Lessius holds this view as well as his brother casuists. You maintain "that Lessius quotes this opinion solely for the purpose of refuting it, and that I, therefore, attribute to him a sentiment which he produces only to overthrow—the basest and most disgraceful act of which a writer can be guilty." Now I maintain, fathers, that he quotes the opinion solely for the purpose of supporting it. Here is a question of fact, which it will be very easy to settle. Let us see, then, how you prove your allegation, and you will see afterwards how I prove mine.

To show that Lessius is not of that opinion, you tell us that he condemns the practice of it; and in proof of this, you quote one passage of his (l. 2, c. 9, n. 92), in which he says, in so many words, "I condemn the practice of it." I grant that, on looking for these words, at number 92, to which you refer, they will be found there. But what will people say, fathers, when they discover, at the same time, that he is treating in that place of a question totally different from that of which we are speaking, and that the opinion of which he there says that he condemns the practice has no connection with that now in dispute, but is quite distinct? And yet to be convinced that this is the fact, we have only to open the book to which you refer, and there we find the whole subject in its connection as follows: At number 79 he treats the question, "If it is lawful to kill for a buffet?" and at number 80 he finishes this matter without a single word of condemnation. Having disposed of this question, he opens a new one at 81, namely, "If it is lawful to kill for slanders?" and it is when speaking of *this* question that he employs the words you have quoted: "I condemn the practice of it."

Is it not shameful, fathers, that you should venture to produce these words to make it be believed that Lessius condemns the opinion that it is lawful to kill for a buffet? and that, on the ground of this single proof, you should chuckle over it, as you have done, by saying: "Many persons of honour in Paris have already discovered this notorious falsehood by consulting Lessius, and have thus ascertained the degree of credit due to that slanderer?" Indeed! and is it thus that you abuse the confidence which those persons of honour repose in you? To show them that Lessius does not hold a certain opinion, you open the book to them at a place where he is condemning another opinion; and these persons, not having begun to mistrust your good faith and never thinking of examining whether the author speaks in that place of the subject in dispute, you impose on their credulity. I make no doubt, fathers, that, to shelter yourselves from the guilt of such a scandalous lie, you had recourse to your doctrine of equivocations; and that, having read the passage *in a loud voice*, you would say, *in a lower key*, that the author was speaking there of something else. But I am not so sure whether this saving clause, which is quite enough to satisfy your consciences, will be a very satisfactory answer to the just complaint of those "honourable persons," when they shall discover that you have hoodwinked them in this style.

Take care, then, fathers, to prevent them by all means from seeing my letters; for this is the only method now left to you to preserve your credit for a short time longer. This is not the way in which I deal with your writings: I send them to all my friends; I wish everybody to see them. And I verily believe that both of us are in the right for our own interests; for, after having published with such parade this fourth *Imposture*, were it once discovered that you have made it up by foisting in one passage for another, you would be instantly denounced. It will be easily seen that if you could have found what you wanted in the passage where Lessius treated of this matter, you would not have searched for it elsewhere, and that you had recourse to such a trick only because you could find nothing in that passage favourable to your purpose.

You would have us believe that we may find in Lessius what you assert, "that he does *not* allow that this opinion (that a man may be lawfully killed for a buffet) is probable in theory"; whereas Lessius distinctly declares, at number 80: "This opinion, that a man may kill for a buffet, *is* probable in theory." Is not this, word for word, the reverse of your assertion? And can we sufficiently admire the hardihood with which you have advanced, in set phrase, the very reverse of a matter of fact! To your conclusion, from a fabricated passage, that Lessius was *not* of that opinion, we have only to place Lessius himself, who, in the genuine passage, declares that he *is* of that opinion.

Again, you would have Lessius to say "that he condemns the practice of it"; and, as I have just observed, there is not in the original a single word of condemnation; all that he says is: "It appears that it ought not to be *easily* permitted in practice—*In praxi non videtur* facile *permittenda.*" Is that, fathers, the language of a man who *condemns* a maxim? Would you say that adultery and incest ought not to be *easily permitted* in practice? Must we not, on the contrary, conclude that as Lessius says no more than that the practice ought not to be easily permitted, his opinion is that it may be permitted sometimes, though rarely? And, as if he had been anxious to apprise everybody when it might be permitted, and to relieve those who have received affronts from being troubled with unreasonable scruples from not knowing on what occasions they might lawfully kill in practice, he has been at pains to inform them what they ought to avoid in order to practise the doctrine with a safe conscience. Mark his words: "It seems," says he, "that it ought not to be easily permitted, *because* of the danger that persons may act in this matter out of hatred or revenge, or with excess, or that this may occasion too many murders." From this it appears that murder is freely permitted by Lessius, if one avoids the inconveniences referred to—in other words, if one can act without hatred or revenge and in circumstances that may not open the door to a great many murders. To illustrate the matter, I may give you an example of recent occurrence—the case of the buffet of Compiègne. You will grant that the person who received the blow on that occasion has shown, by the way in which he has acted, that he was sufficiently master of the passions of hatred and revenge. It only remained for him, therefore, to see that he did not give occasion to too many murders; and you need hardly be told, fathers, it is such a rare spectacle to find Jesuits bestowing buffets on the officers of the royal household that he had no great reason to fear that a murder committed on this occasion would be likely to draw many others in its train. You cannot, accordingly, deny that the Jesuit who figured on that occasion was *killable* with a safe conscience, and that the offended party might have converted him into a practical illustration of the doctrine of Lessius. And very likely, fathers, this might have been the result had he been educated in your school, and learnt from Escobar that the man who has received a buffet is held to be disgraced until he has taken the life of him who insulted him. But there is ground to believe that the very different instructions which he received from a curate, who is no great favourite of yours, have contributed not a little in this case to save the life of a Jesuit.

Tell us no more, then, of inconveniences which may, in many instances, be so easily got over, and in the absence of which, according to Lessius, murder is permissible even in practice. This is frankly avowed by your authors, as quoted by Escobar, in his *Practice of Homicide, according to your Society.* "Is it allowable," asks this casuist, "to kill him who has given me a buffet? Lessius says it is permissible in speculation, though not to be followed in practice—*non consulendum in praxi*—on account of the risk of hatred, or of murders prejudicial to the State. Others, however, have judged that, *by avoiding these inconveniences, this is permissible and safe in practice—in praxi probabilem et tutam judicarunt Henriquez,*" &c. See how your opinions mount up, by little and little, to the climax of probabilism! The present one you have at last elevated to this position, by permitting murder without any distinction between speculation and practice, in the following terms: "It is lawful, when one has received a buffet, to return the blow immediately with the sword, not to avenge one's self, but to preserve one's honour." Such is the decision of your fathers of Caen in 1644, embodied in their publications produced by the university before parliament, when they presented their third remonstrance against your doctrine of homicide, as shown in the book then emitted by them, on page 339.

Mark, then, fathers, that your own authors have themselves demolished this absurd distinction between speculative and practical murder—a distinction which the university treated with ridicule, and the invention of which is a secret of your policy, which it may now be worth while to explain. The knowledge of it, besides being necessary to the right understanding of your 15th, 16th, 17th, and 18th charges, is well calculated, in general, to open up, by little and little, the principles of that mysterious policy.

In attempting, as you have done, to decide cases of conscience in the most agreeable and accommodating manner, while you met with some questions in which religion alone was concerned—such as those of contrition, penance, love to God, and others only affecting the inner court of conscience—you encountered another class of cases in which civil society was interested as well as religion —such as those relating to usury, bankruptcy, homicide, and the like. And it is truly distressing to all that love the Church to observe that, in a vast number of instances, in which you had only Religion to contend with, you have violated her laws without reservation, without distinction, and without compunction; because you knew that it is not here that God visibly administers his justice. But in those cases in which the State is interested as well as Religion, your apprehension of man's justice has induced you to divide your decisions into two shares. To the first of these you give the name of *speculation;* under which category crimes, considered in themselves, without regard to society, but merely to the law of God, you have permitted, without the least scruple, and in the way of trampling on the divine law which condemns them. The second you rank under the denomination of *practice;* and here, considering the injury which may be done to society, and the presence of magistrates who look after the public peace, you take care, in order to keep yourselves on the safe side of the law, not to approve always in practice the murders and other crimes which you have sanctioned in speculation. Thus, for example, on the question, "If it be lawful to kill for slanders?" your authors, Filiutius, Reginald, and others, reply: "This is permitted in speculation —*ex probabile opinione licet;* but is not to be approved in *practice,* on account of the great number of murders which might ensue, and which might injure the State, if all slanderers were to be killed, *and also because one might be punished in a court of justice for having killed another for that matter.*" Such is the style in which your opinions begin to develop themselves, under the shelter of this distinction, in virtue of which, without doing any sensible injury to society, you only ruin religion. In acting thus, you consider yourselves quite safe. You suppose that, on the one hand, the influence you have in the Church will effectually shield from punishment your assaults on truth; and that, on the other, the precautions you have taken against too easily reducing your permissions to practice will save you on the part of the civil powers, who, not being judges in cases of conscience, are properly concerned only with the outward practice. Thus an opinion which would be condemned under the name of *practice*, comes out quite safe under the name of *speculation*. But this basis once established, it is not difficult to erect on it the rest of your maxims. There is an infinite distance between God's prohibition of murder and your speculative permission of the crime; but between that permission and the practice the distance is very small indeed. It only remains to show that what is allowable in speculation is also so in practice; and there can be no want of reasons for this. You have contrived to find them in far more difficult cases. Would you like to see, fathers, how this may be managed? I refer you to the reasoning of Escobar, who has distinctly decided the point in the first six volumes of his grand *Moral Theology*, of which I have already spoken—a work in which he shows quite another spirit from that which appears in his former compilation from your four-and-twenty elders. At that time he thought that there might be opinions probable in speculation, which might not be safe in practice; but he has now come to form an opposite judgment, and has, in this, his latest work, confirmed it. Such is the wonderful growth attained by the doctrine of probability in general, as well as by every probable opinion in particular, in the course of time. Attend, then, to what he says: "I cannot see how it can be that an action which seems allowable in speculation should not be so likewise in practice; because what may be done in practice depends on what is found to be lawful in speculation, and the things differ from each other only as cause and effect. Speculation is that which determines to action. *Whence it follows that opinions probable in speculation may be followed with a safe conscience in practice*, and that even with more safety than those which have not been so well examined as matters of speculation."

Verily, fathers, your friend Escobar reasons uncommonly well sometimes; and, in point of fact, there is such a close connection between speculation and practice, that when the former has once taken root, you have no difficulty in permitting the latter, without any disguise. A good illustration of this we have in the permission "to kill for a buffet," which, from being a point of simple speculation, was boldly raised by Lessius into a practice "which ought not easily to be allowed"; from that promoted by Escobar to the character of "an easy practice"; and from thence elevated by your fathers of Caen, as we have seen, without any distinction between theory and practice, into a full permission. Thus you bring your opinions to their full growth very gradually. Were they presented all at once in their finished extravagance, they would beget horror; but this slow imperceptible progress gradually habituates men to the sight of them and hides their offensiveness. And in this way the permission to murder, in itself so odious both to Church and State, creeps first into the Church, and then from the Church into the State.

A similar success has attended the opinion of "killing for slander," which has now reached the climax of a permission without any distinction. I should not have stopped to quote my authorities on this point from your writings, had it not been necessary in order to put down the effrontery with which you have asserted, twice over, in your fifteenth *Imposture*, "that there never was a Jesuit who permitted killing for slander." Before making this statement, fathers, you should have taken care to prevent it from coming under my notice, seeing that it is so easy for me to answer it. For, not to mention that your fathers Reginald, Filiutius, and others, have permitted it in speculation, as I have already shown, and that the principle laid down by Escobar leads us safely on to the practice, I have to tell you that you have authors who have permitted it in so many words, and among others Father Hereau in his public lectures, on the conclusion of which the king put him under arrest in your house, for having taught, among other errors, that when a person who has slandered us in the presence of men of honour, continues to do so after being warned to desist, it is allowable to kill him, not publicly, indeed, for fear of scandal, but *in a private way—sed clam.*

I have had occasion already to mention Father Lamy, and you do not need to be informed that his doctrine on this subject was censured in 1649 by the University of Louvain. And yet two months have not elapsed since your Father Des Bois maintained this very censured doctrine of Father Lamy and taught that "it was allowable for a monk to defend the honour which he acquired by his virtue, *even by killing* the person who assails his reputation—*etiam cum morte invasoris*"; which has raised such a scandal in that town that the whole of the curés united to impose silence on him, and to oblige him, by a canonical process, to retract his doctrine. The case is now pending in the Episcopal court.

What say you now, fathers? Why attempt, after that, to maintain that "no Jesuit ever held that it was lawful to kill for slander?" Is anything more necessary to convince you of this than the very opinions of your fathers which you quote, since they do not condemn murder in speculation, but only in practice, and that, too, "on account of the injury that might thereby accrue to the State"? And here I would just beg to ask whether the whole matter in dispute between us is not simply and solely to ascertain if you have or have not subverted the law of God which condemns murder? The point in question is, not whether you have injured the commonwealth, but whether you have injured religion. What purpose, then, can it serve, in a dispute of this kind, to show that you have spared the State, when you make it apparent, at the same time, that you have destroyed the faith? Is this not evident from your saying that the meaning of Reginald, on the question of killing for slanders, is, "that a private individual has a right to employ that mode of defence, viewing it simply *in itself*"? I desire nothing beyond this concession to confute you. "A private individual," you say, "has a right to employ that mode of defence" (that is, killing for slanders), "viewing the thing in itself"; and, consequently, fathers, the law of God, which forbids us to kill, is nullified by that decision.

It serves no purpose to add, as you have done, "that such a mode is unlawful and criminal, even according to the law of God, on account of the murders and disorders which would follow in society, because the law of God obliges us to have regard to the good of society." This is to evade the question: for there are two laws to be observed—one forbidding us to kill, and another forbidding us to harm society. Reginald has not, perhaps, broken the law which forbids us to do harm to society; but he has most certainly violated that which forbids us to kill.

Now this is the only point with which we have to do. I might have shown, besides, that your other writers, who have permitted these murders in practice, have subverted the one law as well as the other. But, to proceed, we have seen that you *sometimes* forbid doing harm to the State; and you allege that your design in that is to fulfil the law of God, which obliges us to consult the interests of society. That may be true, though it is far from being certain, as you might do the same thing purely from fear of the civil magistrate. With your permission, then, we shall scrutinize the real secret of this movement.

Is it not certain, fathers, that if you had really any regard to God, and if the observance of his law had been the prime and principal object in your thoughts, this respect would have invariably predominated in all your leading decisions and would have engaged you at all times on the side of religion? But, if it turns out, on the contrary, that you violate, in innumerable instances, the most sacred commands that God has laid upon men, and that, as in the instances before us, you annihilate the law of God, which forbids these actions as criminal in themselves, and that you only scruple to approve of them in practice, from bodily fear of the civil magistrate, do you not afford us ground to conclude that you have no respect to God in your apprehensions, and that if you yield an apparent obedience to his law, in so far as regards the obligation to do no harm to the State, this is not done out of any regard to the law itself, but to compass your own ends, as has ever been the way with politicians of no religion?

What, fathers! will you tell us that, looking simply to the law of God, which says, "Thou shalt not kill," we have a right to kill for slanders? And after having thus trampled on the eternal law of God, do you imagine that you atone for the scandal you have caused, and can persuade us of your reverence for Him, by adding that you prohibit the practice for State reasons and from dread of the civil arm? Is not this, on the contrary, to raise a fresh scandal? I mean not by the respect which you testify for the magistrate; that is not my charge against you, and it is ridiculous in you to banter, as you have done, on this matter. I blame you, not for fearing the magistrate, but for fearing none but the magistrate. And I blame you for this, because it is making God less the enemy of vice than man. Had you said that to kill for slander was allowable according to men, but not according to God, that might have been something more endurable; but when you maintain that what is too criminal to be tolerated among men may yet be innocent and right in the eyes of that Being who is righteousness itself, what is this but to declare before the whole world, by a subversion of principle as shocking in itself as it is alien to the spirit of the saints, that while you can be braggarts before God, you are cowards before men?

Had you really been anxious to condemn these homicides, you would have allowed the commandment of God which forbids them to remain intact; and had you dared at once to permit them, you would have permitted them openly, in spite of the laws of God and men. But, your object being to permit them imperceptibly, and to cheat the magistrate, who watches over the public safety, you have gone craftily to work. You separate your maxims into two portions. On the one side, you hold out "that it is lawful in speculation to kill a man for slander"; and nobody thinks of hindering you from taking a speculative view of matters. On the other side, you come out with this detached axiom, "that what is permitted in speculation is also permissible in practice"; and what concern does society seem to have in this general and metaphysical-looking proposition? And thus these two principles, so little suspected, being embraced in their separate form, the vigilance of the magistrate is eluded; while it is only necessary to combine the two together to draw from them the conclusion which you aim at—namely, that it is lawful in practice to put a man to death for a simple slander.

It is, indeed, fathers, one of the most subtle tricks of your policy to scatter through your publications the maxims which you club together in your decisions. It is partly in this way that you establish your doctrine of probabilities, which I have frequently had occasion to explain. That general principle once established, you advance propositions harmless enough when viewed apart, but which, when taken in connection with that pernicious dogma, become positively horrible. An example of this, which demands an answer, may be found in the 11th page of your *Impostures*, where you allege that "several famous theologians have decided that it is lawful to kill a man for a box on the ear." Now, it is certain that, if that had been said by a person who did not hold probabilism, there would be nothing to find fault with in it; it would in this case amount to no more than a harmless statement, and nothing could be elicited from it. But you, fathers, and all who hold that dangerous tenet, "that whatever has been approved by celebrated authors is probable and safe in conscience," when *you* add to this "that several celebrated authors are of opinion that it is lawful to kill a man for a box on the ear," what is this but to put a dagger into the hand of all Christians, for the purpose of plunging it into the heart of the first person that insults them, and to assure them that, having the judgement of so many grave authors on their side, they may do so with a perfectly safe conscience?

What monstrous species of language is this, which, in announcing that certain authors hold a detestable opinion, is at the same time giving a decision in favour of that opinion—which solemnly teaches whatever it simply tells! We have learnt, fathers, to understand this peculiar dialect of the Jesuitical school; and it is astonishing that you have the hardihood to speak it out so freely, for it betrays your sentiments somewhat too broadly. It convicts you of permitting murder for a buffet, as often as you repeat that many celebrated authors have maintained that opinion.

This charge, fathers, you will never be able to repel; nor will you be much helped out by those passages from Vasquez and Suarez that you adduce against me, in which they condemn the murders which their associates have approved. These testimonies, disjoined from the rest of your doctrine, may hoodwink those who know little about it; but we, who know better, put your principles and maxims together. You say, then, that Vasquez condemns murders; but what say you on the other side of the question, my reverend fathers? Why, "that the probability of one sentiment does not hinder the probability of the opposite sentiment; and that it is warrantable to follow the less probable and less safe opinion, giving up the more probable and more safe one." What follows from all this taken in connection, but that we have perfect freedom of conscience to adopt any one of these conflicting judgements which pleases us best? And what becomes of all the effect which you fondly anticipate from your quotations? It evaporates in smoke, for we have no more to do than to conjoin for your condemnation the maxims which you have disjoined for your exculpation. Why, then, produce those passages of your authors which I have not quoted, to qualify those which I have quoted, as if the one could excuse the other? What right does that give you to call me an "impostor"? Have I said that all your fathers are implicated in the same corruptions? Have I not, on the contrary, been at pains to show that your interest lay in having them of all different minds, in order to suit all your purposes? Do you wish to kill your man?—here is Lessius for you. Are you inclined to spare him?—here is Vasquez. Nobody need go away in ill humour—nobody without the authority of a grave doctor. Lessius will talk to you like a Heathen on homicide, and like a Christian, it may be, on charity. Vasquez, again, will descant like a Heathen on charity, and like a Christian on homicide. But by means of probabilism, which is held both by Vasquez and Lessius, and which renders all your opinions common property, they will lend their opinions to one another, and each will be held bound to absolve those who have acted according to opinions which each of them has condemned. It is this very variety, then, that confounds you. Uniformity, even in evil, would be better than this. Nothing is more contrary to the orders of St. Ignatius and the first generals of your Society than this confused medley of all sorts of opinions, good and bad. I may, perhaps, enter on this topic at some future period; and it will astonish many to see how far you have degenerated from the original spirit of your institution, and that your own generals have foreseen that the corruption of your doctrine on morals might prove fatal, not only to your Society, but to the Church universal.

Meanwhile, I repeat that you can derive no advantage from the doctrine of Vasquez. It would be strange, indeed, if, out of all the Jesuits that have written on morals, one or two could not be found who may have hit upon a truth which has been confessed by all Christians. There is no glory in maintaining the truth, according to the Gospel, that it is unlawful to kill a man for smiting us on the face; but it is foul shame to deny it. So far, indeed, from justifying you, nothing tells more fatally against you than the fact that, having doctors among you who have told you the truth, you abide not in the truth, but love the darkness rather than the light. You have been taught by Vasquez that it is a Heathen, and not a Christian, opinion to hold that we may knock down a man for a blow on the cheek; and that it is subversive both of the Gospel and of the Decalogue to say that we may kill for such a matter. The most profligate of men will acknowledge as much. And yet you have allowed Lessius, Escobar, and others, to decide, in the face of these well-known truths, and in spite of all the laws of God against manslaughter, that it is quite allowable to kill a man for a buffet!

What purpose, then, can it serve to set this passage of Vasquez over against the sentiment of Lessius, unless you mean to show that, in the opinion of Vasquez, Lessius is a "Heathen" and a "profligate"? and that, fathers, is more than I durst have said myself. What else can be deduced from it than that Lessius "subverts both the Gospel and the Decalogue"; that, at the last day, Vasquez will condemn Lessius on this point, as Lessius will condemn Vasquez on another; and that all your fathers will rise up in judgement one against another, mutually condemning each other for their sad outrages on the law of Jesus Christ?

To this conclusion, then, reverend fathers, must we come at length, that, as your probabilism renders the good opinions of some of your authors useless to the Church, and useful only to your policy, they merely serve to betray, by their contrariety, the duplicity of your hearts. This you have completely unfolded, by telling us, on the one hand, that Vasquez and Suarez are against homicide, and on the other hand, that many celebrated authors are for homicide; thus presenting two roads to our choice and destroying the simplicity of the Spirit of God, who denounces his anathema on the deceitful and the double-hearted: *"Væ duplici corde, et ingredienti duabus viis!*—Woe be to the double hearts, and the sinner that goeth two ways!"

LETTER XIV

To the Reverend Fathers, the Jesuits

October 23, 1656

REVEREND FATHERS,

If I had merely to reply to the three remaining charges on the subject of homicide, there would be no need for a long discourse, and you will see them refuted presently in a few words; but as I think it of much more importance to inspire the public with a horror at your opinions on this subject than to justify the fidelity of my quotations, I shall be obliged to devote the greater part of this letter to the refutation of your maxims, to show you how far you have departed from the sentiments of the Church and even of nature itself. The permissions of murder, which you have granted in such a variety of cases, render it very apparent, that you have so far forgotten the law of God, and quenched the light of nature, as to require to be remanded to the simplest principles of religion and of common sense. What can be a plainer dictate of nature than that "no private individual has a right to take away the life of another"? "So well are we taught this of ourselves," says St. Chrysostom, "that God, in giving the commandment not to kill, did not add as a reason that homicide was an evil; because," says that father, "the law supposes that nature has taught us that truth already." Accordingly, this commandment has been binding on men in all ages. The Gospel has confirmed the requirement of the law; and the Decalogue only renewed the command which man had received from God before the law, in the person of Noah, from whom all men are descended. On that renovation of the world, God said to the patriarch: "At the hand of man, and at the hand of every man's brother, will I require the life of man. Whoso sheddeth man's blood, by man shall his blood be shed; for man is made in the image of God." (Gen. ix. 5, 6.) This general prohibition deprives man of all power over the life of man. And so exclusively has the Almighty reserved this prerogative in His own hand that, in accordance with Christianity, which is at utter variance with the false maxims of Paganism, man has no power even over his own life. But, as it has seemed good to His providence to take human society under His protection, and to punish the evil-doers that give it disturbance, He has Himself established laws for depriving criminals of life; and thus those executions which, without His sanction, would be punishable outrages, become, by virtue of His authority, which is the rule of justice, praiseworthy penalties. St. Augustine takes an admirable view of this subject. "God," he says, "has himself qualified this general prohibition against manslaughter, both by the laws which He has instituted for the capital punishment of malefactors, and by the special orders which He has sometimes issued to put to death certain individuals. And when death is inflicted in such cases, it is not man that kills, but God, of whom man may be considered as only the instrument, in the same way as a sword in the hand of him that wields it. But, these instances excepted, whosoever kills incurs the guilt of murder."

It appears, then, fathers, that the right of taking away the life of man is the sole prerogative of God, and that, having ordained laws for executing death on criminals, He has deputed kings or commonwealths as the depositaries of that power—a truth which St. Paul teaches us, when, speaking of the right which sovereigns possess over the lives of their subjects, he deduces it from Heaven in these words: "He beareth not the sword in vain; for he is the minister of God to execute wrath upon him that doeth evil." (Rom. 13. 4.) But as it is God who has put this power into their hands, so He requires them to exercise it in the same manner as He does himself; in other words, with perfect justice; according to what St. Paul observes in the same passage: "Rulers are not a terror to good works, but to the evil. Wilt thou, then, not be afraid of the power? Do that which is good: for he is the minister of God to thee for good." And this restriction, so far from lowering their prerogative, exalts it, on the contrary, more than ever; for it is thus assimilated to that of God who has no power to do evil, but is all-powerful to do good; and it is thus distinguished from that of devils, who are impotent in that which is good, and powerful only for evil. There is this difference only to be observed betwixt the King of Heaven and earthly sovereigns, that God, being justice and wisdom itself, may inflict death instantaneously on whomsoever and in whatsoever manner He pleases; for, besides His being the sovereign Lord of human life, it is certain that He never takes it away either without cause or without judgement, because He is as incapable of injustice as He is of error. Earthly potentates, however, are not at liberty to act in this manner; for, though the ministers of God, still they are but men, and not gods. They may be misguided by evil counsels, irritated by false suspicions, transported by passion, and hence they find themselves obliged to have recourse, in their turn also, to human agency, and appoint magistrates in their dominions, to whom they delegate their power, that the authority which God has bestowed on them may be employed solely for the purpose for which they received it.

I hope you understand, then, fathers, that, to avoid the crime of murder, we must act at once by the authority of God, and according to the justice of God; and that, when these two conditions are not united, sin is contracted; whether it be by taking away life with his authority, but without his justice; or by taking it away with justice, but without his authority. From this indispensable connection it follows, according to St. Augustine, "that he who, without proper authority, kills a criminal, becomes a criminal himself, chiefly for this reason, that he usurps an authority which God has not given him"; and on the other hand, magistrates, though they possess this authority, are nevertheless chargeable with murder, if, contrary to the laws which they are bound to follow, they inflict death on an innocent man.

Such are the principles of public safety and tranquillity which have been admitted at all times and in all places, and on the basis of which all legislators, sacred and profane, from the beginning of the world, have founded their laws. Even Heathens have never ventured to make an exception to this rule, unless in cases where there was no other way of escaping the loss of chastity or life, when they conceived, as Cicero tells us, "that the law itself seemed to put its weapons into the hands of those who were placed in such an emergency."

But with this single exception, which has nothing to do with my present purpose, that such a law was ever enacted, authorizing or tolerating, as you have done, the practice of putting a man to death, to atone for an insult, or to avoid the loss of honour or property, where life is not in danger at the same time; that, fathers, is what I deny was ever done, even by infidels. They have, on the contrary, most expressly forbidden the practice. The law of the Twelve Tables of Rome bore, "that it is unlawful to kill a robber in the daytime, when he does not defend himself with arms"; which, indeed, had been prohibited long before in the 22d chapter of Exodus. And the law *Furem*, in the *Lex Cornelia*, which is borrowed from Ulpian, forbids the killing of robbers even by night, if they do not put us in danger of our lives.

Tell us now, fathers, what authority you have to permit what all laws, human as well as divine, have forbidden; and who gave Lessius a right to use the following language? "The book of Exodus forbids the killing of thieves by day, when they do not employ arms in their defence; and in a court of justice, punishment is inflicted on those who kill under these circumstances. *In conscience*, however, no blame can be attached to this practice, when a person is not sure of being able otherwise to recover his stolen goods, or entertains a doubt on the subject, as Sotus expresses it; for he is not obliged to run the risk of losing any part of his property merely to save the life of a robber. The same privilege extends even to clergymen." Such extraordinary assurance! The law of Moses punishes those who kill a thief when he does not threaten our lives, and the law of the Gospel, according to you, will absolve them! What, fathers! has Jesus Christ come to destroy the law, and not to fulfil it? "The civil judge," says Lessius, "would inflict punishment on those who should kill under such circumstances; but no blame can be attached to the deed in conscience." Must we conclude, then, that the morality of Jesus Christ is more sanguinary, and less the enemy of murder, than that of Pagans, from whom our judges have borrowed their civil laws which condemn that crime? Do Christians make more account of the good things of this earth, and less account of human life, than infidels and idolaters? On what principle do you proceed, fathers? Assuredly not upon any law that ever was enacted either by God or man—on nothing, indeed, but this extraordinary reasoning: "The laws," say you, "permit us to defend ourselves against robbers, and to repel force by force; self-defence, therefore, being permitted, it follows that murder, without which self-defence is often impracticable, may be considered as permitted also."

It is false, fathers, that, because self-defence is allowed, murder may be allowed also. This barbarous method of self-vindication lies at the root of all your errors, and has been justly stigmatized by the Faculty of Louvain, in their censure of the doctrine of your friend Father Lamy, as "*a murderous defence—defensio occisiva.*" I maintain that the laws recognize such a wide difference between murder and self-defence that, in those very cases in which the latter is sanctioned, they have made a provision against murder, when the person is in no danger of his life. Read the words, fathers, as they run in the same passage of Cujas: "It is lawful to repulse the person who comes to invade our property; but *we are not permitted to kill him.*" And again: "If any should threaten to strike us, and not to deprive us of life, it is quite allowable to repulse him; but *it is against all law to put him to death.*"

Who, then, has given you a right to say, as Molina, Reginald, Filiutius, Escobar, Lessius, and others among you, have said, "that it is lawful to kill the man who offers to strike us a blow"? or, "that it is lawful to take the life of one who means to insult us, by the common consent of all the casuists," as Lessius says. By what authority do you, who are mere private individuals, confer upon other private individuals, not excepting clergymen, this right of killing and slaying? And how dare you usurp the power of life and death, which belongs essentially to none but God, and which is the most glorious mark of sovereign authority? These are the points that demand explanation; and yet you conceive that you have furnished a triumphant reply to the whole, by simply remarking, in your thirteenth *Imposture*, "that the value for which Molina permits us to kill a thief, who flies without having done us any violence, is not so small as I have said, and that it must be a much larger sum than six ducats!" How extremely silly! Pray, fathers, where would you have the price to be fixed? At fifteen or sixteen ducats? Do not suppose that this will produce any abatement in my accusations. At all events, you cannot make it exceed the value of a horse; for Lessius is clearly of opinion, "that we may lawfully kill the thief that runs off with our horse." But I must tell you, moreover, that I was perfectly correct when I said that Molina estimates the value of the thief's life at six ducats; and, if you will not take it upon my word, we shall refer it to an umpire to whom you cannot object. The person whom I fix upon for this office is your own Father Reginald, who, in his explanation of the same passage of Molina (1.28, n. 68), declares that "Molina there *determines* the sum for which it is not allowable to kill at three, or four, or five ducats." And thus, fathers, I shall have Reginald, in addition to Molina, to bear me out.

It will be equally easy for me to refute your fourteenth *Imposture*, touching Molina's permission to "kill a thief who offers to rob us of a crown." This palpable fact is attested by Escobar, who tells us "that Molina has regularly determined the sum for which it is lawful to take away life, at one crown." And all you have to lay to my charge in the fourteenth *Imposture* is, that I have suppressed the last words of this passage, namely, "that in this matter every one ought to study the moderation of a just self-defence." Why do you not complain that Escobar has also omitted to mention these words? But how little tact you have about you! You imagine that nobody understands what you mean by *self-defence*. Don't we know that it is to employ "*a murderous defence*"? You would persuade us that Molina meant to say that if a person, in defending his crown, finds himself in danger of his life, he is then at liberty to kill his assailant, in self-preservation. If that were true, fathers, why should Molina say in the same place that "in this matter he was of a contrary judgement from Carrer and Bald," who give permission to kill in self-preservation? I repeat, therefore, that his plain meaning is that, provided the person can save his crown without killing the thief, he ought not to kill him; but that, if he cannot secure his object without shedding blood, even though he should run no risk of his own life, as in the case of the robber being unarmed, he is permitted to take up arms and kill the man, in order to save his crown; and in so doing, according to him, the person does not transgress "the moderation of a just defence." To show you that I am in the right, just allow him to explain himself: "One does not exceed the moderation of a just defence," says he, "when he takes up arms against a thief who has none, or employs weapons which give him the advantage over his assailant. I know there are some who are of a contrary judgement; but I do not approve of their opinion, even in the external tribunal."

Thus, fathers, it is unquestionable that your authors have given permission to kill in defence of property and honour, though life should be perfectly free from danger. And it is upon the same principle that they authorize duelling, as I have shown by a great variety of passages from their writings, to which you have made no reply. You have animadverted in your writings only on a single passage taken from Father Layman, who sanctions the above practice, "when otherwise a person would be in danger of sacrificing his fortune or his honour"; and here you accuse me with having suppressed what he adds, "that such a case happens very rarely." You astonish me, fathers: these are really curious impostures you charge me withal. You talk as if the question were whether that is a rare case? when the real question is if, in such a case, duelling is lawful? These are two very different questions. Layman, in the quality of a casuist, ought to judge whether duelling is lawful in the case supposed; and he declares that it is. We can judge without his assistance whether the case be a rare one; and we can tell him that it is a very ordinary one. Or, if you prefer the testimony of your good friend Diana, he will tell you that "the case is exceedingly common." But, be it rare or not, and let it be granted that Layman follows in this the example of Navarre, a circumstance on which you lay so much stress, is it not shameful that he should consent to such an opinion as that, to preserve a false honour, it is lawful in conscience to accept of a challenge, in the face of the edicts of all Christian states, and of all the canons of the Church, while in support of these diabolical maxims you can produce neither laws, nor canons, nor authorities from Scripture, or from the fathers, nor the example of a single saint, nor, in short, anything but the following impious syllogism: "Honour is more than life; it is allowable to kill in defence of life; therefore it is allowable to kill in defence of honour!" What, fathers! because the depravity of men disposes them to prefer that factitious honour before the life which God hath given them to be devoted to his service, must they be permitted to murder one another for its preservation? To love that honour more than life is in itself a heinous evil; and yet this vicious passion, which, when proposed as the end of our conduct, is enough to tarnish the holiest of actions, is considered by you capable of sanctifying the most criminal of them!

What a subversion of all principle is here, fathers! And who does not see to what atrocious excesses it may lead? It is obvious, indeed, that it will ultimately lead to the commission of murder for the most trifling things imaginable, when one's honour is considered to be staked for their preservation—murder, I venture to say, even *for an apple!* You might complain of me, fathers, for drawing sanguinary inferences from your doctrine with a malicious intent, were I not fortunately supported by the authority of the grave Lessius, who makes the following observation, in number 68: "It is not allowable to take life for an article of small value, such as for a crown or *for an apple—aut pro pomo*—unless it would be deemed dishonourable to lose it. In this case, one may recover the article, and even, if necessary, *kill the aggressor*, for this is not so much defending one's property as retrieving one's honour." This is plain speaking, fathers; and, just to crown your doctrine with a maxim which includes all the rest, allow me to quote the following from Father Hereau, who has taken it from Lessius: "The right of self-defence extends to whatever is necessary to protect ourselves from all injury."

What strange consequences does this inhuman principle involve! and how imperative is the obligation laid upon all, and especially upon those in public stations, to set their face against it! Not the general good alone, but their own personal interest should engage them to see well to it; for the casuists of your school whom I have cited in my letters extend their permissions to kill far enough to reach even them. Factious men, who dread the punishment of their outrages, which never appear to them in a criminal light, easily persuade themselves that they are the victims of violent oppression, and will be led to believe at the same time, "that the right of self-defence extends to whatever is necessary to protect themselves from all injury." And thus, relieved from contending against the checks of conscience, which stifle the greater number of crimes at their birth, their only anxiety will be to surmount external obstacles.

I shall say no more on this subject, fathers; nor shall I dwell on the other murders, still more odious and important to governments, which you sanction, and of which Lessius, in common with many others of your authors, treats in the most unreserved manner. It was to be wished that these horrible maxims had never found their way out of hell; and that the devil, who is their original author, had never discovered men sufficiently devoted to his will to publish them among Christians.

From all that I have hitherto said, it is easy to judge what a contrariety there is betwixt the licentiousness of your opinions and the severity of civil laws, not even excepting those of Heathens. How much more apparent must the contrast be with ecclesiastical laws, which must be incomparably more holy than any other, since it is the Church alone that knows and possesses the true holiness! Accordingly, this chaste spouse of the Son of God, who, in imitation of her heavenly husband, can shed her own blood for others, but never the blood of others for herself, entertains a horror at the crime of murder altogether singular, and proportioned to the peculiar illumination which God has vouchsafed to bestow upon her. She views man, not simply as man, but as the image of the God whom she adores. She feels for every one of the race a holy respect, which imparts to him, in her eyes, a venerable character, as redeemed by an infinite price, to be made the temple of the living God. And therefore she considers the death of a man, slain without the authority of his Maker, not as murder only, but as sacrilege, by which she is deprived of one of her members; for, whether he be a believer or an unbeliever, she uniformly looks upon him, if not as one, at least as capable of becoming one, of her own children.

Such, fathers, are the holy reasons which, ever since the time that God became man for the redemption of men, have rendered their condition an object of such consequence to the Church that she uniformly punishes the crime of homicide, not only as destructive to them, but as one of the grossest outrages that can possibly be perpetrated against God. In proof of this I shall quote some examples, not from the idea that all the severities to which I refer ought to be kept up (for I am aware that the Church may alter the arrangement of such exterior discipline), but to demonstrate her immutable spirit upon this subject. The penances which she ordains for murder may differ according to the diversity of the times, but no change of time can ever effect an alteration of the horror with which she regards the crime itself.

For a long time the Church refused to be reconciled, till the very hour of death, to those who had been guilty of wilful murder, as those are to whom you give your sanction. The celebrated Council of Ancyra adjudged them to penance during their whole lifetime; and, subsequently, the Church deemed it an act of sufficient indulgence to reduce that term to a great many years. But, still more effectually to deter Christians from wilful murder, she has visited with most severe punishment even those acts which have been committed through inadvertence, as may be seen in St. Basil, in St. Gregory of Nyssen, and in the decretals of Popes Zachary and Alexander II. The canons quoted by Isaac, bishop of Langres (tr. 2. 13), "ordain seven years of penance for having killed another in self-defence." And we find St. Hildebert, bishop of Mans, replying to Yves de Chartres, "that he was right in interdicting for life a priest who had, in self-defence, killed a robber with a stone."

After this, you cannot have the assurance to persist in saying that your decisions are agreeable to the spirit or the canons of the Church. I defy you to show one of them that permits us to kill solely in defence of our property (for I speak not of cases in which one may be called upon to defend his life—*se suaquae liberando*); your own authors, and, among the rest, Father Lamy, confess that no such canon can be found. "There is no authority," he says, "human or divine, which gives an express permission to kill a robber who makes no resistance." And yet this is what you permit most expressly. I defy you to show one of them that permits us to kill in vindication of honour, for a buffet, for an affront, or for a slander. I defy you to show one of them that permits the killing of witnesses, judges, or magistrates, whatever injustice we may apprehend from them. The spirit of the church is diametrically opposite to these seditious maxims, opening the door to insurrections to which the mob is naturally prone enough already. She has invariably taught her children that they ought not to render evil for evil; that they ought to give place unto wrath; to make no resistance to violence; to give unto every one his due—honour, tribute, submission; to obey magistrates and superiors, even though they should be unjust, because we ought always to respect in them the power of that God who has placed them over us. She forbids them, still more strongly than is done by the civil law, to take justice into their own hands; and it is in her spirit that Christian kings decline doing so in cases of high treason, and remit the criminals charged with this grave offence into the hands of the judges, that they may be punished according to the laws and the forms of justice, which in this matter exhibit a contrast to your mode of management so striking and complete that it may well make you blush for shame.

As my discourse has taken this turn, I beg you to follow the comparison which I shall now draw between the style in which you would dispose of your enemies, and that in which the judges of the land dispose of criminals. Everybody knows, fathers, that no private individual has a right to demand the death of another individual; and that though a man should have ruined us, maimed our body, burnt our house, murdered our father, and was prepared, moreover, to assassinate ourselves, or ruin our character, our private demand for the death of that person would not be listened to in a court of justice. Public officers have been appointed for that purpose, who make the demand in the name of the king, or rather, I would say, in the name of God. Now, do you conceive, fathers, that Christian legislators have established this regulation out of mere show and grimace? Is it not evident that their object was to harmonize the laws of the state with those of the Church, and thus prevent the external practice of justice from clashing with the sentiments which all Christians are bound to cherish in their hearts? It is easy to see how this, which forms the commencement of a civil process, must stagger you; its subsequent procedure absolutely overwhelms you.

Suppose then, fathers, that these official persons have demanded the death of the man who has committed all the above-mentioned crimes, what is to be done next? Will they instantly plunge a dagger in his breast? No, fathers; the life of man is too important to be thus disposed of; they go to work with more decency; the laws have committed it, not to all sorts of persons, but exclusively to the judges, whose probity and competency have been duly tried. And is one judge sufficient to condemn a man to death? No; it requires seven at the very least; and of these seven there must not be one who has been injured by the criminal, lest his judgement should be warped or corrupted by passion. You are aware also, fathers, that, the more effectually to secure the purity of their minds, they devote the hours of the morning to these functions. Such is the care taken to prepare them for the solemn action of devoting a fellow-creature to death; in performing which they occupy the place of God, whose ministers they are, appointed to condemn such only as have incurred his condemnation.

For the same reason, to act as faithful administrators of the divine power of taking away human life, they are bound to form their judgement solely according to the depositions of the witnesses, and according to all the other forms prescribed to them; after which they can pronounce conscientiously only according to law, and can judge worthy of death those only whom the law condemns to that penalty. And then, fathers, if the command of God obliges them to deliver over to punishment the bodies of the unhappy culprits, the same divine statute binds them to look after the interests of their guilty souls, and binds them the more to this just because they are guilty; so that they are not delivered up to execution till after they have been afforded the means of providing for their consciences. All this is quite fair and innocent; and yet, such is the abhorrence of the Church to blood that she judges those to be incapable of ministering at her altars who have borne any share in passing or executing a sentence of death, accompanied though it be with these religious circumstances; from which we may easily conceive what idea the Church entertains of murder.

Such, then, being the manner in which human life is disposed of by the legal forms of justice, let us now see how you dispose of it. According to your modern system of legislation, there is but one judge, and that judge is no other than the offended party. He is at once the judge, the party, and the executioner. He himself demands from himself the death of his enemy; he condemns him, he executes him on the spot; and, without the least respect either for the soul or the body of his brother, he murders and damns him for whom Jesus Christ died; and all this for the sake of avoiding a blow on the cheek, or a slander, or an offensive word, or some other offence of a similar nature, for which, if a magistrate, in the exercise of legitimate authority, were condemning any to die, he would himself be impeached; for, in such cases, the laws are very far indeed from condemning any to death. In one word, to crown the whole of this extravagance, the person who kills his neighbour in this style, without authority and in the face of all law, contracts no sin and commits no disorder, though he should be religious and even a priest! Where are we, fathers? Are these really religious, and priests, who talk in this manner? Are they Christians? are they Turks? are they men? or are they demons? And are these "the mysteries revealed by the Lamb to his Society"? or are they not rather abominations suggested by the Dragon to those who take part with him?

To come to the point, with you, fathers, whom do you wish to be taken for?—for the children of the Gospel, or for the enemies of the Gospel? You must be ranged either on the one side or on the other; for there is no medium here. "He that is not with Jesus Christ is against him." Into these two classes all mankind are divided. There are, according to St. Augustine, two peoples and two worlds, scattered abroad over the earth. There is the world of the children of God, who form one body, of which Jesus Christ is the king and the head; and there is the world at enmity with God, of which the devil is the king and the head. Hence Jesus Christ is called the King and God of the world, because he has everywhere his subjects and worshippers; and hence the devil is also termed in Scripture the *prince* of this world, and the god of this world, because he has everywhere his agents and his slaves. Jesus Christ has imposed upon the Church, which is his empire, such laws as he, in his eternal wisdom, was pleased to ordain; and the devil has imposed on the world, which is his kingdom, such laws as he chose to establish. Jesus Christ has associated honour with suffering; the devil with not-suffering. Jesus Christ has told those who are smitten on the one cheek to turn the other also; and the devil has told those who are threatened with a buffet to kill the man that would do them such an injury. Jesus Christ pronounces those happy who share in his reproach; and the devil declares those to be unhappy who lie under ignominy. Jesus Christ says: Woe unto you when men shall speak well of you! and the devil says: Woe unto those of whom the world does not speak with esteem!

Judge, then, fathers, to which of these kingdoms you belong. You have heard the language of the city of peace, the mystical Jerusalem; and you have heard the language of the city of confusion, which Scripture terms "the spiritual Sodom." Which of these two languages do you understand? which of them do you speak? Those who are on the side of Jesus Christ have, as St. Paul teaches us, the same mind which was also in him; and those who are the children of the devil—*ex patre diabolo*—who has been a murderer from the beginning, according to the saying of Jesus Christ, follow the maxims of the devil. Let us hear, therefore, the language of your school. I put this question to your doctors: When a person has given me a blow on the cheek, ought I rather to submit to the injury than kill the offender? or may I not kill the man in order to escape the affront? Kill him by all means—it is quite lawful! exclaim, in one breath, Lessius, Molina, Escobar, Reginald, Filiutius, Baldelle, and other Jesuits. Is that the language of Jesus Christ? One question more: Would I lose my honour by tolerating a box on the ear, without killing the person that gave it? "Can there be a doubt," cries Escobar, "that so long as a man suffers another to live who has given him a buffet, that man remains without honour?" Yes, fathers, without that honour which the devil transfuses, from his own proud spirit into that of his proud children. This is the honour which has ever been the idol of worldly-minded men. For the preservation of this false glory, of which the god of this world is the appropriate dispenser, they sacrifice their lives by yielding to the madness of duelling; their honour, by exposing themselves to ignominious punishments; and their salvation, by involving themselves in the peril of damnation—a peril which, according to the canons of the Church, deprives them even of Christian burial. We have reason to thank God, however, for having enlightened the mind of our monarch with ideas much purer than those of your theology. His edicts bearing so severely on this subject, have not made duelling a crime—they only punish the crime which is inseparable from duelling. He has checked, by the dread of his rigid justice, those who were not restrained by the fear of the justice of God; and his piety has taught him that the honour of Christians consists in their observance of the mandates of Heaven and the rules of Christianity, and not in the pursuit of that phantom which, airy and unsubstantial as it is, you hold to be a legitimate apology for murder. Your murderous decisions being thus universally detested, it is highly advisable that you should now change your sentiments, if not from religious principle, at least from motives of policy. Prevent, fathers, by a spontaneous condemnation of these inhuman dogmas, the melancholy consequences which may result from them, and for which you will be responsible. And to impress your minds with a deeper horror at homicide, remember that the first crime of fallen man was a murder, committed on the person of the first holy man; that the greatest crime was a murder, perpetrated on the person of the King of saints; and that, of all crimes, murder is the only one which involves in a common destruction the Church and the state, nature and religion.

I have just seen the answer of your apologist to my *Thirteenth Letter;* but if he has nothing better to produce in the shape of a reply to that letter, which obviates the greater part of his objections, he will not deserve a rejoinder. I am sorry to see him perpetually digressing from his subject, to indulge in rancorous abuse both of the living and the dead. But, in order to gain some credit to the stories with which you have furnished him, you should not have made him publicly disavow a fact so notorious as that of the buffet of Compiègne. Certain it is, fathers, from the deposition of the injured party, that he received upon his cheek a blow from the hand of a Jesuit; and all that your friends have been able to do for you has been to raise a doubt whether he received the blow with the back or the palm of the hand, and to discuss the question whether a stroke on the cheek with the back of the hand can be properly denominated a *buffet*. I know not to what tribunal it belongs to decide this point; but shall content myself, in the meantime, with believing that it was, to say the very least, *a probable buffet*. This gets me off with a safe conscience.

LETTER XV

To the reverend fathers, the jesuits

November 25, 1656

Reverend Fathers,

As your scurrilities are daily increasing, and as you are employing them in the merciless abuse of all pious persons opposed to your errors, I feel myself obliged, for their sake and that of the Church, to bring out that grand secret of your policy, which I promised to disclose some time ago, in order that all may know, through means of your own maxims, what degree of credit is due to your calumnious accusations.

I am aware that those who are not very well acquainted with you are at a great loss what to think on this subject, as they find themselves under the painful necessity, either of believing the incredible crimes with which you charge your opponents, or (what is equally incredible) of setting you down as slanderers. "Indeed!" they exclaim, "were these things not true, would clergymen publish them to the world—would they debauch their consciences and damn themselves by venting such libels?" Such is their way of reasoning, and thus it is that the palpable proof of your falsifications coming into collision with their opinion of your honesty, their minds hang in a state of suspense between the evidence of truth, which they cannot gainsay, and the demands of charity, which they would not violate. It follows that since their high esteem for you is the only thing that prevents them from discrediting your calumnies, if we can succeed in convincing them that you have quite a different idea of calumny from that which they suppose you to have, and that you actually believe that in blackening and defaming your adversaries you are working out your own salvation, there can be little question that the weight of truth will determine them immediately to pay no regard to your accusations. This, fathers, will be the subject of the present letter.

My design is not simply to show that your writings are full of calumnies; I mean to go a step beyond this. It is quite possible for a person to say a number of false things believing them to be true; but the character of a liar implies the intention to tell lies. Now I undertake to prove, fathers, that it is your deliberate intention to tell lies, and that it is both knowingly and purposely that you load your opponents with crimes of which you know them to be innocent, because you believe that you may do so without falling from a state of grace. Though you doubtless know this point of your morality as well as I do, this need not prevent me from telling you about it; which I shall do, were it for no other purpose than to convince all men of its existence, by showing them that I can maintain it to your face, while you cannot have the assurance to disavow it, without confirming, by that very disavowment, the charge which I bring against you.

The doctrine to which I allude is so common in your schools that you have maintained it not only in your books, but, such is your assurance, even in your public theses; as, for example, in those delivered at Louvain in the year 1645, where it occurs in the following terms: "What is it but a venial sin to culminate and forge false accusations to ruin the credit of those who speak evil of us?" So settled is this point among you that, if any one dare to oppose it, you treat him as a blockhead and a hare-brained idiot. Such was the way in which you treated Father Quiroga, the German Capuchin, when he was so unfortunate as to impugn the doctrine. The poor man was instantly attacked by Dicastille, one of your fraternity; and the following is a specimen of the manner in which he manages the dispute: "A certain rueful-visaged, bare-footed, cowled friar—*cucullatus gymnopoda*—whom I do not choose to name, had the boldness to denounce this opinion, among some women and ignorant people, and to allege that it was scandalous and pernicious against all good manners, hostile to the peace of states and societies, and, in short, contrary to the judgement not only of all Catholic doctors, but of all true Catholics. But in opposition to him I maintained, as I do still, that calumny, when employed against a calumniator, though it should be a falsehood, is not a mortal sin, either against justice or charity: and, to prove the point, I referred him to the whole body of our fathers, and to whole universities, exclusively composed of them whom I had consulted on the subject; and among others the reverend Father John Gans, confessor to the Emperor; the reverend Father Daniel Bastele, confessor to the Archduke Leopold; Father Henri, who was preceptor to these two princes; all the public and ordinary professors of the university of Vienna" (wholly composed of Jesuits); "all the professors of the university of Gratz" (all Jesuits); "all the professors of the university of Prague" (where Jesuits are the masters);—"from all of whom I have in my possession approbations of my opinions, written and signed with their own hands; besides having on my side the reverend Father Panalossa, a Jesuit, preacher to the Emperor and the King of Spain; Father Pilliceroli, a Jesuit, and many others, who had all judged this opinion to be probable, before our dispute began." You perceive, fathers, that there are few of your opinions which you have been at more pains to establish than the present, as indeed there were few of them of which you stood more in need. For this reason, doubtless, you have authenticated it so well that the casuists appeal to it as an indubitable principle. "There can be no doubt," says Caramuel, "that it is a probable opinion that we contract no mortal sin by calumniating another, in order to preserve our own reputation. For it is maintained by more than twenty grave doctors, by Gaspard Hurtado, and Dicastille, Jesuits, &c.; so that, were this doctrine not probable, it would be difficult to find any one such in the whole compass of theology."

Wretched indeed must that theology be, and rotten to the very core, which, unless it has been decided to be safe in conscience to defame our neighbor's character to preserve our own, can hardly boast of a safe decision on any other point! How natural is it, fathers, that those who hold this principle should occasionally put it in practice! The corrupt propensity of mankind leans so strongly in that direction of itself that, the obstacle of conscience once being removed, it would be folly to suppose that it will not burst forth with all its native impetuosity. If you desire an example of this, Caramuel will furnish you with one that occurs in the same passage: "This maxim of Father Dicastille," he says, "having been communicated by a German countess to the daughters of the Empress, the belief thus impressed on their minds that calumny was only a venial sin, gave rise in the course of a few days to such an immense number of false and scandalous tales that the whole court was thrown into a flame and filled with alarm. It is easy, indeed, to conceive what a fine use these ladies would make of the new light they had acquired. Matters proceeded to such a length, that it was found necessary to call in the assistance of a worthy Capuchin friar, a man of exemplary life, called Father Quiroga" (the very man whom Dicastille rails at so bitterly), "who assured them that the maxim was most pernicious, especially among women, and was at the greatest pains to prevail upon the Empress to abolish the practice of it entirely." We have no reason, therefore, to be surprised at the bad effects of this doctrine; on the contrary, the wonder would be if it had failed to produce them. Self-love is always ready enough to whisper in our ear, when we are attacked, that we suffer wrongfully; and more particularly in your case, fathers, whom vanity has blinded so egregiously as to make you believe that to wound the honour of your Society is to wound that of the Church. There would have been good ground to look on it as something miraculous, if you had *not* reduced this maxim to practice. Those who do not know you are ready to say: How could these good fathers slander their enemies, when they cannot do so but at the expense of their own salvation? But, if they knew you better, the question would be: How could these good fathers forego the advantage of decrying their enemies, when they have it in their power to do so without hazarding their salvation? Let none, therefore, henceforth be surprised to find the Jesuits calumniators; they can exercise this vocation with a safe conscience; there is no obstacle in heaven or on earth to prevent them. In virtue of the credit they have acquired in the world, they can practise defamation without dreading the justice of mortals; and, on the strength of their self-assumed authority in matters of conscience, they have invented maxims for enabling them to do it without any fear of the justice of God.

This, fathers, is the fertile source of your base slanders. On this principle was Father Brisacier led to scatter his calumnies about him, with such zeal as to draw down on his head the censure of the late Archbishop of Paris. Actuated by the same motives, Father D'Anjou launched his invectives from the pulpit of the Church of St. Benedict in Paris on the 8th of March, 1655, against those honourable gentlemen who were intrusted with the charitable funds raised for the poor of Picardy and Champagne, to which they themselves had largely contributed; and, uttering a base falsehood, calculated (if your slanders had been considered worthy of any credit) to dry up the stream of that charity, he had the assurance to say, "that he knew, from good authority, that certain persons had diverted that money from its proper use, to employ it against the Church and the State"; a calumny which obliged the curate of the parish, who is a doctor of the Sorbonne, to mount the pulpit the very next day, in order to give it the lie direct. To the same source must be traced the conduct of your Father Crasset, who preached calumny at such a furious rate in Orleans that the Archbishop of that place was under the necessity of interdicting him as a public slanderer. In this mandate, dated the 9th of September last, his lordship declares: "That whereas he had been informed that Brother Jean Crasset, priest of the Society of Jesus, had delivered from the pulpit a discourse filled with falsehoods and calumnies against the ecclesiastics of this city, falsely and maliciously charging them with maintaining impious and heretical propositions, such as: That the commandments of God are impracticable; that internal grace is irresistible; that Jesus Christ did not die for all men; and others of a similar kind, condemned by Innocent X: he therefore hereby interdicts the aforesaid Crasset from preaching in his diocese, and forbids all his people to hear him, on pain of mortal disobedience." The above, fathers, is your ordinary accusation, and generally among the first that you bring against all whom it is your interest to denounce. And, although you should find it as impossible to substantiate the charge against any of them, as Father Crasset did in the case of the clergy of Orleans, your peace of conscience will not be in the least disturbed on that account; for you believe that this mode of calumniating your adversaries is permitted you with such certainty that you have no scruple to avow it in the most public manner, and in the face of a whole city.

A remarkable proof of this may be seen in the dispute you had with M. Puys, curate of St. Nisier at Lyons; and the story exhibits so complete an illustration of your spirit that I shall take the liberty of relating some of its leading circumstances. You know, fathers, that, in the year 1649, M. Puys translated into French an excellent book, written by another Capuchin friar, *On the duty which Christians owe to their own parishes, against those that would lead them away from them*, without using a single invective, or pointing to any monk or any order of monks in particular. Your fathers, however, were pleased to put the cap on their own heads;

and without any respect to an aged pastor, a judge in the Primacy of France, and a man who was held in the highest esteem by the whole city, Father Alby wrote a furious tract against him, which you sold in your own church upon Assumption Day; in which book, among other various charges, he accused him of having "made himself scandalous by his gallantries," described him as suspected of having no religion, as a heretic, excommunicated, and, in short, worthy of the stake. To this M. Puys made a reply; and Father Alby, in a second publication, supported his former allegations. Now, fathers, is it not a clear point either that you were calumniators, or that you believed all that you alleged against that worthy priest to be true; and that, on this latter assumption, it became you to see him purified from all these abominations before judging him worthy of your friendship? Let us see, then, what happened at the accommodation of the dispute, which took place in the presence of a great number of the principal inhabitants of the town on the 25th of September, 1650. Before all these witnesses M. Puys made a declaration, which was neither more nor less than this: "That what he had written was not directed against the fathers of the Society of Jesus; that he had spoken in general of those who alienated the faithful from their parishes, without meaning by that to attack the Society; and that, so far from having such an intention, the Society was the object of his esteem and affection." By virtue of these words alone, without either retraction or absolution, M. Puys recovered, all at once, from his apostasy, his scandals, and his excommunication; and Father Alby immediately thereafter addressed him in the following express terms: "Sir, it was in consequence of my believing that you meant to attack the Society to which I have the honour to belong that I was induced to take up the pen in its defence; and I considered that the mode of reply which I adopted was *such as I was permitted to employ*. But, on a better understanding of your intention, I am now free to declare that *there is nothing in your work* to prevent me from regarding you as a man of genius, enlightened in judgement, profound and *orthodox* in doctrine, and *irreproachable* in manners; in one word, as a pastor worthy of your Church. It is with much pleasure that I make this declaration, and I beg these gentlemen to remember what I have now said."

They do remember it, fathers; and, allow me to add, they were more scandalized by the reconciliation than by the quarrel. For who can fail to admire this speech of Father Alby? He does not say that he retracts, in consequence of having learnt that a change had taken place in the faith and manners of M. Puys, but solely because, *having understood that he had no intention of attacking your Society*, there was nothing further to prevent him from regarding the author as a good Catholic. He did not then believe him to be actually a heretic! And yet, after having, contrary to his conviction, accused him of this crime, he will not acknowledge he was in the wrong, but has the hardihood to say that he considered the method he adopted to be "such as he was *permitted* to employ!"

What can you possibly mean, fathers, by so publicly avowing the fact that you measure the faith and the virtue of men only by the sentiments they entertain towards your Society? Had you no apprehension of making yourselves pass, by your own acknowledgement, as a band of swindlers and slanderers? What, fathers! must the same individual without undergoing any personal transformation, but simply according as you judge him to have honoured or assailed your community, be "pious" or "impious," "irreproachable" or "excommunicated," "a pastor worthy of the Church," or "worthy of the stake"; in short, "a Catholic" or "a heretic"? To attack your Society and to be a heretic are, therefore, in your language, convertible terms! An odd sort of heresy this, fathers! And so it would appear that, when we see many good Catholics branded, in your writings, by the name of *heretics*, it means nothing more than that *you think they attack you!* It is well, fathers, that we understand this strange dialect, according to which there can be no doubt that I must be a great heretic. It is in *this* sense, then, that you so often favour me with this appellation! Your sole reason for cutting me off from the Church is because you conceive that my letters have done you harm; and, accordingly, all that I have to do, in order to become a good Catholic, is either to approve of your extravagant morality, or to convince you that my sole aim in exposing it has been your advantage. The former I could not do without renouncing every sentiment of piety that I ever possessed; and the latter you will be slow to acknowledge till you are well cured of your errors. Thus am I involved in heresy, after a very singular fashion; for, the purity of my faith being of no avail for my exculpation, I have no means of escaping from the charge, except either by turning traitor to my own conscience, or by reforming yours. Till one or other of these events happen, I must remain a reprobate and a slanderer; and, let me be ever so faithful in my citations from your writings, you will go about crying everywhere: "What an instrument of the devil must that man be, to impute to us things of which there is not the least mark or vestige to be found in our books!" And, by doing so, you will only be acting in conformity with your fixed maxim and your ordinary practice: to such latitude does your privilege of telling lies extend! Allow me to give you an example of this, which I select on purpose; it will give me an opportunity of replying, at the same time, to your ninth *Imposture:* for, in truth, they only deserve to be refuted in passing.

About ten or twelve years ago, you were accused of holding that maxim of Father Bauny, "that it is permissible to seek directly (*primo et per se*) a proximate occasion of sin, for the spiritual or temporal good of ourselves or our neighbour" (tr. 4, q. 14); as an example of which, he observes: "It is allowable to visit infamous places, for the purpose of converting abandoned females, even although the practice should be very likely to lead into sin, as in the case of one who has found from experience that he has frequently yielded to their temptations." What answer did your Father Caussin give to this charge in the year 1644? "Just let any one look at the passage in Father Bauny," said he, "let him peruse the page, the margins, the preface, the appendix, in short, the whole book from beginning to end, and he will not discover the slightest vestige of such a sentence, which could only enter into the mind of a man totally devoid of conscience, and could hardly have been forged by any other but an instrument of Satan." Father Pintereau talks in the same style: "That man must be lost to all conscience who would teach so detestable a doctrine; but he must be worse than a devil who attributes it to Father Bauny. Reader, there is not a single trace or vestige of it in the whole of his book." Who would not believe that persons talking in this tone have good reason to complain, and that Father Bauny has, in very deed, been misrepresented? Have you ever asserted anything against me in stronger terms? And, after such a solemn asseveration, that "there was not a single trace or vestige of it in the whole book," who would imagine that the passage is to be found, word for word, in the place referred to?

Truly, fathers, if this be the means of securing your reputation, so long as you remain unanswered, it is also, unfortunately, the means of destroying it forever, so soon as an answer makes its appearance. For so certain is it that you told a lie at the period before mentioned, that you make no scruple of acknowledging, in your apologies of the present day, that the maxim in question is to be found in the very place which had been quoted; and, what is most extraordinary, the same maxim which, twelve years ago, was "detestable," has now become so innocent that in your ninth *Imposture* (p. 10) you accuse me of "ignorance and malice, in quarrelling with Father Bauny for an opinion which has not been rejected in the School." What an advantage it is, fathers, to have to do with people that deal in contradictions! I need not the aid of any but yourselves to confute you; for I have only two things to show: first, That the maxim in dispute is a worthless one; and, secondly, That it belongs to Father Bauny; and I can prove both by your own confession. In 1644, you confessed that it was "detestable"; and, in 1656, you avow that it is Father Bauny's. This double acknowledgement completely justifies me, fathers; but it does more, it discovers the spirit of your policy. For, tell me, pray, what is the end you propose to yourselves in your writings? Is it to speak with honesty? No, fathers; that cannot be, since your defences destroy each other. Is it to follow the truth of the faith? As little can this be your end; since, according to your own showing, you authorize a "detestable" maxim. But, be it observed that while you said the maxim was "detestable," you denied, at the same time, that it was the property of Father Bauny, and so he was innocent; and when you now acknowledge it to be his, you maintain, at the same time, that it is a good maxim, and so he is innocent still. The innocence of this monk, therefore, being the only thing common to your two answers, it is obvious that this was the sole end which you aimed at in putting them forth; and that, when you say of one and the same maxim, that it is in a certain book, and that it is not; that it is a good maxim, and that it is a bad one; your sole object is to whitewash some one or other of your fraternity; judging in the matter, not according to the truth, which never changes, but according to your own interest, which is varying every hour. Can I say more than this? You perceive that it amounts to a demonstration; but it is far from being a singular instance, and, to omit a multitude of examples of the same thing, I believe you will be contented with my quoting only one more.

You have been charged, at different times, with another proposition of the same Father Bauny, namely: "That absolution ought to be neither denied nor deferred in the case of those who live in the habits of sin against the law of God, of nature, and of the Church, although there should be no apparent prospect of future amendment—*etsi emendationis futuræ spes nulla appareat.*" Now, with regard to this maxim, I beg you to tell me, fathers, which of the apologies that have been made for it is most to your liking; whether that of Father Pintereau, or that of Father Brisacier, both of your Society, who have defended Father Bauny, in your *two different* modes—the one by condemning the proposition, but disavowing it to be Father Bauny's; the other by allowing it to be Father Bauny's, but vindicating the proposition? Listen, then, to their respective deliverances. Here comes that of Father Pintereau (p. 8): "I know not what can be called a transgression of all the bounds of modesty, a step beyond all ordinary impudence, if the imputation to Father Bauny of so damnable a doctrine is not worthy of that designation. Judge, reader, of the baseness of that calumny; see what sort of creatures the

Jesuits have to deal with; and say if the author of so foul a slander does not deserve to be regarded from henceforth as the interpreter of the father of lies." Now for Father Brisacier: "It is true, Father Bauny says what you allege." (That gives the lie direct to Father Pintereau, plain enough.) "But," adds he, in defence of Father Bauny, "if you who find so much fault with this sentiment wait, when a penitent lies at your feet, till his guardian angel find security for his rights in the inheritance of heaven; if you wait till God the Father swear by himself that David told a lie, when he said by the Holy Ghost that 'all men are liars,' fallible and perfidious; if you wait till the penitent be no longer a liar, no longer frail and changeable, no longer a sinner, like other men; if you wait, I say, till then, you will never apply the blood of Jesus Christ to a single soul."

What do you really think now, fathers, of these impious and extravagant expressions? According to them, if we would wait "till there be some hope of amendment" in sinners before granting their absolution, we must wait "till God the Father swear by himself," that they will never fall into sin any more! What, fathers! is no distinction to be made between *hope* and *certainty?* How injurious is it to the grace of Jesus Christ to maintain that it is so impossible for Christians ever to escape from crimes against the laws of God, nature, and the Church, that such a thing cannot be looked for, without supposing "that the Holy Ghost has told a lie"; and, if absolution is not granted to those who give no hope of amendment, the blood of Jesus Christ will be useless, forsooth, and "would never be applied to a single soul!" To what a sad pass have you come, fathers by this extravagant desire of upholding the glory of your authors, when you can find only two ways of justifying them—by imposture or by impiety; and when the most innocent mode by which you can extricate yourselves is by the barefaced denial of facts as patent as the light of day!

This may perhaps account for your having recourse so frequently to that very convenient practice. But this does not complete the sum of your accomplishments in the art of self-defence. To render your opponents odious, you have had recourse to the forging of documents, such as that *Letter of a Minister to M. Arnauld,* which you circulated through all Paris, to induce the belief that the work on *Frequent Communion,* which had been approved by so many bishops and doctors, but which, to say the truth, was rather against you, had been concocted through secret intelligence with the ministers of Charenton. At other times, you attribute to your adversaries writings full of impiety, such as the *Circular Letter of the Jansenists,* the absurd style of which renders the fraud too gross to be swallowed, and palpably betrays the malice of your Father Meynier, who has the impudence to make use of it for supporting his foulest slanders. Sometimes, again, you will quote books which were never in existence, such as *The Constitution of the Holy Sacrament,* from which you extract passages, fabricated at pleasure and calculated to make the hair on the heads of certain good simple people, who have no idea of the effrontery with which you can invent and propagate falsehoods, actually to bristle with horror. There is not, indeed, a single species of calumny which you have not put into requisition; nor is it possible that the maxim which excuses the vice could have been lodged in better hands.

But those sorts of slander to which we have adverted are rather too easily discredited; and, accordingly, you have others of a more subtle character, in which you abstain from specifying particulars, in order to preclude your opponents from getting any hold, or finding any means of reply; as, for example, when Father Brisacier says that "his enemies are guilty of abominable crimes, *which he does not choose to mention.*" Would you not think it were impossible to prove a charge so vague as this to be a calumny? An able man, however, has found out the secret of it; and it is a Capuchin again, fathers. You are unlucky in Capuchins, as times now go; and I foresee that you may be equally so some other time in Benedictines. The name of this Capuchin is Father Valerien, of the house of the Counts of Magnis. You shall hear, by this brief narrative, how he answered your calumnies. He had happily succeeded in converting Prince Ernest, the Landgrave of Hesse-Rheinsfelt. Your fathers, however, seized, as it would appear, with some chagrin at seeing a sovereign prince converted without their having had any hand in it, immediately wrote a book against the friar (for good men are everywhere the objects of your persecution), in which, by falsifying one of his passages, they ascribed to him an heretical doctrine. They also circulated a letter against him, in which they said: "Ah, we have such things to disclose" (without mentioning what) "as will gall you to the quick! If you don't take care, we shall be forced to inform the pope and the cardinals about it." This manœuvre was pretty well executed; and I doubt not, fathers, but you may speak in the same style of me; but take warning from the manner in which the friar answered in his book, which was printed last year at Prague (p. 112, &c.): "What shall I do," he says, "to counteract these vague and indefinite insinuations? How shall I refute charges which have never been specified? Here, however, is my plan. I declare, loudly and publicly, to those who have threatened me, that they are notorious slanderers and most impudent liars, if they do not discover these crimes before the whole world. Come forth, then, mine accusers! and publish your lies upon the house-tops, in place of telling them in the ear, and keeping yourselves out of harm's way by telling them in the ear. Some may think this a scandalous way of managing the dispute. It was scandalous, I grant, to impute to me such a crime as heresy, and to fix upon me the suspicion of many others besides; but, by asserting my innocence, I am merely applying the proper remedy to the scandal already in existence."

Truly, fathers, never were your reverences more roughly handled, and never was a poor man more completely vindicated. Since you have made no reply to such a peremptory challenge, it must be concluded that you are unable to discover the slightest shadow of criminality against him. You have had very awkward scrapes to get through occasionally; but experience has made you nothing the wiser. For, some time after this happened, you attacked the same individual in a similar strain, upon another subject; and he defended himself after the same spirited manner, as follows: "This class of men, who have become an intolerable nuisance to the whole of Christendom, aspire, under the pretext of good works, to dignities and domination, by perverting to their own ends almost all laws, human and divine, natural and revealed. They gain over to their side, by their doctrine, by the force of fear, or of persuasion, the great ones of the earth, whose authority they abuse for the purpose of accomplishing their detestable intrigues. Meanwhile their enterprises, criminal as they are, are neither punished nor suppressed; on the contrary, they are rewarded; and the villains go about them with as little fear or remorse as if they were doing God service. Everybody is aware of the fact I have now stated; everybody speaks of it with execration; but few are found capable of opposing a despotism so powerful. This, however, is what I have done. I have already curbed their insolence; and, by the same means, I shall curb it again. I declare, then, that *they are most impudent liars—mentiris impudentissime.* If the charges they have brought against me be true, let them prove it; otherwise they stand convicted of falsehood, aggravated by the grossest effrontery. Their procedure in this case will show who has the right upon his side. I desire all men to take a particular observation of it; and beg to remark, in the meantime, that this precious cabal, who will not suffer the most trifling charge which they can possibly repel to lie upon them, made a show of enduring, with great patience, those from which they cannot vindicate themselves, and conceal, under a counterfeit virtue, their real impotency. My object, therefore, in provoking their modesty by this sharp retort, is to let the plainest people understand that, if my enemies hold their peace, their forbearance must be ascribed, not to the meekness of their natures, but to the power of a guilty conscience." He concludes with the following sentence: "These gentry, whose history is well known throughout the whole world, are so glaringly iniquitous in their measures, and have become so insolent in their impunity, that if I did not detest their conduct, and publicly express my detestation too, not merely for my own vindication, but to guard the simple against its seducing influence, I must have renounced my allegiance to Jesus Christ and his Church."

Reverend fathers, there is no room for tergiversation. You must pass for convicted slanderers, and take comfort in your old maxim that calumny is no crime. This honest friar has discovered the secret of shutting your mouths; and it must be employed on all occasions when you accuse people without proof. We have only to reply to each slander as it appears, in the words of the Capuchin: "*Mentiris impudentissime*—You are most impudent liars." For instance, what better answer does Father Brisacier deserve when he says of his opponents that they are "the gates of hell; the devil's bishops; persons devoid of faith, hope, and charity; the builders of Antichrist's exchequer"; adding, "I say this of him, not by way of insult, but from deep conviction of its truth"? Who would be at the pains to demonstrate that he is not "a gate of hell," and that he has no concern with "the building up of Antichrist's exchequer"?

In like manner, what reply is due to all the vague speeches of this sort which are to be found in your books and advertisements on my letters; such as the following, for example: "That restitutions have been converted to private uses, and thereby creditors have been reduced to beggary; that bags of money have been offered to learned monks, who declined the bribe; that benefices are conferred for the purpose of disseminating heresies against the faith; that pensioners are kept in the houses of the most eminent churchmen, and in the courts of sovereigns; that I also am a pensioner of Port-Royal; and that, before writing my letters, I had composed *romances*"—I, who never read one in my life, and who do not know so much as the names of those which your apologist has published? What can be said in reply to all this, fathers, if you do not mention the names of all these persons you refer to, their words, the time, and the place, except—*Mentiris impudentissime?* You should either be silent altogether, or relate and prove all the circumstances, as I did when I told you the anecdotes of Father Alby and John d'Alba. Otherwise, you will hurt none but yourselves. Your numerous fables might, perhaps, have done you some service, before your principles were known; but now that the whole has been brought to light, when you begin to whisper as usual, "A man of honor, who desired us to conceal his name, has told us some horrible stories of these same people"—you will be cut short at once, and reminded of the Capuchin's *"Mentiris impudentissime."* Too long by far have you been permitted to deceive the world, and to abuse the confidence which men were ready to place in your calumnious accusations. It is high time to redeem the reputation of the multitudes whom you have defamed. For what innocence can be so generally known, as not to suffer some injury from the daring aspersions of a body of men scattered over the face of the earth, and who, under religious habits, conceal minds so utterly irreligious that they perpetrate crimes like calumny, not in opposition to, but in strict accordance with, their moral maxims? I cannot, therefore, be blamed for destroying the credit which might have been awarded you, seeing it must be allowed to be a much greater act of justice to restore to the victims of your obloquy the character which they did not deserve to lose, than to leave you in the possession of a reputation for sincerity which you do not deserve to enjoy. And, as the one could not be done without the other, how important was it to show you up to the world as you really are! In this letter I have commenced the exhibition; but it will require some time to complete it. Published it shall be, fathers, and all your policy will be inadequate to save you from the disgrace; for the efforts which you may make to avert the blow will only serve to convince the most obtuse observers that you were terrified out of your wits, and that, your consciences anticipating the charges I had to bring against you, you have put every oar in the water to prevent the discovery.

LETTER XVI

TO THE REVEREND FATHERS, THE JESUITS

December 4, 1656

REVEREND FATHERS,

I now come to consider the rest of your calumnies, and shall begin with those contained in your advertisements, which remain to be noticed. As all your other writings, however, are equally well stocked with slander, they will furnish me with abundant materials for entertaining you on this topic as long as I may judge expedient. In the first place, then, with regard to the fable which you have propagated in all your writings against the Bishop of Ypres, I beg leave to say, in one word, that you have maliciously wrested the meaning of some ambiguous expressions in one of his letters which, being capable of a good sense, ought, according to the spirit of the Gospel, to have been taken in good part, and could only be taken otherwise according to the spirit of your Society. For example, when he says to a friend, "Give yourself no concern about your nephew; I will furnish him with what he requires from the money that lies in my hands," what reason have you to interpret this to mean that he would take that money without restoring it, and not that he merely advanced it with the purpose of replacing it? And how extremely imprudent was it for you to furnish a refutation of your own lie, by printing the other letters of the Bishop of Ypres, which clearly show that, in point of fact, it was merely *advanced* money, which he was bound to refund.

This appears, to your confusion, from the following terms in the letter, to which you give the date of July 30, 1619: "Be not uneasy about the money advanced; he shall want for nothing so long as he is here"; and likewise from another, dated January 6, 1620, where he says: "You are in too great haste; when the account shall become due, I have no fear but that the little credit which I have in this place will bring me as much money as I require."

If you are convicted slanderers on this subject, you are no less so in regard to the ridiculous story about the charity-box of St. Merri. What advantage, pray, can you hope to derive from the accusation which one of your worthy friends has trumped up against that ecclesiastic? Are we to conclude that a man is guilty, because he is accused? No, fathers. Men of piety, like him, may expect to be perpetually accused, so long as the world contains calumniators like you. We must judge of him, therefore, not from the accusation, but from the sentence; and the sentence pronounced on the case (February 23, 1656) justifies him completely. Moreover, the person who had the temerity to involve himself in that iniquitous process, was disavowed by his colleagues, and himself compelled to retract his charge. And as to what you allege, in the same place, about "that famous director, who pocketed at once nine hundred thousand livres," I need only refer you to Messieurs the curés of St. Roch and St. Paul, who will bear witness, before the whole city of Paris, to his perfect disinterestedness in the affair, and to your inexcusable malice in that piece of imposition.

Enough, however, for such paltry falsities. These are but the first raw attempts of your novices, and not the master-strokes of your "grand professed." To these do I now come, fathers; I come to a calumny which is certainly one of the basest that ever issued from the spirit of your Society. I refer to the insufferable audacity with which you have imputed to holy nuns, and to their directors, the charge of "disbelieving the mystery of transubstantiation and the real presence of Jesus Christ in the eucharist." Here, fathers, is a slander worthy of yourselves. Here is a crime which God alone is capable of punishing, as you alone were capable of committing it. To endure it with patience would require an humility as great as that of these calumniated ladies; to give it credit would demand a degree of wickedness equal to that of their wretched defamers. I propose not, therefore, to vindicate them; they are beyond suspicion. Had they stood in need of defence, they might have commanded abler advocates than me. My object in what I say here is to show, not their innocence, but your malignity. I merely intend to make you ashamed of yourselves, and to let the whole world understand that, after this, there is nothing of which you are not capable.

You will not fail, I am certain, notwithstanding all this, to say that I belong to Port-Royal; for this is the first thing you say to every one who combats your errors: as if it were only at Port-Royal that persons could be found possessed of sufficient zeal to defend, against your attacks, the purity of Christian morality. I know, fathers, the work of the pious recluses who have retired to that monastery, and how much the Church is indebted to their truly solid and edifying labours. I know the excellence of their piety and their learning. For, though I have never had the honour to belong to their establishment, as you, without knowing who or what I am, would fain have it believed, nevertheless, I do know some of them, and honour the virtue of them all. But God has not confined within the precincts of that society all whom he means to raise up in opposition to your corruptions.

I hope, with his assistance, fathers, to make you feel this; and if he vouchsafe to sustain me in the design he has led me to form, of employing in his service all the resources I have received from him, I shall speak to you in such a strain as will, perhaps, give you reason to regret that you have *not* had to do with a man of Port-Royal. And to convince you of this, fathers, I must tell you that, while those whom you have abused with this notorious slander content themselves with lifting up their groans to Heaven to obtain your forgiveness for the outrage, I feel myself obliged, not being in the least affected by your slander, to make you blush in the face of the whole Church, and so bring you to that wholesome shame of which the Scripture speaks, and which is almost the only remedy for a hardness of heart like yours: "*Imple facies eorum ignominia, et quærent nomen tuum, Domine*— Fill their faces with shame, that they may seek thy name, O Lord."

A stop must be put to this insolence, which does not spare the most sacred retreats. For who can be safe after a calumny of this nature? For shame, fathers! to publish in Paris such a scandalous book, with the name of your Father Meynier on its front, and under this infamous title, *Port-Royal and Geneva in concert against the most holy Sacrament of the Altar*, in which you accuse of this apostasy, not only Monsieur the abbé of St. Cyran, and M. Arnauld, but also Mother Agnes, his sister, and all the nuns of that monastery, alleging that "their faith, in regard to the eucharist, is as suspicious as that of M. Arnauld," whom you maintain to be "a down-right Calvinist." I here ask the whole world if there be any class of persons within the pale of the Church, on whom you could have advanced such an abominable charge with less semblance of truth. For tell me, fathers, if these nuns and their directors had been "in concert with Geneva against the most holy sacrament of the altar" (the very thought of which is shocking), how they should have come to select as the principal object of their piety that very sacrament which they held in abomination? How should they have assumed the habit of the holy sacrament? taken the name of the Daughters of the Holy Sacrament? called their church the Church of the Holy Sacrament? How should they have requested and obtained from Rome the confirmation of that institution, and the right of saying every Thursday the office of the holy sacrament, in which the faith of the Church is so perfectly expressed, if they had conspired with Geneva to banish that faith from the Church? Why would they have bound themselves, by a particular devotion, also sanctioned by the Pope, to have some of their sisterhood, night and day without intermission, in presence of the sacred host, to compensate, by their perpetual adorations towards that perpetual sacrifice, for the impiety of the heresy that aims at its annihilation? Tell me, fathers, if you can, why, of all the mysteries of our religion, they should have passed by those in which they believed, to fix upon that in which they believed not? and how they should have devoted themselves, so fully and entirely, to that mystery of our faith, if they took it, as the heretics do, for the mystery of iniquity? And what answer do you give to these clear evidences, embodied not in words only, but in actions; and not in some particular actions, but in the whole tenor of a life expressly dedicated to the adoration of Jesus Christ, dwelling on our altars? What answer, again, do you give to the books which you ascribe to Port-Royal, all of which are full of the most precise terms employed by the fathers and the councils to mark the essence of that mystery? It is at once ridiculous and disgusting to hear you replying to these as you have done throughout your libel. M. Arnauld, say you, talks very well about transub-

stantiation; but he understands, perhaps, only "a significative transubstantiation."
True, he professes to believe in "the real presence"; who can tell, however, but he
means nothing more than "a true and real figure"? How now, fathers! whom, pray,
will you not make pass for a Calvinist whenever you please, if you are to be allowed
the liberty of perverting the most canonical and sacred expressions by the wicked
subtleties of your modern equivocations? Who ever thought of using any other
terms than those in question, especially in simple discourses of devotion, where
no controversies are handled? And yet the love and the reverence in which they
hold this sacred mystery have induced them to give it such a prominence in all
their writings that I defy you, fathers, with all your cunning, to detect in them
either the least appearance of ambiguity, or the slightest correspondence with
the sentiments of Geneva.

Everybody knows, fathers, that the essence of the Genevan heresy consists, as
it does according to your own showing, in their believing that Jesus Christ is not
contained in this sacrament; that it is impossible he can be in many places at once;
that he is, properly speaking, only in heaven, and that it is as there alone that he
ought to be adored, and not on the altar; that the substance of the bread remains;
that the body of Jesus Christ does not enter into the mouth or the stomach; that
he can only be eaten by faith, and accordingly wicked men do not eat him at all;
and that the mass is not a sacrifice, but an abomination. Let us now hear, then, in
what way "Port-Royal is in concert with Geneva." In the writings of the former
we read, to your confusion, the following statement: That "the flesh and blood
of Jesus Christ are contained under the species of bread and wine"; that "the
Holy of Holies is present in the sanctuary, and that there he ought to be adored";
that "Jesus Christ dwells in the sinners who communicate, by the real and veri-
table presence of his body in their stomach, although not by the presence of his
Spirit in their hearts"; that "the dead ashes of the bodies of the saints derive their
principal dignity from that seed of life which they retain from the touch of the
immortal and vivifying flesh of Jesus Christ"; that "it is not owing to any natural
power, but to the almighty power of God, to whom nothing is impossible, that
the body of Jesus Christ is comprehended under the host, and under the smallest
portion of every host"; that "the divine virtue is present to produce the effect
which the words of consecration signify"; that "Jesus Christ, while he is lowered
and hidden upon the altar, is, at the same time, elevated in his glory; that he
subsists, of himself and by his own ordinary power, in divers places at the same
time—in the midst of the Church triumphant, and in the midst of the Church
militant and travelling"; that "the sacramental species remain suspended, and
subsist extraordinarily, without being upheld by any subject; and that the body
of Jesus Christ is also suspended under the species, and that it does not depend
upon these, as substances depend upon accidents"; that "the substance of the
bread is changed, the immutable accidents remaining the same"; that "Jesus
Christ reposes in the eucharist with the same glory that he has in heaven"; that
"his glorious humanity resides in the tabernacles of the Church, under the species
of bread, which forms its visible covering; and that, knowing the grossness of our
natures, he conducts us to the adoration of his divinity, which is present in all
places, by the adoring of his humanity, which is present in a particular place";
that "we receive the body of Jesus Christ upon the tongue, which is sanctified by
its divine touch"; "that it enters into the mouth of the priest"; that "although

Jesus Christ has made himself accessible in the holy sacrament, by an act of his
love and graciousness, he preserves, nevertheless, in that ordinance, his inaccessibility, as an inseparable condition of his divine nature; because, although the
body alone and the blood alone are there, by virtue of the words—*vi verborum*, as
the schoolmen say—his whole divinity may, notwithstanding, be there also, as
well as his whole humanity, by a necessary conjunction." In fine, that "the eucharist is at the same time sacrament and sacrifice"; and that "although this sacrifice is a commemoration of that of the cross, yet there is this difference between
them, that the sacrifice of the mass is offered for the Church only, and for the
faithful in her communion; whereas that of the cross has been offered for all the
world, as the Scripture testifies."

I have quoted enough, fathers, to make it evident that there was never, perhaps,
a more imprudent thing attempted than what you have done. But I will go a step
farther, and make you pronounce this sentence against yourselves. For what do
you require from a man, in order to remove all suspicion of his being in concert
and correspondence with Geneva? "If M. Arnauld," says your Father Meynier,
p. 93, "had said that, in this adorable mystery, there is no substance of the bread
under the species, but only the flesh and the blood of Jesus Christ, I should have
confessed that he had declared himself absolutely against Geneva." Confess it,
then, ye revilers! and make him a public apology. How often have you seen this
declaration made in the passages I have just cited? Besides this, however, the
Familiar Theology of M. de St. Cyran having been approved by M. Arnauld, it
contains the sentiments of both. Read, then, the whole of lesson 15th, and particularly article 2d, and you will there find the words you desiderate, even more
formally stated than you have done yourselves. "Is there any bread in the host, or
any wine in the chalice? No: for all the substance of the bread and the wine is
taken away, to give place to that of the body and blood of Jesus Christ, the which
substance alone remains therein, covered by the qualities and species of bread and
wine."

How now, fathers! will you still say that Port-Royal teaches "nothing that
Geneva does not receive," and that M. Arnauld has said nothing in his second
letter "which might not have been said by a minister of Charenton"? See if you
can persuade Mestrezat to speak as M. Arnauld does in that letter, on page 237.
Make him say that it is an infamous calumny to accuse him of denying transubstantiation; that he takes for the fundamental principle of his writings the truth of
the real presence of the Son of God, in opposition to the heresy of the Calvinists;
and that he accounts himself happy for living in a place where the Holy of Holies
is continually adored in the sanctuary"—a sentiment which is still more opposed
to the belief of the Calvinists than the real presence itself; for, as Cardinal Richelieu
observes in his *Controversies* (p. 536): "The new ministers of France having agreed
with the Lutherans, who believe the real presence of Jesus Christ in the eucharist;
they have declared that they remain in a state of separation from the Church on
the point of this mystery, only on account of the adoration which Catholics
render to the eucharist." Get all the passages which I have extracted from the
books of Port-Royal subscribed at Geneva, and not the isolated passages merely,
but the entire treatises regarding this mystery, such as the *Book of Frequent Communion*, the *Explication of the Ceremonies of the Mass*, the *Exercise during Mass*, the
Reasons of the Suspension of the Holy Sacrament, the *Translation of the Hymns in the*

Hours of Port-Royal, &c.; in one word, prevail upon them to establish at Charenton that holy institution of adoring, without intermission, Jesus Christ contained in the eucharist, as is done at Port-Royal, and it will be the most signal service which you could render to the Church; for in this case it will turn out, not that Port-Royal is in concert with Geneva, but that Geneva is in concert with Port-Royal and with the whole Church.

Certainly, fathers, you could not have been more unfortunate than in selecting Port-Royal as the object of attack for not believing in the eucharist; but I will show what led you to fix upon it. You know I have picked up some small acquaintance with your policy; in this instance you have acted upon its maxims to admiration. If Monsieur the abbé of St. Cyran, and M. Arnauld, had only spoken of what ought to be believed with great respect to this mystery, and said nothing about what ought to be done in the way of preparation for its reception, they might have been the best Catholics alive; and no equivocations would have been discovered in their use of the terms *real presence* and *transubstantiation*. But, since all who combat your licentious principles must needs be heretics, and heretics, too, in the very point in which they condemn your laxity, how could M. Arnauld escape falling under this charge on the subject of the eucharist, after having published a book expressly against your profanations of that sacrament? What! must he be allowed to say, with impunity, that "the body of Jesus Christ ought not to be given to those who habitually lapse into the same crimes, and who have no prospect of amendment; and that such persons ought to be excluded, for some time, from the altar, to purify themselves by sincere penitence, that they may approach it afterwards with benefit"? Suffer no one to talk in this strain, fathers, or you will find that fewer people will come to your confessionals. Father Brisacier says that "were you to adopt this course, you would never apply the blood of Jesus Christ to a single individual." It would be infinitely more for your interest were every one to adopt the views of your Society, as set forth by your Father Mascarenhas, in a book approved by your doctors, and even by your reverend Father-General, namely: "That persons of every description, and even priests, may receive the body of Jesus Christ on the very day they have polluted themselves with odious crimes; that, so far from such communions implying irreverence, persons who partake of them in this manner act a commendable part; that confessors ought not to keep them back from the ordinance, but, on the contrary, ought to advise those who have recently committed such crimes to communicate immediately; because, although the Church has forbidden it, this prohibition is annulled by the universal practice in all places of the earth."

See what it is, fathers, to have Jesuits in all places of the earth! Behold the universal practice which you have introduced, and which you are anxious everywhere to maintain! It matters nothing that the tables of Jesus Christ are filled with abominations, provided that your churches are crowded with people. Be sure, therefore, cost what it may, to set down all that dare to say a word against your practice as heretics on the holy sacrament. But how can you do this, after the irrefragable testimonies which they have given of their faith? Are you not afraid of my coming out with the four grand proofs of their heresy which you have adduced? You ought, at least, to be so, fathers, and I ought not to spare your blushing. Let us, then, proceed to examine proof the first.

"M. de St. Cyran," says Father Meynier, "consoling one of his friends upon the death of his mother (tom. i., let. 14), says that the most acceptable sacrifice that can be offered up to God, on such occasions, is that of patience; therefore he is a Calvinist." This is marvellously shrewd reasoning, fathers; and I doubt if anybody will be able to discover the precise point of it. Let us learn it, then, from his own mouth. "Because," says this mighty controversialist, "it is obvious that he does not believe in the sacrifice of the mass; for this is, of all other sacrifices, the most acceptable unto God." Who will venture to say now that the Jesuits do not know how to reason? Why, they know the art to such perfection that they will extract heresy out of anything you choose to mention, not even excepting the Holy Scripture itself! For example, might it not be heretical to say, with the wise man in Ecclesiasticus, "There is nothing worse than to love money"; as if adultery, murder, or idolatry, were not far greater crimes? Where is the man who is not in the habit of using similar expressions every day? May we not say, for instance, that the most acceptable of all sacrifices in the eyes of God is that of a contrite and humbled heart; just because, in discourses of this nature, we simply mean to compare certain internal virtues with one another, and not with the sacrifice of the mass, which is of a totally different order, and infinitely more exalted? Is this not enough to make you ridiculous, fathers? And is it necessary, to complete your discomfiture, that I should quote the passages of that letter in which M. de St. Cyran speaks of the sacrifice of the mass as "the most excellent" of all others, in the following terms? "Let there be presented to God, daily and in all places, the sacrifice of the body of his Son, who could not find *a more excellent way* than that by which he might honour his Father." And afterwards: "Jesus Christ has enjoined us to take, when we are dying, his sacrificed body, to render more acceptable to God the sacrifice of our own, and to join himself with us at the hour of dissolution; to the end that he may strengthen us for the struggle, sanctifying, by his presence, the last sacrifice which we make to God of our life and our body"? Pretend to take no notice of all this, fathers, and persist in maintaining, as you do in page 39, that he refused to take the communion on his death-bed, and that he did not believe in the sacrifice of the mass. Nothing can be too gross for calumniators by profession.

Your second proof furnishes an excellent illustration of this. To make a Calvinist of M. de St. Cyran, to whom you ascribe the book of *Petrus Aurelius*, you take advantage of a passage (page 80) in which Aurelius explains in what manner the Church acts towards priests, and even bishops, whom she wishes to degrade or depose. "The Church," he says, "being incapable of depriving them of the power of the order, the character of which is indelible, she does all that she can do: she banishes from her memory the character which she cannot banish from the souls of the individuals who have been once invested with it; she regards them in the same light as if they were not bishops or priests; so that, according to the ordinary language of the Church, it may be said they are no longer such, although they always remain such, in as far as the character is concerned—*ob indelebilitatem characteris.*" You perceive, fathers, that this author, who has been approved by three general assemblies of the clergy of France, plainly declares that the character of the priesthood is indelible; and yet you make him say, on the contrary, in the very same passage, that "the character of the priesthood is *not* indelible." This is what I would call a notorious slander; in other words, according to your nomenclature, a small venial sin. And the reason is, this book has done you some harm by refuting the heresies of your brethren in England touching the Episcopal authority. But the folly of the charge is equally remarkable; for, after having taken it for granted, without any foundation, that M. de St. Cyran holds the priestly character to be not indelible, you conclude from this that he does not believe in the real presence of Jesus Christ in the eucharist.

Do not expect me to answer this, fathers. If you have got no common sense, I am not able to furnish you with it. All who possess any share of it will enjoy a hearty laugh at your expense. Nor will they treat with greater respect your third proof, which rests upon the following words, taken from the *Book of Frequent Communion:* "In the eucharist God vouchsafes us *the same food* that He bestows on the saints in heaven, with this difference only, that here He withholds from us its sensible sight and taste, reserving both of these for the heavenly world." These words express the sense of the Church so distinctly that I am constantly forgetting what reason you have for picking a quarrel with them, in order to turn them to a bad use; for I can see nothing more in them than what the Council of Trent teaches (sess. xiii, c. 8), namely, that there is no difference between Jesus Christ in the eucharist and Jesus Christ in heaven, except that here he is veiled, and there he is not. M. Arnauld does not say that there is no difference in the manner of receiving Jesus Christ, but only that there is no difference in Jesus Christ who is received. And yet you would, in the face of all reason, interpret his language in this passage to mean that Jesus Christ is no more eaten with the mouth in this world than he is in heaven; upon which you ground the charge of heresy against him.

You really make me sorry for you, fathers. Must we explain this further to you? Why do you confound that divine nourishment with the manner of receiving it? There is but one point of difference, as I have just observed, betwixt that nourishment upon earth and in heaven, which is that here it is hidden under veils which deprive us of its sensible sight and taste; but there are various points of dissimilarity in the manner of receiving it here and there, the principal of which is, as M. Arnauld expresses it (p. 3, ch. 16), "that here it enters into the mouth and the breast both of the good and of the wicked," which is not the case in heaven.

And, if you require to be told the reason of this diversity, I may inform you, fathers, that the cause of God's ordaining these different modes of receiving the same food is the difference that exists betwixt the state of Christians in this life and that of the blessed in heaven. The state of the Christian, as Cardinal Perron observes after the fathers, holds a middle place between the state of the blessed and the state of the Jews. The spirits in bliss possess Jesus Christ really, without veil or figure. The Jews possessed Jesus Christ only in figures and veils, such as the manna and the paschal lamb. And Christians possess Jesus Christ in the eucharist really and truly, although still concealed under veils. "God," says St. Eucher, "has made three tabernacles: the synagogue, which had the shadows only, without the truth; the Church, which has the truth and shadows together; and heaven, where there is no shadow, but the truth alone." It would be a departure from our present state, which is the state of faith, opposed by St. Paul alike to the law and to open vision, did we possess the figures only, without Jesus Christ; for it is the property of the law to have the mere figure, and not the substance of things. And it would be equally a departure from our present state if we possessed him visibly; because faith, according to the same apostle, deals not with things that are seen. And thus the eucharist, from its including Jesus Christ truly, though under a veil, is in perfect accordance with our state of faith. It follows that this state would be destroyed, if, as the heretics maintain, Jesus Christ were not really under the species of bread and wine; and it would be equally destroyed if we received him openly, as they do in heaven: since, on these suppositions, our state would be confounded, either with the state of Judaism or with that of glory.

Such, fathers, is the mysterious and divine reason of this most divine mystery. This it is that fills us with abhorrence at the Calvinists, who would reduce us to the condition of the Jews; and this it is that makes us aspire to the glory of the beatified, where we shall be introduced to the full and eternal enjoyment of Jesus Christ. From hence you must see that there are several points of difference between the manner in which he communicates himself to Christians and to the blessed; and that, amongst others, he is in this world received by the mouth, and not so in heaven; but that they all depend solely on the distinction between our state of faith and their state of immediate vision. And this is precisely, fathers, what M. Arnauld has expressed, with great plainness, in the following terms: "There can be no other difference between the purity of those who receive Jesus Christ in the eucharist and that of the blessed, than what exists between faith and the open vision of God, upon which alone depends the different manner in which he is eaten upon earth and in heaven." You were bound in duty, fathers, to have revered in these words the sacred truths they express, instead of wresting them for the purpose of detecting an heretical meaning which they never contained, nor could possibly contain, namely, that Jesus Christ is eaten by faith only, and not by the mouth; the malicious perversion of your Fathers Annat and Meynier, which forms the capital count of their indictment.

Conscious, however, of the wretched deficiency of your proofs, you have had recourse to a new artifice, which is nothing less than to falsify the Council of Trent, in order to convict M. Arnauld of nonconformity with it; so vast is your store of methods for making people heretics. This feat has been achieved by Father Meynier, in fifty different places of his book, and about eight or ten times in the space of a single page (the 54th), wherein he insists that to speak like a true Catholic it is not enough to say, "I believe that Jesus Christ is really present in the eucharist," but we must say, "I believe, *with the council*, that he is present by a true *local presence*, or locally." And, in proof of this, he cites the council, session xiii, canon 3d, canon 4th, and canon 6th. Who would not suppose, upon seeing the term *local presence* quoted from three canons of a universal council, that the phrase was actually to be found in them? This might have served your turn very well, before the appearance of my *Fifteenth Letter;* but, as matters now stand, fathers, the trick has become too stale for us. We go our way and consult the council, and discover only that you are falsifiers. Such terms as *local presence*, *locally*, and *locality*, never existed in the passages to which you refer; and let me tell you further, they are not to be found in any other canon of that council, nor in any other previous council, not in any father of the Church. Allow me, then, to ask you, fathers, if you mean to cast the suspicion of Calvinism upon all that have not made use of that peculiar phrase? If this be the case, the Council of Trent must be suspected of heresy, and all the holy fathers without exception. Have you no other way of making M. Arnauld heretical, without abusing so many other people who never did you any harm, and, among the rest, St. Thomas, who is one of the greatest champions of the eucharist, and who, so far from employing that term, has expressly rejected it—"*Nullo modo corpus Christi est in hoc sacramento localiter.*—By no means is the body of Christ in this sacrament *locally*"? Who are you, then, fathers, to pretend, on your authority, to impose new terms, and ordain them to be used by all for rightly expressing their faith; as if the profession of the faith, drawn up by the popes according to the plan of the council, in which this term has no place, were defective, and left an ambiguity in the creed of the faithful which you had the sole merit of discovering? Such a piece of arrogance, to prescribe these terms, even to learned doctors! such a piece of forgery, to attribute them to general councils! and such ignorance, not to know the objections which the most enlightened saints have made to their reception! "Be ashamed of the error of your ignorance," as the Scripture says of ignorant impostors like you, "*De mendacio ineruditionis tuæ confundere.*"

Give up all further attempts, then, to act the masters; you have neither character nor capacity for the part. If, however, you would bring forward your propositions with a little more modesty, they might obtain a hearing. For, although this phrase, *local presence*, has been rejected, as you have seen, by St. Thomas, on the ground that the body of Jesus Christ is not in the eucharist, in the ordinary extension of bodies in their places, the expression has, nevertheless, been adopted by some modern controversial writers, who understand it simply to mean that the body of Jesus Christ is truly under the species, which being in a particular place, the body of Jesus Christ is there also. And in this sense M. Arnauld will make no scruple to admit the term, as M. de St. Cyran and he have repeatedly declared that Jesus Christ in the eucharist is truly in a particular place, and miraculously in many places at the same time. Thus all your subtleties fall to the ground; and you have failed to give the slightest semblance of plausibility to an accusation which ought not to have been allowed to show its face without being supported by the most unanswerable proofs.

But what avails it, fathers, to oppose their innocence to your calumnies? You impute these errors to them, not in the belief that they maintain heresy, but from the idea that they have done you injury. That is enough, according to your theology, to warrant you to calumniate them without criminality; and you can, without either penance or confession, say mass, at the very time that you charge priests, who say it every day, with holding it to be pure idolatry; which, were it true, would amount to sacrilege no less revolting than that of your own Father Jarrige, whom you yourselves ordered to be hanged in effigy, for having said mass "at the time he was in agreement with Geneva."

What surprises me, therefore, is not the little scrupulosity with which you load them with crimes of the foulest and falsest description, but the little prudence you display, by fixing on them charges so destitute of plausibility. You dispose of sins, it is true, at your pleasure; but do you mean to dispose of men's beliefs too? Verily, fathers, if the suspicion of Calvinism must needs fall either on them or on you, you would stand, I fear, on very ticklish ground. Their language is as Catholic as yours; but their conduct confirms their faith, and your conduct belies it. For if you believe, as well as they do, that the bread is really changed into the body of Jesus Christ, why do you not require, as they do, from those whom you advise to approach the altar, that the heart of stone and ice should be sincerely changed into a heart of flesh and of love? If you believe that Jesus Christ is in that sacrament in a state of death, teaching those that approach it to die to the world, to sin, and to themselves, why do you suffer those to profane it in whose breasts evil passions continue to reign in all their life and vigour? And how do you come to judge those worthy to eat the bread of heaven, who are not worthy to eat that of earth?

Precious votaries, truly, whose zeal is expended in persecuting those who honour this sacred mystery by so many holy communions, and in flattering those who dishonour it by so many sacrilegious desecrations! How comely is it, in these champions of a sacrifice so pure and so venerable, to collect around the table of Jesus Christ a crowd of hardened profligates, reeking from their debaucheries; and to plant in the midst of them a priest, whom his own confessor has hurried from his obscenities to the altar; there, in the place of Jesus Christ, to offer up that most holy victim to the God of holiness, and convey it, with his polluted hands, into mouths as thoroughly polluted as his own! How well does it become those who pursue this course "in all parts of the world," in conformity with maxims sanctioned by their own general to impute to the author of *Frequent Communion*, and to the Sisters of the Holy Sacrament, the crime of not believing in that sacrament!

Even this, however, does not satisfy them. Nothing less will satiate their rage than to accuse their opponents of having renounced Jesus Christ and their baptism. This is no air-built fable, like those of your invention; it is a fact, and denotes a delirious frenzy which marks the fatal consummation of your calumnies. Such a notorious falsehood as this would not have been in hands worthy to support it, had it remained in those of your good friend Filleau, through whom you ushered it into the world: your Society has openly adopted it; and your Father Meynier maintained it the other day to be "*a certain truth*" that Port-Royal has, for the space of thirty-five years, been forming a secret plot, of which M. de St. Cyran and M. d'Ypres have been the ringleaders, "to ruin the mystery of the incarnation —to make the Gospel pass for an apocryphal fable—to exterminate the Christian religion, and to erect Deism upon the ruins of Christianity." Is this enough, fathers? Will you be satisfied if all this be believed of the objects of your hate? Would your animosity be glutted at length, if you could but succeed in making them odious, not only to all within the Church, by the charge of "*consenting with Geneva*," of which you accuse them, but even to all who believe in Jesus Christ, though beyond the pale of the Church, by the imputation of *Deism?*

But whom do you expect to convince, upon your simple asseveration, without the slightest shadow of proof, and in the face of every imaginable contradiction, that priests who preach nothing but the grace of Jesus Christ, the purity of the Gospel, and the obligations of baptism, have renounced at once their baptism, the Gospel, and Jesus Christ? Who will believe it, fathers? Wretched as you are, do you believe it yourselves? What a sad predicament is yours, when you must either prove that they do not believe in Jesus Christ, or must pass for the most abandoned calumniators. Prove it, then, fathers. Name that "*worthy clergyman*" who, you say, attended that assembly at Bourg-Fontaine in 1621, and discovered to Brother Filleau the design there concerted of overturning the Christian religion. Name those six persons whom you allege to have formed that conspiracy. Name the *individual who is designated by the letters A. A.,* who you say "*was not Antony*

Arnauld" (because he convinced you that he was at that time only nine years of age), "*but another person, who you say is still in life, but too good a friend of M. Arnauld not to be known to him.*" You know him, then, fathers; and consequently, if you are not destitute of religion yourselves, you are bound to delate that impious wretch to the king and parliament, that he may be punished according to his deserts. You must speak out, fathers; you must name the person, or submit to the disgrace of being henceforth regarded in no other light than as common liars, unworthy of being ever credited again. Good Father Valerien has taught us that this is the way in which such characters should be "put to the rack" and brought to their senses. Your silence upon the present challenge will furnish a full and satisfactory confirmation of this diabolical calumny. Your blindest admirers will be constrained to admit that it will be "the result, not of your goodness, but your impotency"; and to wonder how you could be so wicked as to extend your hatred even to the nuns of Port-Royal, and to say, as you do in page 14, that *The Secret Chaplet of the Holy Sacrament*, composed by one of their number, was the first fruit of that conspiracy against Jesus Christ; or, as in page 95, that "they have imbibed all the detestable principles of that work"; which is, according to your account, "a lesson in Deism." Your falsehoods regarding that book have already been triumphantly refuted, in the defence of the censure of the late Archbishop of Paris against Father Brisacier. That publication you are incapable of answering; and yet you do not scruple to abuse it in a more shameful manner than ever, for the purpose of charging women, whose piety is universally known, with the vilest blasphemy.

Cruel, cowardly persecutors! Must, then, the most retired cloisters afford no retreat from your calumnies? While these consecrated virgins are employed, night and day, according to their institution, in adoring Jesus Christ in the holy sacrament, you cease not, night nor day, to publish abroad that they do not believe that he is either in the eucharist or even at the right hand of his Father; and you are publicly excommunicating them from the Church, at the very time when they are in secret praying for the whole Church, and for you! You blacken with your slanders those who have neither ears to hear nor mouths to answer you! But Jesus Christ, in whom they are now hidden, not to appear till one day together with him, hears you, and answers for them. At the moment I am now writing, that holy and terrible voice is heard which confounds nature and consoles the Church. And I fear, fathers, that those who now harden their hearts, and refuse with obstinacy to hear him, while he speaks in the character of God, will one day be compelled to hear him with terror, when he speaks to them in the character of a Judge. What account, indeed, fathers, will you be able to render to him of the many calumnies you have uttered, seeing that he will examine them, in that day, not according to the fantasies of Fathers Dicastille, Gans, and Pennalossa, who justify them, but according to the eternal laws of truth, and the sacred ordinances of his own Church, which, so far from attempting to vindicate that crime, abhors it to such a degree that she visits it with the same penalty as wilful murder? By the first and second councils of Arles she has decided that the communion shall be denied to slanderers as well as murderers, till the approach of death. The Council of Lateran has judged those unworthy of admission into the ecclesiastical state who have been convicted of the crime, even though they may have reformed. The popes have even threatened to deprive of the communion at death those who have calumniated bishops, priests, or deacons. And the authors of a defamatory libel, who fail to prove what they have advanced, are condemned by Pope Adrian *to be whipped;*—yes, reverend fathers, *flagellentur* is the word. So strong has been the repugnance of the Church at all times to the errors of your Society—a Society so thoroughly depraved as to invent excuses for the grossest of crimes, such as calumny, chiefly that it may enjoy the greater freedom in perpetrating them itself. There can be no doubt, fathers, that you would be capable of producing abundance of mischief in this way, had God not permitted you to furnish with your own hands the means of preventing the evil, and of rendering your slanders perfectly innocuous; for, to deprive you of all credibility, it was quite enough to publish the strange maxim that it is no crime to calumniate. Calumny is nothing, if not associated with a high reputation for honesty. The defamer can make no impression, unless he has the character of one that abhors defamation as a crime of which he is incapable. And thus, fathers, you are betrayed by your own principle. You establish the doctrine to secure yourselves a safe conscience, that you might slander without risk of damnation, and be ranked with those "pious and holy calumniators" of whom St. Athanasius speaks. To save yourselves from hell, you have embraced a maxim which promises you this security on the faith of your doctors; but this same maxim, while it guarantees you, according to their idea, against the evils you dread in the future world, deprives you of all the advantage you may have expected to reap from it in the present; so that, in attempting to escape the guilt, you have lost the benefit of calumny. Such is the self-contrariety of evil, and so completely does it confound and destroy itself by its own intrinsic malignity.

You might have slandered, therefore, much more advantageously for yourselves, had you professed to hold, with St. Paul, that evil speakers are not worthy to see God; for in this case, though you would indeed have been condemning yourselves, your slanders would at least have stood a better chance of being believed. But, by maintaining, as you have done, that calumny against your enemies is no crime, your slanders will be discredited, and you yourselves damned into the bargain; for two things are certain, fathers: first, That it will never be in the power of your grave doctors to annihilate the justice of God; and, secondly, That you could not give more certain evidence that you are not of the Truth than by your resorting to falsehood. If the Truth were on your side, she would fight for you— she would conquer for you; and whatever enemies you might have to encounter, "the Truth would set you free" from them, according to her promise. But you have had recourse to falsehood, for no other design than to support the errors with which you flatter the sinful children of this world, and to bolster up the calumnies with which you persecute every man of piety who sets his face against these delusions. The truth being diametrically opposed to your ends, it behooved you, to use the language of the prophet, "to put your confidence in lies." You have said: "The scourges which afflict mankind shall not come nigh unto us; for we have made lies our refuge, and under falsehood have we hid ourselves." But what says the prophet in reply to such? "Forasmuch," says he, "as ye have put your trust in calumny and tumult—*sperastis in calumnia et in tumultu*—this iniquity and your ruin shall be like that of a high wall whose breaking cometh suddenly at an instant. And he shall break it as the breaking of the potter's vessel that is shivered in pieces"—with such violence that "there shall not be found in the bursting of it a shred to take fire from the hearth, or to take water withal out of the pit." "Because," as another prophet says, "ye have made the heart of the righteous sad, whom I have not made sad; and ye have flattered and strengthened the malice of the wicked; I will therefore deliver my people out of your hands, and ye shall know that I am their Lord and yours."

Yes, fathers, it is to be hoped that if you do not repent, God will deliver out of your hands those whom you have so long deluded, either by flattering them in their evil courses with your licentious maxims, or by poisoning their minds with your slanders. He will convince the former that the false rules of your casuists will not screen them from His indignation; and He will impress on the minds of the latter the just dread of losing their souls by listening and yielding credit to your slanders, as you lose yours by hatching these slanders and disseminating them through the world. Let no man be deceived; God is not mocked; none may violate with impunity the commandment which He has given us in the Gospel, not to condemn our neighbour without being well assured of his guilt. And, consequently, what profession soever of piety those may make who lend a willing ear to your lying devices, and under what pretence soever of devotion they may entertain them, they have reason to apprehend exclusion from the kingdom of God, solely for having imputed crimes of such a dark complexion as heresy and schism to Catholic priests and holy nuns, upon no better evidence than such vile fabrications as yours. "The devil," says M. de Geneve, "is on the tongue of him that slanders, and in the ear of him that listens to the slanderer." "And evil speaking," says St. Bernard, "is a poison that extinguishes charity in both of the parties; so that a single calumny may prove mortal to an infinite numbers of souls, killing not only those who publish it, but all those besides by whom it is not repudiated."

Reverend fathers, my letters were not wont either to be so prolix, or to follow so closely on one another. Want of time must plead my excuse for both of these faults. The present letter is a very long one, simply because I had no leisure to make it shorter. You know the reason of this haste better than I do. You have been unlucky in your answers. You have done well, therefore, to change your plan; but I am afraid that you will get no credit for it, and that people will say it was done for fear of the Benedictines.

I have just come to learn that the person who was generally reported to be the author of your *Apologies*, disclaims them, and is annoyed at their having been ascribed to him. He has good reason, and I was wrong to have suspected him of any such thing; for, in spite of the assurances which I received, I ought to have considered that he was a man of too much good sense to believe your accusations, and of too much honour to publish them if he did not believe them. There are few people in the world capable of your extravagances; they are peculiar to yourselves, and mark your character too plainly to admit of any excuse for having failed to recognize your hand in their concoction. I was led away by the common report; but this apology, which would be too good for you, is not sufficient for me, who profess to advance nothing without certain proof. In no other instance have I been guilty of departing from this rule. I am sorry for what I said. I retract it; and I only wish that you may profit by my example.

LETTER XVII

To the Reverend Father Annat, Jesuit

January 23, 1657

REVEREND FATHER,

Your former behaviour had induced me to believe that you were anxious for a truce in our hostilities, and I was quite disposed to agree that it should be so. Of late, however, you have poured forth such a volley of pamphlets, in such rapid succession, as to make it apparent that peace rests on a very precarious footing when it depends on the silence of Jesuits. I know not if this rupture will prove very advantageous to you; but, for my part, I am far from regretting the opportunity which it affords me of rebutting that stale charge of heresy with which your writings abound.

It is full time, indeed, that I should, once for all, put a stop to the liberty you have taken to treat me as a heretic—a piece of gratuitous impertinence which seems to increase by indulgence, and which is exhibited in your last book in a style of such intolerable assurance that, were I not to answer the charge as it deserves, I might lay myself open to the suspicion of being actually guilty. So long as the insult was confined to your associates I despised it, as I did a thousand others with which they interlarded their productions. To these my *Fifteenth Letter* was a sufficient reply. But you now repeat the charge with a different air: you make it the main point of your vindication. It is, in fact, almost the only thing in the shape of argument that you employ. You say that, "as a complete answer to my fifteen letters, it is enough to say fifteen times that I am a heretic; and, having been pronounced such, I deserve no credit." In short, you make no question of my apostasy, but assume it as a settled point, on which you may build with all confidence. You are serious then, father, it would seem, in deeming me a heretic. I shall be equally serious in replying to the charge.

You are well aware, sir, that heresy is a charge of so grave a character that it is an act of high presumption to advance, without being prepared to substantiate it. I now demand your proofs. When was I seen at Charenton? When did I fail in my presence at mass, or in my Christian duty to my parish church? What act of union with heretics, or of schism with the Church, can you lay to my charge? What council have I contradicted? What papal constitution have I violated? You *must* answer, father, else—— You know what I mean. And what *do* you answer? I beseech all to observe it: First of all, you assume "that the author of the letters is a Port-Royalist"; then you tell us "that Port-Royal is declared to be heretical"; and, therefore, you conclude, "the author of the letters must be a heretic." It is not on me, then, father, that the weight of this indictment falls, but on Port-Royal; and I am only involved in the crime because you suppose me to belong to that establishment; so that it will be no difficult matter for me to exculpate myself from the charge. I have no more to say than that I am not a member of that community; and to refer you to my letters, in which I have declared that "I am a private individual"; and again in so many words, that "I am not of Port-Royal," as I said in my *Sixteenth Letter*, which preceded your publication.

You must fall on some other way, then, to prove me heretic, otherwise the whole world will be convinced that it is beyond your power to make good your accusation. Prove from my writings that I do not receive the constitution. My letters are not very voluminous—there are but sixteen of them—and I defy you or anybody else to detect in them the slightest foundation for such a charge. I shall, however, with your permission, produce something out of them to prove the reverse. When, for example, I say in the Fourteenth that, "by killing our brethren in mortal sin, according to your maxims, we are damning those for whom Jesus Christ died," do I not plainly acknowledge that Jesus Christ died for those who may be damned, and, consequently, declare it to be false "that he died only for the predestinated," which is the error condemned in the fifth proposition? Certain it is, father, that I have not said a word in behalf of these impious propositions, which I detest with all my heart. And even though Port-Royal should hold them, I protest against your drawing any conclusion from this against me, as, thank God, I have no sort of connection with any community except the Catholic, Apostolic and Roman Church, in the bosom of which I desire to live and die, in communion with the Pope, the head of the Church, and beyond the pale of which I am persuaded there is no salvation.

How are you to get at a person who talks in this way, father? On what quarter will you assail me, since neither my words nor my writings afford the slightest handle to your accusations, and the obscurity in which my person is enveloped forms my protection against your threatenings? You feel yourselves smitten by an invisible hand—a hand, however, which makes your delinquencies visible to all the earth; and in vain do you endeavour to attack me in the person of those with whom you suppose me to be associated. I fear you not, either on my own account or on that of any other, being bound by no tie either to a community or to any individual whatsoever. All the influence which your Society possesses can be of no avail in my case. From this world I have nothing to hope, nothing to dread, nothing to desire. Through the goodness of God, I have no need of any man's money or any man's patronage. Thus, my father, I elude all your attempts to lay hold of me. You may touch Port-Royal, if you choose, but you shall not touch me. You may turn people out of the Sorbonne, but that will not turn me out of my domicile. You may contrive plots against priests and doctors, but not against me, for I am neither the one nor the other. And thus, father, you never perhaps had to do, in the whole course of your experience, with a person so completely beyond your reach, and therefore so admirably qualified for dealing with your errors—one perfectly free—one without engagement, entanglement, relationship, or business of any kind—one, too, who is pretty well versed in your maxims, and determined, as God shall give him light, to discuss them, without permitting any earthly consideration to arrest or slacken his endeavours.

Since, then, you can do nothing against me, what good purpose can it serve to publish so many calumnies, as you and your brethren are doing, against a class of persons who are in no way implicated in our disputes? You shall not escape under these subterfuges: you shall be made to feel the force of the truth in spite of them. How does the case stand? I tell you that you are ruining Christian morality by divorcing it from the love of God, and dispensing with its obligation; and you talk about "the death of Father Mester"—a person whom I never saw in my life. I tell you that your authors permit a man to kill another for the sake of an apple, when it would be dishonourable to lose it; and you reply by informing me that somebody "has broken into the poor-box at St. Merri!" Again, what can you possibly mean by mixing me up perpetually with the book *On the Holy Virginity*, written by some father of the Oratory, whom I never saw any more than his book? It is rather extraordinary, father, that you should thus regard all that are opposed to you as if they were one person. Your hatred would grasp them all at once, and would hold them as a body of reprobates, every one of whom is responsible for all the rest.

There is a vast difference between Jesuits and all their opponents. There can be no doubt that you compose one body, united under one head; and your regulations, as I have shown, prohibit you from printing anything without the approbation of your superiors, who are responsible for all the errors of individual writers, and who "cannot excuse themselves by saying that they did not observe the errors in any publication, for they ought to have observed them." So say your ordinances, and so say the letters of your generals, Aquaviva, Vitelleschi, &c. We have good reason, therefore, for charging upon you the errors of your associates, when we find they are sanctioned by your superiors and the divines of your Society. With me, however, father, the case stands otherwise. I have not subscribed to the book of the Holy Virginity. All the alms-boxes in Paris may be broken into, and yet I am not the less a good Catholic for all that. In short, I beg to inform you, in the plainest terms, that nobody is responsible for my letters but myself, and that I am responsible for nothing but my letters.

Here, father, I might fairly enough have brought our dispute to an issue, without saying a word about those other persons whom you stigmatize as heretics, in order to comprehend me under the condemnation. But, as I have been the occasion of their ill treatment, I consider myself bound in some sort to improve the occasion, and I shall take advantage of it in three particulars. One advantage, not inconsiderable in its way, is that it will enable me to vindicate the innocence of so many calumniated individuals. Another, not inappropriate to my subject, will be to disclose, at the same time, the artifices of your policy in this accusation. But the advantage which I prize most of all is that it affords me an opportunity of apprising the world of the falsehood of that scandalous report which you have been so busily disseminating, namely, "that the Church is divided by a new heresy." And as you are deceiving multitudes into the belief that the points on which you are raising such a storm are essential to the faith, I consider it of the last importance to quash these unfounded impressions, and distinctly to explain here what these points are, so as to show that, in point of fact, there are no heretics in the Church.

I presume, then, that were the question to be asked: Wherein consists the heresy of those called *Jansenists?* the immediate reply would be, "These people hold that the commandments of God are impracticable to men, that grace is irresistible, that we have not free will to do either good or evil, that Jesus Christ did not die for all men, but only for the elect; in short, they maintain the five propositions condemned by the Pope." Do you not give it out to all that this is the ground on which you persecute your opponents? Have you not said as much in your books, in your conversations, in your catechisms? A specimen of this you gave at the late Christmas festival at St. Louis. One of your little shepherdesses was questioned thus:

"For whom did Jesus Christ come into the world, my dear?"

"For all men, father."

"Indeed, my child; so you are not one of those new heretics who say that he came only for the elect?"

Thus children are led to believe you, and many others besides children; for you entertain people with the same stuff in your sermons as Father Crasset did at Orleans, before he was laid under an interdict. And I frankly own that, at one time, I believed you myself. You had given me precisely the same idea of these good people; so that, when you pressed them on these propositions, I narrowly watched their answer, determined never to see them more, if they did not renounce them as palpable impieties.

This, however, they have done in the most unequivocal way. M. de Sainte-Beuve, king's professor in the Sorbonne, censured these propositions in his published writings long before the Pope; and other Augustinian doctors, in various publications, and, among others, in a work *On Victorious Grace*, reject the same articles as both heretical and strange doctrines. In the preface to that work they say that these propositions are "heretical and Lutheran, forged and fabricated at pleasure, and are neither to be found in Jansenius, nor in his defenders." They complain of being charged with such sentiments, and address you in the words of St. Prosper, the first disciple of St. Augustine their master, to whom the semi-Pelagians of France had ascribed similar opinions, with the view of bringing him into disgrace: "There are persons who denounce us, so blinded by passion that they have adopted means for doing so which ruin their own reputation. They have, for this purpose, fabricated propositions of the most impious and blasphemous character, which they industriously circulate, to make people believe that we maintain them in the wicked sense which they are pleased to attach to them. But our reply will show at once our innocence, and the malignity of these persons who have ascribed to us a set of impious tenets, of which they are themselves the sole inventors."

Truly, father, when I found that they had spoken in this way before the appearance of the papal constitution—when I saw that they afterwards received that decree with all possible respect, that they offered to subscribe it, and that M. Arnauld had declared all this in his second letter, in stronger terms than I can report him, I should have considered it a sin to doubt their soundness in the faith. And, in fact, those who were formerly disposed to refuse absolution to M. Arnauld's friends, have since declared that, after his explicit disclaimer of the errors imputed to him, there was no reason left for cutting off either him or them from the communion of the Church. Your associates, however, have acted very differently; and it was this that made me begin to suspect that you were actuated by prejudice.

You threatened first to compel them to sign that constitution, so long as you thought they would resist it; but no sooner did you see them quite ready of their own accord to submit to it than we heard no more about this. Still, however, though one might suppose this ought to have satisfied you, you persisted in calling them heretics, "because," said you, "their heart belies their hand; they are Catholics outwardly, but inwardly they are heretics."

This, father, struck me as very strange reasoning; for where is the person of whom as much may not be said at any time? And what endless trouble and con-

fusion would ensue, were it allowed to go on! "If," says Pope St. Gregory, "we refuse to believe a confession of faith made in conformity to the sentiments of the
Church, we cast a doubt over the faith of all Catholics whatsoever." I am afraid,
father, to use the words of the same pontiff when speaking of a similar dispute
this time, "that your object is to make these persons heretics in spite of themselves; because to refuse to credit those who testify by their confession that they
are in the true faith, is not to purge heresy, but to create it—*hoc non est hæresim pur-
gare, sed facere."* But what confirmed me in my persuasion that there was, indeed,
no heretic in the Church, was finding that our so-called *heretics* had vindicated
themselves so successfully that you were unable to accuse them of a single error
in the faith, and that you were reduced to the necessity of assailing them on
questions of *fact* only, touching Jansenius, which could not possibly be construed
into heresy. You insist, it now appears, on their being compelled to acknowledge
"that these propositions are contained in Jansenius, word for word, every one of
them, in so many terms," or, as you express it, "*Singulares, individuæ, totidem verbis
apud Jansenium contentæ."*

Thenceforth your dispute became, in my eyes, perfectly indifferent. So long as
I believed that you were debating the truth or falsehood of the propositions, I was
all attention, for that quarrel touched the faith; but when I discovered that the bone
of contention was whether they were to be found word for word in Jansenius or
not, as religion ceased to be interested in the controversy, I ceased to be interested
in it also. Not but that there was some presumption that you were speaking the
truth; because to say that such and such expressions are to be found word for
word in an author, is a matter in which there can be no mistake. I do not wonder,
therefore, that so many people, both in France and at Rome, should have been led
to believe, on the authority of a phrase so little liable to suspicion, that Jansenius
has actually taught these obnoxious tenets. And, for the same reason, I was not a
little surprised to learn that this same point of fact, which you had propounded as
so certain and so important, was false; and that, after being challenged to quote
the pages of Jansenius in which you had found these propositions "word for
word," you have not been able to point them out to this day.

I am the more particular in giving this statement, because, in my opinion, it
discovers, in a very striking light, the spirit of your Society in the whole of this
affair; and because some people will be astonished to find that, notwithstanding
all the facts above mentioned, you have not ceased to publish that they are heretics
still. But you have only altered the heresy to suit the time; for no sooner had they
freed themselves from one charge than your fathers, determined that they should
never want an accusation, substituted another in its place. Thus, in 1653, their
heresy lay in the *quality* of the propositions; then came the *word for word* heresy;
after that we had the *heart* heresy. And now we hear nothing of any of these, and
they must be heretics, forsooth, unless they sign a declaration to the effect "*that
the sense of the doctrine of Jansenius is contained in the sense of the five propositions."*

Such is your present dispute. It is not enough for you that they condemn the
five propositions, and everything in Jansenius that bears any resemblance to them,
or is contrary to St. Augustine; for all that they have done already. The point at
issue is not, for example, if Jesus Christ died for the elect only—they condemn
that as much as you do; but, is Jansenius of that opinion, or not? And here I declare, more strongly than ever, that your quarrel affects me as little as it affects the

Church. For although I am no doctor, any more than you, father, I can easily see, nevertheless, that it has no connection with the faith. The only question is to ascertain what is the sense of Jansenius. Did they believe that his doctrine corresponded to the proper and literal sense of these propositions, they would condemn it; and they refuse to do so, because they are convinced it is quite the reverse; so that, although they should misunderstand it, still they would not be heretics, seeing they understand it only in a Catholic sense.

To illustrate this by an example, I may refer to the conflicting sentiments of St. Basil and St. Athanasius, regarding the writings of St. Denis of Alexandria, which St. Basil, conceiving that he found in them the sense of Arius against the equality of the Father and the Son, condemned as heretical, but which St. Athanasius, on the other hand, judging them to contain the genuine sense of the Church, maintained to be perfectly orthodox. Think you, then, father, that St. Basil, who held these writings to be Arian, had a right to brand St. Athanasius as a heretic because he defended them? And what ground would he have had for so doing, seeing that it was not Arianism that his brother defended, but the true faith which he considered these writings to contain? Had these two saints agreed about the true sense of these writings, and had both recognized this heresy in them, unquestionably St. Athanasius could not have approved of them without being guilty of heresy; but as they were at variance respecting the sense of the passage, St. Athanasius was orthodox in vindicating them, even though he may have understood them wrong; because in that case it would have been merely an error in a matter of fact, and because what he defended was really the Catholic faith, which he supposed to be contained in these writings.

I apply this to you, father. Suppose you were agreed upon the sense of Jansenius, and your adversaries were ready to admit with you that he held, for example, *that grace cannot be resisted;* those who refused to condemn him would be heretical. But as your dispute turns upon the meaning of that author, and they believe that, according to this doctrine, *grace may be resisted,* whatever heresy you may be pleased to attribute to him, you have no ground to brand them as heretics, seeing they condemn the sense which you put on Jansenius, and you dare not condemn the sense which they put on him. If, therefore, you mean to convict them, show that the sense which they ascribe to Jansenius is heretical; for then they will be heretical themselves. But how could you accomplish this, since it is certain, according to your own showing, that the meaning which they give to his language has never been condemned?

To elucidate the point still further, I shall assume as a principle what you yourselves acknowledge—*that the doctrine of efficacious grace has never been condemned, and that the pope has not touched it by his constitution.* And, in fact, when he proposed to pass judgement on the five propositions, the question of efficacious grace was protected against all censure. This is perfectly evident from the judgements of the consulters to whom the Pope committed them for examination. These judgements I have in my possession, in common with many other persons in Paris, and, among the rest, the Bishop of Montpelier, who brought them from Rome. It appears from this document that they were divided in their sentiments; that the chief persons among them, such as the Master of the Sacred Palace, the commissary of the Holy Office, the General of the Augustinians, and others, conceiving that these propositions might be understood in the sense of *efficacious grace,* were of opinion that they ought not to be censured; whereas the rest, while they agreed that the propositions would not have merited condemnation had they borne that sense, judged that they ought to be censured, because, as they contended, this was very far from being their proper and natural sense. The Pope, accordingly, condemned them; and all parties have acquiesced in his judgement.

It is certain, then, father, that efficacious grace has not been condemned. Indeed, it is so powerfully supported by St. Augustine, by St. Thomas, and all his school, by a great many popes and councils, and by all tradition, that to tax it with heresy would be an act of impiety. Now, all those whom you condemn as heretics declare that they find nothing in Jansenius, but this doctrine of efficacious grace. And this was the only point which they maintained at Rome. You have acknowledged this yourself when you declare that "when pleading before the pope, they did not say a single word about the propositions, but occupied the whole time in talking about efficacious grace." So that, whether they be right or wrong in this supposition, it is undeniable, at least, that what they suppose to be the sense is not heretical sense; and that, consequently, they are no heretics; for, to state the matter in two words, either Jansenius has merely taught the doctrine of efficacious grace, and in this case he has no errors; or he has taught some other thing, and in this case he has no defenders. The whole question turns on ascertaining whether Jansenius has actually maintained something different from efficacious grace; and, should it be found that he has, you will have the honour of having better understood him, but they will not have the misfortune of having erred from the faith.

It is matter of thankfulness to God, then, father, that there is in reality no heresy in the Church. The question relates entirely to a point of fact, of which no heresy can be made; for the Church, with divine authority, decides the points of *faith*, and cuts off from her body all who refuse to receive them. But she does not act in the same manner in regard to matters of *fact*. And the reason is that our salvation is attached to the faith which has been revealed to us, and which is preserved in the Church by tradition, but that it has no dependence on facts which have not been revealed by God. Thus we are bound to believe that the commandments of God are not impracticable; but we are under no obligation to know what Jansenius has said upon that subject. In the determination of points of faith, God guides the Church by the aid of His unerring Spirit; whereas in matters of fact He leaves her to the direction of reason and the senses, which are the natural judges of such matters. None but God was able to instruct the Church in the faith; but to learn whether this or that proposition is contained in Jansenius, all we require to do is to read his book. And from hence it follows that, while it is heresy to resist the decisions of the faith, because this amounts to an opposing of our own spirit to the Spirit of God, it is no heresy, though it may be an act of presumption, to disbelieve certain particular facts, because this is no more than opposing reason— it may be enlightened reason—to an authority which is great indeed, but in this matter not infallible.

What I have now advanced is admitted by all theologians, as appears from the following axiom of Cardinal Bellarmine, a member of your Society: "General and lawful councils are incapable of error in defining the dogmas of faith; but they may err in questions of fact." In another place he says: "The pope, as pope, and even as the head of a universal council, may err in particular controversies of fact, which depend principally on the information and testimony of men." Cardinal

Baronius speaks in the same manner: "Implicit submission is due to the decisions of councils in points of faith; but, in so far as persons and their writings are concerned, the censures which have been pronounced against them have not been so rigorously observed, because there is none who may not chance to be deceived in such matters." I may add that, to prove this point, the Archbishop of Toulouse has deduced the following rule from the letters of two great popes—St. Leon and Pelagius II: "That the proper object of councils is the faith; and whatsoever is determined by them, independently of the faith, may be reviewed and examined anew: whereas nothing ought to be re-examined that has been decided in a matter of faith; because, as Tertullian observes, the rule of faith alone is immovable and irrevocable."

Hence it has been seen that, while general and lawful councils have never contradicted one another in points of faith, because, as M. de Toulouse has said, "it is not allowable to examine *de novo* decisions in matters of faith"; several instances have occurred in which these same councils have disagreed in points of fact, where the discussion turned upon the sense of an author; because, as the same prelate observes, quoting the popes as his authorities, "everything determined in councils, not referring to the faith, may be reviewed and examined *de novo*." An example of this contrariety was furnished by the fourth and fifth councils, which differed in their interpretation of the same authors. The same thing happened in the case of two popes, about a proposition maintained by certain monks of Scythia. Pope Hormisdas, understanding it in a bad sense, had condemned it; but Pope John II, his successor, upon re-examining the doctrine understood it in a good sense, approved it, and pronounced it to be orthodox. Would you say that for this reason one of these popes was a heretic? And must you not consequently acknowledge that, provided a person condemn the heretical sense which a pope may have ascribed to a book, he is no heretic because he declines condemning that book, while he understands it in a sense which it is certain the pope has not condemned? If this cannot be admitted, one of these popes must have fallen into error.

I have been anxious to familiarize you with these discrepancies among Catholics regarding questions of fact, which involve the understanding of the sense of a writer, showing you father against father, pope against pope, and council against council, to lead you from these to other examples of opposition, similar in their nature, but somewhat more disproportioned in respect of the parties concerned. For, in the instances I am now to adduce, you will see councils and popes ranged on one side, and Jesuits on the other; and yet you have never charged your brethren for this opposition even with presumption, much less with heresy.

You are well aware, father, that the writings of Origen were condemned by a great many popes and councils, and particularly by the fifth general council, as chargeable with certain heresies, and, among others, that of *the reconciliation of the devils at the day of judgement*. Do you suppose that, after this, it became absolutely imperative, as a test of Catholicism, to confess that Origen actually maintained these errors, and that it is not enough to condemn them, without attributing them to him? If this were true, what would become of your worthy Father Halloix, who has asserted the purity of Origen's faith, as well as many other Catholics who have attempted the same thing, such as Pico Mirandola, and Genebrard, doctor of the Sorbonne? Is it not, moreover, a certain fact, that the same fifth general council condemned the writings of Theodoret against St. Cyril, describing them as impious, "contrary to the true faith, and tainted with the Nestorian heresy"? And yet this has not prevented Father Sirmond, a Jesuit, from defending him, or from saying, in his life of that father, that "his writings are entirely free from the heresy of Nestorius."

It is evident, therefore, that as the Church, in condemning a book, assumes that the error which she condemns is contained in that book, it is a point of faith to hold that error as condemned; but it is not a point of faith to hold that the book, in fact, contains the error which the Church supposes it does. Enough has been said, I think, to prove this; I shall, therefore, conclude my examples by referring to that of Pope Honorius, the history of which is so well known. At the commencement of the seventh century, the Church being troubled by the heresy of the Monothelites, that pope, with the view of terminating the controversy, passed a decree which seemed favourable to these heretics, at which many took offence. The affair, nevertheless, passed over without making much disturbance during his pontificate; but fifty years after, the Church being assembled in the sixth general council, in which Pope Agathon presided by his legates, this decree was impeached, and, after being read and examined, was condemned as containing the heresy of the Monothelites, and under that character burnt, in open court, along with the other writings of these heretics. Such was the respect paid to this decision, and such the unanimity with which it was received throughout the whole Church, that it was afterwards ratified by two other general councils, and likewise by two popes, Leo II and Adrian II, the latter of whom lived two hundred years after it had passed; and this universal and harmonious agreement remained undisturbed for seven or eight centuries. Of late years, however, some authors, and among the rest Cardinal Bellarmine, without seeming to dread the imputation of heresy, have stoutly maintained, against all this array of popes and councils, that the writings of Honorius are free from the error which had been ascribed to them; "because," says the cardinal, "general councils being liable to err in questions of fact, we have the best grounds for asserting the sixth council was mistaken with regard to the fact now under consideration; and that, misconceiving the sense of the *Letters* of Honorius, it has placed this pope most unjustly in the rank of heretics." Observe, then, I pray you, father, that a man is not heretical for saying that Pope Honorius was not a heretic; even though a great many popes and councils, after examining his writings, should have declared that he was so.

I now come to the question before us, and shall allow you to state your case as favourably as you can. What will you then say, father, in order to stamp your opponents as heretics? That "Pope Innocent X has declared that the error of the five propositions is to be found in Jansenius?" I grant you that; what inference do you draw from it? That "it is heretical to deny that the error of the five propositions is to be found in Jansenius?" How so, father? Have we not here a question of fact exactly similar to the preceding examples? The Pope has declared that the error of the five propositions is contained in Jansenius, in the same way as his predecessors decided that the errors of the Nestorians and the Monothelites polluted the pages of Theodoret and Honorius. In the latter case, your writers hesitate not to say that, while they condemn the heresies, they do not allow that these authors actually maintained them; and, in like manner, your opponents now say that they condemn the five propositions, but cannot admit that Jansenius has taught them. Truly, the two cases are as like as they could well be; and, if there be any disparity between them, it is easy to see how far it must go in favour of the present question, by a comparison of many particular circumstances, which as they are self-evident, I do not specify. How comes it to pass, then, that when placed in precisely the same predicament, your friends are Catholics and your opponents heretics? On what strange principle of exception do you deprive the latter of a liberty which you freely award to all the rest of the faithful? What answer will you make to this, father? Will you say, "The pope has confirmed his constitution by a brief." To this I would reply, that two general councils and two popes confirmed the condemnation of the letters of Honorius. But what argument do you found upon the language of that brief, in which all that the Pope says is that "he has condemned the doctrine of Jansenius in these five propositions"? What does that add to the constitution, or what more can you infer from it? Nothing, certainly, except that as the sixth council condemned the doctrine of Honorius, in the belief that it was the same with that of the Monothelites, so the Pope has said that he has condemned the doctrine of Jansenius in these five propositions, because he was led to suppose it was the same with that of the five propositions. And how could he do otherwise than suppose it? Your Society published nothing else; and you yourself, father, who have asserted that the said propositions were in that author "word for word," happened to be in Rome (for I know all your motions) at the time when the censure was passed. Was he to distrust the sincerity or the competence of so many grave ministers of religion? And how could he help being convinced of the fact, after the assurance which you had given him that the propositions were in that author "word for word"? It is evident, therefore, that in the event of its being found that Jansenius has not supported these doctrines, it would be wrong to say, as your writers have done in the cases before mentioned, that the Pope has deceived himself in this point of fact, which it is painful and offensive to publish at any time; the proper phrase is that you have deceived the Pope, which, as you are now pretty well known, will create no scandal.

Determined, however, to have a heresy made out, let it cost what it may, you have attempted, by the following manœuvre, to shift the question from the point of fact, and make it bear upon a point of faith. "The Pope," say you, "declares that he has condemned the doctrine of Jansenius in these five propositions; therefore it is essential to the faith to hold that the doctrine of Jansenius touching these five propositions is heretical, *let it be what it may.*" Here is a strange point of faith, that a doctrine is heretical *be what it may.* What! if Jansenius should happen to maintain that "*we are capable of resisting internal grace*" and that "*it is false to say that Jesus Christ died for the elect only,*" would this doctrine be condemned just because it is his doctrine? Will the proposition, that "*man has a freedom of will to do good or evil,*" be true when found in the Pope's constitution, and false when discovered in Jansenius? By what fatality must he be reduced to such a predicament, that truth, when admitted into his book, becomes heresy? You must confess, then, that he is only heretical on the supposition that he is friendly to the errors condemned, seeing that the constitution of the Pope is the rule which we must apply to Jansenius, to judge if his character answer the description there given of him; and, accordingly, the question, "*Is his doctrine heretical?*" must be resolved by another question of fact, "*Does it correspond to the natural sense of these propositions?*" as it must necessarily be heretical if it does correspond to that sense, and must necessarily be orthodox if it be of an opposite character. For, in one word, since, according to the Pope and the bishops, "the propositions are condemned *in their proper and natural sense,*" they cannot possibly be condemned in the sense of Jansenius, except on the understanding that the sense of Jansenius is the same with the proper and natural sense of these propositions; and this I maintain to be purely a question of fact.

The question, then, still rests upon the point of fact, and cannot possibly be tortured into one affecting the faith. But though incapable of twisting it into a matter of heresy, you have it in your power to make it a pretext for persecution, and might, perhaps, succeed in this, were there not good reason to hope that nobody will be found so blindly devoted to your interests as to countenance such a disgraceful proceeding, or inclined to compel people, as you wish to do, to sign a declaration *that they condemn these propositions in the sense of Jansenius,* without explaining what the sense of Jansenius is. Few people are disposed to sign a blank confession of faith. Now this would really be to sign one of that description, leaving you to fill up the blank afterwards with whatsoever you pleased, as you would be at liberty to interpret according to your own taste the unexplained sense of Jansenius. Let it be explained, then, beforehand, otherwise we shall have, I fear, another version of your *proximate power,* without any sense at all—*abstrahendo ab omni sensu.* This mode of proceeding, you must be aware, does not take with the world. Men in general detest all ambiguity, especially in the matter of religion, where it is highly reasonable that one should know at least what one is asked to condemn. And how is it possible for doctors, who are persuaded that Jansenius can bear no other sense than that of efficacious grace, to consent to declare that they condemn his doctrine without explaining it, since, with their present convictions, which no means are used to alter, this would be neither more nor less than to condemn efficacious grace, which cannot be condemned without sin? Would it not, therefore, be a piece of monstrous tyranny to place them in such an unhappy dilemma that they must either bring guilt upon their souls in the sight of God, by signing that condemnation against their consciences, or be denounced as heretics for refusing to sign it?

But there is a mystery under all this. You Jesuits cannot move a step without a stratagem. It remains for me to explain why you do not explain the sense of Jansenius. The sole purpose of my writing is to discover your designs, and, by discovering, to frustrate them. I must, therefore, inform those who are not already aware of the fact that your great concern in this dispute being to uphold the *sufficient grace* of your Molina, you could not effect this without destroying the *efficacious grace* which stands directly opposed to it. Perceiving, however, that the latter was now sanctioned at Rome and by all the learned in the Church, and unable to combat the doctrine on its own merits, you resolved to attack it in a clandestine way, under the name of the doctrine of Jansenius. You were resolved, accordingly, to get Jansenius condemned without explanation; and, to gain your purpose, gave out that his doctrine was not that of efficacious grace, so that every one might think he was at liberty to condemn the one without denying the other. Hence your efforts, in the present day, to impress this idea upon the minds of such as have no acquaintance with that author; an object which you yourself, father, have attempted, by means of the following ingenious syllogism: "The pope has condemned the doctrine of Jansenius; but the pope has not condemned efficacious grace: therefore, the doctrine of efficacious grace must be different from that of Jansenius." If this mode of reasoning were conclusive, it might be demonstrated in the same way that Honorius and all his defenders are heretics of the same kind. "The sixth council has condemned the doctrine of Honorius; but the council has not condemned the doctrine of the Church: therefore the doctrine of Honorius is different from that of the Church; and therefore, all who defend him are heretics." It is obvious that no conclusion can be drawn from this; for the Pope has done no more than condemn the doctrine of the five propositions, which was represented to him as the doctrine of Jansenius.

But it matters not; you have no intention to make use of this logic for any length of time. Poor as it is, it will last sufficiently long to serve your present turn. All that you wish to effect by it, in the meantime, is to induce those who are unwilling to condemn efficacious grace to condemn Jansenius with less scruple. When this object has been accomplished, your argument will soon be forgotten, and their signatures, remaining as an eternal testimony in condemnation of Jansenius, will furnish you with an occasion to make a direct attack upon efficacious grace by another mode of reasoning much more solid than the former, which shall be forthcoming in proper time. "The doctrine of Jansenius," you will argue, "has been condemned by the universal subscriptions of the Church. Now this doctrine is manifestly that of efficacious grace" (and it will be easy for you to prove that); "therefore the doctrine of efficacious grace is condemned even by the confession of his defenders."

Behold your reason for proposing to sign the condemnation of a doctrine without giving an explanation of it! Behold the advantage you expect to gain from subscriptions thus procured! Should your opponents, however, refuse to subscribe, you have another trap laid for them. Having dexterously combined the question of faith with that of fact, and not allowing them to separate between them, nor to sign the one without the other, the consequence will be that, because they could not subscribe the two together, you will publish it in all directions that they have refused the two together. And thus though, in point of fact, they simply decline acknowledging that Jansenius has maintained the propositions which they condemn, which cannot be called heresy, you will boldly assert that they have refused to condemn the propositions themselves, and that it is this that constitutes their heresy.

Such is the fruit which you expect to reap from their refusal, and which will be no less useful to you than what you might have gained from their consent. So that, in the event of these signatures being exacted, they will fall into your snares, whether they sign or not, and in both cases you will gain your point; such is your dexterity in uniformly putting matters into a train for your own advantage, whatever bias they may happen to take in their course!

How well I know you, father! and how grieved am I to see that God has abandoned you so far as to allow you such happy success in such an unhappy course! Your good fortune deserves commiseration, and can excite envy only in the breasts of those who know not what truly good fortune is. It is an act of charity to thwart the success you aim at in the whole of this proceeding, seeing that you can only reach it by the aid of falsehood, and by procuring credit to one of two lies—either that the Church has condemned efficacious grace, or that those who defend that doctrine maintain the five condemned errors.

The world must, therefore, be apprised of two facts: first, That, by your own confession, efficacious grace has not been condemned; and secondly, That nobody supports these errors. So that it may be known that those who refuse to sign what you are so anxious to exact from them, refuse merely in consideration of the question of *fact;* and that, being quite ready to subscribe that of *faith,* they cannot be deemed heretical on that account; because, to repeat it once more, though it be matter of faith to believe these propositions to be heretical, it will never be matter of faith to hold that they are to be found in the pages of Jansenius. They are innocent of all error; that is enough. It may be that they interpret Jansenius too favourably; but it may be also that you do not interpret him favourably enough. I do not enter upon this question. All that I know is that, according to your maxims, you believe that you may, without sin, publish him to be a heretic contrary to your own knowledge; whereas, according to their maxims, they cannot, without sin, declare him to be a Catholic, unless they are persuaded that he is one. They are, therefore, more honest than you, father; they have examined Jansenius more faithfully than you; they are no less intelligent than you; they are, therefore, no less credible witnesses than you. But come what may of this point of fact, they are certainly Catholics; for, in order to be so, it is not necessary to declare that another man is not a Catholic; it is enough, in all conscience, if a person, without charging error upon anybody else, succeed in discharging himself.

Reverend Father, if you have found any difficulty in deciphering this letter, which is certainly not printed in the best possible type, blame nobody but yourself. Privileges are not so easily granted to me as they are to you. You can procure them even for the purpose of combating miracles; I cannot have them even to defend myself. The printing-houses are perpetually haunted. In such circumstances, you yourself would not advise me to write you any more letters, for it is really a sad annoyance to be obliged to have recourse to an Osnabruck impression.

LETTER XVIII

To the Reverend Father Annat, Jesuit

March 24, 1657

REVEREND FATHER,

Long have you laboured to discover some error in the creed or conduct of your opponents; but I rather think you will have to confess, in the end, that it is a more difficult task than you imagined to make heretics of people who, are not only no heretics, but who hate nothing in the world so much as heresy. In my last letter I succeeded in showing that you accuse them of one heresy after another, without being able to stand by one of the charges for any length of time; so that all that remained for you was to fix on their refusal to condemn "the sense of Jansenius," which you insist on their doing without explanation. You must have been sadly in want of heresies to brand them with, when you were reduced to this. For who ever heard of a heresy which nobody could explain? The answer was ready, therefore, that if Jansenius has no errors, it is wrong to condemn him; and if he has, you were bound to point them out, that we might know at least what we were condemning. This, however, you have never yet been pleased to do;

but you have attempted to fortify your position by decrees, which made nothing in your favour, as they gave no sort of explanation of the sense of Jansenius, said to have been condemned in the five propositions. This was not the way to terminate the dispute. Had you mutually agreed as to the genuine sense of Jansenius, and had the only difference between you been as to whether that sense was heretical or not, in that case the decisions which might pronounce it to be heretical would have touched the real question in dispute. But the great dispute being about the sense of Jansenius, the one party saying that they could see nothing in it inconsistent with the sense of St. Augustine and St. Thomas, and the other party asserting that they saw in it an heretical sense which they would not express. It is clear that a constitution which does not say a word about this difference of opinion, and which only condemns in general and without explanation the sense of Jansenius, leaves the point in dispute quite undecided.

You have accordingly been repeatedly told that as your discussion turns on a matter of fact, you would never be able to bring it to a conclusion without declaring what you understand by the sense of Jansenius. But, as you continued obstinate in your refusal to make this explanation, I endeavored, as a last resource, to extort it from you, by hinting in my last letter that there was some mystery under the efforts you were making to procure the condemnation of this sense without explaining it, and that your design was to make this indefinite censure recoil some day or other upon the doctrine of efficacious grace, by showing, as you could easily do, that this was exactly the doctrine of Jansenius. This has reduced you to the necessity of making a reply; for, had you pertinaciously refused, after such an insinuation, to explain your views of that sense, it would have been apparent to persons of the smallest penetration that you condemned it in the sense of efficacious grace—a conclusion which, considering the veneration in which the Church holds holy doctrine, would have overwhelmed you with disgrace.

You have, therefore, been forced to speak out your mind; and we find it expressed in your reply to that part of my letter in which I remarked, that "if Jansenius was capable of any other sense than that of efficacious grace, he had no defenders; but if his writings bore no other sense, he had no errors to defend." You found it impossible to deny this position, father; but you have attempted to parry it by the following distinction: "It is not sufficient," say you, "for the vindication of Jansenius, to allege that he merely holds the doctrine of efficacious grace, for that may be held in two ways—the one heretical, according to Calvin, which consists in maintaining that the will, when under the influence of grace, has not the power of resisting it; the other orthodox, according to the Thomists and the Sorbonists, which is founded on the principles established by the councils, and which is, that efficacious grace of itself governs the will in such a way that it still has the power of resisting it."

All this we grant, father; but you conclude by adding: "Jansenius would be orthodox, if he defended efficacious grace in the sense of the Thomists; but he is heretical, because he opposes the Thomists, and joins issue with Calvin, who denies the power of resisting grace." I do not here enter upon the question of fact, whether Jansenius really agrees with Calvin. It is enough for my purpose that you assert that he does, and that you now inform me that by the sense of Jansenius you have all along understood nothing more than the sense of Calvin. Was this all you meant, then, father? Was it only the error of Calvin that you were so anxious to get condemned, under the name of "the sense of Jansenius?" Why did you not tell us this sooner? You might have saved yourself a world of trouble; for we were all ready, without the aid of bulls or briefs, to join with you in condemning that error. What urgent necessity there was for such an explanation! What a host of difficulties has it removed! We were quite at a loss, my dear father, to know what error the popes and bishops meant to condemn, under the name of "the sense of Jansenius." The whole Church was in the utmost perplexity about it, and not a soul would relieve us by an explanation. This, however, has now been done by you, father—you, whom the whole of your party regard as the chief and prime mover of all their councils, and who are acquainted with the whole secret of this proceeding. You, then, have told us that the sense of Jansenius is neither more nor less than the sense of Calvin, which has been condemned by the council. Why, this explains everything. We know now that the error which they intended to condemn, under these terms—*the sense of Jansenius*—is neither more nor less than the sense of Calvin; and that, consequently, we, by joining with them in the condemnation of Calvin's doctrine, have yielded all due obedience to these decrees. We are no longer surprised at the zeal which the popes and some bishops manifested against "the sense of Jansenius." How, indeed, could they be otherwise than zealous against it, believing, as they did, the declarations of those who publicly affirmed that it was identically the same with that of Calvin?

I must maintain, then, father, that you have no further reason to quarrel with your adversaries; for they detest that doctrine as heartily as you do. I am only astonished to see that you are ignorant of this fact, and that you have such an imperfect acquaintance with their sentiments on this point, which they have so repeatedly expressed in their published works. I flatter myself that, were you more intimate with these writings, you would deeply regret your not having made yourself acquainted sooner, in the spirit of peace, with a doctrine which is in every respect so holy and so Christian, but which passion, in the absence of knowledge, now prompts you to oppose. You would find, father, that they not only hold that an effective resistance may be made to those feebler graces which go under the name of *exciting* or *inefficacious*, from their not terminating in the good with which they inspire us; but that they are, moreover, as firm in maintaining, in opposition to Calvin, the power which the will has to resist even efficacious and victorious grace, as they are in contending against Molina for the power of this grace over the will, and fully as jealous for the one of these truths as they are for the other. They know too well that man, of his own nature, has always the power of sinning and of resisting grace; and that, since he became corrupt, he unhappily carries in his breast a fount of concupiscence which infinitely augments that power; but that, notwithstanding this, when it pleases God to visit him with His mercy, He makes the soul do what He wills, and in the manner He wills it to be done, while, at the same time, the infallibility of the divine operation does not in any way destroy the natural liberty of man, in consequence of the secret and wonderful ways by which God operates this change. This has been most admirably explained by St. Augustine, in such a way as to dissipate all those imaginary inconsistencies which the opponents of efficacious grace suppose to exist between the sovereign power of grace over the free-will and the power which the free-will has to resist grace. For, according to this great saint, whom the popes and the

Church have held to be a standard authority on this subject, God transforms the heart of man, by shedding abroad in it a heavenly sweetness, which surmounting the delights of the flesh, and inducing him to feel, on the one hand, his own mortality and nothingness, and to discover, on the other hand, the majesty and eternity of God, makes him conceive a distaste for the pleasures of sin which interpose between him and incorruptible happiness. Finding his chiefest joy in the God who charms him, his soul is drawn towards Him infallibly, but of its own accord, by a motion perfectly free, spontaneous, love-impelled; so that it would be its torment and punishment to be separated from Him. Not but that the person has always the power of forsaking his God, and that he may not actually forsake Him, provided he choose to do it. But how *could* he choose such a course, seeing that the will always inclines to that which is most agreeable to it, and that, in the case we now suppose, nothing can be more agreeable than the possession of that *one good*, which comprises in itself all other good things? "*Quod enim* (says St. Augustine) *amplius nos delectat, secundum operemur necesse est*—Our actions are necessarily determined by that which affords us the greatest pleasure."

Such is the manner in which God regulates the free will of man without encroaching on its freedom, and in which the free will, which always may, but never will, resist His grace, turns to God with a movement as voluntary as it is irresistible, whensoever He is pleased to draw it to Himself by the sweet constraint of His efficacious inspirations.

These, father, are the divine principles of St. Augustine and St. Thomas, according to which it is equally true that *we have the power of resisting grace*, contrary to Calvin's opinion, and that, nevertheless, to employ the language of Pope Clement VIII in his paper addressed to the Congregation *de Auxiliis*, "God forms within us the motion of our will, and effectually disposes of our hearts, by virtue of that empire which His supreme majesty has over the volitions of men, as well as over the other creatures under heaven, according to St. Augustine."

On the same principle, it follows that we act of ourselves, and thus, in opposition to another error of Calvin, that we have merits which are truly and properly *ours;* and yet, as God is the first principle of our actions, and as, in the language of St. Paul, He "worketh in us that which is pleasing in his sight"; "our merits are the gifts of God," as the Council of Trent says.

By means of this distinction we demolish the profane sentiment of Luther, condemned by that Council, namely, that "we co-operate in no way whatever towards our salvation any more than inanimate things"; and, by the same mode of reasoning, we overthrow the equally profane sentiment of the school of Molina, who will not allow that it is by the strength of divine grace that we are enabled to co-operate with it in the work of our salvation, and who thereby comes into hostile collision with that principle of faith established by St. Paul: "That it is God who worketh in us both to will and to do."

In fine, in this way we reconcile all those passages of Scripture which seem quite inconsistent with each other such as the following: "Turn ye unto God"—"Turn thou us, and we shall be turned"—"Cast away iniquity from you"—"It is God who taketh away iniquity from His people"—"Bring forth works meet for repentance"—"Lord, thou hast wrought all our works in us"—"Make ye a new heart and a new spirit"—"A new spirit will I give you, and a new heart will I create within you," &c.

The only way of reconciling these apparent contrarieties, which ascribe our good actions at one time to God and at another time to ourselves, is to keep in view the distinction, as stated by St. Augustine, that "our actions are ours in respect of the free will which produces them; but that they are also of God, in respect of His grace which enables our free will to produce them"; and that, as the same writer elsewhere remarks, "God enables us to do what is pleasing in His sight, by making us will to do even what we might have been unwilling to do."

It thus appears, father, that your opponents are perfectly at one with the modern Thomists, for the Thomists hold with them both the power of resisting grace, and the infallibility of the effect of grace; of which latter doctrine they profess themselves the most strenuous advocates, if we may judge from a common maxim of their theology, which Alvarez, one of the leading men among them, repeats so often in his book, and expresses in the following terms (disp. 72, n. 4): "When efficacious grace moves the free will, it infallibly consents; because the effect of grace is such, that, although the will has the power of withholding its consent, it nevertheless consents in effect." He corroborates this by a quotation from his master, St. Thomas: "The will of God cannot fail to be accomplished; and, accordingly, when it is his pleasure that a man should consent to the influence of grace, he consents infallibly, and even necessarily, not by an absolute necessity, but by a necessity of infallibility." In effecting this, divine grace does not trench upon "the power which man has to resist it, if he wishes to do so"; it merely prevents him from wishing to resist it. This has been acknowledged by your Father Petau, in the following passage (Book i, p. 602): "The grace of Jesus Christ insures infallible perseverance in piety, though not by necessity; for a person may refuse to yield his consent to grace, if he be so inclined, as the council states; but that same grace provides that he shall never be so inclined."

This, father, is the uniform doctrine of St. Augustine, of St. Prosper, of the fathers who followed them, of the councils, of St. Thomas, and of all the Thomists in general. It is likewise, whatever you may think of it, the doctrine of your opponents. And, let me add, it is the doctrine which you yourself have lately sealed with your approbation. I shall quote your own words: "The doctrine of efficacious grace, which admits that we have a power of resisting it, is orthodox, founded on the councils, and supported by the Thomists and Sorbonists." Now, tell us the plain truth, father; if you had known that your opponents really held this doctrine, the interests of your Society might perhaps have made you scruple before pronouncing this public approval of it; but, acting on the supposition that they were hostile to the doctrine, the same powerful motive has induced you to authorize sentiments which you know in your heart to be contrary to those of your Society; and by this blunder, in your anxiety to ruin their principles, you have yourself completely confirmed them. So that, by a kind of prodigy, we now behold the advocates of efficacious grace vindicated by the advocates of Molina—an admirable instance of the wisdom of God in making all things concur to advance the glory of the truth.

Let the whole world observe, then, that, by your own admission, the truth of this efficacious grace, which is so essential to all the acts of piety, which is so dear to the Church, and which is the purchase of her Saviour's blood, is so indisputably Catholic that there is not a single Catholic, not even among the Jesuits, who would not acknowledge its orthodoxy. And let it be noticed, at the same time, that, according to your own confession, not the slightest suspicion of error can fall on those whom you have so often stigmatized with it. For so long as you charged them with clandestine heresies, without choosing to specify them by name, it was as difficult for them to defend themselves as it was easy for you to bring such accusations. But now, when you have come to declare that the error which constrains you to oppose them, is the heresy of Calvin which you supposed them to hold, it must be apparent to every one that they are innocent of all error; for so decidedly hostile are they to this, the only error you charge upon them, that they protest, by their discourses, by their books, by every mode, in short, in which they can testify their sentiments, that they condemn that heresy with their whole heart, and in the same manner as it has been condemned by the Thomists, whom you acknowledge, without scruple, to be Catholics, and who have never been suspected to be anything else.

What will you say against them now, father? Will you say that they are heretics still, because, although they do not adopt the sense of Calvin, they will not allow that the sense of Jansenius is the same with that of Calvin? Will you presume to say that this is matter of heresy? Is it not a pure question of fact, with which heresy has nothing to do? It would be heretical to say that we have not the power of resisting efficacious grace; but would it be so to doubt that Jansenius held that doctrine? Is this a revealed truth? Is it an article of faith which must be believed, on pain of damnation? Or is it not, in spite of you, a point of fact, on account of which it would be ridiculous to hold that there were heretics in the Church?

Drop this epithet, then, father, and give them some other name, more suited to the nature of your dispute. Tell them, they are ignorant and stupid—that they misunderstand Jansenius. These would be charges in keeping with your controversy; but it is quite irrelevant to call them heretics. As this, however, is the only charge from which I am anxious to defend them, I shall not give myself much trouble to show that they rightly understand Jansenius. All I shall say on the point, father, is that it appears to me that, were he to be judged according to your own rules, it would be difficult to prove him not to be a good Catholic. We shall try him by the test you have proposed. "To know," say you, "whether Jansenius is sound or not, we must inquire whether he defends efficacious grace in the manner of Calvin, who denies that man has the power of resisting it—in which case he would be heretical; or in the manner of the Thomists, who admit that it may be resisted—for then he would be Catholic." Judge, then, father, whether he holds that grace may be resisted when he says: "That we have always a power to resist grace, according to the council; that free will may always act or not act, will or not will, consent or not consent, do good or do evil; and that man, in this life, has always these two liberties, which may be called by some contradictions." Judge, likewise, if he be not opposed to the error of Calvin, as you have described it, when he occupies a whole chapter (21st) in showing "that the Church has condemned that heretic who denies that efficacious grace acts on the free will in the manner which has been so long believed in the Church, so as to leave it in the power of free will to consent or not to consent; whereas, according to St. Augustine and the council, we have always the power of withholding our consent if we choose; and according to St. Prosper, God bestows even upon his elect the will to persevere, in such a way as not to deprive them of the power to will the contrary." And,

in one word, judge if he does not agree with the Thomists, from the following declaration in chapter 4th: "That all that the Thomists have written with the view of
reconciling the efficaciousness of grace with the power of resisting it, so entirely
coincides with his judgement that to ascertain his sentiments on this subject we
have only to consult their writings."

Such being the language he holds on these heads my opinion is that he believes
in the power of resisting grace; that he differs from Calvin and agrees with the
Thomists, because he has said so; and that he is, therefore, according to your own
showing, a Catholic. If you have any means of knowing the sense of an author
otherwise than by his expressions; and if, without quoting any of his passages, you
are disposed to maintain, in direct opposition to his own words, that he denies
this power of resistance, and that he is for Calvin and against the Thomists, do
not be afraid, father, that I will accuse you of heresy for that. I shall only say that
you do not seem properly to understand Jansenius; but we shall not be the less on
that account children of the same Church.

How comes it, then, father, that you manage this dispute in such a passionate
spirit, and that you treat as your most cruel enemies, and as the most pestilent of
heretics, a class of persons whom you cannot accuse of any error, nor of anything
whatever, except that they do not understand Jansenius as you do? For what else
in the world do you dispute about, except the sense of that author? You would
have them to condemn it. They ask what you mean them to condemn. You reply
that you mean the error of Calvin. They rejoin that they condemn that error; and
with this acknowledgement (unless it is syllables you wish to condemn, and not
the thing which they signify), you ought to rest satisfied. If they refuse to say
that they condemn the sense of Jansenius, it is because they believe it to be that of
St. Thomas, and thus this unhappy phrase has a very equivocal meaning betwixt
you. In your mouth it signifies the sense of Calvin; in theirs the sense of St.
Thomas. Your dissensions arise entirely from the different ideas which you attach
to the same term. Were I made umpire in the quarrel, I would interdict the use of
the word Jansenius, on both sides; and thus, by obliging you merely to express
what you understand by it, it would be seen that you ask nothing more than the
condemnation of Calvin, to which they willingly agree; and that they ask nothing
more than the vindication of the sense of St. Augustine and St. Thomas, in which
you again perfectly coincide.

I declare, then, father, that for my part I shall continue to regard them as good
Catholics, whether they condemn Jansenius, on finding him erroneous, or refuse
to condemn him, from finding that he maintains nothing more than what you
yourself acknowledge to be orthodox; and that I shall say to them what St. Jerome
said to John, bishop of Jerusalem, who was accused of holding the eight propositions of Origen: "Either condemn Origen, if you acknowledge that he has maintained these errors, or else deny that he has maintained them—*Aut nega hoc dixisse
eum qui arguitur; aut si locutus est talia, eum damna qui dixerit.*"

See, father, how these persons acted, whose sole concern was with principles,
and not with persons; whereas you who aim at persons more than principles, consider it a matter of no consequence to condemn errors, unless you procure the
condemnation of the individuals to whom you choose to impute them.

How ridiculously violent your conduct is, father! and how ill calculated to insure success! I told you before, and I repeat it, violence and verity can make no

impression on each other. Never were your accusations more outrageous, and never was the innocence of your opponents more discernible: never has efficacious grace been attacked with greater subtilty, and never has it been more triumphantly established. You have made the most desperate efforts to convince people that your disputes involved points of faith; and never was it more apparent that the whole controversy turned upon a mere point of fact. In fine, you have moved heaven and earth to make it appear that this point of fact is founded on truth; and never were people more disposed to call it in question. And the obvious reason of this is that you do not take the natural course to make them believe a point of fact, which is to convince their senses and point out to them in a book the words which you allege are to be found in it. The means you have adopted are so far removed from this straightforward course that the most obtuse minds are unavoidably struck by observing it. Why did you not take the plan which I followed in bringing to light the wicked maxims of your authors—which was to cite faithfully the passages of their writings from which they were extracted? This was the mode followed by the curés of Paris, and it never fails to produce conviction. But, when you were charged by them with holding, for example, the proposition of Father Lamy, that a "monk may kill a person who threatens to publish calumnies against himself or his order, when he cannot otherwise prevent the publication," what would you have thought, and what would the public have said, if they had not quoted the place where that sentiment is literally to be found? or if, after having been repeatedly demanded to quote their authority, they still obstinately refused to do it? or if, instead of acceding to this, they had gone off to Rome and procured a bull, ordaining all men to acknowledge the truth of their statement? Would it not be undoubtedly concluded that they had surprised the Pope, and that they would never have had recourse to this extraordinary method, but for want of the natural means of substantiating the truth, which matters of fact furnish to all who undertake to prove them? Accordingly, they had no more to do than to tell us that Father Lamy teaches this doctrine *in Book 5, disp. 36, n. 118, page 544, of the Douay edition;* and by this means everybody who wished to see it found it out, and nobody could doubt about it any longer. This appears to be a very easy and prompt way of putting an end to controversies of fact, when one has got the right side of the question.

How comes it, then, father, that you do not follow this plan? You said, in your book, that the five propositions are in Jansenius, word for word, in the identical terms—*iisdem verbis*. You were told they were not. What had you to do after this, but either to cite the page, if you had really found the words, or to acknowledge that you were mistaken. But you have done neither the one nor the other. In place of this, on finding that all the passages from Jansenius, which you sometimes adduce for the purpose of hoodwinking the people, are not "the condemned propositions in their individual identity," as you had engaged to show us, you present us with Constitutions from Rome, which, without specifying any particular place, declare that the propositions have been extracted from his book.

I am sensible, father, of the respect which Christians owe to the Holy See, and your antagonists give sufficient evidence of their resolution ever to abide by its decisions. Do not imagine that it implied any deficiency in this due deference on their part that they represented to the pope, with all the submission which children owe to their father, and members to their head, that it was possible he might be deceived on this point of fact—that he had not caused it to be investigated during his pontificate; and that his predecessor, Innocent X, had merely examined into the heretical character of the propositions, and not into the fact of their connection with Jansenius. This they stated to the commissary of the Holy Office, one of the principal examiners, stating that they could not be censured according to the sense of any author, because they had been presented for examination on their own merits; and without considering to what author they might belong: further, that upwards of sixty doctors, and a vast number of other persons of learning and piety, had read that book carefully over, without ever having encountered the proscribed propositions, and that they have found some of a quite opposite description: that those who had produced that impression on the mind of the Pope might be reasonably presumed to have abused the confidence he reposed in them, inasmuch as they had an interest in decrying that author, who has convicted Molina of upwards of fifty errors: that what renders this supposition still more probable is that they have a certain maxim among them, one of the best authenticated in their whole system of theology, which is, "that they may, without criminality, calumniate those by whom they conceive themselves to be unjustly attacked"; and that, accordingly, their testimony being so suspicious, and the testimony of the other party so respectable, they had some ground for supplicating his holiness, with the most profound humility, that he would ordain an investigation to be made into this fact, in the presence of doctors belonging to both parties, in order that a solemn and regular decision might be formed on the point in dispute. "Let there be a convocation of able judges (says St. Basil on a similar occasion, Epistle 75); let each of them be left at perfect freedom; let them examine my writings; let them judge if they contain errors against the faith; let them read the objections and the replies; that so a judgement may be given in due form and with proper knowledge of the case, and not a defamatory libel without examination."

It is quite vain for you, father, to represent those who would act in the manner I have now supposed as deficient in proper subjection to the Holy See. The popes are very far from being disposed to treat Christians with that imperiousness which some would fain exercise under their name. "The Church," says Pope St. Gregory, "which has been trained in the school of humility, does not command with authority, but persuades by reason, her children whom she believes to be in error, to obey what she has taught them." And so far from deeming it a disgrace to review a judgement into which they may have been surprised, we have the testimony of St. Bernard for saying that they glory in acknowledging the mistake. "The Apostolic See (he says, Epistle 180) can boast of this recommendation, that it never stands on the point of honour, but willingly revokes a decision that has been gained from it by surprise; indeed, it is highly just to prevent any from profiting by an act of injustice, and more especially before the Holy See."

Such, father, are the proper sentiments with which the popes ought to be inspired; for all divines are agreed that they may be surprised, and that their supreme character, so far from warranting them against mistakes, exposes them the more readily to fall into them, on account of the vast number of cares which claim their attention. This is what the same St. Gregory says to some persons who were astonished at the circumstance of another pope having suffered himself to be deluded: "Why do you wonder," says he, "that we should be deceived, we who are but men? Have you not read that David, a king who had the spirit of prophecy, was induced, by giving credit to the falsehoods of Ziba, to pronounce an unjust judgement against the son of Jonathan? Who will think it strange, then, that we, who are not prophets, should sometimes be imposed upon by deceivers? A multiplicity of affairs presses on us, and our minds, which, by being obliged to attend to so many things at once, apply themselves less closely to each in particular, are the more easily liable to be imposed upon in individual cases." Truly, father, I should suppose that the popes know better than you whether they may be deceived or not. They themselves tell us that popes, as well as the greatest princes, are more exposed to deception than individuals who are less occupied with important avocations. This must be believed on their testimony. And it is easy to imagine by what means they come to be thus overreached. St. Bernard, in the letter which he wrote to Innocent II, gives us the following description of the process: "It is no wonder, and no novelty, that the human mind may be deceived, and is deceived. You are surrounded by monks who come to you in the spirit of lying and deceit. They have filled your ears with stories against a bishop, whose life has been most exemplary, but who is the object of their hatred. These persons bite like dogs, and strive to make good appear evil. Meanwhile, most holy father, you put yourself into a rage against your own son. Why have you afforded matter of joy to his enemies? Believe not every spirit, but try the spirits whether they be of God. I trust that, when you have ascertained the truth, all this delusion, which rests on a false report, will be dissipated. I pray the spirit of truth to grant you the grace to separate light from darkness, and to favour the good by rejecting the evil." You see, then, father, that the eminent rank of the popes does not exempt them from the influence of delusion; and I may now add, that it only serves to render their mistakes more dangerous and important than those of other men. This is the light in which St. Bernard represents them to Pope Eugenius: "There is another fault, so common among the great of this world that I never met one of them who was free from it; and that is, holy father, an excessive credulity, the source of numerous disorders. From this proceed violent persecutions against the innocent, unfounded prejudices against the absent, and tremendous storms about nothing (*pro nihilo*). This, holy father, is a universal evil, from the influence of which, if you are exempt, I shall only say you are the only individual among all your compeers who can boast of that privilege."

I imagine, father, that the proofs I have brought are beginning to convince you that the popes are liable to be surprised. But, to complete your conversion, I shall merely remind you of some examples, which you yourself have quoted in your book, of popes and emperors whom heretics have actually deceived. You will remember, then, that you have told us that Apollinarius surprised Pope Damasius, in the same way that Celestius surprised Zozimus. You inform us, besides, that one called Athanasius deceived the Emperor Heraclius, and prevailed on him to persecute the Catholics. And lastly, that Sergius obtained from Honorius that infamous decretal which was burned at the sixth council, "by playing the busybody," as you say, "about the person of that pope."

It appears, then, father, by your own confession, that those who act this part about the persons of kings and popes do sometimes artfully entice them to persecute the faithful defenders of the truth, under the persuasion that they are persecuting heretics. And hence the popes, who hold nothing in greater horror than these surprisals, have, by a letter of Alexander III, enacted an ecclesiastical statute, which is inserted in the canonical law, to permit the suspension of the execution of their bulls and decretals, when there is ground to suspect that they have been imposed upon. "If," says that pope to the Archbishop of Ravenna, "we sometimes send decretals to your fraternity which are opposed to your sentiments, give yourselves no distress on that account. We shall expect you either to carry them respectfully into execution, or to send us the reason why you conceive they ought not to be executed; for we deem it right that you should not execute a decree which may have been procured from us by artifice and surprise." Such has been the course pursued by the popes, whose sole object is to settle the disputes of Christians, and not to follow the passionate counsels of those who strive to involve them in trouble and perplexity. Following the advice of St. Peter and St. Paul, who in this followed the commandment of Jesus Christ, they avoid domination. The spirit which appears in their whole conduct is that of peace and truth. In this spirit they ordinarily insert in their letters this clause, which is tacitly understood in them all: "*Si ita est; si preces veritate nitantur*—If it be so as we have heard it; if the facts be true." It is quite clear, if the popes themselves give no force to their bulls, except in so far as they are founded on genuine facts, that it is not the bulls alone that prove the truth of the facts, but that, on the contrary, even according to the canonists, it is the truth of the facts which renders the bulls lawfully admissible.

In what way, then, are we to learn the truth of facts? It must be by the eyes, father, which are the legitimate judges of such matters, as reason is the proper judge of things natural and intelligible, and faith of things supernatural and revealed. For, since you will force me into this discussion, you must allow me to tell you that, according to the sentiments of the two greatest doctors of the Church, St. Augustine and St. Thomas, these three principles of our knowledge, the senses, reason, and faith, have each their separate objects and their own degrees of certainty. And as God has been pleased to employ the intervention of the senses to give entrance to faith (for "faith cometh by hearing"), it follows, that so far from faith destroying the certainty of the senses, to call in question the faithful report of the senses would lead to the destruction of faith. It is on this principle that St. Thomas explicitly states that God has been pleased that the sensible accidents should subsist in the eucharist, in order that the senses, which judge only of these accidents, might not be deceived.

We conclude, therefore, from this, that whatever the proposition may be that is submitted to our examination, we must first determine its nature, to ascertain to which of those three principles it ought to be referred. If it relate to a supernatural truth, we must judge of it neither by the senses nor by reason, but by Scripture and the decisions of the Church. Should it concern an unrevealed truth and something within the reach of natural reason, reason must be its proper judge. And if it embrace a point of fact, we must yield to the testimony of the senses, to which it naturally belongs to take cognizance of such matters.

So general is this rule that, according to St. Augustine and St. Thomas, when we meet with a passage even in the Scripture, the literal meaning of which, at first sight, appears contrary to what the senses or reason are certainly persuaded of, we must not attempt to reject their testimony in this case, and yield them up to the authority of that apparent sense of the Scripture, but we must interpret the Scripture, and seek out therein another sense agreeable to that sensible truth; because, the Word of God being infallible in the facts which it records, and the information of the senses and of reason, acting in their sphere, being certain also, it follows that there must be an agreement between these two sources of knowledge. And as Scripture may be interpreted in different ways, whereas the testimony of the senses is uniform, we must in these matters adopt as the true interpretation of Scripture that view which corresponds with the faithful report of the senses. "Two things," says St. Thomas, "must be observed, according to the doctrine of St. Augustine: first, That Scripture has always one true sense; and secondly, That as it may receive various senses, when we have discovered one which reason plainly teaches to be false, we must not persist in maintaining that this is the natural sense, but search out another with which reason will agree."

St. Thomas explains his meaning by the example of a passage in Genesis where it is written that "God created two great lights, the sun and the moon, and also the stars," in which the Scriptures appear to say that the moon is greater than all the stars; but as it is evident, from unquestionable demonstration, that this is false, it is not our duty, says that saint, obstinately to defend the literal sense of that passage; another meaning must be sought, consistent with the truth of the fact, such as the following, "That the phrase *great light*, as applied to the moon, denotes the greatness of that luminary merely as it appears in our eyes, and not the magnitude of its body considered in itself."

An opposite mode of treatment, so far from procuring respect to the Scripture, would only expose it to the contempt of infidels; because, as St. Augustine says, "when they found that we believed, on the authority of Scripture, in things which they assuredly knew to be false, they would laugh at our credulity with regard to its more recondite truths, such as the resurrection of the dead and eternal life." "And by this means," adds St. Thomas, "we should render our religion contemptible in their eyes, and shut up its entrance into their minds."

And let me add, father, that it would in the same manner be the likeliest means to shut up the entrance of Scripture into the minds of heretics, and to render the pope's authority contemptible in their eyes, to refuse all those the name of Catholics who would not believe that certain words were in a certain book, where they are not to be found, merely because a pope by mistake has declared that they are. It is only by examining a book that we can ascertain what words it contains. Matters of fact can only be proved by the senses. If the position which you maintain be true, show it, or else ask no man to believe it—that would be to no purpose. Not all the powers on earth can, by the force of authority, persuade us of a point of fact, any more than they can alter it; for nothing can make that to be not which really is.

It was to no purpose, for example, that the monks of Ratisbon procured from Pope St. Leo IX a solemn decree, by which he declared that the body of St. Denis, the first bishop of Paris, who is generally held to have been the Areopagite, had been transported out of France and conveyed into the chapel of their monastery. It is not the less true, for all this, that the body of that saint always lay, and lies to this hour, in the celebrated abbey which bears his name, and within the walls of which you would find it no easy matter to obtain a cordial reception to this bull, although the pope has therein assured us that he has examined the affair "with all possible diligence (*diligentissime*), and with the advice of many bishops and prelates; so that he strictly enjoins all the French (*districte præcipientes*) to own and confess that these holy relics are no longer in their country." The French, however, who knew that fact to be untrue, by the evidence of their own eyes, and who, upon opening the shrine, found all those relics entire, as the historians of that period inform us, believed then, as they have always believed since, the reverse of what that holy pope had enjoined them to believe, well knowing that even saints and prophets are liable to be imposed upon.

It was to equally little purpose that you obtained against Galileo a decree from Rome condemning his opinion respecting the motion of the earth. It will never be proved by such an argument as this that the earth remains stationary; and if it can be demonstrated by sure observation that it is the earth and not the sun that revolves, the efforts and arguments of all mankind put together will not hinder our planet from revolving, nor hinder themselves from revolving along with her.

Again, you must not imagine that the letters of Pope Zachary, excommunicating St. Virgilius for maintaining the existence of the antipodes, have annihilated the New World; nor must you suppose that, although he declared that opinion to be a most dangerous heresy, the King of Spain was wrong in giving more credence to Christopher Columbus, who came from the place, than to the judgement of the pope, who had never been there, or that the Church has not derived a vast benefit from the discovery, inasmuch as it has brought the knowledge of the Gospel to a great multitude of souls who might otherwise have perished in their infidelity.

You see, then, father, what is the nature of matters of fact, and on what principles they are to be determined; from all which, to recur to our subject, it is easy to conclude that, if the five propositions are not in Jansenius, it is impossible that they can have been extracted from him; and that the only way to form a judgement on the matter, and to produce universal conviction, is to examine that book in a regular conference, as you have been desired to do long ago. Until that be done, you have no right to charge your opponents with contumacy; for they are as blameless in regard to the point of fact as they are of errors in point of faith —Catholics in doctrine, reasonable in fact, and innocent in both.

Who can help feeling astonishment, then, father, to see on the one side a vindication so complete, and on the other accusations so outrageous! Who would suppose that the only question between you relates to a single fact of no importance, which the one party wishes the other to believe without showing it to them! And who would ever imagine that such a noise should have been made in the Church for nothing (*pro nihilo*), as good St. Bernard says! But this is just one of the principal tricks of your policy, to make people believe that everything is at stake, when, in reality, there is nothing at stake; and to represent to those influential persons who listen to you that the most pernicious errors of Calvin, and the most vital principles of the faith, are involved in your disputes, with the view of inducing them, under this conviction, to employ all their zeal and all their authority against your opponents, as if the safety of the Catholic religion depended upon it; whereas, if they came to know that the whole dispute was about this paltry point of fact, they would give themselves no concern about it, but would, on the contrary, regret extremely that, to gratify your private passions, they had made such exertions in an affair of no consequence to the Church. For, in fine, to take the worst view of the matter, even though it should be true that Jansenius maintained these propositions, what great misfortune would accrue from some persons doubting of the fact, provided they detested the propositions, as they have publicly declared that they do? Is it not enough that they are condemned by everybody, without exception, and that, too, in the sense in which you have explained that you wish them to be condemned? Would they be more severely censured by saying that Jansenius maintained them? What purpose, then, would be served by exacting this acknowledgment, except that of disgracing a doctor and bishop, who died in the communion of the Church? I cannot see how that should be accounted so great a blessing as to deserve to be purchased at the expense of so many disturbances. What interest has the state, or the pope, or bishops, or doctors, or the Church at large, in this conclusion? It does not affect them in any way whatever, father; it can affect none but your Society, which would certainly enjoy some pleasure from the defamation of an author who has done you some little injury. Meanwhile everything is in confusion, because you have made people believe that everything is in danger. This is the secret spring giving impulse to all those mighty commotions, which would cease immediately were the real state of the controversy once known. And therefore, as the peace of the Church depended on this explanation, it was, I conceive, of the utmost importance that it should be given that, by exposing all your disguises, it might be manifest to the whole world that your accusations were without foundation, your opponents without error, and the Church without heresy.

Such, father, is the end which it has been my desire to accomplish; an end which appears to me, in every point of view, so deeply important to religion that I am at a loss to conceive how those to whom you furnish so much occasion for speaking can contrive to remain in silence. Granting that they are not affected with the personal wrongs which you have committed against them, those which the Church suffers ought, in my opinion, to have forced them to complain. Besides, I am not altogether sure if ecclesiastics ought to make a sacrifice of their reputation to calumny, especially in the matter of religion. They allow, you, nevertheless, to say whatever you please; so that, had it not been for the opportunity which, by mere accident, you afforded me of taking their part, the scandalous impressions which you are circulating against them in all quarters would, in all probability, have gone forth without contradiction. Their patience, I confess, astonishes me; and the more so that I cannot suspect it of proceeding either from timidity or from incapacity, being well assured that they want neither arguments for their own vindication, nor zeal for the truth. And yet I see them religiously bent on silence, to a degree which appears to me altogether unjustifiable. For my part, father, I do not believe that I can possibly follow their example. Leave the Church in peace, and I shall leave you as you are, with all my heart; but so long as you make it your sole business to keep her in confusion, doubt not but that there shall always be found within her bosom children of peace who will consider themselves bound to employ all their endeavours to preserve her tranquillity.

LETTER XIX

FRAGMENT OF A NINETEENTH PROVINCIAL LETTER, ADDRESSED TO FATHER ANNAT

REVEREND SIR,

If I have caused you some dissatisfaction, in former *Letters*, by my endeavours to establish the innocence of those whom you were labouring to asperse, I shall afford you pleasure in the present by making you acquainted with the sufferings which you have inflicted upon them. Be comforted, my good father, the objects of your enmity are in distress! And if the Reverend the Bishops should be induced to carry out, in their respective dioceses, the advice you have given them, to cause to be subscribed and sworn a certain matter of fact, which is, in itself, not credible, and which it cannot be obligatory upon any one to believe—you will indeed succeed in plunging your opponents to the depth of sorrow, at witnessing the Church brought into so abject a condition.

Yes, sir, I have seen them; and it was with a satisfaction inexpressible! I have seen these holy men; and this was the attitude in which they were found. They were not wrapt up in a philosophic magnanimity; they did not affect to exhibit that indiscriminate firmness which urges implicit obedience to every momentary impulsive duty; nor yet were they in a frame of weakness and timidity, which would prevent them from either discerning the truth, or following it when discerned. But I found them with minds pious, composed, and unshaken; impressed with a meek deference for ecclesiastical authority; with tenderness of spirit, zeal for truth, and a desire to ascertain and obey her dictates: filled with a salutary suspicion of themselves, distrusting their own infirmity, and regretting that it should be thus exposed to trial; yet withal, sustained by a modest hope that their Lord will deign to instruct them by his illuminations, and sustain them by his power; and believing that that peace of their Saviour, whose sacred influences it is their endeavour to maintain, and for whose cause they are brought into suffering, will be at once their guide and their support! I have, in fine, seen them maintaining a character of Christian piety, whose power   .   .   .   .

.   .   .   .

I found them surrounded by their friends, who had hastened to impart those counsels which they deemed the most fitting in their present exigency. I have heard those counsels; I have observed the manner in which they were received, and the answers given: and truly, my father, had you yourself been present, I think you would have acknowledged that, in their whole procedure, there was the entire absence of a spirit of insubordination and schism; and that their only desire and aim was to preserve inviolate two things—to them infinitely precious—peace and truth.

For, after due representations had been made to them of the penalties they would draw upon themselves by their refusal to sign the Constitution, and the scandal it might cause in the Church, their reply was   .   .   .   .   .   .

.   .   .   .

CONTENTS: PENSÉES

NOTE: *Passages* erased by Pascal are enclosed in square brackets, thus [ ]. *Words*, added or corrected by the editor of the text, are similarly denoted, but are in *italics*.

PENSÉES

SECTION I

THOUGHTS ON MIND AND ON STYLE

1. *The difference between the mathematical and the intuitive mind.*—In the one, the principles are palpable, but removed from ordinary use; so that for want of habit it is difficult to turn one's mind in that direction: but if one turns it thither ever so little, one sees the principles fully, and one must have a quite inaccurate mind who reasons wrongly from principles so plain that it is almost impossible they should escape notice.

But in the intuitive mind the principles are found in common use and are before the eyes of everybody. One has only to look, and no effort is necessary; it is only a question of good eyesight, but it must be good, for the principles are so subtle and so numerous that it is almost impossible but that some escape notice. Now the omission of one principle leads to error; thus one must have very clear sight to see all the principles and, in the next place, an accurate mind not to draw false deductions from known principles.

All mathematicians would then be intuitive if they had clear sight, for they do not reason incorrectly from principles known to them; and intuitive minds would be mathematical if they could turn their eyes to the principles of mathematics to which they are unused.

The reason, therefore, that some intuitive minds are not mathematical is that they cannot at all turn their attention to the principles of mathematics. But the reason that mathematicians are not intuitive is that they do not see what is before them, and that, accustomed to the exact and plain principles of mathematics, and not reasoning till they have well inspected and arranged their principles, they are lost in matters of intuition where the principles do not allow of such arrangement. They are scarcely seen; they are felt rather than seen; there is the greatest difficulty in making them felt by those who do not of themselves perceive them. These principles are so fine and so numerous that a very delicate and very clear sense is needed to perceive them, and to judge rightly and justly when they are perceived, without for the most part being able to demonstrate them in order as in mathematics, because the principles are not known to us in the same way, and because it would be an endless matter to undertake it. We must see the matter at once, at one glance, and not by a process of reasoning, at least to a certain degree. And thus it is rare that mathematicians are intuitive and that men of intuition are mathematicians, because mathematicians wish to treat matters of intuition mathematically and make themselves ridiculous, wishing to begin with definitions and then with axioms, which is not the way to proceed in this kind of reasoning. Not that the mind does not do so, but it does it tacitly, naturally, and without technical rules; for the expression of it is beyond all men, and only a few can feel it.

Intuitive minds, on the contrary, being thus accustomed to judge at a single glance, are so astonished when they are presented with propositions of which they understand nothing, and the way to which is through definitions and axioms so sterile, and which they are not accustomed to see thus in detail, that they are repelled and disheartened.

But dull minds are never either intuitive or mathematical.

Mathematicians who are only mathematicians have exact minds, provided all things are explained to them by means of definitions and axioms; otherwise they are inaccurate and insufferable, for they are only right when the principles are quite clear.

And men of intuition who are only intuitive cannot have the patience to reach to first principles of things speculative and conceptual, which they have never seen in the world and which are altogether out of the common.

2. There are different kinds of right understanding; some have right understanding in a certain order of things, and not in others, where they go astray. Some draw conclusions well from a few premises, and this displays an acute judgment.

Others draw conclusions well where there are many premises.

For example, the former easily learn hydrostatics, where the premises are few, but the conclusions are so fine that only the greatest acuteness can reach them.

And in spite of that these persons would perhaps not be great mathematicians, because mathematics contain a great number of premises, and there is perhaps a kind of intellect that can search with ease a few premises to the bottom and cannot in the least penetrate those matters in which there are many premises.

There are then two kinds of intellect: the one able to penetrate acutely and deeply into the conclusions of given premises, and this is the precise intellect; the other able to comprehend a great number of premises without confusing them, and this is the mathematical intellect. The one has force and exactness, the other comprehension. Now the one quality can exist without the other; the intellect can be strong and narrow, and can also be comprehensive and weak.

3. Those who are accustomed to judge by feeling do not understand the process of reasoning, for they would understand at first sight and are not used to seek for principles. And others, on the contrary, who are accustomed to reason from principles, do not at all understand matters of feeling, seeking principles and being unable to see at a glance.

4. *Mathematics, intuition.*—True eloquence makes light of eloquence, true morality makes light of morality; that is to say, the morality of the judgement, which has no rules, makes light of the morality of the intellect.

For it is to judgement that perception belongs, as science belongs to intellect. Intuition is the part of judgement, mathematics of intellect.

To make light of philosophy is to be a true philosopher.

5. Those who judge of a work by rule are in regard to others as those who have a watch are in regard to others. One says, "It is two hours ago"; the other says, "It is only three-quarters of an hour." I look at my watch, and say to the one, "You are weary," and to the other, "Time gallops with you"; for it is only an hour and a half ago, and I laugh at those who tell me that time goes slowly with me and that I judge by imagination. They do not know that I judge by my watch.

6. Just as we harm the understanding, we harm the feelings also.

The understanding and the feelings are moulded by intercourse; the understanding and feelings are corrupted by intercourse. Thus good or bad society improves or corrupts them. It is, then, all-important to know how to choose in order to improve and not to corrupt them; and we cannot make this choice, if they be not already improved and not corrupted. Thus a circle is formed, and those are fortunate who escape it.

7. The greater intellect one has, the more originality one finds in men. Ordinary persons find no difference between men.

8. There are many people who listen to a sermon in the same way as they listen to vespers.

9. When we wish to correct with advantage and to show another that he errs, we must notice from what side he views the matter, for on that side it is usually true, and admit that truth to him, but reveal to him the side on which it is false. He is satisfied with that, for he sees that he was not mistaken and that he only failed to see all sides. Now, no one is offended at not seeing everything; but one does not like to be mistaken, and that perhaps arises from the fact that man naturally cannot see everything, and that naturally he cannot err in the side he looks at, since the perceptions of our senses are always true.

10. People are generally better persuaded by the reasons which they have themselves discovered than by those which have come into the mind of others.

11. All great amusements are dangerous to the Christian life; but among all those which the world has invented there is none more to be feared than the theatre. It is a representation of the passions so natural and so delicate that it excites them and gives birth to them in our hearts, and, above all, to that of love, principally when it is represented as very chaste and virtuous. For the more innocent it appears to innocent souls, the more they are likely to be touched by it. Its violence pleases our self-love, which immediately forms a desire to produce the same effects which are seen so well represented; and, at the same time, we make ourselves a conscience founded on the propriety of the feelings which we see there, by which the fear of pure souls is removed, since they imagine that it cannot hurt their purity to love with a love which seems to them so reasonable.

So we depart from the theatre with our heart so filled with all the beauty and tenderness of love, the soul and the mind so persuaded of its innocence, that we are quite ready to receive its first impressions, or rather to seek an opportunity of awakening them in the heart of another, in order that we may receive the same pleasures and the same sacrifices which we have seen so well represented in the theatre.

12. Scaramouch, who only thinks of one thing.

The doctor, who speaks for a quarter of an hour after he has said everything, so full is he of the desire of talking.

13. One likes to see the error, the passion of Cleobuline, because she is unconscious of it. She would be displeasing, if she were not deceived.

14. When a natural discourse paints a passion or an effect, one feels within oneself the truth of what one reads, which was there before, although one did not know it. Hence one is inclined to love him who makes us feel it, for he has not shown us his own riches, but ours. And thus this benefit renders him pleasing to us, besides that such community of intellect as we have with him necessarily inclines the heart to love.

15. Eloquence, which persuades by sweetness, not by authority; as a tyrant, not as a king.

16. Eloquence is an art of saying things in such a way (1) that those to whom we speak may listen to them without pain and with pleasure; (2) that they feel themselves interested, so that self-love leads them more willingly to reflection upon it.

It consists, then, in a correspondence which we seek to establish between the head and the heart of those to whom we speak, on the one hand, and, on the other, between the thoughts and the expressions which we employ. This assumes that we have studied well the heart of man so as to know all its powers and, then, to find the just proportions of the discourse which we wish to adapt to them. We must put ourselves in the place of those who are to hear us, and make trial on our own heart of the turn which we give to our discourse in order to see whether one is made for the other, and whether we can assure ourselves that the hearer will be, as it were, forced to surrender. We ought to restrict ourselves, so far as possible, to the simple and natural, and not to magnify that which is little, or belittle that which is great. It is not enough that a thing be beautiful; it must be suitable to the subject, and there must be in it nothing of excess or defect.

17. Rivers are roads which move, and which carry us whither we desire to go.

18. When we do not know the truth of a thing, it is of advantage that there should exist a common error which determines the mind of man, as, for example, the moon, to which is attributed the change of seasons, the progress of diseases, etc. For the chief malady of man is restless curiosity about things which he cannot understand; and it is not so bad for him to be in error as to be curious to no purpose.

The manner in which Epictetus, Montaigne, and Salomon de Tultie wrote is the most usual, the most suggestive, the most remembered, and the oftenest quoted, because it is entirely composed of thoughts born from the common talk of life. As when we speak of the common error which exists among men that the moon is the cause of everything, we never fail to say that Salomon de Tultie says that, when we do not know the truth of a thing, it is of advantage that there should exist a common error, etc.; which is the thought above.

19. The last thing one settles in writing a book is what one should put in first.

20. *Order.*—Why should I undertake to divide my virtues into four rather than into six? Why should I rather establish virtue in four, in two, in one? Why into *Abstine et sustine*[1] rather than into "Follow Nature," or, "Conduct your private affairs without injustice," as Plato, or anything else? But there, you will say, everything is contained in one word. Yes, but it is useless without explanation, and when we come to explain it, as soon as we unfold this maxim which contains all the rest, they emerge in that first confusion which you desired to avoid. So, when they are all included in one, they are hidden and useless, as in a chest, and never appear save in their natural confusion. Nature has established them all without including one in the other.

21. Nature has made all her truths independent of one another. Our art makes one dependent on the other. But this is not natural. Each keeps its own place.

22. Let no one say that I have said nothing new; the arrangement of the subject is new. When we play tennis, we both play with the same ball, but one of us places it better.

I had as soon it said that I used words employed before. And in the same way if the same thoughts in a different arrangement do not form a different discourse, no more do the same words in their different arrangement form different thoughts!

23. Words differently arranged have a different meaning, and meanings differently arranged have different effects.

24. *Language.*—We should not turn the mind from one thing to another, except for relaxation, and that when it is necessary and the time suitable, and not otherwise. For he that relaxes out of season wearies, and he who wearies us out of season makes us languid, since we turn quite away. So much does our perverse lust like to do the contrary of what those wish to obtain from us without giving us pleasure, the coin for which we will do whatever is wanted.

25. *Eloquence.*—It requires the pleasant and the real; but the pleasant must itself be drawn from the true.

26. Eloquence is a painting of thought; and thus those who, after having painted it, add something more, make a picture instead of a portrait.

27. *Miscellaneous. Language.*—Those who make antitheses by forcing words are like those who make false windows for symmetry. Their rule is not to speak accurately, but to make apt figures of speech.

[1]"Abstain and uphold." Stoic maxim.

28. Symmetry is what we see at a glance; based on the fact that there is no reason for any difference, and based also on the face of man; whence it happens that symmetry is only wanted in breadth, not in height or depth.

29. When we see a natural style, we are astonished and delighted; for we expected to see an author, and we find a man. Whereas those who have good taste, and who, seeing a book, expect to find a man, are quite surprised to find an author. *Plus poetice quam humane locutus es.*[1] Those honour Nature well who teach that she can speak on everything, even on theology.

30. We only consult the ear because the heart is wanting. The rule is uprightness.
Beauty of omission, of judgement.

31. All the false beauties which we blame in Cicero have their admirers, and in great number.

32. There is a certain standard of grace and beauty which consists in a certain relation between our nature, such as it is, weak or strong, and the thing which pleases us.
Whatever is formed according to this standard pleases us, be it house, song, discourse, verse, prose, woman, birds, rivers, trees, rooms, dress, etc. Whatever is not made according to this standard displeases those who have good taste.
And as there is a perfect relation between a song and a house which are made after a good model, because they are like this good model, though each after its kind; even so there is a perfect relation between things made after a bad model. Not that the bad model is unique, for there are many; but each bad sonnet, for example, on whatever false model it is formed, is just like a woman dressed after that model.
Nothing makes us understand better the ridiculousness of a false sonnet than to consider nature and the standard and, then, to imagine a woman or a house made according to that standard.

33. *Poetical beauty.*—As we speak of poetical beauty, so ought we to speak of mathematical beauty and medical beauty. But we do not do so; and the reason is that we know well what is the object of mathematics, and that it consists in proofs, and what is the object of medicine, and that it consists in healing. But we do not know in what grace consists, which is the object of poetry. We do not know the natural model which we ought to imitate; and through lack of this knowledge, we have coined fantastic terms, "The golden age," "The wonder of our times," "Fatal," etc., and call this jargon poetical beauty.
But whoever imagines a woman after this model, which consists in saying little things in big words, will see a pretty girl adorned with mirrors and chains, at whom he will smile; because we know better wherein consists the charm of woman than the charm of verse. But those who are ignorant would admire her in this dress, and there are many villages in which she would be taken for the queen; hence we call sonnets made after this model "Village Queens."

[1] Petronius, 90. "You have spoken more as a poet than as a man."

34. No one passes in the world as skilled in verse unless he has put up the sign of a poet, a mathematician, etc. But educated people do not want a sign and draw little distinction between the trade of a poet and that of an embroiderer.

People of education are not called poets or mathematicians, etc.; but they are all these and judges of all these. No one guesses what they are. When they come into society, they talk on matters about which the rest are talking. We do not observe in them one quality rather than another, save when they have to make use of it. But then we remember it, for it is characteristic of such persons that we do not say of them that they are fine speakers, when it is not a question of oratory, and that we say of them that they are fine speakers, when it is such a question.

It is therefore false praise to give a man when we say of him, on his entry, that he is a very clever poet; and it is a bad sign when a man is not asked to give his judgement on some verses.

35. We should not be able to say of a man, "He is a mathematician," or "a preacher," or "eloquent"; but that he is "a gentleman." That universal quality alone pleases me. It is a bad sign when, on seeing a person, you remember his book. I would prefer you to see no quality till you meet it and have occasion to use it (*Ne quid minis*),[1] for fear some one quality prevail and designate the man. Let none think him a fine speaker, unless oratory be in question, and then let them think it.

36. Man is full of wants: he loves only those who can satisfy them all. "This one is a good mathematician," one will say. But I have nothing to do with mathematics; he would take me for a proposition. "That one is a good soldier." He would take me for a besieged town. I need, then, an upright man who can accommodate himself generally to all my wants.

37. [Since we cannot be universal and know all that is to be known of everything, we ought to know a little about everything. For it is far better to know something about everything than to know all about one thing. This universality is the best. If we can have both, still better; but if we must choose, we ought to choose the former. And the world feels this and does so; for the world is often a good judge.][2]

38. A poet and not an honest man.

39. If lightning fell on low places, etc., poets, and those who can only reason about things of that kind, would lack proofs.

40. If we wished to prove the examples which we take to prove other things, we should have to take those other things to be examples; for, as we always believe the difficulty is in what we wish to prove, we find the examples clearer and a help to demonstration.

Thus, when we wish to demonstrate a general theorem, we must give the rule

[1]"Nothing in excess."

[2]*Passages* erased by Pascal are enclosed in square brackets. *Words*, added or corrected by the editor of the text, are similarly denoted, but are in *italics*.

as applied to a particular case; but if we wish to demonstrate a particular case, we must begin with the general rule. For we always find the thing obscure which we wish to prove and that clear which we use for the proof; for, when a thing is put forward to be proved, we first fill ourselves with the imagination that it is, therefore, obscure and, on the contrary, that what is to prove it is clear, and so we understand it easily.

41. *Epigrams of Martial.*—Man loves malice, but not against one-eyed men nor the unfortunate, but against the fortunate and proud. People are mistaken in thinking otherwise.

For lust is the source of all our actions, and humanity, etc. We must please those who have humane and tender feelings. That epigram about two one-eyed people is worthless, for it does not console them and only gives a point to the author's glory. All that is only for the sake of the author is worthless. *Ambitiosa recident ornamenta.*[1]

42. To call a king "Prince" is pleasing, because it diminishes his rank.

43. Certain authors, speaking of their works, say: "My book," "My commentary," "My history," etc. They resemble middle-class people who have a house of their own and always have "My house" on their tongue. They would do better to say: "Our book," "Our commentary," "Our history," etc., because there is in them usually more of other people's than their own.

44. Do you wish people to believe good of you? Don't speak.

45. Languages are ciphers, wherein letters are not changed into letters, but words into words, so that an unknown language is decipherable.

46. A maker of witticisms, a bad character.

47. There are some who speak well and write badly. For the place and the audience warm them, and draw from their minds more than they think of without that warmth.

48. When we find words repeated in a discourse and, in trying to correct them, discover that they are so appropriate that we would spoil the discourse, we must leave them alone. This is the test; and our attempt is the work of envy, which is blind, and does not see that repetition is not in this place a fault; for there is no general rule.

49. To mask nature and disguise her. No more king, pope, bishop—but *august monarch*, etc.; not Paris—*the capital of the kingdom*. There are places in which we ought to call Paris, *Paris*, and others in which we ought to call it *the capital of the kingdom*.

50. The same meaning changes with the words which express it. Meanings re-

[1]Horace, *Epistle to the Pisos*, 447. "They curtailed pretentious ornaments."

ceive their dignity from words instead of giving it to them. Examples should be sought . . . .

51. Sceptic, for obstinate.

52. No one calls another a Cartesian but he who is one himself, a pedant but a pedant, a provincial but a provincial; and I would wager it was the printer who put it on the title of *Letters to a Provincial*.

53. A carriage *upset* or *overturned*, according to the meaning. *To spread abroad* or *upset*, according to the meaning. (The argument by force of M. le Maître over the friar.)

54. *Miscellaneous.*—A form of speech, "I should have liked to apply myself to that."

55. The *aperitive* virtue of a key, the *attractive* virtue of a hook.

56. To guess: "The part that I take in your trouble." The Cardinal did not want to be guessed.
"My mind is disquieted." *I am disquieted* is better.

57. I always feel uncomfortable under such compliments as these: "I have given you a great deal of trouble," "I am afraid I am boring you," "I fear this is too long." We either carry our audience with us, or irritate them.

58. You are ungraceful: "Excuse me, pray." Without that excuse I would not have known there was anything amiss. "With reverence be it spoken . . ." The only thing bad is their excuse.

59. "To extinguish the torch of sedition"; too luxuriant. "The restlessness of his genius"; two superfluous grand words.

SECTION II

THE MISERY OF MAN WITHOUT GOD

60. *First part:* Misery of man without God.
Second part: Happiness of man with God.
Or, *First part:* That nature is corrupt. Proved by nature itself.
Second part: That there is a Redeemer. Proved by Scripture.

61. *Order.*—I might well have taken this discourse in an order like this: to show the vanity of all conditions of men, to show the vanity of ordinary lives, and then the vanity of philosophic lives, sceptics, stoics; but the order would not have been kept. I know a little what it is, and how few people understand it. No human

science can keep it. Saint Thomas did not keep it. Mathematics keep it, but they are useless on account of their depth.

62. *Preface to the first part.*—To speak of those who have treated of the knowledge of self; of the divisions of Charron, which sadden and weary us; of the confusion of Montaigne; that he was quite aware of his want of method and shunned it by jumping from subject to subject; that he sought to be fashionable.

His foolish project of describing himself! And this not casually and against his maxims, since every one makes mistakes, but by his maxims themselves, and by first and chief design. For to say silly things by chance and weakness is a common misfortune, but to say them intentionally is intolerable, and to say such as that . . .

63. *Montaigne.*—Montaigne's faults are great. Lewd words; this is bad, notwithstanding Mademoiselle de Gournay. Credulous; *people without eyes.* Ignorant; *squaring the circle, a greater world.* His opinions on suicide, on death. He suggests an indifference about salvation, *without fear and without repentance.* As his book was not written with a religious purpose, he was not bound to mention religion; but it is always our duty not to turn men from it. One can excuse his rather free and licentious opinions on some relations of life; but one cannot excuse his thoroughly pagan views on death, for a man must renounce piety altogether, if he does not at least wish to die like a Christian. Now, through the whole of his book his only conception of death is a cowardly and effeminate one.

64. It is not in Montaigne, but in myself, that I find all that I see in him.

65. What good there is in Montaigne can only have been acquired with difficulty. The evil that is in him, I mean apart from his morality, could have been corrected in a moment, if he had been informed that he made too much of trifles and spoke too much of himself.

66. One must know oneself. If this does not serve to discover truth, it at least serves as a rule of life, and there is nothing better.

67. *The vanity of the sciences.*—Physical science will not console me for the ignorance of morality in the time of affliction. But the science of ethics will always console me for the ignorance of the physical sciences.

68. Men are never taught to be gentlemen and are taught everything else; and they never plume themselves so much on the rest of their knowledge as on knowing how to be gentlemen. They only plume themselves on knowing the one thing they do not know.

69. *The infinites, the mean.*—When we read too fast or too slowly, we understand nothing.

70. *Nature . . .*—[Nature has set us so well in the centre, that if we change one side of the balance, we change the other also. *I act.* Τά ζῶα τρέχει. This makes me

believe that the springs in our brain are so adjusted that he who touches one touches also its contrary.]

71. Too much and too little wine. Give him none, he cannot find truth; give him too much, the same.

72. *Man's disproportion.*—[This is where our innate knowledge leads us. If it be not true, there is no truth in man; and if it be true, he finds therein great cause for humiliation, being compelled to abase himself in one way or another. And since he cannot exist without this knowledge, I wish that, before entering on deeper researches into nature, he would consider her both seriously and at leisure, that he would reflect upon himself also, and knowing what proportion there is . . .] Let man then contemplate the whole of nature in her full and grand majesty, and turn his vision from the low objects which surround him. Let him gaze on that brilliant light, set like an eternal lamp to illumine the universe; let the earth appear to him a point in comparison with the vast circle described by the sun; and let him wonder at the fact that this vast circle is itself but a very fine point in comparison with that described by the stars in their revolution round the firmament. But if our view be arrested there, let our imagination pass beyond; it will sooner exhaust the power of conception than nature that of supplying material for conception. The whole visible world is only an imperceptible atom in the ample bosom of nature. No idea approaches it. We may enlarge our conceptions beyond all imaginable space; we only produce atoms in comparison with the reality of things. It is an infinite sphere, the centre of which is everywhere, the circumference nowhere. In short, it is the greatest sensible mark of the almighty power of God that imagination loses itself in that thought.

Returning to himself, let man consider what he is in comparison with all existence; let him regard himself as lost in this remote corner of nature; and from the little cell in which he finds himself lodged, I mean the universe, let him estimate at their true value the earth, kingdoms, cities, and himself. What is a man in the Infinite?

But to show him another prodigy equally astonishing, let him examine the most delicate things he knows. Let a mite be given him, with its minute body and parts incomparably more minute, limbs with their joints, veins in the limbs, blood in the veins, humours in the blood, drops in the humours, vapours in the drops. Dividing these last things again, let him exhaust his powers of conception, and let the last object at which he can arrive be now that of our discourse. Perhaps he will think that here is the smallest point in nature. I will let him see therein a new abyss. I will paint for him not only the visible universe, but all that he can conceive of nature's immensity in the womb of this abridged atom. Let him see therein an infinity of universes, each of which has its firmament, its planets, its earth, in the same proportion as in the visible world; in each earth animals, and in the last mites, in which he will find again all that the first had, finding still in these others the same thing without end and without cessation. Let him lose himself in wonders as amazing in their littleness as the others in their vastness. For who will not be astounded at the fact that our body, which a little while ago was imperceptible in the universe, itself imperceptible in the bosom of the whole, is now a colossus, a world, or rather a whole, in respect of the nothingness which we cannot reach?

He who regards himself in this light will be afraid of himself, and observing himself sustained in the body given him by nature between those two abysses of the Infinite and Nothing, will tremble at the sight of these marvels; and I think that, as his curiosity changes into admiration, he will be more disposed to contemplate them in silence than to examine them with presumption.

For, in fact, what is man in nature? A Nothing in comparison with the Infinite, an All in comparison with the Nothing, a mean between nothing and everything. Since he is infinitely removed from comprehending the extremes, the end of things and their beginning are hopelessly hidden from him in an impenetrable secret; he is equally incapable of seeing the Nothing from which he was made, and the Infinite in which he is swallowed up.

What will he do then, but perceive the appearance of the middle of things, in an eternal despair of knowing either their beginning or their end. All things proceed from the Nothing, and are borne towards the Infinite. Who will follow these marvellous processes? The Author of these wonders understands them. None other can do so.

Through failure to contemplate these Infinites, men have rashly rushed into the examination of nature, as though they bore some proportion to her. It is strange that they have wished to understand the beginnings of things, and thence to arrive at the knowledge of the whole, with a presumption as infinite as their object. For surely this design cannot be formed without presumption or without a capacity infinite like nature.

If we are well informed, we understand that, as nature has graven her image and that of her Author on all things, they almost all partake of her double infinity. Thus we see that all the sciences are infinite in the extent of their researches. For who doubts that geometry, for instance, has an infinite infinity of problems to solve? They are also infinite in the multitude and fineness of their premises; for it is clear that those which are put forward as ultimate are not self-supporting, but are based on others which, again having others for their support, do not permit of finality. But we represent some as ultimate for reason, in the same way as in regard to material objects we call that an indivisible point beyond which our senses can no longer perceive anything, although by its nature it is infinitely divisible.

Of these two Infinites of science, that of greatness is the most palpable, and hence a few persons have pretended to know all things. "I will speak of the whole," said Democritus.

But the infinitely little is the least obvious. Philosophers have much oftener claimed to have reached it, and it is here they have all stumbled. This has given rise to such common titles as *First Principles*, *Principles of Philosophy*, and the like, as ostentatious in fact, though not in appearance, as that one which blinds us, *De omni scibili*.[1]

We naturally believe ourselves far more capable of reaching the centre of things than of embracing their circumference. The visible extent of the world visibly exceeds us; but as we exceed little things, we think ourselves more capable of knowing them. And yet we need no less capacity for attaining the Nothing than the All. Infinite capacity is required for both, and it seems to me that whoever shall have understood the ultimate principles of being might also attain to the knowledge of the Infinite. The one depends on the other, and one leads to the

[1] Title given by Pico della Mirandola to one of his proposed nine hundred theses, in 1486.

other. These extremes meet and reunite by force of distance and find each other in God, and in God alone.

Let us, then, take our compass; we are something, and we are not everything. The nature of our existence hides from us the knowledge of first beginnings which are born of the Nothing; and the littleness of our being conceals from us the sight of the Infinite.

Our intellect holds the same position in the world of thought as our body occupies in the expanse of nature.

Limited as we are in every way, this state which holds the mean between two extremes is present in all our impotence. Our senses perceive no extreme. Too much sound deafens us; too much light dazzles us; too great distance or proximity hinders our view. Too great length and too great brevity of discourse tend to obscurity; too much truth is paralysing (I know some who cannot understand that to take four from nothing leaves nothing). First principles are too self-evident for us; too much pleasure disagrees with us. Too many concords are annoying in music; too many benefits irritate us; we wish to have the wherewithal to overpay our debts. *Beneficia eo usque læta sunt dum videntur exsolvi posse; ubi multum antevenere, pro gratia odium redditur.*[1] We feel neither extreme heat nor extreme cold. Excessive qualities are prejudicial to us and not perceptible by the senses; we do not feel but suffer them. Extreme youth and extreme age hinder the mind, as also too much and too little education. In short, extremes are for us as though they were not, and we are not within their notice. They escape us, or we them.

This is our true state; this is what makes us incapable of certain knowledge and of absolute ignorance. We sail within a vast sphere, ever drifting in uncertainty, driven from end to end. When we think to attach ourselves to any point and to fasten to it, it wavers and leaves us; and if we follow it, it eludes our grasp, slips past us, and vanishes for ever. Nothing stays for us. This is our natural condition and yet most contrary to our inclination; we burn with desire to find solid ground and an ultimate sure foundation whereon to build a tower reaching to the Infinite. But our whole groundwork cracks, and the earth opens to abysses.

Let us, therefore, not look for certainty and stability. Our reason is always deceived by fickle shadows; nothing can fix the finite between the two Infinites, which both enclose and fly from it.

If this be well understood, I think that we shall remain at rest, each in the state wherein nature has placed him. As this sphere which has fallen to us as our lot is always distant from either extreme, what matters it that man should have a little more knowledge of the universe? If he has it, he but gets a little higher. Is he not always infinitely removed from the end, and is not the duration of our life equally removed from eternity, even if it lasts ten years longer?

In comparison with these Infinites, all finites are equal, and I see no reason for fixing our imagination on one more than on another. The only comparison which we make of ourselves to the finite is painful to us.

If man made himself the first object of study, he would see how incapable he is of going further. How can a part know the whole? But he may perhaps aspire to know at least the parts to which he bears some proportion. But the parts of the

---

[1]Tacitus, *Annals*, iv.18. "Kindnesses are agreeable so long as one thinks them possible to render; further, recognition makes way for hatred."

world are all so related and linked to one another that I believe it impossible to know one without the other and without the whole.

Man, for instance, is related to all he knows. He needs a place wherein to abide, time through which to live, motion in order to live, elements to compose him, warmth and food to nourish him, air to breathe. He sees light; he feels bodies; in short, he is in a dependent alliance with everything. To know man, then, it is necessary to know how it happens that he needs air to live, and, to know the air, we must know how it is thus related to the life of man, etc. Flame cannot exist without air; therefore, to understand the one, we must understand the other.

Since everything, then, is cause and effect, dependent and supporting, mediate and immediate, and all is held together by a natural though imperceptible chain which binds together things most distant and most different, I hold it equally impossible to know the parts without knowing the whole and to know the whole without knowing the parts in detail.

[The eternity of things in itself or in God must also astonish our brief duration. The fixed and constant immobility of nature, in comparison with the continual change which goes on within us, must have the same effect.]

And what completes our incapability of knowing things is the fact that they are simple and that we are composed of two opposite natures, different in kind, soul and body. For it is impossible that our rational part should be other than spiritual; and if any one maintain that we are simply corporeal, this would far more exclude us from the knowledge of things, there being nothing so inconceivable as to say that matter knows itself. It is impossible to imagine how it should know itself.

So, if we are simply material, we can know nothing at all; and if we are composed of mind and matter, we cannot know perfectly things which are simple, whether spiritual or corporeal. Hence it comes that almost all philosophers have confused ideas of things, and speak of material things in spiritual terms, and of spiritual things in material terms. For they say boldly that bodies have a tendency to fall, that they seek after their centre, that they fly from destruction, that they fear the void, that they have inclinations, sympathies, antipathies, all of which attributes pertain only to mind. And in speaking of minds, they consider them as in a place, and attribute to them movement from one place to another; and these are qualities which belong only to bodies.

Instead of receiving the ideas of these things in their purity, we colour them with our own qualities, and stamp with our composite being all the simple things which we contemplate.

Who would not think, seeing us compose all things of mind and body, but that this mixture would be quite intelligible to us? Yet it is the very thing we least understand. Man is to himself the most wonderful object in nature; for he cannot conceive what the body is, still less what the mind is, and least of all how a body should be united to a mind. This is the consummation of his difficulties, and yet it is his very being. *Modus quo corporibus adhærent spiritus comprehendi ab hominibus non potest, et hoc tamen homo est.*[1] Finally, to complete the proof of our weakness, I shall conclude with these two considerations. . .

[1]St. Augustine, *City of God,* xxi. 10." The manner in which the spirit is united to the body can not be understood by man; and yet it is man."

73. [But perhaps this subject goes beyond the capacity of reason. Let us therefore examine her solutions to problems within her powers. If there be anything to which her own interest must have made her apply herself most seriously, it is the inquiry into her own sovereign good. Let us see, then, wherein these strong and clear-sighted souls have placed it and whether they agree.

One says that the sovereign good consists in virtue, another in pleasure, another in the knowledge of nature, another in truth, *Felix qui potuit rerum cognoscere causas*,[1] another in total ignorance, another in indolence, others in disregarding appearances, another in wondering at nothing, *nihil admirari prope res una quæ possit facere et servare beatum*,[2] and the true sceptics in their indifference, doubt, and perpetual suspense, and others, wiser, think to find a better definition. We are well satisfied.

To transpose after the laws to the following title.

We must see if this fine philosophy has gained nothing certain from so long and so intent study; perhaps at least the soul will know itself. Let us hear the rulers of the world on this subject. What have they thought of her substance? 394.[3] Have they been more fortunate in locating her? 395.[3] What have they found out about her origin, duration, and departure? 399.[3]

Is, then, the soul too noble a subject for their feeble lights? Let us, then, abase her to matter and see if she knows whereof is made the very body which she animates and those others which she contemplates and moves at her will. What have those great dogmatists, who are ignorant of nothing, known of this matter? *Harum sententiarum*,[4] 393.[3]

This would doubtless suffice, if Reason were reasonable. She is reasonable enough to admit that she has been unable to find anything durable, but she does not yet despair of reaching it; she is as ardent as ever in this search, and is confident she has within her the necessary powers for this conquest. We must therefore conclude, and, after having examined her powers in their effects, observe them in themselves, and see if she has a nature and a grasp capable of laying hold of the truth.]

74. A letter *On the Foolishness of Human Knowledge and Philosophy.*
This letter before *Diversion.*
Felix qui potuit . . . Nihil admirari.
280 kinds of sovereign good in Montaigne.

75. Part I, 1, 2, c. 1, section 4.[5]
[*Probability.*—It will not be difficult to put the case a stage lower, and make it appear ridiculous. To begin at the very beginning.] What is more absurd than to say that lifeless bodies have passions, fears, hatreds—that insensible bodies, lifeless and incapable of life, have passions which presuppose at least a sensitive soul to feel them, nay more, that the object of their dread is the void? What is there in the void that could make them afraid? Nothing is more shallow and ridiculous.

[1]Virgil, *Georgics*, ii.489. "Happy is he who is able to know the causes of things."
[2]Horace, *Epistles*, I.vi.1. "To be astonished at nothing is nearly the only thing which can give and conserve happiness."
[3]Montaigne, *Essays*, ii.12
[4]Cicero, *Disputationes Tusculanae*, i, 11. *Harum sententiarum quae vera sit, Deus aliquis viderit.* "Which of these opinions is the truth, a god will see."
[5]*Treatise on the Vacuum.*

This is not all; it is said that they have in themselves a source of movement to shun the void. Have they arms, legs, muscles, nerves?

76. To write against those who made too profound a study of science: Descartes.

77. I cannot forgive Descartes. In all his philosophy he would have been quite willing to dispense with God. But he had to make Him give a fillip to set the world in motion; beyond this, he has no further need of God.

78. Descartes useless and uncertain.

79. [*Descartes.*—We must say summarily: "This is made by figure and motion," for it is true. But to say what these are, and to compose the machine, is ridiculous. For it is useless, uncertain, and painful. And were it true, we do not think all philosophy is worth one hour of pain.]

80. How comes it that a cripple does not offend us, but that a fool does? Because a cripple recognises that we walk straight, whereas a fool declares that it is we who are silly; if it were not so, we should feel pity and not anger.

Epictetus asks still more strongly: "Why are we not angry if we are told that we have a headache, and why are we angry if we are told that we reason badly, or choose wrongly"? The reason is that we are quite certain that we have not a headache, or are not lame, but we are not so sure that we make a true choice. So, having assurance only because we see with our whole sight, it puts us into suspense and surprise when another with his whole sight sees the opposite, and still more so when a thousand others deride our choice. For we must prefer our own lights to those of so many others, and that is bold and difficult. There is never this contradiction in the feelings towards a cripple.

81. It is natural for the mind to believe and for the will to love; so that, for want of true objects, they must attach themselves to false.

82. *Imagination.*—It is that deceitful part in man, that mistress of error and falsity, the more deceptive that she is not always so; for she would be an infallible rule of truth, if she were an infallible rule of falsehood. But being most generally false, she gives no sign of her nature, impressing the same character on the true and the false.

I do not speak of fools, I speak of the wisest men; and it is among them that the imagination has the great gift of persuasion. Reason protests in vain; it cannot set a true value on things.

This arrogant power, the enemy of reason, who likes to rule and dominate it, has established in man a second nature to show how all-powerful she is. She makes men happy and sad, healthy and sick, rich and poor; she compels reason to believe, doubt, and deny; she blunts the senses, or quickens them; she has her fools and sages; and nothing vexes us more than to see that she fills her devotees with a satisfaction far more full and entire than does reason. Those who have a lively imagination are a great deal more pleased with themselves than the wise can reasonably be. They look down upon men with haughtiness; they argue with boldness and confidence, others with fear and diffidence; and this gaiety of coun-tenance often gives them the advantage in the opinion of the hearers, such favour have the imaginary wise in the eyes of judges of like nature. Imagination cannot make fools wise; but she can make them happy, to the envy of reason which can only make its friends miserable; the one covers them with glory, the other with shame.

What but this faculty of imagination dispenses reputation, awards respect and veneration to persons, works, laws, and the great? How insufficient are all the riches of the earth without her consent!

Would you not say that this magistrate, whose venerable age commands the re-spect of a whole people, is governed by pure and lofty reason, and that he judges causes according to their true nature without considering those mere trifles which only affect the imagination of the weak? See him go to sermon, full of devout zeal, strengthening his reason with the ardour of his love. He is ready to listen with exemplary respect. Let the preacher appear, and let nature have given him a hoarse voice or a comical cast of countenance, or let his barber have given him a bad shave, or let by chance his dress be more dirtied than usual, then, however great the truths he announces, I wager our senator loses his gravity.

If the greatest philosopher in the world find himself upon a plank wider than actually necessary, but hanging over a precipice, his imagination will prevail, though his reason convince him of his safety. Many cannot bear the thought with-out a cold sweat. I will not state all its effects.

Every one knows that the sight of cats or rats, the crushing of a coal, etc., may unhinge the reason. The tone of voice affects the wisest, and changes the force of a discourse or a poem.

Love or hate alters the aspect of justice. How much greater confidence has an advocate, retained with a large fee, in the justice of his cause! How much better does his bold manner make his case appear to the judges, deceived as they are by appearances! How ludicrous is reason, blown with a breath in every direction!

I should have to enumerate almost every action of men who scarce waver save under her assaults. For reason has been obliged to yield, and the wisest reason takes as her own principles those which the imagination of man has everywhere rashly introduced. [He who would follow reason only would be deemed foolish by the generality of men. We must judge by the opinion of the majority of man-kind. Because it has pleased them, we must work all day for pleasures seen to be imaginary; and, after sleep has refreshed our tired reason, we must forthwith start up and rush after phantoms, and suffer the impressions of this mistress of the world. This is one of the sources of error, but it is not the only one.]

Our magistrates have known well this mystery. Their red robes, the ermine in which they wrap themselves like furry cats, the courts in which they administer justice, the *fleurs-de-lis*, and all such august apparel were necessary; if the physicians had not their cassocks and their mules, if the doctors had not their square caps and their robes four times too wide, they would never have duped the world, which cannot resist so original an appearance. If magistrates had true justice, and if physicians had the true art of healing, they would have no occasion for square caps; the majesty of these sciences would of itself be venerable enough. But having only imaginary knowledge, they must employ those silly tools that strike the imagination with which they have to deal; and thereby, in fact, they inspire respect.

Soldiers alone are not disguised in this manner, because indeed their part is the most essential; they establish themselves by force, the others by show.

Therefore our kings seek out no disguises. They do not mask themselves in extraordinary costumes to appear such; but they are accompanied by guards and halberdiers. Those armed and red-faced puppets who have hands and power for them alone, those trumpets and drums which go before them, and those legions round about them, make the stoutest tremble. They have not dress only, they have might. A very refined reason is required to regard as an ordinary man the Grand Turk, in his superb seraglio, surrounded by forty thousand janissaries.

We cannot even see an advocate in his robe and with his cap on his head, without a favourable opinion of his ability. The imagination disposes of everything; it makes beauty, justice, and happiness, which is everything in the world. I should much like to see an Italian work, of which I only know the title, which alone is worth many books, *Della opinione regina del mondo*. I approve of the book without knowing it, save the evil in it, if any. These are pretty much the effects of that deceptive faculty, which seems to have been expressly given us to lead us into necessary error. We have, however, many other sources of error.

Not only are old impressions capable of misleading us; the charms of novelty have the same power. Hence arise all the disputes of men, who taunt each other either with following the false impressions of childhood or with running rashly after the new. Who keeps the due mean? Let him appear and prove it. There is no principle, however natural to us from infancy, which may not be made to pass for a false impression either of education or of sense.

"Because," say some, "you have believed from childhood that a box was empty when you saw nothing in it, you have believed in the possibility of a vacuum. This is an illusion of your senses, strengthened by custom, which science must correct." "Because," say others, "you have been taught at school that there is no vacuum, you have perverted your common sense which clearly comprehended it, and you must correct this by returning to your first state." Which has deceived you, your senses or your education?

We have another source of error in diseases. They spoil the judgement and the senses; and if the more serious produce a sensible change, I do not doubt that slighter ills produce a proportionate impression.

Our own interest is again a marvellous instrument for nicely putting out our eyes. The justest man in the world is not allowed to be judge in his own cause; I know some who, in order not to fall into this self-love, have been perfectly unjust out of opposition. The sure way of losing a just cause has been to get it recommended to these men by their near relatives.

Justice and truth are two such subtle points that our tools are too blunt to touch them accurately. If they reach the point, they either crush it, or lean all round, more on the false than on the true.

[Man is so happily formed that he has no . . . good of the true, and several excellent of the false. Let us now see how much . . . But the most powerful cause of error is the war existing between the senses and reason.]

83. *We must thus begin the chapter on the deceptive powers.* Man is only a subject full of error, natural and ineffaceable, without grace. Nothing shows him the truth. Everything deceives him. These two sources of truth, reason and the senses, be-

sides being both wanting in sincerity, deceive each other in turn. The senses mislead the Reason with false appearances, and receive from Reason in their turn the same trickery which they apply to her; Reason has her revenge. The passions of the soul trouble the senses, and make false impressions upon them. They rival each other in falsehood and deception.

But besides those errors which arise accidentally and through lack of intelligence, with these heterogeneous faculties . . .

84. The imagination enlarges little objects so as to fill our souls with a fantastic estimate; and, with rash insolence, it belittles the great to its own measure, as when talking of God.

85. Things which have most hold on us, as the concealment of our few possessions, are often a mere nothing. It is a nothing which our imagination magnifies into a mountain. Another turn of the imagination would make us discover this without difficulty.

86. [My fancy makes me hate a croaker, and one who pants when eating. Fancy has great weight. Shall we profit by it? Shall we yield to this weight because it is natural? No, but by resisting it . . .]

87. *Næ iste magno conatu magnas nugas dixerit.*[1]
583.[2] *Quasi quidquam infelicius sit homini cui sua figmenta dominantur.*[3]

88. Children who are frightened at the face they have blackened are but children. But how shall one who is so weak in his childhood become really strong when he grows older? We only change our fancies. All that is made perfect by progress perishes also by progress. All that has been weak can never become absolutely strong. We say in vain, "He has grown, he has changed"; he is also the same.

89. Custom is our nature. He who is accustomed to the faith believes in it, can no longer fear hell, and believes in nothing else. He who is accustomed to believe that the king is terrible . . . etc. Who doubts, then, that our soul, being accustomed to see number, space, motion, believes that and nothing else?

90. *Quod crebro videt non miratur, etiamsi cur fiat nescit; quod ante non viderit, id si evenerit, ostentum esse censet.*[4]

91. *Spongia solis.*—When we see the same effect always recur, we infer a natural necessity in it, as that there will be a tomorrow, etc. But Nature often deceives us, and does not subject herself to her own rules.

[1]Terence, *Heauton Timorumenos*, III.v.8. "There is one who will say great foolishness with great effort."
[2]Montaigne, *Essays*, ii.12.
[3]Pliny, ii.7. "As though there were anyone more unhappy than a man dominated by his imagination."
[4]Cicero, *De Divinatione* ii.22. "A common happening does not astonish, even though the cause is unknown; an event such as one has never seen before passes for a prodigy."

92. What are our natural principles but principles of custom? In children they are those which they have received from the habits of their fathers, as hunting in animals. A different custom will cause different natural principles. This is seen in experience; and if there are some natural principles ineradicable by custom, there are also some customs opposed to nature, ineradicable by nature or by a second custom. This depends on disposition.

93. Parents fear lest the natural love of their children may fade away. What kind of nature is that which is subject to decay? Custom is a second nature which destroys the former. But what is nature? For is custom not natural? I am much afraid that nature is itself only a first custom, as custom is a second nature.

94. The nature of man is wholly natural, *omne animal*.[1]
There is nothing he may not make natural; there is nothing natural he may not lose.

95. Memory, joy, are intuitions; and even mathematical propositions become intuitions, for education produces natural intuitions, and natural intuitions are erased by education.

96. When we are accustomed to use bad reasons for proving natural effects, we are not willing to receive good reasons when they are discovered. An example may be given from the circulation of the blood as a reason why the vein swells below the ligature.

97. The most important affair in life is the choice of a calling; chance decides it. Custom makes men masons, soldiers, slaters. "He is a good slater," says one, and, speaking of soldiers, remarks, "They are perfect fools." But others affirm, "There is nothing great but war; the rest of men are good for nothing." We choose our callings according as we hear this or that praised or despised in our childhood, for we naturally love truth and hate folly. These words move us; the only error is in their application. So great is the force of custom that, out of those whom nature has only made men, are created all conditions of men. For some districts are full of masons, others of soldiers, etc. Certainly nature is not so uniform. It is custom then which does this, for it constrains nature. But sometimes nature gains the ascendancy and preserves man's instinct, in spite of all custom, good or bad.

98. *Bias leading to error.*—It is a deplorable thing to see all men deliberating on means alone, and not on the end. Each thinks how he will acquit himself in his condition; but as for the choice of condition, or of country, chance gives them to us.

It is a pitiable thing to see so many Turks, heretics, and infidels follow the way of their fathers for the sole reason that each has been imbued with the prejudice that it is the best. And that fixes for each man his condition of locksmith, soldier, etc.

Hence savages care nothing for Providence.

[1]Allusion to Gen. 7.14. *Ipsi et omne animal secundus genus suum.* "And every beast after his kind."

99. There is an universal and essential difference between the actions of the will and all other actions.

The will is one of the chief factors in belief, not that it creates belief, but because things are true or false according to the aspect in which we look at them. The will, which prefers one aspect to another, turns away the mind from considering the qualities of all that it does not like to see; and thus the mind, moving in accord with the will, stops to consider the aspect which it likes and so judges by what it sees.

100. *Self-love.*—The nature of self-love and of this human Ego is to love self only and consider self only. But what will man do? He cannot prevent this object that he loves from being full of faults and wants. He wants to be great, and he sees himself small. He wants to be happy, and he sees himself miserable. He wants to be perfect, and he sees himself full of imperfections. He wants to be the object of love and esteem among men, and he sees that his faults merit only their hatred and contempt. This embarrassment in which he finds himself produces in him the most unrighteous and criminal passion that can be imagined; for he conceives a mortal enmity against that truth which reproves him and which convinces him of his faults. He would annihilate it, but, unable to destroy it in its essence, he destroys it as far as possible in his own knowledge and in that of others; that is to say, he devotes all his attention to hiding his faults both from others and from himself, and he cannot endure either that others should point them out to him, or that they should see them.

Truly it is an evil to be full of faults; but it is a still greater evil to be full of them and to be unwilling to recognise them, since that is to add the further fault of a voluntary illusion. We do not like others to deceive us; we do not think it fair that they should be held in higher esteem by us than they deserve; it is not, then, fair that we should deceive them and should wish them to esteem us more highly than we deserve.

Thus, when they discover only the imperfections and vices which we really have, it is plain they do us no wrong, since it is not they who cause them; they rather do us good, since they help us to free ourselves from an evil, namely, the ignorance of these imperfections. We ought not to be angry at their knowing our faults and despising us; it is but right that they should know us for what we are and should despise us, if we are contemptible.

Such are the feelings that would arise in a heart full of equity and justice. What must we say then of our own heart, when we see it in a wholly different disposition? For is it not true that we hate truth and those who tell it us, and that we like them to be deceived in our favour, and prefer to be esteemed by them as being other than what we are in fact? One proof of this makes me shudder. The Catholic religion does not bind us to confess our sins indiscriminately to everybody; it allows them to remain hidden from all other men save one, to whom she bids us reveal the innermost recesses of our heart and show ourselves as we are. There is only this one man in the world whom she orders us to undeceive, and she binds him to an inviolable secrecy, which makes this knowledge to him as if it were not. Can we imagine anything more charitable and pleasant? And yet the corruption of man is such that he finds even this law harsh; and it is one of the main reasons which has caused a great part of Europe to rebel against the Church.

How unjust and unreasonable is the heart of man, which feels it disagreeable to be obliged to do in regard to one man what in some measure it were right to do to all men! For is it right that we should deceive men?

There are different degrees in this aversion to truth; but all may perhaps be said to have it in some degree, because it is inseparable from self-love. It is this false delicacy which makes those who are under the necessity of reproving others choose so many windings and middle courses to avoid offence. They must lessen our faults, appear to excuse them, intersperse praises and evidence of love and esteem. Despite all this, the medicine does not cease to be bitter to self-love. It takes as little as it can, always with disgust, and often with a secret spite against those who administer it.

Hence it happens that, if any have some interest in being loved by us, they are averse to render us a service which they know to be disagreeable. They treat us as we wish to be treated. We hate the truth, and they hide it from us. We desire flattery, and they flatter us. We like to be deceived, and they deceive us.

So each degree of good fortune which raises us in the world removes us farther from truth, because we are most afraid of wounding those whose affection is most useful and whose dislike is most dangerous. A prince may be the byword of all Europe, and he alone will know nothing of it. I am not astonished. To tell the truth is useful to those to whom it is spoken, but disadvantageous to those who tell it, because it makes them disliked. Now those who live with princes love their own interests more than that of the prince whom they serve; and so they take care not to confer on him a benefit so as to injure themselves.

This evil is no doubt greater and more common among the higher classes; but the lower are not exempt from it, since there is always some advantage in making men love us. Human life is thus only a perpetual illusion; men deceive and flatter each other. No one speaks of us in our presence as he does of us in our absence. Human society is founded on mutual deceit; few friendships would endure if each knew what his friend said of him in his absence, although he then spoke in sincerity and without passion.

Man is, then, only disguise, falsehood, and hypocrisy, both in himself and in regard to others. He does not wish any one to tell him the truth; he avoids telling it to others, and all these dispositions, so removed from justice and reason, have a natural root in his heart.

101. I set it down as a fact that if all men knew what each said of the other, there would not be four friends in the world. This is apparent from the quarrels which arise from the indiscreet tales told from time to time. [I say, further, all men would be . . .]

102. Some vices only lay hold of us by means of others, and these, like branches, fall on removal of the trunk.

103. The example of Alexander's chastity has not made so many continent as that of his drunkenness has made intemperate. It is not shameful not to be as virtuous as he, and it seems excusable to be no more vicious. We do not believe ourselves to be exactly sharing in the vices of the vulgar when we see that we are sharing in those of great men; and yet we do not observe that in these matters they

are ordinary men. We hold on to them by the same end by which they hold on to the rabble; for, however exalted they are, they are still united at some point to the lowest of men. They are not suspended in the air, quite removed from our society. No, no; if they are greater than we, it is because their heads are higher; but their feet are as low as ours. They are all on the same level, and rest on the same earth; and by that extremity they are as low as we are, as the meanest folk, as infants, and as the beasts.

104. When our passion leads us to do something, we forget our duty; for example, we like a book and read it, when we ought to be doing something else. Now, to remind ourselves of our duty, we must set ourselves a task we dislike; we then plead that we have something else to do and by this means remember our duty.

105. How difficult it is to submit anything to the judgement of another, without prejudicing his judgement by the manner in which we submit it! If we say, "I think it beautiful," "I think it obscure," or the like, we either entice the imagination into that view, or irritate it to the contrary. It is better to say nothing; and then the other judges according to what really is, that is to say, according as it then is and according as the other circumstances, not of our making, have placed it. But we at least shall have added nothing, unless it be that silence also produces an effect, according to the turn and the interpretation which the other will be disposed to give it, or as he will guess it from gestures or countenance, or from the tone of the voice, if he is a physiognomist. So difficult is it not to upset a judgement from its natural place, or, rather, so rarely is it firm and stable!

106. By knowing each man's ruling passion, we are sure of pleasing him; and yet each has his fancies, opposed to his true good, in the very idea which he has of the good. It is a singularly puzzling fact.

107. *Lustravit lampade terras.*[1]—The weather and my mood have little connection. I have my foggy and my fine days within me; my prosperity or misfortune has little to do with the matter. I sometimes struggle against luck, the glory of mastering it makes me master it gaily; whereas I am sometimes surfeited in the midst of good fortune.

108. Although people may have no interest in what they are saying, we must not absolutely conclude from this that they are not lying; for there are some people who lie for the mere sake of lying.

109. When we are well we wonder what we would do if we were ill, but when we are ill we take medicine cheerfully; the illness persuades us to do so. We have no longer the passions and desires for amusements and promenades which health gave to us, but which are incompatible with the necessities of illness. Nature gives us, then, passions and desires suitable to our present state. We are only troubled by the fears which we, and not nature, give ourselves, for they add to the state in which we are the passions of the state in which we are not.

[1]Homer, *Odyssey*, xviii.135.

As nature makes us always unhappy in every state, our desires picture to us a happy state; because they add to the state in which we are the pleasures of the state in which we are not. And if we attained to these pleasures, we should not be happy after all; because we should have other desires natural to this new state.

We must particularise this general proposition. . . .

110. The consciousness of the falsity of present pleasures, and the ignorance of the vanity of absent pleasures, cause inconstancy.

111. *Inconstancy.*—We think we are playing on ordinary organs when playing upon man. Men are organs, it is true, but, odd, changeable, variable [with pipes not arranged in proper order.] Those who only know how to play on ordinary organs will not produce harmonies on these. We must know where [*the keys*] are.

112. *Inconstancy.*—Things have different qualities, and the soul different inclinations; for nothing is simple which is presented to the soul, and the soul never presents itself simply to any object. Hence it comes that we weep and laugh at the same thing.

113. *Inconstancy and oddity.*—To live only by work, and to rule over the most powerful State in the world, are very opposite things. They are united in the person of the great Sultan of the Turks.

114. Variety is as abundant as all tones of the voice, all ways of walking, coughing, blowing the nose, sneezing. We distinguish vines by their fruit, and call them the Condrien, the Desargues, and such and such a stock. Is this all? Has a vine ever produced two bunches exactly the same, and has a bunch two grapes alike, etc.?

I can never judge of the same thing exactly in the same way. I cannot judge of my work, while doing it. I must do as the artists, stand at a distance, but not too far. How far, then? Guess.

115. *Variety.*—Theology is a science, but at the same time how many sciences? A man is a whole; but if we dissect him, will he be the head, the heart, the stomach, the veins, each vein, each portion of a vein, the blood, each humour in the blood?

A town, a country-place, is from afar a town and a country-place. But, as we draw near, there are houses, trees, tiles, leaves, grass, ants, limbs of ants, in infinity. All this is contained under the name of *country-place.*

116. *Thoughts.*—All is one, all is different. How many natures exist in man? How many vocations? And by what chance does each man ordinarily choose what he has heard praised? A well-turned heel.

117. *The heel of a slipper.*—"Ah! How well this is turned! Here is a clever workman! How brave is this soldier!" This is the source of our inclinations and of the choice of conditions. "How much this man drinks! How little that one"! This makes people sober or drunk, soldiers, cowards, etc.

118. Chief talent, that which rules the rest.

119. Nature imitates herself. A seed grown in good ground brings forth fruit. A principle instilled into a good mind brings forth fruit. Numbers imitate space, which is of a different nature.

All is made and led by the same master, root, branches, and fruits; principles and consequences.

120. [Nature diversifies and imitates; art imitates and diversifies.]

121. Nature always begins the same things again, the years, the days, the hours; in like manner spaces and numbers follow each other from beginning to end. Thus is made a kind of infinity and eternity. Not that anything in all this is infinite and eternal, but these finite realities are infinitely multiplied. Thus it seems to me to be only the number which multiplies them that is infinite.

122. Time heals griefs and quarrels, for we change and are no longer the same persons. Neither the offender nor the offended are any more themselves. It is like a nation which we have provoked, but meet again after two generations. They are still Frenchmen, but not the same.

123. He no longer loves the person whom he loved ten years ago. I quite believe it. She is no longer the same, nor is he. He was young, and she also; she is quite different. He would perhaps love her yet, if she were what she was then.

124. We view things not only from different sides, but with different eyes; we have no wish to find them alike.

125. *Contraries.*—Man is naturally credulous and incredulous, timid and rash.

126. Description of man: dependency, desire of independence, need.

127. Condition of man: inconstancy, weariness, unrest.

128. The weariness which is felt by us in leaving pursuits to which we are attached. A man dwells at home with pleasure; but if he sees a woman who charms him, or if he enjoys himself in play for five or six days, he is miserable if he returns to his former way of living. Nothing is more common than that.

129. Our nature consists in motion; complete rest is death.

130. *Restlessness.*—If a soldier, or labourer, complain of the hardship of his lot, set him to do nothing.

131. *Weariness.*—Nothing is so insufferable to man as to be completely at rest, without passions, without business, without diversion, without study. He then feels his nothingness, his forlornness, his insufficiency, his dependence, his weakness, his emptiness. There will immediately arise from the depth of his heart weariness, gloom, sadness, fretfulness, vexation, despair.

132. Methinks Cæsar was too old to set about amusing himself with conquering the world. Such sport was good for Augustus or Alexander. They were still young men and thus difficult to restrain. But Cæsar should have been more mature.

133. Two faces which resemble each other make us laugh, when together, by their resemblance, though neither of them by itself makes us laugh.

134. How useless is painting, which attracts admiration by the resemblance of things, the originals of which we do not admire!

135. The struggle alone pleases us, not the victory. We love to see animals fighting, not the victor infuriated over the vanquished. We would only see the victorious end; and, as soon as it comes, we are satiated. It is the same in play, and the same in the search for truth. In disputes we like to see the clash of opinions, but not at all to contemplate truth when found. To observe it with pleasure, we have to see it emerge out of strife. So in the passions, there is pleasure in seeing the collision of two contraries; but when one acquires the mastery, it becomes only brutality. We never seek things for themselves, but for the search. Likewise in plays, scenes which do not rouse the emotion of fear are worthless, so are extreme and hopeless misery, brutal lust, and extreme cruelty.

136. A mere trifle consoles us, for a mere trifle distresses us.

137. Without examining every particular pursuit, it is enough to comprehend them under diversion.

138. Men naturally slaters and of all callings, save in their own rooms.

139. *Diversion.*—When I have occasionally set myself to consider the different distractions of men, the pains and perils to which they expose themselves at court or in war, whence arise so many quarrels, passions, bold and often bad ventures, etc., I have discovered that all the unhappiness of men arises from one single fact, that they cannot stay quietly in their own chamber. A man who has enough to live on, if he knew how to stay with pleasure at home, would not leave it to go to sea or to besiege a town. A commission in the army would not be bought so dearly, but that it is found insufferable not to budge from the town; and men only seek conversation and entering games, because they cannot remain with pleasure at home.

But, on further consideration, when, after finding the cause of all our ills, I have sought to discover the reason of it, I have found that there is one very real reason, namely, the natural poverty of our feeble and mortal condition, so miserable that nothing can comfort us when we think of it closely.

Whatever condition we picture to ourselves, if we muster all the good things which it is possible to possess, royalty is the finest position in the world. Yet, when we imagine a king attended with every pleasure he can feel, if he be without diversion and be left to consider and reflect on what he is, this feeble happiness will not sustain him; he will necessarily fall into forebodings of dangers, of revolutions which may happen, and, finally, of death and inevitable disease; so that, if he be without what is called diversion, he is unhappy and more unhappy than the least of his subjects who plays and diverts himself.

Hence it comes that play and the society of women, war and high posts, are so sought after. Not that there is in fact any happiness in them, or that men imagine true bliss to consist in money won at play, or in the hare which they hunt; we would not take these as a gift. We do not seek that easy and peaceful lot which permits us to think of our unhappy condition, nor the dangers of war, nor the labour of office, but the bustle which averts these thoughts of ours and amuses us.

Reasons why we like the chase better than the quarry.

Hence it comes that men so much love noise and stir; hence it comes that the prison is so horrible a punishment; hence it comes that the pleasure of solitude is a thing incomprehensible. And it is, in fact, the greatest source of happiness in the condition of kings that men try incessantly to divert them and to procure for them all kinds of pleasures.

The king is surrounded by persons whose only thought is to divert the king and to prevent his thinking of self. For he is unhappy, king though he be, if he think of himself.

This is all that men have been able to discover to make themselves happy. And those who philosophise on the matter, and who think men unreasonable for spending a whole day in chasing a hare which they would not have bought, scarce know our nature. The hare in itself would not screen us from the sight of death and calamities; but the chase, which turns away our attention from these, does screen us.

The advice given to Pyrrhus, to take the rest which he was about to seek with so much labour, was full of difficulties.

[To bid a man live quietly is to bid him live happily. It is to advise him to be in a state perfectly happy, in which he can think at leisure without finding therein a cause of distress. This is to misunderstand nature.]

As men who naturally understand their own condition avoid nothing so much as rest, so there is nothing they leave undone in seeking turmoil. Not that they have an instinctive knowledge of true happiness . . .

So we are wrong in blaming them. Their error does not lie in seeking excitement, if they seek it only as a diversion; the evil is that they seek it as if the possession of the objects of their quest would make them really happy. In this respect it is right to call their quest a vain one. Hence in all this both the censurers and the censured do not understand man's true nature.]

And thus, when we take the exception against them, that what they seek with such fervour cannot satisfy them, if they replied—as they should do if they considered the matter thoroughly—that they sought in it only a violent and impetuous occupation which turned their thoughts from self, and that they therefore chose an attractive object to charm and ardently attract them, they would leave their opponents without a reply. But they do not make this reply, because they do not know themselves. They do not know that it is the chase, and not the quarry, which they seek.

Dancing: We must consider rightly where to place our feet.—A gentleman sincerely believes that hunting is great and royal sport; but a beater is not of this opinion.

They imagine that, if they obtained such a post, they would then rest with pleasure and are insensible of the insatiable nature of their desire. They think they are truly seeking quiet, and they are only seeking excitement.

They have a secret instinct which impels them to seek amusement and occupation abroad, and which arises from the sense of their constant unhappiness. They have another secret instinct, a remnant of the greatness of our original nature, which teaches them that happiness in reality consists only in rest and not in stir. And of these two contrary instincts they form within themselves a confused idea, which hides itself from their view in the depths of their soul, inciting them to aim at rest through excitement, and always to fancy that the satisfaction which they have not will come to them, if, by surmounting whatever difficulties confront them, they can thereby open the door to rest.

Thus passes away all man's life. Men seek rest in a struggle against difficulties; and when they have conquered these, rest becomes insufferable. For we think either of the misfortunes we have or of those which threaten us. And even if we should see ourselves sufficiently sheltered on all sides, weariness of its own accord would not fail to arise from the depths of the heart wherein it has its natural roots and to fill the mind with its poison.

Thus so wretched is man that he would weary even without any cause for weariness from the peculiar state of his disposition; and so frivolous is he that, though full of a thousand reasons for weariness, the least thing, such as playing billiards or hitting a ball, is sufficient to amuse him.

But will you say what object has he in all this? The pleasure of bragging tomorrow among his friends that he has played better than another. So others sweat in their own rooms to show to the learned that they have solved a problem in algebra, which no one had hitherto been able to solve. Many more expose themselves to extreme perils, in my opinion as foolishly, in order to boast afterwards that they have captured a town. Lastly, others wear themselves out in studying all these things, not in order to become wiser, but only in order to prove that they know them; and these are the most senseless of the band, since they are so knowingly, whereas one may suppose of the others that, if they knew it, they would no longer be foolish.

This man spends his life without weariness in playing every day for a small stake. Give him each morning the money he can win each day, on condition he does not play; you make him miserable. It will perhaps be said that he seeks the amusement of play and not the winnings. Make him, then, play for nothing; he will not become excited over it and will feel bored. It is, then, not the amusement alone that he seeks; a languid and passionless amusement will weary him. He must get excited over it and deceive himself by the fancy that he will be happy to win what he would not have as a gift on condition of not playing; and he must make for himself an object of passion, and excite over it his desire, his anger, his fear, to obtain his imagined end, as children are frightened at the face they have blackened.

Whence comes it that this man, who lost his only son a few months ago, or who this morning was in such trouble through being distressed by lawsuits and quarrels, now no longer thinks of them? Do not wonder; he is quite taken up in looking out for the boar which his dogs have been hunting so hotly for the last six hours. He requires nothing more. However full of sadness a man may be, he is happy for the time, if you can prevail upon him to enter into some amusement; and however happy a man may be, he will soon be discontented and wretched, if he be not diverted and occupied by some passion or pursuit which prevents weariness from overcoming him. Without amusement there is no joy; with amusement there is no sadness. And this also constitutes the happiness of persons in high position, that they have a number of people to amuse them and have the power to keep themselves in this state.

Consider this. What is it to be superintendent, chancellor, first president, but to be in a condition wherein from early morning a large number of people come from all quarters to see them, so as not to leave them an hour in the day in which they can think of themselves? And when they are in disgrace and sent back to their country houses, where they lack neither wealth nor servants to help them on occasion, they do not fail to be wretched and desolate, because no one prevents them from thinking of themselves.

140. [How does it happen that this man, so distressed at the death of his wife and his only son, or who has some great lawsuit which annoys him, is not at this moment sad, and that he seems so free from all painful and disquieting thoughts? We need not wonder; for a ball has been served him, and he must return it to his companion. He is occupied in catching it in its fall from the roof, to win a game. How can he think of his own affairs, pray, when he has this other matter in hand? Here is a care worthy of occupying this great soul and taking away from him every other thought of the mind. This man, born to know the universe, to judge all causes, to govern a whole state, is altogether occupied and taken up with the business of catching a hare. And if he does not lower himself to this and wants always to be on the strain, he will be more foolish still, because he would raise himself above humanity; and after all, he is only a man, that is to say capable of little and of much, of all and of nothing; he is neither angel nor brute, but man.]

141. Men spend their time in following a ball or a hare; it is the pleasure even of kings.

142. *Diversion*—Is not the royal dignity sufficiently great in itself to make its possessor happy by the mere contemplation of what he is? Must he be diverted from this thought like ordinary folk? I see well that a man is made happy by diverting him from the view of his domestic sorrows so as to occupy all his thoughts with the care of dancing well. But will it be the same with a king, and will he be happier in the pursuit of these idle amusements than in the contemplation of his greatness? And what more satisfactory object could be presented to his mind? Would it not be a deprivation of his delight for him to occupy his soul with the thought of how to adjust his steps to the cadence of an air, or of how to throw a [ball] skilfully, instead of leaving it to enjoy quietly the contemplation of the majestic glory which encompasses him? Let us make the trial; let us leave a king all alone to reflect on himself quite at leisure, without any gratification of the senses, without any care in his mind, without society; and we will see that a king without diversion is a man full of wretchedness. So this is carefully avoided, and near the persons of kings there never fail to be a great number of people who see to it that amusement follows business, and who watch all the time of their leisure to supply them with delights and games, so that there is no blank in it. In fact, kings are sur-

rounded with persons who are wonderfully attentive in taking care that the king be not alone and in a state to think of himself, knowing well that he will be miserable, king though he be, if he meditate on self.

In all this I am not talking of Christian kings as Christians, but only as kings.

143. *Diversion.*—Men are entrusted from infancy with the care of their honour, their property, their friends, and even with the property and the honour of their friends. They are overwhelmed with business, with the study of languages, and with physical exercise; and they are made to understand that they cannot be happy unless their health, their honour, their fortune and that of their friends be in good condition, and that a single thing wanting will make them unhappy. Thus they are given cares and business which make them bustle about from break of day.— It is, you will exclaim, a strange way to make them happy! What more could be done to make them miserable?—Indeed! what could be done? We should only have to relieve them from all these cares; for then they would see themselves: they would reflect on what they are, whence they came, whither they go, and thus we cannot employ and divert them too much. And this is why, after having given them so much business, we advise them, if they have some time for relaxation, to employ it in amusement, in play, and to be always fully occupied.

How hollow and full of ribaldry is the heart of man!

144. I spent a long time in the study of the abstract sciences, and was disheartened by the small number of fellow-students in them. When I commenced the study of man, I saw that these abstract sciences are not suited to man and that I was wandering farther from my own state in examining them than others in not knowing them. I pardoned their little knowledge; but I thought at least to find many companions in the study of man and that it was the true study which is suited to him. I have been deceived; still fewer study it than geometry. It is only from the want of knowing how to study this that we seek the other studies. But is it not that even here is not the knowledge which man should have and that for the purpose of happiness it is better for him not to know himself?

145. [One thought alone occupies us; we cannot think of two things at the same time. This is lucky for us according to the world, not according to God.]

146. Man is obviously made to think. It is his whole dignity and his whole merit; and his whole duty is to think as he ought. Now, the order of thought is to begin with self, and with its Author and its end.

Now, of what does the world think? Never of this, but of dancing, playing the lute, singing, making verses, running at the ring, etc., fighting, making oneself king, without thinking what it is to be a king and what to be a man.

147. We do not content ourselves with the life we have in ourselves and in our own being; we desire to live an imaginary life in the mind of others, and for this purpose we endeavour to shine. We labour unceasingly to adorn and preserve this imaginary existence and neglect the real. And if we possess calmness, or generosity, or truthfulness, we are eager to make it known, so as to attach these virtues to that imaginary existence. We would rather separate them from ourselves to join

them to it; and we would willingly be cowards in order to acquire the reputation of being brave. A great proof of the nothingness of our being, not to be satisfied with the one without the other, and to renounce the one for the other! For he would be infamous who would not die to preserve his honour.

148. We are so presumptuous that we would wish to be known by all the world, even by people who shall come after, when we shall be no more; and we are so vain that the esteem of five or six neighbours delights and contents us.

149. We do not trouble ourselves about being esteemed in the towns through which we pass. But if we are to remain a little while there, we are so concerned. How long is necessary? A time commensurate with our vain and paltry life.

150. Vanity is so anchored in the heart of man that a soldier, a soldier's servant, a cook, a porter brags and wishes to have his admirers. Even philosophers wish for them. Those who write against it want to have the glory of having written well; and those who read it desire the glory of having read it. I who write this have perhaps this desire, and perhaps those who will read it . . .

151. *Glory.*—Admiration spoils all from infancy. Ah! How well said! Ah! How well done! How well-behaved he is! etc.

The children of Port-Royal, who do not receive this stimulus of envy and glory, fall into carelessness.

152. *Pride.*— Curiosity is only vanity. Most frequently we wish to know but to talk. Otherwise we would not take a sea voyage in order never to talk of it, and for the sole pleasure of seeing without hope of ever communicating it.

153. *Of the desire of being esteemed by those with whom we are.*—Pride takes such natural possession of us in the midst of our woes, errors, etc. We even lose our life with joy, provided people talk of it.

Vanity: play, hunting, visiting, false shame, a lasting name.

154. [I have no friends to your advantage.]

155. A true friend is so great an advantage, even for the greatest lords, in order that he may speak well of them and back them in their absence, that they should do all to have one. But they should choose well; for, if they spend all their efforts in the interests of fools, it will be of no use, however well these may speak of them; and these will not even speak well of them if they find themselves on the weakest side, for they have no influence; and thus they will speak ill of them in company.

156. *Ferox gens, nullam esse vitam sine armis rati.*[1]—They prefer death to peace; others prefer death to war.

Every opinion may be held preferable to life, the love of which is so strong and so natural.

[1]Livy, xxxiv.17. "A brutal people, for whom, when they have not armour, there is not life."

157. Contradiction: comtempt for our existence, to die for nothing, hatred of our existence.

158. *Pursuits.*—The charm of fame is so great that we like every object to which it is attached, even death.

159. Noble deeds are most estimable when hidden. When I see some of these in history, they please me greatly. But after all they have not been quite hidden, since they have been known; and though people have done what they could to hide them, the little publication of them spoils all, for what was best in them was the wish to hide them.

160. Sneezing absorbs all the functions of the soul, as well as work does; but we do not draw therefrom the same conclusions against the greatness of man, because it is against his will. And although we bring it on ourselves, it is nevertheless against our will that we sneeze. It is not in view of the act itself; it is for another end. And thus it is not a proof of the weakness of man and of his slavery under that action.

It is not disgraceful for man to yield to pain, and it is disgraceful to yield to pleasure. This is not because pain comes to us from without, and we ourselves seek pleasure; for it is possible to seek pain, and yield to it purposely, without this kind of baseness. Whence comes it, then, that reason thinks it honourable to succumb under stress of pain, and disgraceful to yield to the attack of pleasure? It is because pain does not tempt and attract us. It is we ourselves who choose it voluntarily, and will it to prevail over us. So that we are masters of the situation; and in this man yields to himself. But in pleasure it is man who yields to pleasure. Now only mastery and sovereignty bring glory, and only slavery brings shame.

161. *Vanity.*—How wonderful it is that a thing so evident as the vanity of the world is so little known, that it is a strange and surprising thing to say that it is foolish to seek greatness?

162. He who will know fully the vanity of man has only to consider the causes and effects of love. The cause is a *je ne sais quoi* (Corneille), and the effects are dreadful. This *je ne sais quoi*, so small an object that we cannot recognise it, agitates a whole country, princes, armies, the entire world.

Cleopatra's nose: had it been shorter, the whole aspect of the world would have been altered.

163. *Vanity.*—The cause and the effects of love: Cleopatra.

164. He who does not see the vanity of the world is himself very vain. Indeed who do not see it but youths who are absorbed in fame, diversion, and the thought of the future? But take away diversion, and you will see them dried up with weariness. They feel then their nothingness without knowing it; for it is indeed to be unhappy to be in insufferable sadness as soon as we are reduced to thinking of self and have no diversion.

165. *Thoughts.—In omnibus requiem quæsivi.*[1] If our condition were truly happy, we would not need diversion from thinking of it in order to make ourselves happy.

166. *Diversion.—*Death is easier to bear without thinking of it than is the thought of death without peril.

167. The miseries of human life has established all this: as men have seen this, they have taken up diversion.

168. *Diversion.—*As men are not able to fight against death, misery, ignorance, they have taken it into their heads, in order to be happy, not to think of them at all.

169. Despite these miseries, man wishes to be happy, and only wishes to be happy, and cannot wish not to be so. But how will he set about it? To be happy he would have to make himself immortal; but, not being able to do so, it has occurred to him to prevent himself from thinking of death.

170. *Diversion.—*If man were happy, he would be the more so, the less he was diverted, like the Saints and God. Yes; but is it not to be happy to have a faculty of being amused by diversion? No; for that comes from elsewhere and from without, and thus is dependent, and therefore subject to be disturbed by a thousand accidents, which bring inevitable griefs.

171. *Misery.—*The only thing which consoles us for our miseries is diversion, and yet this is the greatest of our miseries. For it is this which principally hinders us from reflecting upon ourselves and which makes us insensibly ruin ourselves. Without this we should be in a state of weariness, and this weariness would spur us to seek a more solid means of escaping from it. But diversion amuses us, and leads us unconsciously to death.

172. We do not rest satisfied with the present. We anticipate the future as too slow in coming, as if in order to hasten its course; or we recall the past, to stop its too rapid flight. So imprudent are we that we wander in the times which are not ours and do not think of the only one which belongs to us; and so idle are we that we dream of those times which are no more and thoughtlessly overlook that which alone exists. For the present is generally painful to us. We conceal it from our sight, because it troubles us; and, if it be delightful to us, we regret to see it pass away. We try to sustain it by the future and think of arranging matters which are not in our power, for a time which we have no certainty of reaching.

Let each one examine his thoughts, and he will find them all occupied with the past and the future. We scarcely ever think of the present; and if we think of it, it is only to take light from it to arrange the future. The present is never our end. The past and the present are our means; the future alone is our end. So we never live, but we hope to live; and, as we are always preparing to be happy, it is inevitable we should never be so.

173. They say that eclipses foretoken misfortune, because misfortunes are com-

[1]Ecclus. 24.11. "With all these I have sought rest."

mon, so that, as evil happens so often, they often foretell it; whereas if they said that they predict good fortune, they would often be wrong. They attribute good fortune only to rare conjunctions of the heavens; so they seldom fail in prediction.

174. *Misery.*—Solomon and Job have best known and best spoken of the misery of man; the former the most fortunate, and the latter the most unfortunate of men; the former knowing the vanity of pleasures from experience, the latter the reality of evils.

175. We know ourselves so little that many think they are about to die when they are well, and many think they are well when they are near death, unconscious of approaching fever, or of the abscess ready to form itself.

176. Cromwell was about to ravage all Christendom; the royal family was undone, and his own for ever established, save for a little grain of sand which formed in his ureter. Rome herself was trembling under him; but this small piece of gravel having formed there, he is dead, his family cast down, all is peaceful, and the king is restored.

177. [Three hosts.] Would he who had possessed the friendship of the King of England, the King of Poland, and the Queen of Sweden, have believed he would lack a refuge and shelter in the world?

178. Macrobius: on the innocents slain by Herod.

179. When Augustus learnt that Herod's own son was amongst the infants under two years of age, whom he had caused to be slain, he said that it was better to be Herod's pig than his son. Macrobius, *Saturnalia*, ii. 4.

180. The great and the humble have the same misfortunes, the same griefs, the same passions; but the one is at the top of the wheel, and the other near the centre, and so less disturbed by the same revolutions.

181. We are so unfortunate that we can only take pleasure in a thing on condition of being annoyed if it turn out ill, as a thousand things can do, and do every hour. He who should find the secret of rejoicing in the good, without troubling himself with its contrary evil, would have hit the mark. It is perpetual motion.

182. Those who have always good hope in the midst of misfortunes, and who are delighted with good luck, are suspected of being very pleased with the ill success of the affair, if they are not equally distressed by bad luck; and they are overjoyed to find these pretexts of hope, in order to show that they are concerned and to conceal by the joy which they feign to feel that which they have at seeing the failure of the matter.

183. We run carelessly to the precipice, after we have put something before us to prevent us seeing it.

SECTION III

OF THE NECESSITY OF THE WAGER

184. A letter to incite to the search after God.

And then to make people seek Him among the philosophers, sceptics, and dog-matists, who disquiet him who inquires of them.

185. The conduct of God, who disposes all things kindly, is to put religion into the mind by reason, and into the heart by grace. But to will to put it into the mind and heart by force and threats is not to put religion there, but terror; *terrorrem potius quam religionem.*[1]

186. *Nisi terrerentur et non docerentur, improba quasi dominatio videretur* (St. Augustine, *Epistle* 48 or 49),[2] *Contra Mendacium ad Consentium.*

187. *Order.*—Men despise religion; they hate it and fear it is true. To remedy this, we must begin by showing that religion is not contrary to reason; that it is venerable, to inspire respect for it; then we must make it lovable, to make good men hope it is true; finally, we must prove it is true.

Venerable, because it has perfect knowledge of man; lovable because it promises the true good.

188. In every dialogue and discourse, we must be able to say to those who take offence, "Of what do you complain?"

189. To begin by pitying unbelievers; they are wretched enough by their condition. We ought only to revile them where it is beneficial; but this does them harm.

190. To pity atheists who seek, for are they not unhappy enough? To inveigh against those who make a boast of it.

191. And will this one scoff at the other? Who ought to scoff? And yet, the latter does not scoff at the other, but pities him.

192. To reproach Milton with not being troubled, since God will reproach him.

193. *Quid fiet hominibus qui minima contemnunt, majora non credunt?*[3]

194. . . . Let them at least learn what is the religion they attack, before attacking

---

[1]"Terror which is more powerful than religion."
[2]"From fear that they are being led by terror, without guidance, domination appears tyrannical."
[3]"What will become of men who mistake small things and do not believe in greater?"

it. If this religion boasted of having a clear view of God, and of possessing it open and unveiled, it would be attacking it to say that we see nothing in the world which shows it with this clearness. But since, on the contrary, it says that men are in darkness and estranged from God, that He has hidden Himself from their knowledge, that this is in fact the name which He gives Himself in the Scriptures, *Deus absconditus;*[1] and finally, if it endeavours equally to establish these two things: that God has set up in the Church visible signs to make Himself known to those who should seek Him sincerely, and that He has nevertheless so disguised them that He will only be perceived by those who seek Him with all their heart; what advantage can they obtain, when, in the negligence with which they make profession of being in search of the truth, they cry out that nothing reveals it to them; and since that darkness in which they are, and with which they upbraid the Church, establishes only one of the things which she affirms, without touching the other, and, very far from destroying, proves her doctrine?

In order to attack it, they should have protested that they had made every effort to seek Him everywhere, and even in that which the Church proposes for their instruction, but without satisfaction. If they talked in this manner, they would in truth be attacking one of her pretensions. But I hope here to show that no reasonable person can speak thus, and I venture even to say that no one has ever done so. We know well enough how those who are of this mind behave. They believe they have made great efforts for their instruction when they have spent a few hours in reading some book of Scripture and have questioned some priests on the truths of the faith. After that, they boast of having made vain search in books and among men. But, verily, I will tell them what I have often said, that this negligence is insufferable. We are not here concerned with the trifling interests of some stranger, that we should treat it in this fashion; the matter concerns ourselves and our all.

The immortality of the soul is a matter which is of so great consequence to us and which touches us so profoundly that we must have lost all feeling to be indifferent as to knowing what it is. All our actions and thoughts must take such different courses, according as there are or are not eternal joys to hope for, that it is impossible to take one step with sense and judgment unless we regulate our course by our view of this point which ought to be our ultimate end.

Thus our first interest and our first duty is to enlighten ourselves on this subject, whereon depends all our conduct. Therefore among those who do not believe, I make a vast difference between those who strive with all their power to inform themselves and those who live without troubling or thinking about it.

I can have only compassion for those who sincerely bewail their doubt, who regard it as the greatest of misfortunes, and who, sparing no effort to escape it, make of this inquiry their principal and most serious occupation.

But as for those who pass their life without thinking of this ultimate end of life, and who, for this sole reason that they do not find within themselves the lights which convince them of it, neglect to seek them elsewhere, and to examine thoroughly whether this opinion is one of those which people receive with credulous simplicity, or one of those which, although obscure in themselves, have nevertheless a solid and immovable foundation, I look upon them in a manner quite different.

This carelessness in a matter which concerns themselves, their eternity, their all,

[1] Is. 45.15. "Thou art a God that hidest thyself."

moves me more to anger than pity; it astonishes and shocks me; it is to me monstrous. I do not say this out of the pious zeal of a spiritual devotion. I expect, on the contrary, that we ought to have this feeling from principles of human interest and self-love; for this we need only see what the least enlightened persons see.

We do not require great education of the mind to understand that here is no real and lasting satisfaction; that our pleasures are only vanity; that our evils are infinite; and, lastly, that death, which threatens us every moment, must infallibly place us within a few years under the dreadful necessity of being for ever either annihilated or unhappy.

There is nothing more real than this, nothing more terrible. Be we as heroic as we like, that is the end which awaits the noblest life in the world. Let us reflect on this and then say whether it is not beyond doubt that there is no good in this life but in the hope of another; that we are happy only in proportion as we draw near it; and that, as there are no more woes for those who have complete assurance of eternity, so there is no more happiness for those who have no insight into it.

Surely then it is a great evil thus to be in doubt, but it is at least an indispensable duty to seek when we are in such doubt; and thus the doubter who does not seek is altogether completely unhappy and completely wrong. And if besides this he is easy and content, professes to be so, and indeed boasts of it; if it is this state itself which is the subject of his joy and vanity, I have no words to describe so silly a creature.

How can people hold these opinions? What joy can we find in the expectation of nothing but hopeless misery? What reason for boasting that we are in impenetrable darkness? And how can it happen that the following argument occurs to a reasonable man?

"I know not who put me into the world, nor what the world is, nor what I myself am. I am in terrible ignorance of everything. I know not what my body is, nor my senses, nor my soul, not even that part of me which thinks what I say, which reflects on all and on itself, and knows itself no more than the rest. I see those frightful spaces of the universe which surround me, and I find myself tied to one corner of this vast expanse, without knowing why I am put in this place rather than in another, nor why the short time which is given me to live is assigned to me at this point rather than at another of the whole eternity which was before me or which shall come after me. I see nothing but infinites on all sides, which surround me as an atom and as a shadow which endures only for an instant and returns no more. All I know is that I must soon die, but what I know least is this very death which I cannot escape.

"As I know not whence I come, so I know not whither I go. I know only that, in leaving this world, I fall for ever either into annihilation or into the hands of an angry God, without knowing to which of these two states I shall be for ever assigned. Such is my state, full of weakness and uncertainty. And from all this I conclude that I ought to spend all the days of my life without caring to inquire into what must happen to me. Perhaps I might find some solution to my doubts, but I will not take the trouble, nor take a step to seek it; and after treating with scorn those who are concerned with this care, I will go without foresight and without fear to try the great event, and let myself be led carelessly to death, uncertain of the eternity of my future state."

Who would desire to have for a friend a man who talks in this fashion? Who

would choose him out from others to tell him of his affairs? Who would have recourse to him in affliction? And indeed to what use in life could one put him?

In truth, it is the glory of religion to have for enemies men so unreasonable;
and their opposition to it is so little dangerous that it serves, on the contrary, to
establish its truths. For the Christian faith goes mainly to establish these two facts:
the corruption of nature, and redemption by Jesus Christ. Now I contend that, if
these men do not serve to prove the truth of the redemption by the holiness of
their behaviour, they at least serve admirably to show the corruption of nature by
sentiments so unnatural.

Nothing is so important to man as his own state, nothing is so formidable to
him as eternity; and thus it is not natural that there should be men indifferent to
the loss of their existence, and to the perils of everlasting suffering. They are quite
different with regard to all other things. They are afraid of mere trifles; they foresee them; they feel them. And this same man who spends so many days and nights
in rage and despair for the loss of office, or for some imaginary insult to his
honour, is the very one who knows without anxiety and without emotion that he
will lose all by death. It is a monstrous thing to see in the same heart and at the
same time this sensibility to trifles and this strange insensibility to the greatest objects. It is an incomprehensible enchantment, and a supernatural slumber, which
indicates as its cause an all-powerful force.

There must be a strange confusion in the nature of man, that he should boast of
being in that state in which it seems incredible that a single individual should be.
However, experience has shown me so great a number of such persons that the
fact would be surprising, if we did not know that the greater part of those who
trouble themselves about the matter are disingenuous and not, in fact, what they
say. They are people who have heard it said that it is the fashion to be thus daring.
It is what they call "shaking off the yoke," and they try to imitate this. But it
would not be difficult to make them understand how greatly they deceive themselves in thus seeking esteem. This is not the way to gain it, even I say among those
men of the world who take a healthy view of things and who know that the only
way to succeed in this life is to make ourselves appear honourable, faithful, judicious, and capable of useful service to a friend; because naturally men love only
what may be useful to them. Now, what do we gain by hearing it said of a man
that he has now thrown off the yoke, that he does not believe there is a God who
watches our actions, that he considers himself the sole master of his conduct, and
that he thinks he is accountable for it only to himself? Does he think that he has
thus brought us to have henceforth complete confidence in him and to look to
him for consolation, advice, and help in every need of life? Do they profess to have
delighted us by telling us that they hold our soul to be only a little wind and smoke,
especially by telling us this in a haughty and self-satisfied tone of voice? Is this a
thing to say gaily? Is it not, on the contrary, a thing to say sadly, as the saddest
thing in the world?

If they thought of it seriously, they would see that this is so bad a mistake, so
contrary to good sense, so opposed to decency, and so removed in every respect
from that good breeding which they seek, that they would be more likely to correct than to pervert those who had an inclination to follow them. And, indeed,
make them give an account of their opinions, and of the reasons which they have
for doubting religion, and they will say to you things so feeble and so petty, that

they will persuade you of the contrary. The following is what a person one day said to such a one very appositely: "If you continue to talk in this manner, you will really make me religious." And he was right, for who would not have a horror of holding opinions in which he would have such contemptible persons as companions!

Thus those who only feign these opinions would be very unhappy, if they restrained their natural feelings in order to make themselves the most conceited of men. If, at the bottom of their heart, they are troubled at not having more light, let them not disguise the fact; this avowal will not be shameful. The only shame is to have none. Nothing reveals more an extreme weakness of mind than not to know the misery of a godless man. Nothing is more indicative of a bad disposition of heart than not to desire the truth of eternal promises. Nothing is more dastardly than to act with bravado before God. Let them then leave these impieties to those who are sufficiently ill-bred to be really capable of them. Let them at least be honest men, if they cannot be Christians. Finally, let them recognise that there are two kinds of people one can call reasonable; those who serve God with all their heart because they know Him, and those who seek Him with all their heart because they do not know Him.

But as for those who live without knowing Him and without seeking Him, they judge themselves so little worthy of their own care, that they are not worthy of the care of others; and it needs all the charity of the religion which they despise, not to despise them even to the point of leaving them to their folly. But because this religion obliges us always to regard them, so long as they are in this life, as capable of the grace which can enlighten them, and to believe that they may, in a little time, be more replenished with faith than we are, and that, on the other hand, we may fall into the blindness wherein they are, we must do for them what we would they should do for us if we were in their place, and call upon them to have pity upon themselves, and to take at least some steps in the endeavour to find light. Let them give to reading this some of the hours which they otherwise employ so uselessly; whatever aversion they may bring to the task, they will perhaps gain something, and at least will not lose much. But as for those who bring to the task perfect sincerity and a real desire to meet with truth, those I hope will be satisfied and convinced of the proofs of a religion so divine, which I have here collected, and in which I have followed somewhat after this order . . .

195. Before entering into the proofs of the Christian religion, I find it necessary to point out the sinfulness of those men who live in indifference to the search for truth in a matter which is so important to them, and which touches them so nearly.

Of all their errors, this doubtless is the one which most convicts them of foolishness and blindness, and in which it is easiest to confound them by the first glimmerings of common sense and by natural feelings.

For it is not to be doubted that the duration of this life is but a moment; that the state of death is eternal, whatever may be its nature; and that thus all our actions and thoughts must take such different directions, according to the state of that eternity, that it is impossible to take one step with sense and judgement, unless we regulate our course by the truth of that point which ought to be our ultimate end.

There is nothing clearer than this; and thus, according to the principles of reason, the conduct of men is wholly unreasonable, if they do not take another course.

On this point, therefore, we condemn those who live without thought of the ultimate end of life, who let themselves be guided by their own inclinations and their own pleasures without reflection and without concern, and, as if they could annihilate eternity by turning away their thought from it, think only of making themselves happy for the moment.

Yet this eternity exists, and death, which must open into it and threatens them every hour, must in a little time infallibly put them under the dreadful necessity of being either annihilated or unhappy for ever, without knowing which of these eternities is for ever prepared for them.

This is a doubt of terrible consequence. They are in peril of eternal woe and thereupon, as if the matter were not worth the trouble, they neglect to inquire whether this is one of those opinions which people receive with too credulous a facility, or one of those which, obscure in themselves, have a very firm, though hidden, foundation. Thus they know not whether there be truth or falsity in the matter, nor whether there be strength or weakness in the proofs. They have them before their eyes; they refuse to look at them; and in that ignorance they choose all that is necessary to fall into this misfortune if it exists, to await death to make trial of it, yet to be very content in this state, to make profession of it, and indeed to boast of it. Can we think seriously of the importance of this subject without being horrified at conduct so extravagant?

This resting in ignorance is a monstrous thing, and they who pass their life in it must be made to feel its extravagance and stupidity, by having it shown to them, so that they may be confounded by the sight of their folly. For this is how men reason, when they choose to live in such ignorance of what they are and without seeking enlightenment. "I know not," they say . . .

196. Men lack heart; they would not make a friend of it.

197. To be insensible to the extent of despising interesting things, and to become insensible to the point which interests us most.

198. The sensibility of man to trifles, and his insensibility to great things, indicates a strange inversion.

199. Let us imagine a number of men in chains and all condemned to death, where some are killed each day in the sight of the others, and those who remain see their own fate in that of their fellows and wait their turn, looking at each other sorrowfully and without hope. It is an image of the condition of men.

200. A man in a dungeon, ignorant whether his sentence be pronounced and having only one hour to learn it, but this hour enough, if he knew that it is pronounced, to obtain its repeal, would act unnaturally in spending that hour, not in ascertaining his sentence, but in playing piquet. So it is against nature that man, etc. It is making heavy the hand of God.

Thus not only the zeal of those who seek Him proves God, but also the blindness of those who seek Him not.

201. All the objections of this one and that one only go against themselves, and not against religion. All that infidels say . . .

202. [From those who are in despair at being without faith, we see that God does not enlighten them; but as to the rest, we see there is a God who makes them blind.]

203. *Fascinatio nugacitatis.*[1]—That passion may not harm us, let us act as if we had only eight hours to live.

204. If we ought to devote eight hours of life, we ought to devote a hundred years.

205. When I consider the short duration of my life, swallowed up in the eternity before and after, the little space which I fill and even can see, engulfed in the infinite immensity of spaces of which I am ignorant and which know me not, I am frightened and am astonished at being here rather than there; for there is no reason why here rather than there, why now rather than then. Who has put me here? By whose order and direction have this place and time been allotted to me? *Memoria hospitis unius diei prætereuntis.*[2]

206. The eternal silence of these infinite spaces frightens me.

207. How many kingdoms know us not!

208. Why is my knowledge limited? Why my stature? Why my life to one hundred years rather than to a thousand? What reason has nature had for giving me such, and for choosing this number rather than another in the infinity of those from which there is no more reason to choose one than another, trying nothing else?

209. Art thou less a slave by being loved and favoured by thy master? Thou art indeed well off, slave. Thy master favours thee; he will soon beat thee.

210. The last act is tragic, however happy all the rest of the play is; at the last a little earth is thrown upon our head, and that is the end for ever.

211. We are fools to depend upon the society of our fellow-men. Wretched as we are, powerless as we are, they will not aid us; we shall die alone. We should therefore act as if we were alone, and in that case should we build fine houses, etc. We should seek the truth without hesitation; and, if we refuse it, we show that we value the esteem of men more than the search for truth.

212. *Instability.*—It is a horrible thing to feel all that we possess slipping away.

213. Between us and heaven or hell there is only life, which is the frailest thing in the world.

[1]Wisd. of Sol. 4.12. "Bewitching of naughtiness."
[2]Wisd. of Sol. 5.15. "The remembrance of a guest that tarrieth but a day."

214. *Injustice.*—That presumption should be joined to meanness is extreme injustice.

215. To fear death without danger, and not in danger, for one must be a man.

216. Sudden death alone is feared; hence confessors stay with lords.

217. An heir finds the title-deeds of his house. Will he say, "Perhaps they are forged" and neglect to examine them?

218. *Dungeon.*—I approve of not examining the opinion of Copernicus; but this . . .! It concerns all our life to know whether the soul be mortal or immortal.

219. It is certain that the mortality or immortality of the soul must make an entire difference to morality. And yet philosophers have constructed their ethics independently of this: they discuss to pass an hour.
Plato, to incline to Christianity.

220. The fallacy of philosophers who have not discussed the immortality of the soul. The fallacy of their dilemma in Montaigne.

221. Atheists ought to say what is perfectly evident; now it is not perfectly evident that the soul is material.

222. *Atheists.*—What reason have they for saying that we cannot rise from the dead? What is more difficult, to be born or to rise again; that what has never been should be, or that what has been should be again? Is it more difficult to come into existence than to return to it? Habit makes the one appear easy to us; want of habit makes the other impossible. A popular way of thinking!
Why cannot a virgin bear a child? Does a hen not lay eggs without a cock? What distinguishes these outwardly from others? And who has told us that the hen may not form the germ as well as the cock?

223. What have they to say against the resurrection, and against the child-bearing of the Virgin? Which is the more difficult, to produce a man or an animal, or to reproduce it? And if they had never seen any species of animals, could they have conjectured whether they were produced without connection with each other?

224. How I hate these follies of not believing in the Eucharist, etc.! If the Gospel be true, if Jesus Christ be God, what difficulty is there?

225. Atheism shows strength of mind, but only to a certain degree.

226. Infidels, who profess to follow reason, ought to be exceedingly strong in reason. What say they then? "Do we not see," say they, "that the brutes live and die like men, and Turks like Christians? They have their ceremonies, their prophets, their doctors, their saints, their monks, like us," etc. (Is this contrary to Scripture? Does it not say all this?)

If you care but little to know the truth, here is enough of it to leave you in repose. But if you desire with all your heart to know it, it is not enough; look at it in detail. This would be sufficient for a question in philosophy; but not here, where it concerns your all. And yet, after a trifling reflection of this kind, we go to amuse ourselves, etc. Let us inquire of this same religion whether it does not give a reason for this obscurity; perhaps it will teach it to us.

227. *Order by dialogues.*—What ought I to do? I see only darkness everywhere. Shall I believe I am nothing? Shall I believe I am God?

"All things change and succeed each other." You are mistaken; there is . . .

228. Objection of atheists: "But we have no light."

229. This is what I see and what troubles me. I look on all sides, and I see only darkness everywhere. Nature presents to me nothing which is not matter of doubt and concern. If I saw nothing there which revealed a Divinity, I would come to a negative conclusion; if I saw everywhere the signs of a Creator, I would re-main peacefully in faith. But, seeing too much to deny and too little to be sure, I am in a state to be pitied; wherefore I have a hundred times wished that if a God main-tains Nature, she should testify to Him unequivocally, and that, if the signs she gives are deceptive, she should suppress them altogether; that she should say every-thing or nothing, that I might see which cause I ought to follow. Whereas in my present state, ignorant of what I am or of what I ought to do, I know neither my condition nor my duty. My heart inclines wholly to know where is the true good, in order to follow it; nothing would be too dear to me for eternity.

I envy those whom I see living in the faith with such carelessness and who make such a bad use of a gift of which it seems to me I would make such a different use.

230. It is incomprehensible that God should exist, and it is incomprehensible that He should not exist; that the soul should be joined to the body, and that we should have no soul; that the world should be created, and that it should not be created, etc.; that original sin should be, and that it should not be.

231. Do you believe it to be impossible that God is infinite, without parts? Yes. I wish therefore to show you an infinite and indivisible thing. It is a point moving everywhere with an infinite velocity; for it is one in all places and is all totality in every place.

Let this effect of nature, which previously seemed to you impossible, make you know that there may be others of which you are still ignorant. Do not draw this conclusion from your experiment, that there remains nothing for you to know; but rather that there remains an infinity for you to know.

232. Infinite movement, the point which fills everything, the moment of rest; infinite without quantity, indivisible and infinite.

233. *Infinite—nothing.*—Our soul is cast into a body, where it finds number, time, dimension. Thereupon it reasons, and calls this nature necessity, and can believe nothing else.

Unity joined to infinity adds nothing to it, no more than one foot to an infinite measure. The finite is annihilated in the presence of the infinite, and becomes a pure nothing. So our spirit before God, so our justice before divine justice. There is not so great a disproportion between our justice and that of God as between unity and infinity.

The justice of God must be vast like His compassion. Now justice to the outcast is less vast and ought less to offend our feelings than mercy towards the elect.

We know that there is an infinite, and are ignorant of its nature. As we know it to be false that numbers are finite, it is therefore true that there is an infinity in number. But we do not know what it is. It is false that it is even, it is false that it is odd; for the addition of a unit can make no change in its nature. Yet it is a number, and every number is odd or even (this is certainly true of every finite number). So we may well know that there is a God without knowing what He is. Is there not one substantial truth, seeing there are so many things which are not the truth itself?

We know then the existence and nature of the finite, because we also are finite and have extension. We know the existence of the infinite and are ignorant of its nature, because it has extension like us, but not limits like us. But we know neither the existence nor the nature of God, because He has neither extension nor limits.

But by faith we know His existence; in glory we shall know His nature. Now, I have already shown that we may well know the existence of a thing, without knowing its nature.

Let us now speak according to natural lights.

If there is a God, He is infinitely incomprehensible, since, having neither parts nor limits, He has no affinity to us. We are then incapable of knowing either what He is or if He is. This being so, who will dare to undertake the decision of the question? Not we, who have no affinity to Him.

Who then will blame Christians for not being able to give a reason for their belief, since they profess a religion for which they cannot give a reason? They declare, in expounding it to the world, that it is a foolishness, *stultitiam*;[1] and then you complain that they do not prove it! If they proved it, they would not keep their word; it is in lacking proofs that they are not lacking in sense. "Yes, but although this excuses those who offer it as such and takes away from them the blame of putting it forward without reason, it does not excuse those who receive it." Let us then examine this point, and say, "God is, or He is not." But to which side shall we incline? Reason can decide nothing here. There is an infinite chaos which separated us. A game is being played at the extremity of this infinite distance where heads or tails will turn up. What will you wager? According to reason, you can do neither the one thing nor the other; according to reason, you can defend neither of the propositions.

Do not, then, reprove for error those who have made a choice; for you know nothing about it. "No, but I blame them for having made, not this choice, but a choice; for again both he who chooses heads and he who chooses tails are equally at fault, they are both in the wrong. The true course is not to wager at all."

Yes; but you must wager. It is not optional. You are embarked. Which will you

[1] I Cor. 1.21.

choose then? Let us see. Since you must choose, let us see which interests you least. You have two things to lose, the true and the good; and two things to stake, your reason and your will, your knowledge and your happiness; and your nature has two things to shun, error and misery. Your reason is no more shocked in choosing one rather than the other, since you must of necessity choose. This is one point settled. But your happiness? Let us weigh the gain and the loss in wagering that God is. Let us estimate these two chances. If you gain, you gain all; if you lose, you lose nothing. Wager, then, without hesitation that He is. "That is very fine. Yes, I must wager; but I may perhaps wager too much." Let us see. Since there is an equal risk of gain and of loss, if you had only to gain two lives, instead of one, you might still wager. But if there were three lives to gain, you would have to play (since you are under the necessity of playing), and you would be imprudent, when you are forced to play, not to chance your life to gain three at a game where there is an equal risk of loss and gain. But there is an eternity of life and happiness. And this being so, if there were an infinity of chances, of which one only would be for you, you would still be right in wagering one to win two, and you would act stupidly, being obliged to play, by refusing to stake one life against three at a game in which out of an infinity of chances there is one for you, if there were an infinity of an infinitely happy life to gain. But there is here an infinity of an infinitely happy life to gain, a chance of gain against a finite number of chances of loss, and what you stake is finite. It is all divided; wherever the infinite is and there is not an infinity of chances of loss against that of gain, there is no time to hesitate, you must give all. And thus, when one is forced to play, he must renounce reason to preserve his life, rather than risk it for infinite gain, as likely to happen as the loss of nothingness.

For it is no use to say it is uncertain if we will gain, and it is certain that we risk, and that the infinite distance between the *certainty* of what is staked and the *uncertainty* of what will be gained, equals the finite good which is certainly staked against the uncertain infinite. It is not so, as every player stakes a certainty to gain an uncertainty, and yet he stakes a finite certainty to gain a finite uncertainty, without transgressing against reason. There is not an infinite distance between the certainty staked and the uncertainty of the gain; that is untrue. In truth, there is an infinity between the certainty of gain and the certainty of loss. But the uncertainty of the gain is proportioned to the certainty of the stake according to the proportion of the chances of gain and loss. Hence it comes that, if there are as many risks on one side as on the other, the course is to play even; and then the certainty of the stake is equal to the uncertainty of the gain, so far is it from fact that there is an infinite distance between them. And so our proposition is of infinite force, when there is the finite to stake in a game where there are equal risks of gain and of loss, and the infinite to gain. This is demonstrable; and if men are capable of any truths, this is one.

"I confess it, I admit it. But, still, is there no means of seeing the faces of the cards?" Yes, Scripture and the rest, etc. "Yes, but I have my hands tied and my mouth closed; I am forced to wager, and am not free. I am not released, and am so made that I cannot believe. What, then, would you have me do?"

True. But at least learn your inability to believe, since reason brings you to this, and yet you cannot believe. Endeavour, then, to convince yourself, not by increase of proofs of God, but by the abatement of your passions. You would like

to attain faith and do not know the way; you would like to cure yourself of unbelief and ask the remedy for it. Learn of those who have been bound like you,
and who now stake all their possessions. These are people who know the way
which you would follow, and who are cured of an ill of which you would be
cured. Follow the way by which they began; by acting as if they believed, taking
the holy water, having masses said, etc. Even this will naturally make you believe,
and deaden your acuteness. "But this is what I am afraid of." And why? What
have you to lose?

But to show you that this leads you there, it is this which will lessen the passions, which are your stumbling-blocks.

The end of this discourse.—Now, what harm will befall you in taking this side?
You will be faithful, honest, humble, grateful, generous, a sincere friend, truthful.
Certainly you will not have those poisonous pleasures, glory and luxury; but will
you not have others? I will tell you that you will thereby gain in this life, and that,
at each step you take on this road, you will see so great certainty of gain, so much
nothingness in what you risk, that you will at last recognise that you have wagered
for something certain and infinite, for which you have given nothing.

"Ah! This discourse transports me, charms me," etc.

If this discourse pleases you and seems impressive, know that it is made by a
man who has knelt, both before and after it, in prayer to that Being, infinite and
without parts, before whom he lays all he has, for you also to lay before Him all
you have for your own good and for His glory, that so strength may be given to
lowliness.

234. If we must not act save on a certainty, we ought not to act on religion, for
it is not certain. But how many things we do on an uncertainty, sea voyages, battles! I say then we must do nothing at all, for nothing is certain, and that there is
more certainty in religion than there is as to whether we may see to-morrow; for
it is not certain that we may see to-morrow, and it is certainly possible that we
may not see it. We cannot say as much about religion. It is not certain that it is;
but who will venture to say that it is certainly possible that it is not? Now when
we work for to-morrow, and so on an uncertainty, we act reasonably; for we ought
to work for an uncertainty according to the doctrine of chance which was demonstrated above.

Saint Augustine has seen that we work for an uncertainty, on sea, in battle, etc.
But he has not seen the doctrine of chance which proves that we should do so.
Montaigne has seen that we are shocked at a fool, and that habit is all-powerful;
but he has not seen the reason of this effect.

All these persons have seen the effects, but they have not seen the causes. They
are, in comparison with those who have discovered the causes, as those who have
only eyes are in comparison with those who have intellect. For the effects are
perceptible by sense, and the causes are visible only to the intellect. And although
these effects are seen by the mind, this mind is, in comparison with the mind which
sees the causes, as the bodily senses are in comparison with the intellect.

235. *Rem viderunt, causam non viderunt.*[1]

[1]"They have seen the thing; they have not seen the cause." St. Augustine, *Contra Pelagium,*
iv.60.

236. According to the doctrine of chance, you ought to put yourself to the trouble of searching for the truth; for if you die without worshipping the True Cause, you are lost. "But," say you, "if He had wished me to worship Him, He would have left me signs of His will." He has done so; but you neglect them. Seek them, therefore; it is well worth it.

237. *Chances.*—We must live differently in the world, according to these different assumptions: (1) that we could always remain in it; (2) that it is certain that we shall not remain here long, and uncertain if we shall remain here one hour. This last assumption is our condition.

238. What do you then promise me, in addition to certain troubles, but ten years of self-love (for ten years is the chance), to try hard to please without success?

239. *Objection.*—Those who hope for salvation are so far happy; but they have as a counterpoise the fear of hell.

Reply.—Who has most reason to fear hell: he who is in ignorance whether there is a hell, and who is certain of damnation if there is; or he who certainly believes there is a hell and hopes to be saved if there is?

240. "I would soon have renounced pleasure," say they, "had I faith." For my part I tell you, "You would soon have faith, if you renounced pleasure." Now, it is for you to begin. If I could, I would give you faith. I cannot do so, nor therefore test the truth of what you say. But you can well renounce pleasure and test whether what I say is true.

241. *Order.*—I would have far more fear of being mistaken, and of finding that the Christian religion was true, than of not being mistaken in believing it true.

SECTION IV

OF THE MEANS OF BELIEF

242. *Preface to the second part.*—To speak of those who have treated of this matter.

I admire the boldness with which these persons undertake to speak of God. In addressing their argument to infidels, their first chapter is to prove Divinity from the works of nature. I should not be astonished at their enterprise, if they were addressing their argument to the faithful; for it is certain that those who have the living faith in their hearts see at once that all existence is none other than the work of the God whom they adore. But for those in whom this light is extinguished, and in whom we purpose to rekindle it, persons destitute of faith and grace, who, seeking with all their light whatever they see in nature that can bring them to this knowledge, find only obscurity and darkness; to tell them that they have only to look at the smallest things which surround them, and they will see God openly, to give them, as a complete proof of this great and important matter, the course of the moon and planets, and to claim to have concluded the proof with such an argument, is to give them ground for believing that the proofs of our religion are very weak. And I see by reason and experience that nothing is more calculated to arouse their contempt.

It is not after this manner that Scripture speaks, which has a better knowledge of the things that are of God. It says, on the contrary, that God is a hidden God, and that, since the corruption of nature, He has left men in a darkness from which they can escape only through Jesus Christ, without whom all communion with God is cut off. *Nemo novit Patrem, nisi Filius, et cui voluerit Filius revelare*.[1]

This is what Scripture points out to us, when it says in so many places that those who seek God find Him. It is not of that light, "like the noonday sun," that this is said. We do not say that those who seek the noonday sun, or water in the sea, shall find them; and hence the evidence of God must not be of this nature. So it tells us elsewhere: *Vere tu es Deus absconditus*.[2]

243. It is an astounding fact that no canonical writer has ever made use of nature to prove God. They all strive to make us believe in Him. David, Solomon, etc., have never said, "There is no void, therefore there is a God." They must have had more knowledge than the most learned people who came after them, and who have all made use of this argument. This is worthy of attention.

244. "Why! Do you not say yourself that the heavens and birds prove God?" No. "And does your religion not say so"? No. For although it is true in a sense for some souls to whom God gives this light, yet it is false with respect to the majority of men.

245. There are three sources of belief: reason, custom, inspiration. The Christian religion, which alone has reason, does not acknowledge as her true children those who believe without inspiration. It is not that she excludes reason and custom. On the contrary, the mind must be opened to proofs, must be confirmed by custom and offer itself in humbleness to inspirations, which alone can produce a true and saving effect. *Ne evacuetur crux Christi*.[3]

246. *Order.*—After the letter *That we ought to seek God*, to write the letter *On removing obstacles;* which is the discourse on "the machine," on preparing the machine, on seeking by reason.

247. *Order.*—A letter of exhortation to a friend to induce him to seek. And he will reply, "But what is the use of seeking? Nothing is seen." Then to reply to him, "Do not despair." And he will answer that he would be glad to find some light, but that, according to this very religion, if he believed in it, it will be of no use to him, and that therefore he prefers not to seek. And to answer to that: The machine.

---

[1]Matt 11.27. "Neither knoweth any man the Father, save the Son, and he to whomsoever the Son will reveal him."
[2]Is. 45.15. "Verily, thou art a God that hidest thyself."
[3]I Cor. 1.17. "Lest the cross of Christ should be made of none effect."

248. *A letter which indicates the use of proofs by the machine.*—Faith is different from proof; the one is human, the other is a gift of God. *Justus ex fide vivit.*[1] It is this faith that God Himself puts into the heart, of which the proof is often the instrument, *fides ex auditu;*[2] but this faith is in the heart, and makes us not say *scio*, but *credo*.[3]

249. It is superstition to put one's hope in formalities; but it is pride to be unwilling to submit to them.

250. The external must be joined to the internal to obtain anything from God, that is to say, we must kneel, pray with the lips, etc., in order that proud man, who would not submit himself to God, may be now subject to the creature. To expect help from these externals is superstition; to refuse to join them to the internal is pride.

251. Other religions, as the pagan, are more popular, for they consist in externals. But they are not for educated people. A purely intellectual religion would be more suited to the learned, but it would be of no use to the common people. The Christian religion alone is adapted to all, being composed of externals and internals. It raises the common people to the internal, and humbles the proud to the external; it is not perfect without the two, for the people must understand the spirit of the letter, and the learned must submit their spirit to the letter.

252. For we must not misunderstand ourselves; we are as much automatic as intellectual; and hence it comes that the instrument by which conviction is attained is not demonstrated alone. How few things are demonstrated! Proofs only convince the mind. Custom is the source of our strongest and most believed proofs. It bends the automaton, which persuades the mind without its thinking about the matter. Who has demonstrated that there will be a to-morrow and that we shall die? And what is more believed? It is, then, custom which persuades us of it; it is custom that makes so many men Christians; custom that makes them Turks, heathens, artisans, soldiers, etc. (Faith in baptism is more received among Christians than among Turks.) Finally, we must have recourse to it when once the mind has seen where the truth is, in order to quench our thirst, and steep ourselves in that belief, which escapes us at every hour; for always to have proofs ready is too much trouble. We must get an easier belief, which is that of custom, which, without violence, without art, without argument, makes us believe things and inclines all our powers to this belief, so that our soul falls naturally into it. It is not enough to believe only by force of conviction, when the automaton is inclined to believe the contrary. Both our parts must be made to believe, the mind by reasons which it is sufficient to have seen once in a lifetime, and the automaton by custom, and by not allowing it to incline to the contrary. *Inclina cor meum, Deus.*[4]

The reason acts slowly, with so many examinations and on so many principles, which must be always present, that at every hour it falls asleep, or wanders, through want of having all its principles present. Feeling does not act thus; it acts in a

[1] Rom. 1.17. "The just shall live by faith."
[2] Rom. 10.17. "Faith cometh by hearing."
[3] "I know." "I believe."
[4] Ps. 119.36. "Incline my heart, O Lord."

moment, and is always ready to act. We must then put our faith in feeling; otherwise it will be always vacillating.

253. Two extremes: to exclude reason, to admit reason only.

254. It is not a rare thing to have to reprove the world for too much docility. It is a natural vice like credulity, and as pernicious. Superstition.

255. Piety is different from superstition.

To carry piety as far as superstition is to destroy it.

The heretics reproach us for this superstitious submission. This is to do what they reproach us for . . . .

Infidelity, not to believe in the Eucharist, because it is not seen.

Superstition to believe propositions. Faith, etc.

256. I say there are few true Christians, even as regards faith. There are many who believe but from superstition. There are many who do not believe solely from wickedness. Few are between the two.

In this I do not include those who are of truly pious character, nor all those who believe from a feeling in their heart.

257. There are only three kinds of persons; those who serve God, having found Him; others who are occupied in seeking Him, not having found Him; while the remainder live without seeking Him and without having found Him. The first are reasonable and happy, the last are foolish and unhappy; those between are unhappy and reasonable.

258. *Unusquisque sibi Deum fingit.*[1]

Disgust.

259. Ordinary people have the power of not thinking of that about which they do not wish to think. "Do not meditate on the passages about the Messiah," said the Jew to his son. Thus our people often act. Thus are false religions preserved, and even the true one, in regard to many persons.

But there are some who have not the power of thus preventing thought, and who think so much the more as they are forbidden. These undo false religions and even the true one, if they do not find solid arguments.

260. They hide themselves in the press and call numbers to their rescue. Tumult.

Authority.—So far from making it a rule to believe a thing because you have heard it, you ought to believe nothing without putting yourself into the position as if you had never heard it.

It is your own assent to yourself, and the constant voice of your own reason, and not of others, that should make you believe.

Belief is so important! A hundred contradictions might be true. If antiquity were the rule of belief, men of ancient time would then be without rule. If general consent, if men had perished?

[1] Wisd. of Sol. 15.8,16. "He moulds a God . . . like unto himself."

False humanity, pride.

Lift the curtain. You try in vain; if you must either believe, or deny, or doubt. Shall we then have no rule? We judge that animals do well what they do. Is there no rule whereby to judge men?

To deny, to believe, and to doubt well, are to a man what the race is to a horse. Punishment of those who sin, error.

261. Those who do not love the truth take as a pretext that it is disputed, and that a multitude deny it. And so their error arises only from this, that they do not love either truth or charity. Thus they are without excuse.

262. Superstition and lust. Scruples, evil desires. Evil fear; fear, not such as comes from a belief in God, but such as comes from a doubt whether He exists or not. True fear comes from faith; false fear comes from doubt. True fear is joined to hope, because it is born of faith, and because men hope in the God in whom they believe. False fear is joined to despair, because men fear the God in whom they have no belief. The former fear to lose Him; the latter fear to find Him.

263. "A miracle," says one, "would strengthen my faith." He says so when he does not see one. Reasons, seen from afar, appear to limit our view; but when they are reached, we begin to see beyond. Nothing stops the nimbleness of our mind. There is no rule, say we, which has not some exceptions, no truth so general which has not some aspect in which it fails. It is sufficient that it be not absolutely universal to give us a pretext for applying the exceptions to the present subject and for saying, "This is not always true; there are therefore cases where it is not so." It only remains to show that this is one of them; and that is why we are very awkward or unlucky, if we do not find one some day.

264. We do not weary of eating and sleeping every day, for hunger and sleepiness recur. Without that we should weary of them. So, without the hunger for spiritual things, we weary of them. Hunger after righteousness, the eighth beatitude.

265. Faith indeed tells what the senses do not tell, but not the contrary of what they see. It is above them and not contrary to them.

266. How many stars have telescopes revealed to us which did not exist for our philosophers of old! We freely attack Holy Scripture on the great number of stars, saying, "There are only one thousand and twenty-eight, we know it." There is grass on the earth, we see it—from the moon we would not see it—and on the grass are leaves, and in these leaves are small animals; but after that no more. O presumptuous man! The compounds are composed of elements, and the elements not. O presumptuous man! Here is a fine reflection. We must not say that there is anything which we do not see. We must then talk like others, but not think like them.

267. The last proceeding of reason is to recognise that there is an infinity of

things which are beyond it. It is but feeble if it does not see so far as to know this. But if natural things are beyond it, what will be said of supernatural?

268. *Submission.*—We must know where to doubt, where to feel certain, where to submit. He who does not do so understands not the force of reason. There are some who offend against these three rules, either by affirming everything as demonstrative, from want of knowing what demonstration is; or by doubting everything, from want of knowing where to submit; or by submitting in everything, from want of knowing where they must judge.

269. Submission is the use of reason in which consists true Christianity.

270. *Saint Augustine.*—Reason would never submit, if it did not judge that there are some occasions on which it ought to submit. It is then right for it to submit, when it judges that it ought to submit.

271. Wisdom sends us to childhood. *Nisi efficiamini sicut parvuli.*[1]

272. There is nothing so conformable to reason as this disavowal of reason.

273. If we submit everything to reason, our religion will have no mysterious and supernatural element. If we offend the principles of reason, our religion will be absurd and ridiculous.

274. All our reasoning reduces itself to yielding to feeling.

But fancy is like, though contrary to, feeling, so that we cannot distinguish between these contraries. One person says that my feeling is fancy, another that his fancy is feeling. We should have a rule. Reason offers itself; but it is pliable in every sense; and thus there is no rule.

275. Men often take their imagination for their heart; and they believe they are converted as soon as they think of being converted.

276. M. de Roannez said: "Reasons come to me afterwards, but at first a thing pleases or shocks me without my knowing the reason, and yet it shocks me for that reason which I only discover afterwards." But I believe, not that it shocked him for the reasons which were found afterwards, but that these reasons were only found because it shocked him.

277. The heart has its reasons, which reason does not know. We feel it in a thousand things. I say that the heart naturally loves the Universal Being, and also itself naturally, according as it gives itself to them; and it hardens itself against one or the other at its will. You have rejected the one and kept the other. Is it by reason that you love yourself?

278. It is the heart which experiences God, and not the reason. This, then, is faith: God felt by the heart, not by the reason.

[1]Matt. 18.3. "Except ye become as little children."

Faith is a gift of God; do not believe that we said it was a gift of reasoning. Other religions do not say this of their faith. They only give reasoning in order to arrive at it, and yet it does not bring them to it.

279. Faith is a gift of God; do not believe that we said it was a gift of reasoning. Other religions do not say this of their faith. They only gave reasoning in order to arrive at it, and yet it does not bring them to it.

280. The knowledge of God is very far from the love of Him.

281. Heart, instinct, principles.

282. We know truth, not only by the reason, but also by the heart, and it is in this last way that we know first principles; and reason, which has no part in it, tries in vain to impugn them. The sceptics, who have only this for their object, labour to no purpose. We know that we do not dream, and, however impossible it is for us to prove it by reason, this inability demonstrates only the weakness of our reason, but not, as they affirm, the uncertainty of all our knowledge. For the knowledge of first principles, as space, time, motion, number, is as sure as any of those which we get from reasoning. And reason must trust these intuitions of the heart, and must base them on every argument. (We have intuitive knowledge of the tri-dimensional nature of space and of the infinity of number, and reason then shows that there are no two square numbers one of which is double of the other. Principles are intuited, propositions are inferred, all with certainty, though in different ways.) And it is as useless and absurd for reason to demand from the heart proofs of her first principles, before admitting them, as it would be for the heart to demand from reason an intuition of all demonstrated propositions before accepting them.

This inability ought, then, to serve only to humble reason, which would judge all, but not to impugn our certainty, as if only reason were capable of instructing us. Would to God, on the contrary, that we had never need of it, and that we knew everything by instinct and intuition! But nature has refused us this boon. On the contrary, she has given us but very little knowledge of this kind; and all the rest can be acquired only by reasoning.

Therefore, those to whom God has imparted religion by intuition are very fortunate and justly convinced. But to those who do not have it, we can give it only by reasoning, waiting for God to give them spiritual insight, without which faith is only human and useless for salvation.

283. *Order.—Against the objection that Scripture has no order.*
The heart has its own order; the intellect has its own, which is by principle and demonstration. The heart has another. We do not prove that we ought to be loved by enumerating in order the causes of love; that would be ridiculous.

Jesus Christ and Saint Paul employ the rule of love, not of intellect; for they would warm, not instruct. It is the same with Saint Augustine. This order consists chiefly in digressions on each point to indicate the end, and keep it always in sight.

284. Do not wonder to see simple people believe without reasoning. God imparts

to them love of Him and hatred of self. He inclines their heart to believe. Men will never believe with a saving and real faith, unless God inclines their heart; and they will believe as soon as He inclines it. And this is what David knew well, when he said: *Inclina cor meum, Deus, in . . .*[1]

285. Religion is suited to all kinds of minds. Some pay attention only to its establishment, and this religion is such that its very establishment suffices to prove its truth. Others trace it even to the apostles. The more learned go back to the beginning of the world. The angels see it better still, and from a more distant time.

286. Those who believe without having read the Testaments, do so because they have an inward disposition entirely holy, and all that they hear of our religion conforms to it. They feel that a God has made them; they desire only to love God; they desire to hate themselves only. They feel that they have no strength in themselves; that they are incapable of coming to God; and that if God does not come to them, they can have no communion with Him. And they hear our religion say that men must love God only, and hate self only; but that, all being corrupt and unworthy of God, God made Himself man to unite Himself to us. No more is required to persuade men who have this disposition in their heart, and who have this knowledge of their duty and of their inefficiency.

287. Those whom we see to be Christians without the knowledge of the prophets and evidences, nevertheless judge of their religion as well as those who have that knowledge. They judge of it by the heart, as others judge of it by the intellect. God Himself inclines them to believe, and thus they are most effectively convinced.

I confess indeed that one of those Christians who believe without proofs will not, perhaps, be capable of convincing an infidel who will say the same of himself. But those who know the proofs of religion will prove without difficulty that such a believer is truly inspired by God, though he cannot prove it himself.

For God having said in His prophecies (which are undoubtedly prophecies) that in the reign of Jesus Christ He would spread His spirit abroad among nations, and that the youths and maidens and children of the Church would prophesy; it is certain that the Spirit of God is in these and not in the others.

288. Instead of complaining that God had hidden Himself, you will give Him thanks for not having revealed so much of Himself; and you will also give Him thanks for not having revealed Himself to haughty sages, unworthy to know so holy a God.

Two kinds of persons know Him: those who have a humble heart, and who love lowliness, whatever kind of intellect they may have, high or low; and those who have sufficient understanding to see the truth, whatever opposition they may have to it.

289. *Proof.*—1. The Christian religion, by its establishment, having established itself so strongly, so gently, whilst so contrary to nature. 2. The sanctity, the dig-

[1]Ps. 119.36. "Incline my heart, O Lord, unto thy testimonies."

nity, and the humility of a Christian soul. 3. The miracles of Holy Scripture. 4. Jesus Christ in particular. 5. The apostles in particular. 6. Moses and the prophets in particular. 7. The Jewish people. 8. The prophecies. 9. Perpetuity; no religion has perpetuity. 10. The doctrine which gives a reason for everything. 11. The sanctity of this law. 12. By the course of the world.

Surely, after considering what is life and what is religion, we should not refuse to obey the inclination to follow it, if it comes into our heart; and it is certain that there is no ground for laughing at those who follow it.

290. *Proofs of religion.*—Morality, doctrine, miracles, prophecies, types.

SECTION V

JUSTICE AND THE REASON OF EFFECTS

291. In the letter *On Injustice* can come the ridiculousness of the law that the elder gets all. "My friend, you were born on this side of the mountain, it is therefore just that your elder brother gets everything."

"Why do you kill me"?

292. He lives on the other side of the water.

293. "Why do you kill me? What! do you not live on the other side of the water? If you lived on this side, my friend, I should be an assassin, and it would be unjust to slay you in this manner. But since you live on the other side, I am a hero, and it is just."

294. On what shall man found the order of the world which he would govern? Shall it be on the caprice of each individual? What confusion! Shall it be on justice? Man is ignorant of it.

Certainly, had he known it, he would not have established this maxim, the most general of all that obtain among men, that each should follow the custom of his own country. The glory of true equity would have brought all nations under subjection, and legislators would not have taken as their model the fancies and caprice of Persians and Germans instead of this unchanging justice. We would have seen it set up in all the States on earth and in all times; whereas we see neither justice nor injustice which does not change its nature with change in climate. Three degrees of latitude reverse all jurisprudence; a meridian decides the truth. Fundamental laws change after a few years of possession; right has its epochs; the entry of Saturn into the Lion marks to us the origin of such and such a crime. A strange justice that is bounded by a river! Truth on this side of the Pyrenees, error on the other side.

Men admit that justice does not consist in these customs, but that it resides in natural laws, common to every country. They would certainly maintain it obstinately, if reckless chance which has distributed human laws had encountered even one which was universal; but the farce is that the caprice of men has so many vagaries that there is no such law.

Theft, incest, infanticide, parricide, have all had a place among virtuous actions. Can anything be more ridiculous than that a man should have the right to kill me because he lives on the other side of the water, and because his ruler has a quarrel with mine, though I have none with him?

Doubtless there are natural laws; but good reason once corrupted has corrupted all. *Nihil amplius nostrum est; quod nostrum dicimus, artis est.*[1] *Ex senatus—consultis et plebiscitis crimina exercentur.*[2] *Ut olim vitiis, sic nunc legibus laboramus.*[3]

The result of this confusion is that one affirms the essence of justice to be the authority of the legislator; another, the interest of the sovereign; another, present ustom, and this is the most sure. Nothing, according to reason alone, is just in itself; all changes with time. Custom creates the whole of equity, for the simple reason that it is accepted. It is the mystical foundation of its authority; whoever carries it back to first principles destroys it. Nothing is so faulty as those laws which correct faults. He who obeys them because they are just obeys a justice which is imaginary and not the essence of law; it is quite self-contained, it is law and nothing more. He who will examine its motive will find it so feeble and so trifling that, if he be not accustomed to contemplate the wonders of human imagination, he will marvel that one century has gained for it so much pomp and reverence. The art of opposition and of revolution is to unsettle established customs, sounding them even to their source, to point out their want of authority and justice. We must, it is said, get back to the natural and fundamental laws of the State, which an unjust custom has abolished. It is a game certain to result in the loss of all; nothing will be just on the balance. Yet people readily lend their ear to such arguments. They shake off the yoke as soon as they recognise it; and the great profit by their ruin and by that of these curious investigators of accepted customs. But from a contrary mistake men sometimes think they can justly do everything which is not without an example. That is why the wisest of legislators said that it was necessary to deceive men for their own good; and another, a good politician, *Cum veritatem qua liberetur ignoret, expedit quod fallatur.*[4] We must not see the fact of usurpation; law was once introduced without reason, and has become reasonable. We must make it regarded as authoritative, eternal, and conceal its origin, if we do not wish that it should soon come to an end.

295. *Mine, thine.*—"This dog is mine," said those poor children; "that is my place in the sun." Here is the beginning and the image of the usurpation of all the earth.

296. When the question for consideration is whether we ought to make war and kill so many men—condemn so many Spaniards to death—only one man is judge, and he is an interested party. There should be a third, who is disinterested.

[1] Cicero, *De finibus*, v.21. "There is no longer anything which is ours; what I call ours is conventional."

[2] Seneca, *Epistles*, xcv. "It is by virtue of *senatus-consultes* and plebiscites that one commits crimes."

[3] Tacitus, *Annals*, iii.25. "Once we suffered from our vices; today we suffer from our laws."

[4] Saint Augustine, *City of God*, iv.27. "As he has ignored the truth which frees, it is right he is mistaken."

297. *Veri juris.*[1]—We have it no more; if we had it, we should take conformity to the customs of a country as the rule of justice. It is here that, not finding justice, we have found force, etc.

298. *Justice, might.*—It is right that what is just should be obeyed; it is necessary that what is strongest should be obeyed. Justice without might is helpless; might without justice is tyrannical. Justice without might is gainsaid, because there are always offenders; might without justice is condemned. We must then combine justice and might and, for this end, make what is just strong, or what is strong just.

Justice is subject to dispute; might is easily recognised and is not disputed. So we cannot give might to justice, because might has gainsaid justice and has declared that it is she herself who is just. And thus, being unable to make what is just strong, we have made what is strong just.

299. The only universal rules are the laws of the country in ordinary affairs and of the majority in others. Whence comes this? From the might which is in them. Hence it comes that kings, who have power of a different kind, do not follow the majority of their ministers.

No doubt equality of goods is just; but, being unable to cause might to obey justice, men have made it just to obey might. Unable to strengthen justice, they have justified might; so that the just and the strong should unite, and there should be peace, which is the sovereign good.

300. "When a strong man armed keepeth his goods, his goods are in peace."

301. Why do we follow the majority? Is it because they have more reason? No, because they have more power.

Why do we follow the ancient laws and opinions? Is it because they are more sound? No, but because they are unique and remove from us the root of difference.

302. . . . It is the effect of might, not of custom. For those who are capable of originality are few; the greater number will only follow and refuse glory to those inventors who seek it by their inventions. And if these are obstinate in their wish to obtain glory and despise those who do not invent, the latter will call them ridiculous names and will beat them with a stick. Let no one, then, boast of his subtlety, or let him keep his complacency to himself.

303. Might is the sovereign of the world, and not opinion. But opinion makes use of might. It is might that makes opinion. Gentleness is beautiful in our opinion. Why? Because he who will dance on a rope will be alone, and I will gather a stronger mob of people who will say that it is unbecoming.

304. The cords which bind the respect of men to each other are in general cords of necessity; for there must be different degrees, all men wishing to rule, and not all being able to do so, but some being able.

Let us, then, imagine we see society in the process of formation. Men will

[1]Cicero, *De officiis,* iii,17. "Concerning true law."

doubtless fight till the stronger party overcomes the weaker, and a dominant party is established. But when this is once determined, the masters, who do not desire the continuation of strife, then decree that the power which is in their hands shall be transmitted as they please. Some place it in election by the people, others in hereditary succession, etc.

And this is the point where imagination begins to play its part. Till now power makes fact; now power is sustained by imagination in a certain party, in France in the nobility, in Switzerland in the burgesses, etc.

These cords which bind the respect of men to such and such an individual are therefore the cords of imagination.

305. The Swiss are offended by being called *gentlemen*, and prove themselves true plebeians in order to be thought worthy of great office.

306. As duchies, kingships, and magistracies are real and necessary, because might rules all, they exist everywhere and always. But since only caprice makes such and such a one a ruler, the principle is not constant, but subject to variation, etc.

307. The chancellor is grave and clothed with ornaments, for his position is unreal. Not so the king; he has power and has nothing to do with the imagination. Judges, physicians, etc., appeal only to the imagination.

308. The habit of seeing kings accompanied by guards, drums, officers, and all the paraphernalia which mechanically inspire respect and awe, makes their countenance, when sometimes seen alone without these accompaniments, impress respect and awe on their subjects; because we cannot separate in thought their persons from the surroundings with which we see them usually joined. And the world, which knows not that this effect is the result of habit, believes that it arises by a natural force, whence come these words, "The character of Divinity is stamped on his countenance," etc.

309. *Justice.*—As custom determines what is agreeable, so also does it determine justice.

310. *King and tyrant.*—I, too, will keep my thoughts secret.
I will take care on every journey.
Greatness of establishment, respect for establishment.
The pleasure of the great is the power to make people happy.
The property of riches is to be given liberally.
The property of each thing must be sought. The property of power is to protect.
When force attacks humbug, when a private soldier takes the square cap off a first president, and throws it out of the window.

311. The government founded on opinion and imagination reigns for some time, and this government is pleasant and voluntary; that founded on might lasts for ever. Thus opinion is the queen of the world, but might is its tyrant.

312. Justice is what is established; and thus all our established laws will necessarily be regarded as just without examination, since they are established.

313. *Sound opinions of the people.*—Civil wars are the greatest of evils. They are inevitable, if we wish to reward desert; for all will say they are deserving. The evil we have to fear from a fool who succeeds by right of birth, is neither so great nor so sure.

314. God has created all for Himself. He has bestowed upon Himself the power of pain and pleasure.

You can apply it to God, or to yourself. If to God, the Gospel is the rule. If to yourself, you will take the place of God. As God is surrounded by persons full of charity, who ask of Him the blessings of charity that are in His power, so . . . recognise, then, and learn that you are only a king of lust, and take the ways of lust.

315. *The reason of effects.*—It is wonderful that men would not have me honour a man clothed in brocade and followed by seven or eight lackeys! Why! He will have me thrashed, if I do not salute him. This custom is a farce. It is the same with a horse in fine trappings in comparison with another! Montaigne is a fool not to see what difference there is, to wonder at our finding any, and to ask the reason. "Indeed," says he, "how comes it," etc. . . .

316. *Sound opinions of the people.*—To be spruce is not altogether foolish, for it proves that a great number of people work for one. It shows by one's hair, that one has a valet, a perfumer, etc., by one's band, thread, lace, . . . etc. Now it is not merely superficial nor merely outward show to have many arms at command. The more arms one has, the more powerful one is. To be spruce is to show one's power.

317. Deference means, "Put yourself to inconvenience." This is apparently silly, but is quite right. For it is to say, "I would indeed put myself to inconvenience if you required it, since indeed I do so when it is of no service to you." Deference further serves to distinguish the great. Now if deference was displayed by sitting in an arm-chair, we should show deference to everybody, and so no distinction would be made; but, being put to inconvenience, we distinguish very well.

318. He has four lackeys.

319. How rightly do we distinguish men by external appearances rather than by internal qualities! Which of us two shall have precedence? Who will give place to the other? The least clever. But I am as clever as he. We should have to fight over this. He has four lackeys, and I have only one. This can be seen; we have only to count. It falls to me to yield, and I am a fool if I contest the matter. By this means we are at peace, which is the greatest of boons.

320. The most unreasonable things in the world become most reasonable, because of the unruliness of men. What is less reasonable than to choose the eldest son of a queen to rule a State? We do not choose as captain of a ship the passenger who is of the best family.

This law would be absurd and unjust; but, because men are so themselves and always will be so, it becomes reasonable and just. For whom will men choose, as the most virtuous and able? We at once come to blows, as each claims to be the most virtuous and able. Let us then attach this quality to something indisputable. This is the king's eldest son. That is clear, and there is no dispute. Reason can do no better, for civil war is the greatest of evils.

321. Children are astonished to see their comrades respected.

322. To be of noble birth is a great advantage. In eighteen years it places a man within the select circle, known and respected, as another would have merited in fifty years. It is a gain of thirty years without trouble.

323. What is the Ego?

Suppose a man puts himself at a window to see those who pass by. If I pass by, can I say that he placed himself there to see me? No; for he does not think of me in particular. But does he who loves someone on account of beauty really love that person? No; for the small-pox, which will kill beauty without killing the person, will cause him to love her no more.

And if one loves me for my judgement, memory, he does not love *me*, for I can lose these qualities without losing myself. Where, then, is this Ego, if it be neither in the body nor in the soul? And how love the body or the soul, except for these qualities which do not constitute *me*, since they are perishable? For it is impossible and would be unjust to love the soul of a person in the abstract and whatever qualities might be therein. We never, then, love a person, but only qualities.

Let us, then, jeer no more at those who are honoured on account of rank and office; for we love a person only on account of borrowed qualities.

324. The people have very sound opinions, for example:

1. In having preferred diversion and hunting to poetry. The half-learned laugh at it, and glory in being above the folly of the world; but the people are right for a reason which these do not fathom.

2. In having distinguished men by external marks, as birth or wealth. The world again exults in showing how unreasonable this is; but it is very reasonable. Savages laugh at an infant king.

3. In being offended at a blow, or in desiring glory so much. But it is very desirable on account of the other essential goods which are joined to it; and a man who has received a blow, without resenting it, is overwhelmed with taunts and indignities.

4. In working for the uncertain; in sailing on the sea; in walking over a plank.

325. Montaigne is wrong. Custom should be followed only because it is custom, and not because it is reasonable or just. But people follow it for this sole reason, that they think it just. Otherwise they would follow it no longer, although it were the custom; for they will only submit to reason or justice. Custom without this would pass for tyranny; but the sovereignty of reason and justice is no more tyrannical than that of desire. They are principles natural to man.

It would, therefore, be right to obey laws and customs, because they are laws; but we should know that there is neither truth nor justice to introduce into them, that we know nothing of these, and so must follow what is accepted. By this means we would never depart from them. But people cannot accept this doctrine; and, as they believe that truth can be found, and that it exists in law and custom, they believe them and take their antiquity as a proof of their truth, and not simply of their authority apart from truth. Thus they obey laws, but they are liable to revolt when these are proved to be valueless; and this can be shown of all, looked at from a certain aspect.

326. *Injustice.*—It is dangerous to tell the people that the laws are unjust; for they obey them only because they think them just. Therefore it is necessary to tell them at the same time that they must obey them because they are laws, just as they must obey superiors, not because they are just, but because they are superiors. In this way all sedition is prevented, if this can be made intelligible and it be understood what is the proper definition of justice.

327. The world is a good judge of things, for it is in natural ignorance, which is man's true state. The sciences have two extremes which meet. The first is the pure natural ignorance in which all men find themselves at birth. The other extreme is that reached by great intellects, who, having run through all that men can know, find they know nothing, and come back again to that same ignorance from which they set out; but this is a learned ignorance which is conscious of itself. Those between the two, who have departed from natural ignorance and not been able to reach the other, have some smattering of this vain knowledge and pretend to be wise. These trouble the world and are bad judges of everything. The people and the wise constitute the world; these despise it, and are despised. They judge badly of everything, and the world judges rightly of them.

328. *The reason of effects.*—Continual alternation of pro and con.
We have, then, shown that man is foolish, by the estimation he makes of things which are not essential; and all these opinions are destroyed. We have next shown that all these opinions are very sound and that thus, since all these vanities are well founded, the people are not so foolish as is said. And so we have destroyed the opinion which destroyed that of the people.
But we must now destroy this last proposition and show that it remains always true that the people are foolish, though their opinions are sound because they do not perceive the truth where it is, and, as they place it where it is not, their opinions are always very false and very unsound.

329. *The reason of effects.*—The weakness of man is the reason why so many things are considered fine, as to be good at playing the lute. It is only an evil because of our weakness.

330. The power of kings is founded on the reason and on the folly of the people, and specially on their folly. The greatest and most important thing in the world has weakness for its foundation, and this foundation is wonderfully sure; for there is nothing more sure than this, that the people will be

weak. What is based on sound reason is very ill-founded as the estimate of wisdom.

331. We can only think of Plato and Aristotle in grand academic robes. They were honest men, like others, laughing with their friends, and, when they diverted themselves with writing their *Laws* and the *Politics*, they did it as an amusement. That part of their life was the least philosophic and the least serious; the most philosophic was to live simply and quietly. If they wrote on politics, it was as if laying down rules for a lunatic asylum; and if they presented the appearance of speaking of a great matter, it was because they knew that the madmen, to whom they spoke, thought they were kings and emperors. They entered into their principles in order to make their madness as little harmful as possible.

332. Tyranny consists in the desire of universal power beyond its scope.

There are different assemblies of the strong, the fair, the sensible, the pious, in which each man rules at home, not elsewhere. And sometimes they meet, and the strong and the fair foolishly fight as to who shall be master, for their mastery is of different kinds. They do not understand one another, and their fault is the desire to rule everywhere. Nothing can effect this, not even might, which is of no use in the kingdom of the wise, and is only mistress of external actions.

Tyranny— . . . So these expressions are false and tyrannical: "I am fair, therefore I must be feared. I am strong, therefore I must be loved. I am . . ."

Tyranny is the wish to have in one way what can only be had in another. We render different duties to different merits; the duty of love to the pleasant; the duty of fear to the strong; duty of belief to the learned.

We must render these duties; it is unjust to refuse them, and unjust to ask others. And so it is false and tyrannical to say, "He is not strong, therefore I will not esteem him; he is not able, therefore I will not fear him."

333. Have you never seen people who, in order to complain of the little fuss you make about them, parade before you the example of great men who esteem them? In answer I reply to them, "Show me the merit whereby you have charmed these persons, and I also will esteem you."

334. *The reason of effects.*—Lust and force are the source of all our actions; lust causes voluntary actions, force involuntary ones.

335. *The reason of effects.*—It is, then, true to say that all the world is under a delusion; for, although the opinions of the people are sound, they are not so as conceived by them, since they think the truth to be where it is not. Truth is indeed in their opinions, but not at the point where they imagine it. [Thus] it is true that we must honour noblemen, but not because noble birth is real superiority, etc.

336. *The reason of effects.*—We must keep our thought secret, and judge everything by it, while talking like the people.

337. *The reason of effects*. Degrees. The people honour persons of high birth. The semi-learned despise them, saying that birth is not a personal, but a chance superiority. The learned honour them, not for popular reasons, but for secret reasons.

Devout persons, who have more zeal than knowledge, despise them, in spite of that consideration which makes them honoured by the learned, because they judge them by a new light which piety gives them. But perfect Christians honour them by another and higher light. So arise a succession of opinions for and against, according to the light one has.

338. True Christians, nevertheless, comply with folly, not because they respect folly, but the command of God, who for the punishment of men has made them subject to these follies. *Omnis creatura subjecta est vanitati.*[1] *Liberabitur.*[2] Thus Saint Thomas explains the passage in Saint James on giving place to the rich, that, if they do it not in the sight of God, they depart from the command of religion.

SECTION VI

THE PHILOSOPHERS

339. I can well conceive a man without hands, feet, head (for it is only experience which teaches us that the head is more necessary than feet). But I cannot conceive man without thought; he would be a stone or a brute.

340. The arithmetical machine produces effects which approach nearer to thought than all the actions of animals. But it does nothing which would enable us to attribute will to it, as to the animals.

341. The account of the pike and frog of Liancourt. They do it always, and never otherwise, nor any other thing showing mind.

342. If an animal did by mind what it does by instinct, and if it spoke by mind what it speaks by instinct, in hunting and in warning its mates that the prey is found or lost, it would indeed also speak in regard to those things which affect it closer, as example, "Gnaw me this cord which is wounding me, and which I cannot reach."

343. The beak of the parrot, which it wipes, although it is clean.

344. Instinct and reason, marks of two natures.

345. Reason commands us far more imperiously than a master; for in disobeying the one we are unfortunate, and in disobeying the other we are fools.

346. Thought constitutes the greatness of man.

347. Man is but a reed, the most feeble thing in nature; but he is a thinking reed. The entire universe need not arm itself to crush him. A vapour, a drop of

[1]Eccles. 3.19. "for all is vanity."
[2]Rom. 8.20-21. "It shall be delivered."

water suffices to kill him. But, if the universe were to crush him, man would still be more noble than that which killed him, because he knows that he dies and the advantage which the universe has over him; the universe knows nothing of this.

All our dignity consists, then, in thought. By it we must elevate ourselves, and not by space and time which we cannot fill. Let us endeavour, then, to think well; this is the principle of morality.

348. *A thinking reed.*—It is not from space that I must seek my dignity, but from the government of my thought. I shall have no more if I possess worlds. By space the universe encompasses and swallows me up like an atom; by thought I comprehend the world.

349. *Immateriality of the soul.*—Philosophers who have mastered their passions. What matter could do that?

350. *The Stoics.*—They conclude that what has been done once can be done always, and that, since the desire of glory imparts some power to those whom it possesses, others can do likewise. There are feverish movements which health cannot imitate.

Epictetus concludes that, since there are consistent Christians, every man can easily be so.

351. Those great spiritual efforts, which the soul sometimes assays, are things on which it does not lay hold. It only leaps to them, not as upon a throne, for ever, but merely for an instant.

352. The strength of a man's virtue must not be measured by his efforts, but by his ordinary life.

353. I do not admire the excess of a virtue as of valour, except I see at the same time the excess of the opposite virtue, as in Epaminondas, who had the greatest valour and the greatest kindness. For otherwise it is not to rise, it is to fall. We do not display greatness by going to one extreme, but in touching both at once, and filling all the intervening space. But perhaps this is only a sudden movement of the soul from one to the other extreme, and in fact it is ever at one point only, as in the case of a firebrand. Be it so, but at least this indicates agility if not expanse of soul.

354. Man's nature is not always to advance; it has its advances and retreats.

Fever has its cold and hot fits; and the cold proves as well as the hot the greatness of the fire of fever.

The discoveries of men from age to age turn out the same. The kindness and the malice of the world in general are the same. *Plerumque gratæ principibus vices.*[1]

355. Continuous eloquence wearies.

Princes and kings sometimes play. They are not always on their thrones. They weary there. Grandeur must be abandoned to be appreciated. Continuity in everything is unpleasant. Cold is agreeable, that we may get warm.

[1]Horace, *Odes*, III.xxix.13. "Changes nearly always please the great."

Nature acts by progress, *itus et reditus*. It goes and returns, then advances further, then twice as much backwards, then more forward than ever, etc.

The tide of the sea behaves in the same manner; and so, apparently, does the sun in its course.

356. The nourishment of the body is little by little. Fullness of nourishment and smallness of substance.

357. When we would pursue virtues to their extremes on either side, vices present themselves, which insinuate themselves insensibly there, in their insensible journey towards the infinitely little; and vices present themselves in a crowd towards the infinitely great, so that we lose ourselves in them and no longer see virtues. We find fault with perfection itself.

358. Man is neither angel nor brute, and the unfortunate thing is that he who would act the angel acts the brute.

359. We do not sustain ourselves in virtue by our own strength, but by the balancing of two opposed vices, just as we remain upright amidst two contrary gales. Remove one of the vices, and we fall into the other.

360. What the Stoics propose is so difficult and foolish!

The Stoics lay down that all those who are not at the high degree of wisdom are equally foolish and vicious, as those who are two inches under water.

361. *The sovereign good. Dispute about the sovereign good.—Ut sis contentus temetipso et ex te nascentibus bonis.*[1] There is a contradiction, for in the end they advise suicide. Oh! What a happy life, from which we are to free ourselves as from the plague!

362. *Ex senatus-consultis et plebiscitis* . . .

To ask like passages.

363. *Ex senatus-consultis et plebiscitis scelera exercentur.* Seneca.[2] 588.[3]

Nihil tam absurde dici potest quod non dicatur ab aliquo philosophorum.[4]

Quibusdam destinatis sententiis consecrati quæ non probant coguntur defendere.[5]

Ut omnium rerum sic litterarum quoque intemperantia laboramus.[6]

Id maxime quemque decet, quod est cujusque suum maxime.[7]

Hos natura modos primum dedit.[8]

---

[1]Seneca, *Epistles*, xx.8. "In order that you are satisfied with yourself and the good that is born from you."

[2]See P. 226, Note [2]

[3]Montaigne, *Essays*, ii.12.

[4]Cicero, *De Divinatione*, ii.58. "There is nothing so absurd that it has not been said by some philosopher."

[5]Cicero, *Disputationes Tusculanae*, ii.2. "Devoted to certain fixed opinions, they are forced to defend what they hardly approve."

[6]Seneca, *Epistles*, cvi. "We suffer from an excess of literature as from an excess of anything."

[7]Cicero, *De officiis*, i.31. "What suits each one best is what is to him the most natural."

[8]Virgil, *The Georgics*, ii, 20. "Nature gave them first these limits."

Paucis opus est litteris ad bonam mentem.[1]
Si quando turpe non sit, tamen non est non turpe quum id a multitudine laudetur.[2]
Mihi sic usus est, tibi ut opus est facto, fac.[3]

364. *Rarum est enim ut satis se quisque vereatur.*[4]
Tot circa unum caput tumultuantes deos.[5]
Nihil turpius quam cognitioni assertionem præcurrere.[6]
Nec me pudet, ut istos, fateri nescire quid nesciam.[7]
Melius non incipient.[8]

365. *Thought.*—All the dignity of man consists in thought. Thought is, therefore, by its nature a wonderful and incomparable thing. It must have strange defects to be contemptible. But it has such, so that nothing is more ridiculous. How great it is in its nature! How vile it is in its defects!

But what is this thought? How foolish it is!

366. The mind of this sovereign judge of the world is not so independent that it is not liable to be disturbed by the first din about it. The noise of a cannon is not necessary to hinder its thoughts; it needs only the creaking of a weathercock or a pulley. Do not wonder if at present it does not reason well; a fly is buzzing in its ears; that is enough to render it incapable of good judgement. If you wish it to be able to reach the truth, chase away that animal which holds its reason in check and disturbs that powerful intellect which rules towns and kingdoms. Here is a comical god! *O ridicolosissimo eroe!*

367. The power of flies; they win battles, hinder our soul from acting, eat our body.

368. When it is said that heat is only the motions of certain molecules, and light the *conatus recedendi* which we feel, it astonishes us. What! Is pleasure only the ballet of our spirits? We have conceived so different an idea of it! And these sensations seem so removed from those others which we say are the same as those with which we compare them! The sensation from the fire, that warmth which affects us in a manner wholly different from touch, the reception of sound and light, all this appears to us mysterious, and yet it is material like the blow of a stone. It is true that the smallness of the spirits which enter into the pores touches other nerves, but there are always some nerves touched.

369. Memory is necessary for all the operations of reason.

[1] Seneca, *Epistles*, cvi. "Wisdom does not demand much teaching."
[2] Cicero, *De finibus bonorum et malorum*. "What is not shameful begins to become so when it is approved by the multitude."
[3] Terence, *Heauton Timorumenos*, I.i.21. "That is how I use it; you must do as you wish."
[4] Quintillian, x.7. "It is rare that one sufficiently respects one's self."
[5] Seneca the Elder, *Suasoriae*, i.4. "So many gods are busy around a single head."
[6] Cicero, *Academica*, i.45. "Nothing is more shameful than to affirm before knowing."
[7] Cicero, *Disputationes Tusculanae*, i.25. "I have not shame, as they do, to admit that I know not what I do not know."
[8] Seneca, *Epistles*, lxxii. "It is easier not to begin . . . ."

370. [Chance gives rise to thoughts, and chance removes them; no art can keep or acquire them.

A thought has escaped me. I wanted to write it down. I write instead that it has escaped me.]

371. [When I was small, I hugged my book; and because it sometimes happened to me to . . . in believing I hugged it, I doubted. . . .]

372. In writing down my thought, it sometimes escapes me; but this makes me remember my weakness, that I constantly forget. This is as instructive to me as my forgotten thought; for I strive only to know my nothingness.

373. *Scepticism.*—I shall here write my thoughts without order, and not perhaps in unintentional confusion; that is true order, which will always indicate my object by its very disorder. I should do too much honour to my subject, if I treated it with order, since I want to show that it is incapable of it.

374. What astonishes me most is to see that all the world is not astonished at its own weakness. Men act seriously, and each follows his own mode of life, not because it is in fact good to follow since it is the custom, but as if each man knew certainly where reason and justice are. They find themselves continually deceived, and, by a comical humility, think it is their own fault and not that of the art which they claim always to possess. But it is well there are so many such people in the world, who are not sceptics for the glory of scepticism, in order to show that man is quite capable of the most extravagant opinions, since he is capable of believing that he is not in a state of natural and inevitable weakness, but, on the contrary, of natural wisdom.

Nothing fortifies scepticism more than that there are some who are not sceptics; if all were so, they would be wrong.

375. [I have passed a great part of my life believing that there was justice, and in this I was not mistaken; for there is justice according as God has willed to reveal it to us. But I did not take it so, and this is where I made a mistake; for I believed that our justice was essentially just, and that I had that whereby to know and judge of it. But I have so often found my right judgement at fault, that at last I have come to distrust myself and then others. I have seen changes in all nations and men, and thus, after many changes of judgement regarding true justice, I have recognised that our nature was but in continual change, and I have not changed since; and if I changed, I would confirm my opinion.

The sceptic Arcesilaus, who became a dogmatist.]

376. This sect derives more strength from its enemies than from its friends; for the weakness of man is far more evident in those who know it not than in those who know it.

377. Discourses on humility are a source of pride in the vain and of humility in the humble. So those on scepticism cause believers to affirm. Few men speak humbly of humility, chastely of chastity, few doubtingly of scepticism. We are only

falsehood, duplicity, contradiction; we both conceal and disguise ourselves from ourselves.

378. *Scepticism.*—Excess, like defect of intellect, is accused of madness. Nothing is good but mediocrity. The majority has settled that and finds fault with him who escapes it at whichever end. I will not oppose it. I quite consent to put myself there, and refuse to be at the lower end, not because it is low, but because it is an end; for I would likewise refuse to be placed at the top. To leave the mean is to abandon humanity. The greatness of the human soul consists in knowing how to preserve the mean. So far from greatness consisting in leaving it, it consists in not leaving it.

379. It is not good to have too much liberty. It is not good to have all one wants.

380. All good maxims are in the world. We only need to apply them. For instance, we do not doubt that we ought to risk our lives in defence of the public good; but for religion, no.

It is true there must be inequality among men; but if this be conceded, the door is opened not only to the highest power, but to the highest tyranny.

We must relax our minds a little; but this opens the door to the greatest debauchery. Let us mark the limits. There are no limits in things. Laws would put them there, and the mind cannot suffer it.

381. When we are too young, we do not judge well; so, also, when we are too old. If we do not think enough, or if we think too much on any matter, we get obstinate and infatuated with it. If one considers one's work immediately after having done it, one is entirely prepossessed in its favour; by delaying too long, one can no longer enter into the spirit of it. So with pictures seen from too far or too near; there is but one exact point which is the true place wherefrom to look at them: the rest are too near, too far, too high, or too low. Perspective determines that point in the art of painting. But who shall determine it in truth and morality?

382. When all is equally agitated, nothing appears to be agitated, as in a ship. When all tend to debauchery, none appears to do so. He who stops draws attention to the excess of others, like a fixed point.

383. The licentious tell men of orderly lives that they stray from nature's path, while they themselves follow it; as people in a ship think those move who are on the shore. On all sides the language is similar. We must have a fixed point in order to judge. The harbour decides for those who are in a ship; but where shall we find a harbour in morality?

384. Contradiction is a bad sign of truth; several things which are certain are contradicted; several things which are false pass without contradiction. Contradiction is not a sign of falsity, nor the want of contradiction a sign of truth.

385. *Scepticism.*—Each thing here is partly true and partly false. Essential truth is

not so; it is altogether pure and altogether true. This mixture dishonours and an-
nihilates it. Nothing is purely true, and thus nothing is true, meaning by that
pure truth. You will say it is true that homicide is wrong. Yes; for we know well
the wrong and the false. But what will you say is good? Chastity? I say no; for the
world would come to an end. Marriage? No; continence is better. Not to kill? No;
for lawlessness would be horrible, and the wicked would kill all the good. To kill?
No; for that destroys nature. We possess truth and goodness only in part, and
mingled with falsehood and evil.

386. If we dreamt the same thing every night, it would affect us as much as the
objects we see every day. And if an artisan were sure to dream every night for
twelve hours' duration that he was a king, I believe he would be almost as happy
as a king, who should dream every night for twelve hours on end that he was an
artisan.

If we were to dream every night that we were pursued by enemies and harassed
by these painful phantoms, or that we passed every day in different occupations,
as in making a voyage, we should suffer almost as much as if it were real, and should
fear to sleep, as we fear to wake when we dread in fact to enter on such mishaps.
And, indeed, it would cause pretty nearly the same discomforts as the reality.

But since dreams are all different, and each single one is diversified, what is seen
in them affects us much less than what we see when awake, because of its continuity, which is not, however, so continuous and level as not to change too; but
it changes less abruptly, except rarely, as when we travel, and then we say, "It
seems to me I am dreaming." For life is a dream a little less inconstant.

387. [It may be that there are true demonstrations; but this is not certain. Thus,
this proves nothing else but that it is not certain that all is uncertain, to the glory
of scepticism.]

388. *Good sense.*—They are compelled to say, "You are not acting in good
faith; we are not asleep," etc. How I love to see this proud reason humiliated and
suppliant! For this is not the language of a man whose right is disputed, and who
defends it with the power of armed hands. He is not foolish enough to declare
that men are not acting in good faith, but he punishes this bad faith with force.

389. Ecclesiastes shows that man without God is in total ignorance and inevitable misery. For it is wretched to have the wish, but not the power. Now he
would be happy and assured of some truth, and yet he can neither know, nor
desire not to know. He cannot even doubt.

390. My God! How foolish this talk is! "Would God have made the world to
damn it? Would He ask so much from persons so weak"? etc. Scepticism is the
cure for this evil, and will take down this vanity.

391. *Conversation.*—Great words: Religion, I deny it.
Conversation.—Scepticism helps religion.

392. *Against Scepticism.*—[. . . It is, then, a strange fact that we cannot define

these things without obscuring them, while we speak of them with all assurance.]
We assume that all conceive of them in the same way; but we assume it quite
gratuitously, for we have no proof of it. I see, in truth, that the same words are applied on the same occasions, and that every time two men see a body change its
place, they both express their view of this same fact by the same word, both saying that it has moved; and from this conformity of application we derive a strong
conviction of a conformity of ideas. But this is not absolutely or finally convincing
though there is enough to support a bet on the affirmative, since we know that we
often draw the same conclusions from different premises.

This is enough, at least, to obscure the matter; not that it completely extinguishes
the natural light which assures us of these things. The academicians would have
won. But this dulls it and troubles the dogmatists to the glory of the sceptical
crowd, which consists in this doubtful ambiguity and in a certain doubtful dim-
ness from which our doubts cannot take away all the clearness, nor our own
natural lights chase away all the darkness.

393. It is a singular thing to consider that there are people in the world who,
having renounced all the laws of God and nature, have made laws for themselves
which they strictly obey, as, for instance, the soldiers of Mahomet, robbers,
heretics, etc. It is the same with logicians. It seems that their license must be without any limits or barriers, since they have broken through so many that are so just
and sacred.

394. All the principles of sceptics, stoics, atheists, etc., are true. But their conclusions are false, because the opposite principles are also true.

395. *Instinct, reason.*—We have an incapacity of proof, insurmountable by all
dogmatism. We have an idea of truth, invincible to all scepticism.

396. Two things instruct man about his whole nature; instince and experience.

397. The greatness of man is great in that he knows himself to be miserable. A
tree does not know itself to be miserable. It is then being miserable to know oneself to be miserable; but it is also being great to know that one is miserable.

398. All these same miseries prove man's greatness. They are the miseries of a
great lord, of a deposed king.

399. We are not miserable without feeling it. A ruined house is not miserable.
Man only is miserable. *Ego vir videns.*[1]

400. *The greatness of man.*—We have so great an idea of the soul of man that we
cannot endure being despised, or not being esteemed by any soul; and all the
happiness of men consists in this esteem.

401. *Glory.*—The brutes do not admire each other. A horse does not admire his
companion. Not that there is no rivalry between them in a race, but that is of no

[1]Lam. 3. 1. "I am the man that hath seen."

consequence; for, when in the stable, the heaviest and most ill-formed does not give up his oats to another, as men would have others do to them. Their virtue is satisfied with itself.

402. The greatness of man even in his lust, to have known how to extract from it a wonderful code, and to have drawn from it a picture of benevolence.

403. *Greatness.*—The reasons of effects indicate the greatness of man, in having extracted so fair an order from lust.

404. The greatest baseness of man is the pursuit of glory. But is is also the greatest mark of his excellence; for whatever possessions he may have on earth, whatever health and essential comfort, he is not satisfied if he has not the esteem of men. He values human reason so highly that, whatever advantages he may have on earth, he is not content if he is not also ranked highly in the judgement of man. This is the finest position in the world. Nothing can turn him from that desire, which is the most indelible quality of man's heart.

And those who must despise men, and put them on a level with the brutes, yet wish to be admired and believed by men, and contradict themselves by their own feelings; their nature, which is stronger than all, convincing them of the greatness of man more forcibly than reason convinces them of their baseness.

405. *Contradiction.*—Pride counterbalancing all miseries. Man either hides his miseries, or, if he disclose them, glories in knowing them.

406. Pride counterbalances and takes away all miseries. Here is a strange monster and a very plain aberration. He is fallen from his place and is anxiously seeking it. This is what all men do. Let us see who will have found it.

407. When malice has reason on its side, it becomes proud and parades reason in all its splendour. When austerity or stern choice has not arrived at the true good and must needs return to follow nature, it becomes proud by reason of this return.

408. Evil is easy, and has infinite forms; good is almost unique. But a certain kind of evil is as difficult to find as what we call good; and often on this account such particular evil gets passed off as good. An extraordinary greatness of soul is needed in order to attain to it as well as to good.

409. *The greatness of man.*—The greatness of man is so evident that it is even proved by his wretchedness. For what in animals is *nature*, we call in man *wretchedness;* by which we recognise that, his nature being now like that of animals, he has fallen from a better nature which once was his.

For who is unhappy at not being a king, except a deposed king? Was Paulus Æmilius unhappy at being no longer consul? On the contrary, everybody thought him happy in having been consul, because the office could only be held for a time. But men thought Perseus so unhappy in being no longer king, because the condition of kingship implied his being always king, that they thought it strange that he endured life. Who is unhappy at only having one mouth? And who is not unhappy at having only one eye? Probably no man ever ventured to mourn at not having three eyes. But any one is inconsolable at having none.

410. *Perseus, King of Macedon.*—Paulus Æmilius reproached Perseus for not killing himself.

411. Notwithstanding the sight of all our miseries, which press upon us and take us by the throat, we have an instinct which we cannot repress and which lifts us up.

412. There is internal war in man between reason and the passions.
If he had only reason without passions . . .
If he had only passions without reason . . .
But having both, he cannot be without strife, being unable to be at peace with the one without being at war with the other. Thus he is always divided against and opposed to himself.

413. This internal war of reason against the passions has made a division of those who would have peace into two sects. The first would renounce their passions and become gods; the others would renounce reason and become brute beasts. (Des Barreaux.) But neither can do so, and reason still remains, to condemn the vileness and injustice of the passions and to trouble the repose of those who abandon themselves to them; and the passions keep always alive in those who would renounce them.

414. Men are so necessarily mad that not to be mad would amount to another form of madness.

415. The nature of man may be viewed in two ways: the one according to its end, and then he is great and incomparable; the other according to the multitude, just as we judge of the nature of the horse and the dog, popularly, by seeing its fleetness, *et animum arcendi;* and then man is abject and vile. These are the two ways which make us judge of him differently and which occasion such disputes among philosophers. For one denies the assumption of the other. One says, "He is not born for this end, for all his actions are repugnant to it." The other says, "He forsakes his end, when he does these base actions."

416. *For Port-Royal. Greatness and wretchedness.*—Wretchedness being deduced from greatness, and greatness from wretchedness, some have inferred man's wretchedness all the more because they have taken his greatness as a proof of it, and others have inferred his greatness with all the more force, because they have inferred it from his very wretchedness. All that the one party has been able to say in proof of his greatness has only served as an argument of his wretchedness to the others, because the greater our fall, the more wretched we are, and *vice versa*. The one party is brought back to the other in an endless circle, it being certain that, in proportion as men possess light, they discover both the greatness and the wretchedness of man. In a word, man knows that he is wretched. He is therefore wretched, because he is so; but he is really great because he knows it.

417. This twofold nature of man is so evident that some have thought that we had two souls. A single subject seemed to them incapable of such sudden variations from unmeasured presumption to a dreadful dejection of heart.

418. It is dangerous to make man see too clearly his equality with the brutes without showing him his greatness. It is also dangerous to make his see his greatness too clearly, apart from his vileness. It is still more dangerous to leave him in ignorance of both. But it is very advantageous to show him both. Man must not think that he is on a level either with the brutes or with the angels, nor must he be ignorant of both sides of his nature; but he must know both.

419. I will not allow man to depend upon himself, or upon another, to the end that, being without a resting-place and without repose . . .

420. If he exalt himself, I humble him; if he humble himself, I exalt him; and I always contradict him, till he understands that he is an incomprehensible monster.

421. I blame equally those who choose to praise man, those who choose to blame him, and those who choose to amuse themselves; and I can only approve of those who seek with lamentation.

422. It is good to be tired and wearied by the vain search after the true good, that we may stretch out our arms to the Redeemer.

423. *Contraries. After having shown the vileness and the greatness of man.*—Let man now know his value. Let him love himself, for there is in him a nature capable of good; but let him not for this reason love the vileness which is in him. Let him despise himself, for this capacity is barren; but let him not therefore despise this natural capacity. Let him hate himself, let him love himself; he has within him the capacity of knowing the truth and of being happy, but he possesses no truth, either constant or satisfactory.

I would then lead man to the desire of finding truth; to be free from passions, and ready to follow it where he may find it, knowing how much his knowledge is obscured by the passions. I would, indeed, that he should hate in himself the lust which determined his will by itself so that it may not blind him in making his choice, and may not hinder him when he has chosen.

424. All these contradictions, which seem most to keep me from the knowledge of religion, have led me most quickly to the true one.

SECTION VII

MORALITY AND DOCTRINE

425. *Second part.*—*That man without faith cannot know the true good, nor justice.*
All men seek happiness. This is without exception. Whatever different means

they employ, they all tend to this end. The cause of some going to war, and of others avoiding it, is the same desire in both, attended with different views. The will never takes the least step but to this object. This is the motive of every action of every man, even of those who hang themselves.

And yet, after such a great number of years, no one without faith has reached the point to which all continually look. All complain, princes and subjects, noblemen and commoners, old and young, strong and weak, learned and ignorant, healthy and sick, of all countries, all times, all ages, and all conditions.

A trial so long, so continuous, and so uniform, should certainly convince us of our inability to reach the good by our own efforts. But example teaches us little. No resemblance is ever so perfect that there is not some slight difference; and hence we expect that our hope will not be deceived on this occasion as before. And thus, while the present never satisfies us, experience dupes us and, from misfortune to misfortune, leads us to death, their eternal crown.

What is it, then, that this desire and this inability proclaim to us, but that there was once in man a true happiness of which there now remain to him only the mark and empty trace, which he in vain tries to fill from all his surroundings, seeking from things absent the help he does not obtain in things present? But these are all inadequate, because the infinite abyss can only be filled by an infinite and immutable object, that is to say, only by God Himself.

He only is our true good, and since we have forsaken him, it is a strange thing that there is nothing in nature which has not been serviceable in taking His place; the stars, the heavens, earth, the elements, plants, cabbages, leeks, animals, insects, calves, serpents, fever, pestilence, war, famine, vices, adultery, incest. And since man has lost the true good, everything can appear equally good to him, even his own destruction, though so opposed to God, to reason, and to the whole course of nature.

Some seek good in authority, others in scientific research, others in pleasure. Others, who are in fact nearer the truth, have considered it necessary that the universal good, which all men desire, should not consist in any of the particular things which can only be possessed by one man, and which, when shared, afflict their possessors more by the want of the part he has not than they please him by the possession of what he has. They have learned that the true good should be such as all can possess at once, without diminution and without envy, and which no one can lose against his will. And their reason is that this desire, being natural to man, since it is necessarily in all, and that it is impossible not to have it, they infer from it . . .

426. True nature being lost, everything becomes its own nature; as the true good being lost, everything becomes its own true good.

427. Man does not know in what rank to place himself. He has plainly gone astray and fallen from his true place without being able to find it again. He seeks it anxiously and unsuccessfully everywhere in impenetrable darkness.

428. If it is a sign of weakness to prove God by nature, do not despise Scripture; if it is a sign of strength to have known these contradictions, esteem Scripture.

429. The vileness of man in submitting himself to the brutes and in even worshipping them.

430. *For Port-Royal. The beginning, after having explained the incomprehensibility.*— The greatness and the wretchedness of man are so evident that the true religion must necessarily teach us both that there is in man some great source of greatness and a great source of wretchedness. It must then give us a reason for these astonishing contradictions.

In order to make man happy, it must prove to him that there is a God; that we ought to love Him; that our true happiness is to be in Him, and our sole evil to be separated from Him; it must recognise that we are full of darkness which hinders us from knowing and loving Him; and that thus, as our duties compel us to love God, and our lusts turn us away from Him, we are full of unrighteousness. It must give us an explanation of our opposition to God and to our own good. It must teach us the remedies for these infirmities and the means of obtaining these remedies. Let us, therefore, examine all the religions of the world and see if there be any other than the Christian which is sufficient for this purpose.

Shall it be that of the philosophers, who put forward, as the chief good, the good which is in ourselves? Is this the true good? Have they found the remedy for our ills? Is man's pride cured by placing him on an equality with God? Have those who have made us equal to the brutes, or the Mohammedans who have offered us earthly pleasures as the chief good even in eternity, produced the remedy for our lusts? What religion, then, will teach us to cure pride and lust? What religion will, in fact, teach us our good, our duties, the weakness which turns us from them, the cause of this weakness, the remedies which can cure it, and the means of obtaining these remedies?

All other religions have not been able to do so. Let us see what the wisdom of God will do.

"Expect neither truth," she says, "nor consolation from men. I am she who formed you, and who alone can teach you what you are. But you are now no longer in the state in which I formed you. I created man holy, innocent, perfect. I filled him with light and intelligence. I communicated to him my glory and my wonders. The eye of man saw then the majesty of God. He was not then in the darkness which blinds him, nor subject to mortality and the woes which afflict him. But he has not been able to sustain so great glory without falling into pride. He wanted to make himself his own centre and independent of my help. He withdrew himself from my rule; and, on his making himself equal to me by the desire of finding his happiness in himself, I abandoned him to himself. And setting in revolt the creatures that were subject to him, I made them his enemies; so that man is now become like the brutes and so estranged from me that there scarce remains to him a dim vision of his Author. So far has all his knowledge been extinguished or disturbed! The senses, independent of reason, and often the masters of reason, have led him into pursuit of pleasure. All creatures either torment or tempt him, and domineer over him, either subduing him by their strength, or fascinating him by their charms, a tyranny more awful and more imperious.

"Such is the state in which men now are. There remains to them some feeble instinct of the happiness of their former state; and they are plunged in the evils of their blindness and their lust, which have become their second nature.

"From this principle which I disclose to you, you can recognize the cause of those contradictions which have astonished all men and have divided them into parties holding so different views. Observe, now, all the feelings of greatness and glory which the experience of so many woes cannot stifle, and see if the cause of them must not be in another nature."

For Port-Royal to-morrow (Prosopopæa).—"It is in vain, O men, that you seek within yourselves the remedy for your ills. All your light can only reach the knowledge that not in yourselves will you find truth or good. The philosophers have promised you that, and you have been unable to do it. They neither know what is your true good, nor what is your true state. How could they have given remedies for your ills, when they did not even know them? Your chief maladies are pride, which takes you away from God, and lust, which binds you to earth; and they have done nothing else but cherish one or other of these diseases. If they gave you God as an end, it was only to administer to your pride; they made you think that you are by nature like Him and conformed to Him. And those who saw the absurdity of this claim put you on another precipice, by making you understand that your nature was like that of the brutes, and led you to seek your good in the lusts which are shared by the animals. This is not the way to cure you of your unrighteousness, which these wise men never knew. I alone can make you understand who you are. . . ."

Adam, Jesus Christ.

If you are united to God, it is by grace, not by nature. If you are humbled, it is by penitence, not by nature.

Thus this double capacity . . .

You are not in the state of your creation.

As these two states are open, it is impossible for you not to recognise them. Follow your own feelings, observe yourselves, and see if you do not find the lively characteristics of these two natures. Could so many contradictions be found in a simple subject?

Incomprehensible. Not all that is incomprehensible ceases to exist. Infinite number. An infinite space equal to a finite.

Incredible that God should unite Himself to us. This consideration is drawn only from the sight of our vileness. But if you are quite sincere over it, follow it as far as I have done and recognise that we are indeed so vile that we are incapable in ourselves of knowing if His mercy cannot make us capable of Him. For I would know how this animal, who knows himself to be so weak, has the right to measure the mercy of God and set limits to it, suggested by his own fancy. He has so little knowledge of what God is that he does not know what he himself is, and, completely disturbed at the sight of his own state, dares to say that God cannot make him capable of communion with Him.

But I would ask him if God demands anything else from him than the knowledge and love of Him, and why, since his nature is capable of love and knowledge, he believes that God cannot make Himself known and loved by him. Doubtless he knows at least that he exists, and that he loves something. Therefore, if he sees anything in the darkness wherein he is, and if he finds some object of his love among the things on earth, why, if God impart to him some ray of His essence, will he not be capable of knowing and of loving Him in the manner in which it shall please Him to communicate Himself to us? There must, then, be certainly an intolerable presumption in arguments of this sort, although they seem founded on an apparent humility, which is neither sincere nor reasonable, if it does not make us admit that, not knowing of ourselves what we are, we can only learn it from God.

"I do not mean that you should submit your belief to me without reason, and I do not aspire to overcome you by tyranny. In fact, I do not claim to give you a reason for everything. And to reconcile these contradictions, I intend to make you see clearly, by convincing proofs, those divine signs in me, which may convince you of what I am, and may gain authority for me by wonders and proofs which you cannot reject; so that you may then believe without . . . the things which I teach you, since you will find no other ground for rejecting them, except that you cannot know of yourselves if they are true or not.

"God has willed to redeem men and to open salvation to those who seek it. But men render themselves so unworthy of it that it is right that God should refuse to some, because of their obduracy, what He grants others from a compassion which is not due to them. If He had willed to overcome the obstinacy of the most hardened, He could have done so by revealing Himself so manifestly to them that they could not have doubted of the truth of His essence; as it will appear at the last day, with such thunders and such a convulsion of nature that the dead will rise again, and the blindest will see Him.

"It is not in this manner that He has willed to appear in His advent of mercy, because, as so many make themselves unworthy of His mercy, He has willed to leave them in the loss of the good which they do not want. It was not, then, right that He should appear in a manner manifestly divine, and completely capable of convincing all men; but it was also not right that He should come in so hidden a manner that He could not be known by those who should sincerely seek Him. He has willed to make Himself quite recognisable by those; and thus, willing to appear openly to those who seek Him with all their heart, and to be hidden from those who flee from Him with all their heart, He so regulates the knowledge of Himself that He has given signs of Himself, visible to those who seek Him, and not to those who seek Him not. There is enough light for those who only desire to see, and enough obscurity for those who have a contrary disposition."

431. No other religion has recognised that man is the most excellent creature. Some, which have quite recognised the reality of his excellence, have considered as mean and ungrateful the low opinions which men naturally have of themselves; and others, which have thoroughly recognised how real is this vileness, have treated with proud ridicule those feelings of greatness, which are equally natural to man.

"Lift your eyes to God," say the first; "see Him whom you resemble and who has created you to worship Him. You can make yourselves like unto Him; wisdom will make you equal to Him, if you will follow it." "Raise your heads, free men," says Epictetus. And others say, "Bend your eyes to the earth, wretched worm that you are, and consider the brutes whose companion you are."

What, then, will man become? Will he be equal to God or the brutes? What a frightful difference! What, then, shall we be? Who does not see from all this that man has gone astray, that he has fallen from his place, that he anxiously seeks it, that he cannot find it again? And who shall then direct him to it? The greatest men have failed.

432. Scepticism is true; for, after all, men before Jesus Christ did not know where they were, nor whether they were great or small. And those who have said the one or the other knew nothing about it and guessed without reason and by chance. They also erred always in excluding the one or the other.

Quod ergo ignorantes, quæritis, religio annuntiat vobis.[1]

433. *After having understood the whole nature of man.*—That a religion may be true, it must have knowledge of our nature. It ought to know its greatness and littleness, and the reason of both. What religion but the Christian has known this?

434. The chief arguments of the sceptics—I pass over the lesser ones—are that we have no certainty of the truth of these principles apart from faith and revelation, except in so far as we naturally perceive them in ourselves. Now this natural intuition is not a convincing proof of their truth; since, having no certainty, apart from faith, whether man was created by a good God, or by a wicked demon, or by chance, it is doubtful whether these principles given to us are true, or false, or uncertain, according to our origin. Again, no person is certain, apart from faith, whether he is awake or sleeps, seeing that during sleep we believe that we are awake as firmly as we do when we *are* awake; we believe that we see space, figure, and motion; we are aware of the passage of time, we measure it; and in fact we act as if we were awake. So that half of our life being passed in sleep, we have on our own admission no idea of truth, whatever we may imagine. As all our intuitions are, then, illusions, who knows whether the other half of our life, in which we think we are awake, is not another sleep a little different from the former, from which we awake when we suppose ourselves asleep?

[And who doubts that, if we dreamt in company, and the dreams chanced to agree, which is common enough, and if we were always alone when awake, we should believe that matters were reversed? In short, as we often dream that we dream, heaping dream upon dream, may it not be that this half of our life, wherein we think ourselves awake, is itself only a dream on which the others are grafted, from which we wake at death, during which we have as few principles of truth and good as during natural sleep, these different thoughts which disturb us being perhaps only illusions like the flight of time and the vain fancies of our dreams?]

These are the chief arguments on one side and the other.

I omit minor ones, such as the sceptical talk against the impressions of custom, education, manners, country and the like. Though these influence the majority of common folk, who dogmatise only on shallow foundations, they are upset by the least breath of the sceptics. We have only to see their books if we are not sufficiently convinced of this, and we shall very quickly become so, perhaps too much.

I notice the only strong point of the dogmatists, namely, that, speaking in good faith and sincerely, we cannot doubt natural principles. Against this the sceptics set up in one word the uncertainty of our origin, which includes that of our nature. The dogmatists have been trying to answer this objection ever since the world began.

So there is open war among men, in which each must take a part and side either

[1] "What you seek without knowing, religion will announce to you." Pascal misquotes Acts 17.23. "Whom therefore ye ignorantly worship, him declare I unto you."

with dogmatism or scepticism. For he who thinks to remain neutral is above all a sceptic. This neutrality is the essence of the sect; he who is not against them is essentially for them. [In this appears their advantage.] They are not for themselves; they are neutral, indifferent, in suspense as to all things, even themselves being no exception.

What, then, shall man do in this state? Shall he doubt everything? Shall he doubt whether he is awake, whether he is being pinched, or whether he is being burned? Shall he doubt whether he doubts? Shall he doubt whether he exists? We cannot go so far as that; and I lay it down as a fact that there never has been a real complete sceptic. Nature sustains our feeble reason and prevents it raving to this extent.

Shall he, then, say, on the contrary, that he certainly possesses truth—he who, when pressed ever so little, can show no title to it and is forced to let go his hold?

What a chimera, then, is man! What a novelty! What a monster, what a chaos, what a contradiction, what a prodigy! Judge of all things, imbecile worm of the earth; depositary of truth, a sink of uncertainty and error; the pride and refuse of the universe!

Who will unravel this tangle? Nature confutes the sceptics, and reason confutes the dogmatists. What, then, will you become, O men! who try to find out by your natural reason what is your true condition? You cannot avoid one of these sects, nor adhere to one of them.

Know then, proud man, what a paradox you are to yourself. Humble yourself, weak reason; be silent, foolish nature; learn that man infinitely transcends man, and learn from your Master your true condition, of which you are ignorant. Hear God.

For in fact, if man had never been corrupt, he would enjoy in his innocence both truth and happiness with assurance; and if man had always been corrupt, he would have no idea of truth or bliss. But, wretched as we are, and more so than if there were no greatness in our condition, we have an idea of happiness and cannot reach it. We perceive an image of truth and possess only a lie. Incapable of absolute ignorance and of certain knowledge, we have thus been manifestly in a degree of perfection from which we have unhappily fallen.

It is, however, an astonishing thing that the mystery furthest removed from our knowledge, namely, that of the transmission of sin, should be a fact without which we can have no knowledge of ourselves. For it is beyond doubt that there is nothing which more shocks our reason than to say that the sin of the first man has rendered guilty those who, being so removed from this source, seem incapable of participation in it. This transmission does not only seem to us impossible, it seems also very unjust. For what is more contrary to the rules of our miserable justice than to damn eternally an infant incapable of will, for a sin wherein he seems to have so little a share that it was committed six thousand years before he was in existence? Certainly nothing offends us more rudely than this doctrine; and yet, without this mystery, the most incomprehensible of all, we are incomprehensible to ourselves. The knot of our condition takes its twists and turns in this abyss, so that man is more inconceivable without this mystery than this mystery is inconceivable to man.

[Whence it seems that God, willing to render the difficulty of our existence unintelligible to ourselves, has concealed the knot so high, or, better speaking, so

low, that we are quite incapable of reaching it; so that it is not by the proud exertions of our reason, but by the simple submissions of reason, that we can truly
know ourselves.

These foundations, solidly established on the inviolable authority of religion,
make us know that there are two truths of faith equally certain: the one, that man,
in the state of creation, or in that of grace, is raised above all nature, made like
unto God and sharing in His divinity; the other, that in the state of corruption
and sin, he is fallen from this state and made like unto the beasts.

These two propositions are equally sound and certain. Scripture manifestly de-
clares this to us, when it says in some places: *Deliciæ meæ esse cum filiis hominum.*[1]
Effundam spiritum meum super omnem carnem.[2] *Dii estis,*[3] etc.; and in other places,
Omnis caro fœnum.[4] *Homo assimilatus est jumentis insipientibus, et similis factus est illis.*[5]
Dixi in corde meo de filiis hominum.[6]

Whence it clearly seems that man by grace is made like unto God, and a par-
taker in His divinity, and that without grace he is like unto the brute beasts.]

435. Without this divine knowledge what could men do but either become
elated by the inner feeling of their past greatness which still remains to them, or
become despondent at the sight of their present weakness? For, not seeing the
whole truth, they could not attain to perfect virtue. Some considering nature as incorrupt, others as incurable, they could not escape either pride or sloth, the two
sources of all vice; since they cannot but either abandon themselves to it through
cowardice, or escape it by pride. For if they knew the excellence of man, they
were ignorant of his corruption; so that they easily avoided sloth, but fell into
pride. And if they recognized the infirmity of nature, they were ignorant of its
dignity; so that they could easily avoid vanity, but it was to fall into despair.
Thence arise the different schools of the Stoics and Epicureans, the Dogmatists,
Academicians, etc.

The Christian religion alone has been able to cure these two vices, not by expelling the one through means of the other according to the wisdom of the world,
but by expelling both according to the simplicity of the Gospel. For it teaches the
righteous that it raises them even to a participation in divinity itself; that in this
lofty state they still carry the source of all corruption, which renders them during
all their life subject to error, misery, death, and sin; and it proclaims to the most
ungodly that they are capable of the grace of their Redeemer. So making those
tremble whom it justifies, and consoling those whom it condemns, religion so
justly tempers fear with hope through that double capacity of grace and of sin,
common to all, that it humbles infinitely more than reason alone can do, but without despair; and it exalts infinitely more than natural pride, but without inflating;
thus making it evident that alone being exempt from error and vice, it alone fulfils
the duty of instructing and correcting men.

Who, then, can refuse to believe and adore this heavenly light? For is it not
clearer than day that we perceive within ourselves ineffaceable marks of excel-

[1]Prov. 8.31. "And my delights were with the sons of men."
[2]Joel 2.28. "I will pour out my spirit upon all flesh."
[3]Ps. 82.6. "Ye are gods."
[4]Is. 40.6. "All flesh is grass."
[5]Ps. 49.12,13. "He is like the beasts that perish; this their way is their folly."
[6]Eccles. 3.18. "I said in mine heart concerning the estate of the sons of men."

lence? And is it not equally true that we experience every hour the results of our deplorable condition? What does this chaos and monstrous confusion proclaim to us but the truth of these two states, with a voice so powerful that it is impossible to resist it?

436. *Weakness.*—Every pursuit of men is to get wealth; and they cannot have a title to show that they possess it justly, for they have only that of human caprice; nor have they strength to hold it securely. It is the same with knowledge, for disease takes it away. We are incapable both of truth and goodness.

437. We desire truth, and find within ourselves only uncertainty.

We seek happiness, and find only misery and death.

We cannot but desire truth and happiness, and are incapable of certainty or happiness. This desire is left to us, partly to punish us, partly to make us perceive wherefrom we are fallen.

438. If man is not made for God, why is he only happy in God? If man is made for God, why is he so opposed to God?

439. *Nature corrupted.*—Man does not act by reason, which constitutes his being.

440. The corruption of reason is shown by the existence of so many different and extravagant customs. It was necessary that truth should come, in order that man should no longer dwell within himself.

441. For myself, I confess that, so soon as the Christian religion reveals the principle that human nature is corrupt and fallen from God, that opens my eyes to see everywhere the mark of this truth: for nature is such that she testifies everywhere, both within man and without him, to a lost God and a corrupt nature.

442. Man's true nature, his true good, true virtue, and true religion, are things of which the knowledge is inseparable.

443. *Greatness, wretchedness.*—The more light we have, the more greatness and the more baseness we discover in man. Ordinary men—those who are more educated: philosophers, they astonish ordinary men—Christians, they astonish philosophers.

Who will then be surprised to see that religion only makes us know profoundly what we already know in proportion to our light?

444. This religion taught to her children what men have only been able to discover by their greatest knowledge.

445. Original sin is foolishness to men, but it is admitted to be such. You must not, then, reproach me for the want of reason in this doctrine, since I admit it to be without reason. But this foolishness is wiser than all the wisdom of men,

sapientius est hominibus.[1] For without this, what can we say that man is? His whole state depends on this imperceptible point. And how should it be perceived by his reason, since it is a thing against reason, and since reason, far from finding it out by her own ways, is averse to it when it is presented to her?

446. *Of original sin. Ample tradition of original sin according to the Jews.*
On the saying in Genesis 8.21: "The imagination of man's heart is evil from his youth."

R. Moses Haddarschan: This evil leaven is placed in man from the time that he is formed.

Massechet Succa: This evil leaven has seven names in Scritpure. It is called *evil, the foreskin, uncleanness, an enemy, a scandal, a heart of stone, the north wind;* all this signifies the malignity which is concealed and impressed in the heart of man.

Midrasch Tillim says the same thing and that God will deliver the good nature of man from the evil.

This malignity is renewed every day against man, as it is written, Psalm xxxvii. 32: "The wicked watcheth the righteous, and seeketh to slay him"; but God will not abandon him. This malignity tries the heart of man in this life and will accuse him in the other. All this is found in the Talmud.

Midrasch Tillim on Psalm 4.4: "Stand in awe and sin not." Stand in awe and be afraid of your lust, and it will not lead you into sin. And on Psalm 36.1: "The wicked has said within his own heart: Let not the fear of God be before me." That is to say that the malignity natural to man has said that to the wicked.

Midrasch el Kohelet: "Better is a poor and wise child than an old and foolish king who cannot foresee the future." The child is virtue, and the king is the malignity of man. It is called *king* because all the members obey it, and *old* because it is in the human heart from infancy to old age, and *foolish* because it leads man in the way of [*perdition*], which he does not foresee. The same thing is in *Midrasch Tillim.*

Bereschist Rabba on Psalm 35.10: "Lord, all my bones shall bless Thee, which deliverest the poor from the tyrant." And is there a greater tyrant than the evil leaven? And on Proverbs 25.21: "If thine enemy be hungry, give him bread to eat." That is to say, if the evil leaven hunger, give him the bread of wisdom of which it is spoken in Proverbs 9, and if he be thirsty, give him the water of which it is spoken in Isaiah 55.

Midrasch Tillim says the same thing, and that Scripture in that passage, speaking of the enemy, means the evil leaven; and that, in [*giving*] him that bread and that water, we heap coals of fire on his head.

Midrasch el Kohelet on Ecclesiastes 9.14: "A great king besieged a little city." This great king is the evil leaven; the great bulwarks built against it are temptations; and there has been found a poor wise man who has delivered it—that is to say, virtue.

And on Psalm 41.1: "Blessed is he that considereth the poor."

And on Psalm 78.39: "The spirit passeth away, and cometh not again"; whence some have erroneously argued against the immortality of the soul. But the sense is that this spirit is the evil leaven, which accompanies man till death and will not return at the resurrection.

[1] I Cor. 1.25 "The foolishness of God is wiser than men; and the weakness of God is stronger than men."

And on Psalm 103 the same thing.
And on Psalm 16.
Principles of Rabbinism: two Messiahs.

447. Will it be said that, as men have declared that righteousness has departed the earth, they therefore knew of original sin?—*Nemo ante obitum beatus est*[1]—that is to say, they knew death to be the beginning of eternal and essential happiness?

448. [*Milton*] sees well that nature is corrupt and that men are averse to virtue; but he does not know why they cannot fly higher.

449. *Order.*—After *Corruption* to say: "It is right that all those who are in that state should know it, both those who are content with it, and those who are not content with it; but it is not right that all should see Redemption."

450. If we do not know ourselves to be full of pride, ambition, lust, weakness, misery, and injustice, we are indeed blind. And if, knowing this, we do not desire deliverance, what can we say of a man . . .?
    What, then, can we have but esteem for a religion which knows so well the defects of man, and desire for the truth of a religion which promises remedies so desirable?

451. All men naturally hate one another. They employ lust as far as possible in the service of the public weal. But this is only a [*pretence*] and a false image of love; for at bottom it is only hate.

452. To pity the unfortunate is not contrary to lust. On the contrary, we can quite well give such evidence of friendship, and acquire the reputation of kindly feeling, without giving anything.

453. From lust men have found and extracted excellent rules of policy, morality, and justice; but in reality this vile root of man, this *figmentum malum*, is only covered, it is not taken away.

454. *Injustice.*—They have not found any other means of satisfying lust without doing injury to others.

455. Self is hateful. You, Milton, conceal it; you do not for that reason destroy it; you are, then, always hateful.
    No; for in acting as we do to oblige everybody, we give no more occasion for hatred of us. That is true, if we only hated in Self the vexation which comes to us from it. But if I hate it because it is unjust and because it makes itself the centre of everything, I shall always hate it.
    In a word, the Self has two qualities: it is unjust in itself since it makes itself the centre of everything; it is inconvenient to others since it would enslave them; for

---

[1]Ovid, *Metamorphoses*, iii.135. "No one is happy before death."

each Self is the enemy, and would like to be the tyrant of all others. You take away its inconvenience, but not its injustice, and so you do not render it lovable to those who hate injustice; you render it lovable only to the unjust, who do not any longer find in it an enemy. And thus you remain unjust and can please only the unjust.

456. It is a perverted judgement that makes every one place himself above the rest of the world, and prefer his own good, and the continuance of his own good fortune and life, to that of the rest of the world!

457. Each one is all in all to himself; for he being dead, all is dead to him. Hence it comes that each believes himself to be all in all to everybody. We must not judge of nature by ourselves, but by it.

458. "All that is in the world is the lust of the flesh, or the lust of the eyes, or the pride of life; *libido sentiendi, libido sciendi, libido dominandi.*"[1] Wretched is the cursed land which these three rivers of fire enflame rather than water! Happy they who, on these rivers, are not overwhelmed nor carried away, but are immovably fixed, not standing but seated on a low and secure base, whence they do not rise before the light, but, having rested in peace, stretch out their hands to Him, who must lift them up, and make them stand upright and firm in the porches of the holy Jerusalem! There pride can no longer assail them nor cast them down; and yet they weep, not to see all those perishable things swept away by the torrents, but at the remembrance of their loved country, the heavenly Jerusalem, which they remember without ceasing during their prolonged exile.

459. The rivers of Babylon rush and fall and sweep away.
O holy Zion, where all is firm and nothing falls!
We must sit upon the waters, not under them or in them, but on them; and not standing but seated; being seated to be humble, and being above them to be secure. But we shall stand in the porches of Jerusalem.
Let us see if this pleasure is stable or transitory; if it pass away, it is a river of Babylon.

460. *The lust of the flesh, the lust of the eyes, pride, etc.*—There are three orders of things: the flesh, the spirit, and the will. The carnal are the rich and kings; they have the body as their object. Inquirers and scientists; they have the mind as their object. The wise; they have righteousness as their object.
God must reign over all, and all men must be brought back to Him. In things of the flesh lust reigns specially; in intellectual matters, inquiry specially; in wisdom, pride specially. Not that a man cannot boast of wealth or knowledge, but it is not the place for pride; for in granting to a man that he is learned, it is easy to convince him that he is wrong to be proud. The proper place for pride is in wisdom, for it cannot be granted to a man that he has made himself wise, and that he is wrong to be proud; for that is right. Now God alone gives wisdom, and that is why *Qui gloriatur, in Domino glorietur.*[2]

[1] I John 2.16.
[2] I Cor. 1.31. "He that glorieth, let him glory in the Lord."

461. The three lusts have made three sects; and the philosophers have done no other thing than follow one of the three lusts.

462. *Search for the true good.*—Ordinary men place the good in fortune and external goods, or at least in amusement. Philosophers have shown the vanity of all this and have placed it where they could.

463. [*Against the philosophers who believe in God without Jesus Christ.*]
Philosophers.—They believe that God alone is worthy to be loved and admired; and they have desired to be loved and admired of men and do not know their own corruption. If they feel full of feelings of love and admiration and find therein their chief delight, very well, let them think themselves good. But if they find themselves averse to Him, if they have no inclination but the desire to establish themselves in the esteem of men, and if their whole perfection consists only in making men—but without constraint—find their happiness in loving them, I declare that this perfection is horrible. What! they have known God and have not desired solely that men should love Him, but that men should stop short at them! They have wanted to be the object of the voluntary delight of men.

464. *Philosophers.*—We are full of things which take us out of ourselves.
Our instinct makes us feel that we must seek our happiness outside ourselves. Our passions impel us outside, even when no objects present themselves to excite them. External objects tempt us of themselves, and call to us, even when we are not thinking of them. And thus philosophers have said in vain: "Retire within yourselves, you will find your good there." We do not believe them, and those who believe them are the most empty and the most foolish.

465. The Stoics say, "Retire within yourselves; it is there you will find your rest." And that is not true.
Others say, "Go out of yourselves; seek happiness in amusement." And this is not true. Illness comes.
Happiness is neither without us nor within us. It is in God, both without us and within us.

466. Had Epictetus seen the way perfectly, he would have said to men, "You follow a wrong road"; he shows that there is another, but he does not lead to it. It is the way of willing what God wills. Jesus Christ alone leads to it: *Via, veritas.*[1]
The vices of Zeno himself.

467. *The reason of effects.*—Epictetus. Those who say, "You have a headache"; this is not the same thing. We are assured of health, and not of justice; and in fact his own was nonsense.
And yet he believed it demonstrable, when he said, "It is either in our power or it is not." But he did not perceive that it is not in our power to regulate the heart, and he was wrong to infer from this the fact that there were some Christians.

468. No other religion has proposed to men to hate themselves. No other reli-
[1]John 14.6. "I am the way, the truth, and the life."

gion, then, can please those who hate themselves, and who seek a Being truly lovable. And these, if they had never heard of the religion of a God humiliated, would embrace it at once.

469. I feel that I might not have been; for the Ego consists in my thoughts. Therefore I, who think, would not have been, if my mother had been killed before I had life. I am not, then, a necessary being. In the same way I am not eternal or infinite; but I see plainly that there exists in nature a necessary Being, eternal and infinite.

470. "Had I seen a miracle," say men, "I should become converted." How can they be sure they would do a thing of the nature of which they are ignorant? They imagine that this conversion consists in a worship of God which is like commerce, and in a communion such as they picture to themselves. True religion consists in annihilating self before that Universal Being, whom we have so often provoked, and who can justly destroy us at any time; in recognising that we can do nothing without Him, and have deserved nothing from Him but His displeasure. It consists in knowing that there is an unconquerable opposition between us and God, and that without a mediator there can be no communion with Him.

471. It is unjust that men should attach themselves to me, even though they do it with pleasure and voluntarily. I should deceive those in whom I had created this desire; for I am not the end of any, and I have not the wherewithal to satisfy them. Am I not about to die? And thus the object of their attachment will die. Therefore, as I would be blamable in causing a falsehood to be believed, though I should employ gentle persuasion, though it should be believed with pleasure, and though it should give me pleasure; even so I am blamable in making myself loved and if I attract persons to attach themselves to me. I ought to warn those who are ready to consent to a lie that they ought not to believe it, whatever advantage comes to me from it; and likewise that they ought not to attach themselves to me; for they ought to spend their life and their care in pleasing God, or in seeking Him.

472. Self-will will never be satisfied, though it should have command of all it would; but we are satisfied from the moment we renounce it. Without it we cannot be discontented; with it we cannot be content.

473. Let us imagine a body full of thinking members.

474. *Members. To commence with that.*—To regulate the love which we owe to ourselves, we must imagine a body full of thinking members, for we are members of the whole, and must see how each member should love itself, etc. . . .

475. If the feet and the hands had a will of their own, they could only be in their order in submitting this particular will to the primary will which governs the whole body. Apart from that, they are in disorder and mischief; but in willing only the good of the body, they accomplish their own good.

476. We must love God only and hate self only.

If the foot had always been ignorant that it belonged to the body, and that there was a body on which it depended, if it had only had the knowledge and the love of self, and if it came to know that it belonged to a body on which it depended, what regret, what shame for its past life, for having been useless to the body which inspired its life, which would have annihilated it if it had rejected it and separated it from itself, as it kept itself apart from the body! What prayers for its preservation in it! And with what submission would it allow itself to be governed by the will which rules the body, even to consenting, if necessary, to be cut off, or it would lose its character as member! For every member must be quite willing to perish for the body, for which alone the whole is.

477. It is false that we are worthy of the love of others; it is unfair that we should desire it. If we were born reasonable and impartial, knowing ourselves and others, we should not give this bias to our will. However, we are born with it; therefore born unjust, for all tends to self. This is contrary to all order. We must consider the general good; and the propensity to self is the beginning of all disorder, in war, in politics, in economy, and in the particular body of man. The will is therefore depraved.

If the members of natural and civil communities tend towards the weal of the body, the communities themselves ought to look to another more general body of which they are members. We ought, therefore, to look to the whole. We are, therefore, born unjust and depraved.

478. When we want to think of God, is there nothing which turns us away, and tempts us to think of something else? All this is bad, and is born in us.

479. If there is a God, we must love Him only and not the creatures of a day. The reasoning of the ungodly in the Book of Wisdom is only based upon the nonexistence of God. "On that supposition," say they, "let us take delight in the creatures." That is the worst that can happen. But if there were a God to love, they would not have come to this conclusion, but to quite the contrary. And this is the conclusion of the wise: "There is a God; let us therefore not take delight in the creatures."

Therefore all that incites us to attach ourselves to the creatures is bad; since it prevents us from serving God if we know Him, or from seeking Him if we know Him not. Now we are full of lust. Therefore we are full of evil; therefore we ought to hate ourselves and all that excited us to attach ourselves to any other object than God only.

480. To make the members happy, they must have one will and submit it to the body.

481. The examples of the noble deaths of the Lacedæmonians and others scarce touch us. For what good is it to us? But the example of the death of the martyrs touches us; for they are "our members." We have a common tie with them. Their resolution can form ours, not only by example, but because it has perhaps deserved ours. There is nothing of this in the examples of the heathen. We have no tie with them; as we do not become rich by seeing a stranger who is so, but in fact by seeing a father or a husband who is so.

482. *Morality.*—God having made the heavens and the earth, which do not feel the happiness of their being, He has willed to make beings who should know it, and who should compose a body of thinking members. For our members do not feel the happiness of their union, of their wonderful intelligence, of the care which has been taken to infuse into them minds, and to make them grow and endure. How happy they would be if they saw and felt it! But for this the) would need to have intelligence to know it, and good-will to consent to that of the universal soul. But if, having received intelligence, they employed it to retain nourishment for themselves without allowing it to pass to the other members, they would be not only unjust, but also miserable, and would hate rather than love themselves; their blessedness, as well as their duty, consisting in their consent to the guidance of the whole soul to which they belong, which loves them better than they love themselves.

483. To be a member is to have neither life, being, nor movement, except through the spirit of the body, and for the body.

The separate member, seeing no longer the body to which it belongs, has only a perishing and dying existence. Yet it believes it is a whole, and, seeing not the body on which it depends, it believes it depends only on self and desires to make itself both centre and body. But not having in itself a principle of life, it only goes astray and is astonished in the uncertainty of its being; perceiving in fact that it is not a body, and still not seeing that it is a member of a body. In short, when it comes to know itself, it has returned, as it were, to its own home, and loves itself only for the body. It deplores its past wanderings.

It cannot by its nature love any other thing, except for itself and to subject it to self, because each thing loves itself more than all. But, in loving the body, it loves itself, because it only exists in it, by it, and for it. *Qui adhæret Deo unus spiritus est.*[1]

The body loves the hand; and the hand, if it had a will, should love itself in the same way as it is loved by the soul. All love which goes beyond this is unfair.

Adhærens Deo unus spiritus est. We love ourselves, because we are members of Jesus Christ. We love Jesus Christ, because He is the body of which we are members. All is one, one is in the other, like the Three Persons.

484. Two laws suffice to rule the whole Christian Republic better than all the laws of statecraft.

485. The true and only virtue, then, is to hate self (for we are hateful on account of lust) and to seek a truly lovable being to love. But as we cannot love what is outside ourselves, we must love a being who is in us and is not ourselves; and that is true of each and all men. Now, only the Universal Being is such. The kingdom of God is within us; the universal good is within us, is ourselves—and not ourselves.

486. The dignity of man in his innocence consisted in using and having dominion over the creatures, but now in separating himself from them and subjecting himself to them.

487. Every religion is false which, as to its faith, does not worship one God as

[1] I Cor. 6.17. "But he that is joined unto the Lord is one spirit."

the origin of everything and which, as to its morality, does not love one only God as the object of everything.

488. . . . But it is impossible that God should ever be the end, if He is not the beginning. We lift our eyes on high, but lean upon the sand; and the earth will dissolve, and we shall fall whilst looking at the heavens.

489. If there is one sole source of everything, there is one sole end of everything; everything through Him, everything for Him. The true religion, then, must teach us to worship Him only, and to love Him only. But as we find ourselves unable to worship what we know not, and to love any other object but ourselves, the religion which instructs us in these duties must instruct us also of this inability, and teach us also the remedies for it. It teaches us that by one man all was lost, and the bond broken between God and us, and that by one man the bond is renewed.

We are born so averse to this love of God, and it is so necessary, that we must be born guilty, or God would be unjust.

490. Men, not being accustomed to form merit, but only to recompense it where they find it formed, judge of God by themselves.

491. The true religion must have as a characteristic the obligation to love God. This is very just, and yet no other religion has commanded this; ours has done so. It must also be aware of human lust and weakness; ours is so. It must have adduced remedies for this; one is prayer. No other religion has asked of God to love and follow Him.

492. He who hates not in himself his self-love, and that instinct which leads him to make himself God, is indeed blinded. Who does not see that there is nothing so opposed to justice and truth? For it is false that we deserve this, and it is unfair and impossible to attain it, since all demand the same thing. It is, then, a manifest injustice which is innate in us, of which we cannot get rid, and of which we must get rid.

Yet no religion has indicated that this was a sin; or that we were born in it; or that we were obliged to resist it; or has thought of giving us remedies for it.

493. The true religion teaches our duties; our weaknesses, pride, and lust; and the remedies, humility and mortification.

494. The true religion must teach greatness and misery; must lead to the esteem and contempt of self, to love and to hate.

495. If it is an extraordinary blindness to live without investigating what we are, it is a terrible one to live an evil life, while believing in God.

496. Experience makes us see an enormous difference between piety and goodness.

497. *Against those who, trusting to the mercy of God, live heedlessly, without doing good works.*—As the two sources of our sins are pride and sloth, God has revealed to us

two of His attributes to cure them, mercy and justice. The property of justice is to humble pride, however holy may be our works, *et non intres in judicium*, etc.; and the property of mercy is to combat sloth by exhorting to good works, according to that passage: "The goodness of God leadeth to repentance," and that other of the Ninevites: "Let us do penance to see if peradventure He will pity us." And thus mercy is so far from authorising slackness that it is on the contrary the quality which formally attacks it; so that instead of saying, "If there were no mercy in God we should have to make every kind of effort after virtue," we must say, on the contrary, that it is because there is mercy in God that we must make every kind of effort.

498. It is true there is difficulty in entering into godliness. But this difficulty does not arise from the religion which begins in us, but from the irreligion which is still there. If our senses were not opposed to penitence, and if our corruption were not opposed to the purity of God, there would be nothing in this painful to us. We suffer only in proportion as the vice which is natural to us resists supernatural grace. Our heart feels torn asunder between these opposed efforts. But it would be very unfair to impute this violence to God, who is drawing us on, instead of to the world, which is holding us back. It is as a child, which a mother tears from the arms of robbers, in the pain it suffers, should love the loving and legitimate violence of her who procures its liberty, and detest only the impetuous and tyrannical violence of those who detain it unjustly. The most cruel war which God can make with men in this life is to leave them without that war which He came to bring. "I came to send war," He says, "and to teach them of this war. I came to bring fire and the sword." Before Him the world lived in this false peace.

499. *External works.*—There is nothing so perilous as what pleases God and man. For those states, which please God and man, have one property which pleases God, and another which pleases men; as the greatness of Saint Teresa. What pleased God was her deep humility in the midst of her revelations; what pleased men was her light. And so we torment ourselves to imitate her discourses, thinking to imitate her conditions, and not so much to love what God loves and to put ourselves in the state which God loves.

It is better not to fast, and be thereby humbled, than to fast and be self-satisfied therewith. The Pharisee and the Publican.

What use will memory be to me, if it can alike hurt and help me, and all depends upon the blessing of God, who gives only to things done for Him, according to His rules and in His ways, the manner being thus as important as the thing and perhaps more; since God can bring forth good out of evil, and without God we bring forth evil out of good?

500. The meaning of the words, *good* and *evil*.

501. First step: to be blamed for doing evil, and praised for doing good. Second step: to be neither praised nor blamed.

502. Abraham took nothing for himself, but only for his servants. So the righteous man takes for himself nothing of the world, nor of the applause of the world,

but only for his passions, which he uses as their master, saying to the one, "Go," and to another, "Come." *Sub te erit appetitus tuus.*[1] The passions thus subdued are virtues. Even God attributes to Himself avarice, jealousy, anger; and these are virtues as well as kindness, pity, constancy, which are also passions. We must employ them as slaves, and, leaving to them their food, prevent the soul from taking any of it. For, when the passions become masters, they are vices; and they give their nutriment to the soul, and the soul nourishes itself upon it and is poisoned.

503. Philosophers have consecrated the vices by placing them in God Himself. Christians have consecrated the virtues.

504. The just man acts by faith in the least things; when he reproves his servants, he desires their conversion by the Spirit of God, and prays God to correct them; and he expects as much from God as from his own reproofs, and prays God to bless his corrections. And so in all his other actions he proceeds with the Spirit of God; and his actions deceive us by reason of the ... or suspension of the Spirit of God in him; and he repents in his affliction.

505. All things can be deadly to us, even the things made to serve us; as in nature walls can kill us, and stairs can kill us, if we do not walk circumspectly.

The least movement affects all nature; the entire sea changes because of a rock. Thus, in grace, the least action affects everything by its consequences; therefore everything is important.

In each action we must look beyond the action at our past, present, and future state, and at others whom it affects, and see the relations of all those things. And then we shall be very cautious.

506. Let God not impute to us our sins, that is to say, all the consequences and results of our sins, which are dreadful, even those of the smallest faults, if we wish to follow them out mercilessly!

507. The spirit of grace; the hardness of the heart; external circumstances.

508. Grace is indeed needed to turn a man into a saint; and he who doubts it does not know what a saint or a man is.

509. *Philosophers.*—A fine thing to cry to a man who does not know himself, that he should come of himself to God! And a fine thing to say so to a man who does know himself!

510. Man is not worthy of God, but he is not incapable of being made worthy.

It is unworthy of God to unite Himself to wretched man; but it is not unworthy of God to pull him out of his misery.

511. If we would say that man is too insignificant to deserve communion with God, we must indeed be very great to judge of it.

[1]Gen. 4.7. "Unto thee shall be his desire."

512. It is, in peculiar phraseology, wholly the body of Jesus Christ, but it cannot be said to be the whole body of Jesus Christ. The union of two things without change does not enable us to say that one becomes the other; the soul thus being united to the body, the fire to the timber, without change. But change is necessary to make the form of the one become the form of the other; thus the union of the Word to man. Because my body without my soul would not make the body of a man; therefore my soul united to any matter whatsoever will make my body. It does not distinguish the necessary condition from the sufficient condition; the union is necessary, but not sufficient. The left arm is not the right.

Impenetrability is a property of matter.

Identity *de numero* in regard to the same time requires the identity of matter.

Thus if God united my soul to a body in China, the same body, *idem numero* would be in China.

The same river which runs there is *idem numero* as that which runs at the same time in China.

513. Why God has established prayer.

1. To communicate to His creatures the dignity of causality.
2. To teach us from whom our virtue comes.
3. To make us deserve other virtues by work.

(But to keep His own pre-eminence, He grants prayer to whom He pleases.)

Objection: But we believe that we hold prayer of ourselves.

This is absurd; for since, though having faith, we cannot have virtues, how should we have faith? Is there a greater distance between infidelity and faith than between faith and virtue?

Merit. This word is ambiguous.

Meruit habere Redemptorem.[1]

Meruit tam sacra membra tangere.[2]

Digno tam sacra membra tangere.[3]

Non sum dignus.[4]

Qui manducat indignus.[5]

Dignus est accipere.[6]

Dignare me.[7]

God is only bound according to His promises. He has promised to grant justice to prayers; He has never promised prayer only to the children of promise.

Saint Augustine has distinctly said that strength would be taken away from the righteous. But it is by chance that he said it; for it might have happened that the occasion of saying it did not present itself. But his principles make us see that, when the occasion for it presented itself, it was impossible that he should not say it, or that he should say anything to the contrary. It is then rather that he was forced to say it, when the occasion presented itself, than that he said it, when the

---

[1] Office for Holy Saturday. "Which won for us a Saviour."
[2] Office for Good Friday. "Which won for us God's hallowed members to embrace."
[3] Hymn *Vexilla regis*. "Worthy God's hallowed members to embrace."
[4] Luke 7.6 "I am not worthy."
[5] I Cor. 11.29. "Who eateth unworthily."
[6] Rev. 4.11. "Thou art worthy to receive."
[7] Office of the Holy Virgin. "Make me worthy."

occasion presented itself, the one being of necessity, the other of chance. But the two are all that we can ask.

514. "Work out your own salvation with fear."

Proofs of prayer. *Petenti dabitur.*[1]

Therefore it is in our power to ask. On the other hand, there is God. So it is not in our power, since the obtaining of (the grace) to pray to Him is not in our power. For since salvation is not in us, and the obtaining of such grace is from Him, prayer is not in our power.

The righteous man should then hope no more in God, for he ought not to hope, but to strive to obtain what he wants.

Let us conclude then that, since man is now unrighteous since the first sin, and God is unwilling that he should thereby not be estranged from Him, it is only by a first effect that he is not estranged.

Therefore, those who depart from God have not this first effect without which they are not estranged from God, and those who do not depart from God have this first effect. Therefore, those whom we have seen possessed for some time of grace by this first effect, cease to pray, for want of this first effect.

Then God abandons the first in this sense.

515. The elect will be ignorant of their virtues, and the outcast of the greatness of their sins: "Lord, when saw we Thee an hungered, thirsty"? etc.

516. Romans 3.27. Boasting is excluded. By what law? Of works? Nay, but by faith. Then faith is not within our power like the deeds of the law, and it is given to us in another way.

517. Comfort yourselves. It is not from yourselves that you should expect grace; but, on the contrary, it is in expecting nothing from yourselves that you must hope for it.

518. Every condition, and even the martyrs, have to fear, according to Scripture.

The greatest pain of purgatory is the uncertainty of the judgement. *Deus absconditus.*[2]

519. John 8. *Multi crediderunt in eum. Dicebat ergo Jesus: "Si manseritis . . . VERE mei discipuli eritis, et VERITAS LIBERABIT VOS." Responderunt: "Semen Abrahæ sumus, et nemini servimus unquam."*[3]

There is a great difference between disciples and true disciples. We recognise them by telling them that the truth will make them free; for if they answer that they are free and that it is in their power to come out of slavery to the devil, they are indeed disciples, but not true disciples.

520. The law has not destroyed nature, but has instructed it; grace has not de-

[1]Matthew, 7.7, "Ask and it shall be given you."

[2]Is. 45.15.

[3]30-33. "Many believed on him. Then Jesus said: 'If ye continue . . . then ye are my disciples indeed, and the truth shall make you free.' They answered him: 'We be Abraham's seed, and were never in bondage to any man.'"

stroyed the law, but has made it act. Faith received at baptism is the source of the whole life of Christians and of the converted.

521. Grace will always be in the world, and nature also; so that the former is in some sort natural. And thus there will always be Pelagians, and always Catholics, and always strife; because the first birth makes the one, and the grace of the second birth the other.

522. The law imposed what it did not give. Grace gives what it imposes.

523. All faith consists in Jesus Christ and in Adam, and all morality in lust and in grace.

524. There is no doctrine more appropriate to man than this, which teaches him his double capacity of receiving and of losing grace, because of the double peril to which he is exposed, of despair or of pride.

525. The philosophers did not prescribe feelings suitable to the two states.
They inspired feelings of pure greatness, and that is not man's state.
They inspired feelings of pure littleness, and that is not man's state.
There must be feelings of humility, not from nature, but from penitence, not to rest in them, but to go on to greatness. There must be feelings of greatness, not from merit, but from grace, and after having passed through humiliation.

526. Misery induces despair, pride induces presumption. The Incarnation shows man the greatness of his misery by the greatness of the remedy which he required.

527. The knowledge of God without that of man's misery causes pride. The knowledge of man's misery without that of God causes despair. The knowledge of Jesus Christ constitutes the middle course, because in Him we find both God and our misery.

528. Jesus Christ is a God whom we approach without pride and before whom we humble ourselves without despair.

529. . . . Not a degradation which renders us incapable of good, nor a holiness exempt from evil.

530. A person told me one day that on coming from confession he felt great joy and confidence. Another told me that he remained in fear. Whereupon I thought that these two together would make one good man, and that each was wanting in that he had not the feeling of the other. The same often happens in other things.

531. He who knows the will of his master will be beaten with more blows, because of the power he has by his knowledge. *Qui justus est, justificetur adhuc,*[1] because of the power he has by justice. From him who has received most, will the greatest reckoning be demanded, because of the power he has by this help.

[1]Rev. 22.11. "He that is righteous, let him be righteous still."

532. Scripture has provided passages of consolation and of warning for all conditions.

Nature seems to have done the same thing by her two infinities, natural and moral; for we shall always have the higher and the lower, the more clever and the less clever, the most exalted and the meanest, in order to humble our pride and exalt our humility.

533. *Comminutum cor* (Saint Paul).[1] This is the Christian character. *Alba has named you, I know you no more* (Corneille). That is the inhuman character. The human character is the opposite.

534. There are only two kinds of men: the righteous who believe themselves sinners; the rest, sinners, who believe themselves righteous.

535. We owe a great debt to those who point out faults. For they mortify us. They teach us that we have been despised. They do not prevent our being so in the future; for we have many other faults for which we may be despised. They prepare for us the exercise of correction and freedom from fault.

536. Man is so made that by continually telling him he is a fool he believes it, and by continually telling it to himself he makes himself believe it. For man holds an inward talk with his self alone, which it behoves him to regulate well: *Corrumpunt bonos mores colloquia prava*.[2] We must keep silent as much as possible and talk with ourselves only of God, whom we know to be true; and thus we convince ourselves of the truth.

537. Christianity is strange. It bids man recognise that he is vile, even abominable, and bids him desire to be like God. Without such a counterpoise, this dignity would make him horribly vain, or this humiliation would make him terribly abject.

538. With how little pride does a Christian believe himself united to God! With how little humiliation does he place himself on a level with the worms of earth!

A glorious manner to welcome life and death, good and evil!

539. What difference in point of obedience is there between a soldier and a Carthusian monk? For both are equally under obedience and dependent, both engaged in equally painful exercises. But the soldier always hopes to command and never attains this, for even captains and princes are ever slaves and dependants; still he ever hopes and ever works to attain this. Whereas the Carthusian monk makes a vow to be always dependent. So they do not differ in their perpetual thraldom, in which both of them always exist, but in the hope, which one always has, and the other never.

540. The hope which Christians have of possessing an infinite good is mingled with real enjoyment as well as with fear; for it is not as with those who should

[1] *Circumcidentes cor*. Rom. 2. "Circumcision is that of the heart."
[2] I Cor. 15.33. "Evil communications corrupt good manners."

hope for a kingdom, of which they, being subjects, would have nothing; but they hope for holiness, for freedom from injustice, and they have something of this.

541. None is so happy as a true Christian, nor so reasonable, virtuous, or amiable.

542. The Christian religion alone makes man altogether *lovable and happy*. In honesty, we cannot perhaps be altogether lovable and happy.

543. *Preface.*—The metaphysical proofs of God are so remote from the reasoning of men, and so complicated, that they make little impression; and if they should be of service to some, it would be only during the moment that they see such demonstration; but an hour afterwards they fear they have been mistaken.

Quod curiositate cognoverunt superbia amiserunt.[1]

This is the result of the knowledge of God obtained without Jesus Christ; it is communion without a mediator with the God whom they have known without a mediator. Whereas those who have known God by a mediator know their own wretchedness.

544. The God of the Christians is a God who makes the soul feel that He is her only good, that her only rest is in Him, that her only delight is in loving Him; and who makes her at the same time abhor the obstacles which keep her back and prevent her from loving God with all her strength. Self-love and lust, which hinder us, are unbearable to her. Thus God makes her feel that she has this root of self-love which destroys her, and which He alone can cure.

545. Jesus Christ did nothing but teach men that they loved themselves, that they were slaves, blind, sick, wretched, and sinners; that He must deliver them, enlighten, bless, and heal them; that this would be effected by hating self, and by following Him through suffering and the death on the cross.

546. Without Jesus Christ man must be in vice and misery; with Jesus Christ man is free from vice and misery; in Him is all our virtue and all our happiness. Apart from Him there is but vice, misery, darkness, death, despair.

547. We know God only by Jesus Christ. Without this mediator, all communion with God is taken away; through Jesus Christ we know God. All those who have claimed to know God, and to prove Him without Jesus Christ, have had only weak proofs. But in proof of Jesus Christ we have the prophecies, which are solid and palpable proofs. And these prophecies, being accomplished and proved true by the event, mark the certainty of these truths and, therefore, the divinity of Christ. In Him, then, and through Him, we know God. Apart from Him, and without the Scripture, without original sin, without a necessary mediator promised and come, we cannot absolutely prove God, nor teach right doctrine and right morality. But through Jesus Christ, and in Jesus Christ, we prove God, and teach morality and doctrine. Jesus Christ is, then, the true God of men.

[1]"What they have found by their curiosity, they have lost by their pride." *Quod curiositate invenerunt, superbia perdiderunt.* St. Augustine, *Sermon* cxli.

But we know at the same time our wretchedness; for this God is none other than the Saviour of our wretchedness. So we can only know God well by knowing our iniquities. Therefore those who have known God, without knowing their wretchedness, have not glorified Him, but have glorified themselves. *Quia . . . non cognovit per sapientiam . . . placuit Deo per stultitiam prædicationis salvos facere.*[1]

548. Not only do we know God by Jesus Christ alone, but we know ourselves only by Jesus Christ. We know life and death only through Jesus Christ. Apart from Jesus Christ, we do not know what is our life, nor our death, nor God, nor ourselves.

Thus without the Scripture, which has Jesus Christ alone for its object, we know nothing, and see only darkness and confusion in the nature of God and in our own nature.

549. It is not only impossible but useless to know God without Jesus Christ. They have not departed from Him, but approached; they have not humbled themselves, but . . .

Quo quisque optimus est, pessimus, si hoc ipsum, quod optimus est, adscribat sibi.[2]

550. I love poverty because He loved it. I love riches because they afford me the means of helping the very poor. I keep faith with everybody; I do not render evil to those who wrong me, but I wish them a lot like mine, in which I receive neither evil nor good from men. I try to be just, true, sincere, and faithful to all men; I have a tender heart for those to whom God has more closely united me; and whether I am alone, or seen of men, I do all my actions in the sight of God, who must judge of them, and to whom I have consecrated them all.

These are my sentiments; and every day of my life I bless my Redeemer, who has implanted them in me, and who, of a man full of weakness, of miseries, of lust, of pride, and of ambition, has made a man free from all these evils by the power of His grace, to which all the glory of it is due, as of myself I have only misery and error.

551. *Dignior plagis quam osculis non timeo quia amo.*[3]

552. *The Sepulchre of Jesus Christ.*—Jesus Christ was dead, but seen on the Cross. He was dead, and hidden in the Sepulchre.

Jesus Christ was buried by the saints alone.

Jesus Christ wrought no miracle at the Sepulchre.

Only the saints entered it.

It is there, not on the Cross, that Jesus Christ takes a new life.

It is the last mystery of the Passion and the Redemption.

Jesus Christ had nowhere to rest on earth but in the Sepulchre. His enemies only ceased to persecute Him at the Sepulchre.

---

[1] I Cor. 1.21. "Which . . . by wisdom knew not . . . it pleased God by the foolishness of preaching to save them that believe."

[2] St. Bernard, *Sermones in Cantica Canticorum*, lxxxiv. "The better one is, the worse one becomes, if one attributes the cause of this goodness to one's self."

[3] *Ibid.* "Meriting blows more than kisses, I fear not, because I love."

553. *The Mystery of Jesus.*—Jesus suffers in His passions the torments which men inflict upon Him; but in His agony He suffers the torments which He inflicts on Himself; *turbare semetipsum.*[1] This is a suffering from no human, but an almighty hand, for He must be almighty to bear it.

Jesus seeks some comfort at least in His three dearest friends, and they are asleep. He prays them to bear with Him for a little, and they leave Him with entire indifference, having so little compassion that it could not prevent their sleeping even for a moment. And thus Jesus was left alone to the wrath of God.

Jesus is alone on the earth, without any one not only to feel and share His suffering, but even to know of it; He and Heaven were alone in that knowledge.

Jesus is in a garden, not of delight as the first Adam, where he lost himself and the whole human race, but in one of agony, where He saved Himself and the whole human race.

He suffers this affliction and this desertion in the horror of night.

I believe that Jesus never complained but on this single occasion; but then He complained as if he could no longer bear His extreme suffering. "My soul is sorrowful, even unto death."

Jesus seeks companionship and comfort from men. This is the sole occasion in all His life, as it seems to me. But He receives it not, for His disciples are asleep.

Jesus will be in agony even to the end of the world. We must not sleep during that time.

Jesus, in the midst of this universal desertion, including that of His own friends chosen to watch with Him, finding them asleep, is vexed because of the danger to which they expose, not Him, but themselves; He cautions them for their own safety and their own good, with a sincere tenderness for them during their ingratitude, and warns them that the spirit is willing and the flesh weak.

Jesus, finding them still asleep, without being restrained by any consideration for themselves or for Him, has the kindness not to waken them and leaves them in repose.

Jesus prays, uncertain of the will of His Father, and fears death; but, when He knows it, He goes forward to offer Himself to death. *Eamus.*[2] *Processit* (John).[3]

Jesus asked of men and was not heard.

Jesus, while His disciples slept, wrought their salvation. He has wrought that of each of the righteous while they slept, both in their nothingness before their birth, and in their sins after their birth.

He prays only once that the cup pass away, and then with submission; and twice that it come if necessary.

Jesus is weary.

Jesus, seeing all His friends asleep and all His enemies wakeful, commits Himself entirely to His Father.

Jesus does not regard in Judas his enmity, but the order of God, which He loves and admits, since He calls him friend.

Jesus tears Himself away from His disciples to enter into His agony; we must tear ourselves away from our nearest and dearest to imitate Him.

Jesus being in agony and in the greatest affliction, let us pray longer.

[1]John 11.33. *Et turbarit seipsum.* "And he troubled himself."
[2]Matt. 26.46. "Let us be going."
[3]18.2. "Jesus went forth."

We implore the mercy of God, not that He may leave us at peace in our vices, but that He may deliver us from them.

If God gave us masters by His own hand, oh! how necessary for us to obey them with a good heart! Necessity and events follow infallibly.

"Console thyself, thou wouldst not seek Me, if thou hadst not found Me.

"I thought of thee in Mine agony, I have sweated such drops of blood for thee.

"It is tempting Me rather than proving thyself, to think if thou wouldst do such and such a thing on an occasion which has not happened; I shall act in thee if it occur.

"Let thyself be guided by My rules; see how well I have led the Virgin and the saints who have let Me act in them.

"The Father loves all that I do.

"Dost thou wish that it always cost Me the blood of My humanity, without thy shedding tears?

"Thy conversion is My affair; fear not, and pray with confidence as for Me.

"I am present with thee by My Word in Scripture, by My Spirit in the Church and by inspiration, by My power in the priests, by My prayer in the faithful.

"Physicians will not heal thee, for thou wilt die at last. But it is I who heal thee and make the body immortal.

"Suffer bodily chains and servitude, I deliver thee at present only from spiritual servitude.

"I am more a friend to thee than such and such an one, for I have done for thee more then they; they would not have suffered what I have suffered from thee, and they would not have died for thee as I have done in the time of thine infidelities and cruelties, and as I am ready to do, and do, among My elect and at the Holy Sacrament."

"If thou knewest thy sins, thou wouldst lose heart."

I shall lose it then, Lord, for on Thy assurance I believe their malice.

"No, for I, by whom thou learnest, can heal thee of them, and what I say to thee is a sign that I will heal thee. In proportion to thy expiation of them, thou wilt know them, and it will be said to thee: 'Behold, thy sins are forgiven thee.' Repent, then, for thy hidden sins, and for the secret malice of those which thou knowest."

Lord, I give Thee all.

"I love thee more ardently than thou hast loved thine abominations, *ut immundus pro luto.*

"To Me be the glory, not to thee, worm of the earth.

"Ask thy confessor, when My own words are to thee occasion of evil, vanity, or curiosity."

I see in me depths of pride, curiosity, and lust. There is no relation between me and God, nor Jesus Christ the Righteous. But He has been made sin for me; all Thy scourges are fallen upon Him. He is more abominable than I, and, far from abhorring me, He holds Himself honoured that I go to Him and succour Him.

But He has healed Himself, and still more so will He heal me.

I must add my wounds to His, and join myself to Him; and He will save me in saving Himself. But this must not be postponed to the future.

Eritis sicut dii scientes bonum et malum.[1] Each one creates his god, when judging,

[1] Gen. 3.5. "Ye shall be as gods, knowing good and evil."

"This is good or bad"; and men mourn or rejoice too much at events.

Do little things as though they were great, because of the majesty of Jesus Christ who does them in us and who lives our life; and do the greatest things as though they were little and easy, because of His omnipotence.

554. It seems to me that Jesus Christ only allowed His wounds to be touched after His resurrection: *Noli me tangere*.[1] We must unite ourselves only to His sufferings.

At the Last Supper He gave Himself in communion as about to die; to the disciples at Emmaus as risen from the dead; to the whole Church as ascended into heaven.

555. "Compare not thyself with others, but with Me. If thou dost not find Me in those with whom thou comparest thyself, thou comparest thyself to one who is abominable. If thou findest Me in them, compare thyself to Me. But whom wilt thou compare? Thyself, or Me in thee? If it is thyself, it is one who is abominable. If it is I, thou comparest Me to Myself. Now I am God in all.

"I speak to thee, and often counsel thee, because thy director cannot speak to thee, for I do not want thee to lack a guide.

"And perhaps I do so at his prayers, and thus he leads thee without thy seeing it. Thou wouldst not seek Me, if thou didst not possess Me.

"Be not therefore troubled."

SECTION VIII

THE FUNDAMENTALS OF THE CHRISTIAN RELIGION

556. . . . Men blaspheme what they do not know. The Christian religion consists in two points. It is of equal concern to men to know them, and it is equally dangerous to be ignorant of them. And it is equally of God's mercy that He has given indications of both.

And yet they take occasion to conclude that one of these points does not exist, from that which should have caused them to infer the other. The sages who have said there is only one God have been persecuted, the Jews were hated, and still more the Christians. They have seen by the light of nature that if there be a true religion on earth, the course of all things must tend to it as to a centre.

The whole course of things must have for its object the establishment and the greatness of religion. Men must have within them feelings suited to what religion teaches us. And, finally, religion must so be the object and the centre to which all things tend that whoever knows the principles of religion can give an explanation both of the whole nature of man in particular and of the whole course of the world in general.

And on this ground they take occasion to revile the Christian religion, because they misunderstand it. They imagine that it consists simply in the worship of a God considered as great, powerful, and eternal; which is strictly deism, almost as

[1]John 20.17. "Touch me not."

far removed from the Christian religion as atheism, which is its exact opposite. And thence they conclude that this religion is not true, because they do not see that all things concur to the establishment of this point, that God does not manifest Himself to men with all the evidence which He could show.

But let them conclude what they will against deism, they will conclude nothing against the Christian religion, which properly consists in the mystery of the Redeemer, who, uniting in Himself the two natures, human and divine, has redeemed men from the corruption of sin in order to reconcile them in His divine person to God.

The Christian religion, then, teaches men these two truths; that there is a God whom men can know, and that there is a corruption in their nature which renders them unworthy of Him. It is equally important to men to know both these points; and it is equally dangerous for man to know God without knowing his own wretchedness, and to know his own wretchedness without knowing the Redeemer who can free him from it. The knowledge of only one of these points gives rise either to the pride of philosophers, who have known God, and not their own wretchedness, or to the despair of atheists, who know their own wretchedness, but not the Redeemer.

And, as it is alike necessary to man to know these two points, so is it alike merciful of God to have made us know them. The Christian religion does this; it is in this that it consists.

Let us herein examine the order of the world and see if all things do not tend to establish these two chief points of this religion: Jesus Christ is the end of all, and the centre to which all tends. Whoever knows Him knows the reason of everything.

Those who fall into error err only through failure to see one of these two things. We can, then, have an excellent knowledge of God without that of our own wretchedness and of our own wretchedness without that of God. But we cannot know Jesus Christ without knowing at the same time both God and our own wretchedness.

Therefore I shall not undertake here to prove by natural reasons either the existence of God, or the Trinity, or the immortality of the soul, or anything of that nature; not only because I should not feel myself sufficiently able to find in nature arguments to convince hardened atheists, but also because such knowledge without Jesus Christ is useless and barren. Though a man should be convinced that numerical proportions are immaterial truths, eternal and dependent on a first truth, in which they subsist and which is called God, I should not think him far advanced towards his own salvation.

The God of Christians is not a God who is simply the author of mathematical truths, or of the order of the elements; that is the view of heathens and Epicureans. He is not merely a God who exercises His providence over the life and fortunes of men, to bestow on those who worship Him a long and happy life. That was the portion of the Jews. But the God of Abraham, the God of Isaac, the God of Jacob, the God of Christians, is a God of love and of comfort, a God who fills the soul and heart of those whom He possesses, a God who makes them conscious of their inward wretchedness, and His infinite mercy, who unites Himself to their inmost soul, who fills it with humility and joy, with confidence and love, who renders them incapable of any other end than Himself.

All who seek God without Jesus Christ, and who rest in nature, either find no light to satisfy them, or come to form for themselves a means of knowing God and serving Him without a mediator. Thereby they fall either into atheism, or into deism, two things which the Christian religion abhors almost equally.

Without Jesus Christ the world would not exist; for it should needs be either that it would be destroyed or be a hell.

If the world existed to instruct man of God, His divinity would shine through every part in it in an indisputable manner; but as it exists only by Jesus Christ, and for Jesus Christ, and to teach men both their corruption and their redemption, all displays the proofs of these two truths.

All appearance indicates neither a total exclusion nor a manifest presence of divinity, but the presence of a God who hides Himself. Everything bears this character.

. . . Shall he alone who knows his nature know it only to be miserable? Shall he alone who knows it be alone unhappy?

. . . He must not see nothing at all, nor must he see sufficient for him to believe he possesses it; but he must see enough to know that he has lost it. For to know of his loss, he must see and not see; and that is exactly the state in which he naturally is.

. . . Whatever part he takes, I shall not leave him at rest . . .

557. . . . It is, then, true that everything teaches man his condition, but he must understand this well. For it is not true that all reveals God, and it is not true that all conceals God. But it is at the same time true that He hides Himself from those who tempt Him, and that He reveals Himself to those who seek Him, because men are both unworthy and capable of God; unworthy by their corruption, capable by their original nature.

558. What shall we conclude from all our darkness, but our unworthiness?

559. If there never had been any appearance of God, this eternal deprivation would have been equivocal, and might have as well corresponded with the absence of all divinity, as with the unworthiness of men to know Him; but His occasional, though not continual, appearances remove the ambiguity. If He appeared once, He exists always; and thus we cannot but conclude both that there is a God and that men are unworthy of Him.

560. We do not understand the glorious state of Adam, nor the nature of his sin, nor the transmission of it to us. These are matters which took place under conditions of a nature altogether different from our own and which transcend our present understanding.

The knowledge of all this is useless to us as a means of escape from it; and all that we are concerned to know is that we are miserable, corrupt, separated from God, but ransomed by Jesus Christ, whereof we have wonderful proofs on earth.

So the two proofs of corruption and redemption are drawn from the ungodly, who live in indifference to religion, and from the Jews who are irreconcilable enemies.

561. There are two ways of proving the truths of our religion; one by the power of reason, the other by the authority of him who speaks.

We do not make use of the latter, but of the former. We do not say, "This must be believed, for Scripture, which says it, is divine." But we say that it must be believed for such and such a reason, which are feeble arguments, as reason may be bent to everything.

562. There is nothing on earth that does not show either the wretchedness of man, or the mercy of God; either the weakness of man without God, or the strength of man with God.

563. It will be one of the confusions of the damned to see that they are condemned by their own reason, by which they claimed to condemn the Christian religion.

564. The prophecies, the very miracles and proofs of our religion, are not of such a nature that they can be said to be absolutely convincing. But they are also of such a kind that it cannot be said that it is unreasonable to believe them. Thus there is both evidence and obscurity to enlighten some and confuse others. But the evidence is such that it surpasses, or at least equals, the evidence to the contrary; so that it is not reason which can determine men not to follow it, and thus it can only be lust or malice of heart. And by this means there is sufficient evidence to condemn, and insufficient to convince; so that it appears in those who follow it that it is grace, and not reason, which makes them follow it; and in those who shun it, that it is lust, not reason, which makes them shun it.

Vere discipuli, vere Israëlita, vere liberi, vere cibus.[1]

565. Recognise, then, the truth of religion in the very obscurity of religion, in the little light we have of it, and in the indifference which we have to knowing it.

566. We understand nothing of the works of God, if we do not take as a principle that He has willed to blind some and enlighten others.

567. The two contrary reasons. We must begin with that; without that we understand nothing, and all is heretical; and we must even add at the end of each truth that the opposite truth is to be remembered.

568. *Objection.* The Scripture is plainly full of matters not dictated by the Holy Spirit. *Answer.* Then they do not harm faith. *Objection.* But the Church has decided that all is of the Holy Spirit. *Answer.* I answer two things: first, the Church has not so decided; secondly, if she should so decide, it could be maintained.

Do you think that the prophecies cited in the Gospel are related to make you believe? No, it is to keep you from believing.

569. *Canonical.*—The heretical books in the beginning of the Church serve to prove the canonical.

570. To the chapter on the *Fundamentals* must be added that on *Typology* touch-

[1]Allusion to John 6.56; 1.47; 8.36; 6.32. "True disciple; an Israëlite indeed; free indeed; true bread."

ing the reason of types: why Jesus Christ was prophesied as to His first coming; why prophesied obscurely as to the manner.

571. *The reason why. Types.*—[They had to deal with a carnal people and to render them the depositary of the spiritual covenant.] To give faith to the Messiah, it was necessary there should have been precedent prophesies, and that these should be conveyed by persons above suspicion, diligent, faithful, unusually zealous, and known to all the world.

To accomplish all this, God chose this carnal people, to whom He entrusted the prophecies which foretell the Messiah as a deliverer and as a dispenser of those carnal goods which this people loved. And thus they have had an extraordinary passion for their prophets and, in sight of the whole world, have had charge of these books which foretell their Messiah, assuring all nations that He should come and in the way foretold in the books, which they held open to the whole world. Yet this people, deceived by the poor and ignominious advent of the Messiah, have been His most cruel enemies. So that they, the people least open to suspicion in the world of favouring us, the most strict and most zealous that can be named for their law and their prophets, have kept the books incorrupt. Hence those who have rejected and crucified Jesus Christ, who has been to them an offence, are those who have charge of the books which testify of Him, and state that He will be an offence and rejected. Therefore they have shown it was He by rejecting Him, and He has been alike proved both by the righteous Jews who received Him and by the unrighteous who rejected Him, both facts having been foretold.

Wherefore the prophecies have a hidden and spiritual meaning to which this people were hostile, under the carnal meaning which they loved. If the spiritual meaning had been revealed, they would not have loved it, and, unable to bear it, they would not have been zealous of the preservation of their books and their ceremonies; and if they had loved these spiritual promises, and had preserved them incorrupt till the time of the Messiah, their testimony would have had no force, because they had been his friends.

Therefore it was well that the spiritual meaning should be concealed; but, on the other hand, if this meaning had been so hidden as not to appear at all, it could not have served as a proof of the Messiah. What then was done? In a crowd of passages it has been hidden under the temporal meaning, and in a few has been clearly revealed; besides that, the time and the state of the world have been so clearly foretold that it is clearer than the sun. And in some places this spiritual meaning is so clearly expressed that it would require a blindness, like that which the flesh imposes on the spirit when it is subdued by it, not to recognise it.

See, then, what has been the prudence of God. This meaning is concealed under another in an infinite number of passages, and in some, though rarely, it is revealed; but yet so that the passages in which it is concealed are equivocal and can suit both meanings; whereas the passages where it is disclosed are unequivocal and can only suit the spiritual meaning.

So that this cannot lead us into error and could only be misunderstood by so carnal a people.

For when blessings are promised in abundance, what was to prevent them from understanding the true blessings, but their covetousness, which limited the meaning to worldly goods? But those whose only good was in God referred them to

God alone. For there are two principles, which divide the wills of men, covetousness and charity. Not that covetousness cannot exist along with faith in God, nor charity with worldly riches; but covetousness uses God and enjoys the world, and charity is the opposite.

Now the ultimate end gives names to things. All which prevents us from attaining it is called an enemy to us. Thus the creatures, however good, are the enemies of the righteous, when they turn them away from God, and God Himself is the enemy of those whose covetousness He confounds.

Thus as the significance of the word *enemy* is dependent on the ultimate end, the righteous understood by it their passions, and the carnal the Babylonians; and so these terms were obscure only for the unrighteous. And this is what Isaiah says: *Signa legem in electis meis,*[1] and that Jesus Christ shall be a stone of stumbling. But, "Blessed are they who shall not be offended in him." Hosea, 14.9, says excellently, "Where is the wise? and he shall understand what I say. The righteous shall know them, for the ways of God are right; but the transgressors shall fall therein."

572. Hypothesis that the apostles were impostors. The time clearly, the manner obscurely. Five typical proofs.

$$2000 \begin{cases} \text{1600 prophets.} \\ \text{400 scattered.} \end{cases}$$

573. *Blindness of Scripture.*—"The Scripture," said the Jews, "says that we shall not know whence Christ will come (John 7.27, and 12.34). The Scripture says that Christ abideth for ever, and He said that He should die." Therefore, says Saint John, they believed not, though He had done so many miracles, that the word of Isaiah might be fulfilled: "He hath blinded them," etc.

574. *Greatness.*—Religion is so great a thing that it is right that those who will not take the trouble to seek it, if it be obscure, should be deprived of it. Why, then, do any complain, if it be such as can be found by seeking?

575. All things work together for good to the elect, even the obscurities of Scripture; for they honour them because of what is divinely clear. And all things work together for evil to the rest of the world, even what is clear; for they revile such, because of the obscurities which they do not understand.

576. *The general conduct of the world towards the Church: God willing to blind and to enlighten.*—The event having proved the divinity of these prophecies, the rest ought to be believed. And thereby we see the order of the world to be of this kind. The miracles of the Creation and the Deluge being forgotten, God sends the law and the miracles of Moses, the prophets who prophesied particular things; and to prepare a lasting miracle, He prepares prophecies and their fulfilment; but, as the prophecies could be suspected, He desires to make them above suspicion, etc.

577. God has made the blindness of this people subservient to the good of the elect.

[1] *In discipulis meis.* Isaiah 8.16. "Seal the law among my disciples."

578. There is sufficient clearness to enlighten the elect, and sufficient obscurity to humble them. There is sufficient obscurity to blind the reprobate, and sufficient clearness to condemn them and make them inexcusable. Saint Augustine, Montaigne, Sébond.

The genealogy of Jesus Christ in the Old Testament is intermingled with so many others that are useless that it cannot be distinguished. If Moses had kept only the record of the ancestors of Christ, that might have been too plain. If he had not noted that of Jesus Christ, it might not have been sufficiently plain. But, after all, whoever looks closely sees that of Jesus Christ expressly traced through Tamar, Ruth, etc.

Those who ordained these sacrifices knew their uselessness; those who have declared their uselessness, have not ceased to practise them.

If God had permitted only one religion, it has been too easily known; but when we look at it closely, we clearly discern the truth amidst this confusion.

The premiss.—Moses was a clever man. If, then, he ruled himself by his reason, he would say nothing clearly which was directly against reason.

Thus all the very apparent weaknesses are strength. Example; the two genealogies in Saint Matthew and Saint Luke. What can be clearer than that this was not concerted?

579. God (and the Apostles), foreseeing that the seeds of pride would make heresies spring up, and being unwilling to give them occasion to arise from correct expressions, has put in Scripture and the prayers of the Church contrary words and sentences to produce their fruit in time.

So in morals He gives charity, which produces fruits contrary to lust.

580. Nature has some perfections to show that she is the image of God, and some defects to show that she is only His image.

581. God prefers rather to incline the will than the intellect. Perfect clearness would be of use to the intellect and would harm the will. To humble pride.

582. We make an idol of truth itself; for truth apart from charity is not God, but His image and idol, which we must neither love nor worship; and still less must we love or worship its opposite, namely, falsehood.

I can easily love total darkness; but if God keeps me in a state of semi-darkness, such partial darkness displeases me, and, because I do not see therein the advantage of total darkness, it is unpleasant to me. This is a fault and a sign that I make for myself an idol of darkness, apart from the order of God. Now only His order must be worshipped.

583. The feeble-minded are people who know the truth, but only affirm it so far as consistent with their own interest. But, apart from that, they renounce it.

584. The world exists for the exercise of mercy and judgement, not as if men were placed in it out of the hands of God, but as hostile to God; and to them He grants by grace sufficient light, that they may return to Him, if they desire to seek

and follow Him; and also that they may be punished, if they refuse to seek or follow Him.

585. *That God has willed to hide Himself.*—If there were only one religion, God would indeed be manifest. The same would be the case if there were no martyrs but in our religion.

God being thus hidden, every religion which does not affirm that God is hidden is not true; and every religion which does not give the reason of it is not instructive. Our religion does all this: *Vere tu es Deus absconditus.*[1]

586. If there were no obscurity, man would not be sensible of his corruption; if there were no light, man would not hope for a remedy. Thus, it is not only fair, but advantageous to us, that God be partly hidden and partly revealed; since it is equally dangerous to man to know God without knowing his own wretchedness, and to know his own wretchedness without knowing God.

587. This religion, so great in miracles, saints, blameless Fathers, learned and great witnesses, martyrs, established kings as David, and Isaiah, a prince of the blood, and so great in science, after having displayed all her miracles and all her wisdom, rejects all this, and declares that she has neither wisdom nor signs, but only the cross and foolishness.

For those, who, by these signs and that wisdom, have deserved your belief, and who have proved to you their character, declare to you that nothing of all this can change you, and render you capable of knowing and loving God, but the power of the foolishness of the cross without wisdom and signs, and not the signs without this power. Thus our religion is foolish in respect to the effective cause and wise in respect to the wisdom which prepares it.

588. Our religion is wise and foolish. Wise, because it is the most learned and the most founded on miracles, prophecies, etc. Foolish, because it is not all this which makes us belong to it. This makes us, indeed, condemn those who do not belong to it; but it does not cause belief in those who do belong to it. It is the cross that makes them believe, *ne evacuata sit crux.*[2] And so Saint Paul, who came with wisdom and signs, says that he has come neither with wisdom nor with signs; for he came to convert. But those who come only to convince can say that they come with wisdom and with signs.

SECTION IX

PERPETUITY

589. *On the fact that the Christian religion is not the only religion.*—So far is this from being a reason for believing that it is not the true one that, on the contrary, it makes us see that it is so.

[1]Is. 45.15.
[2]I Cor. 1.17. "Lest the cross of Christ should be made of none effect."

590. Men must be sincere in all religions; true heathens, true Jews, true Christians.

591.   J. C.
                    Heathens | Mahomet
                    ‾‾‾‾‾‾‾‾‾‾‾‾‾‾‾‾‾‾‾‾
                     Ignorance of God

592. *The falseness of other religions.*—They have no witnesses. Jews have. God defies other religions to produce such signs: Isaiah 43. 9; 44. 8.

593. *History of China.*—I believe only the histories, whose witnesses got themselves killed.

[Which is the more credible of the two, Moses or China?]

It is not a question of seeing this summarily. I tell you there is in it something to blind, and something to enlighten.

By this one word I destroy all your reasoning. "But China obscures," say you; and I answer, "China obscures, but there is clearness to be found; seek it."

Thus all that you say makes for one of the views and not at all against the other. So this serves, and does no harm.

We must, then, see this in detail; we must put the papers on the table.

594. *Against the history of China.*—The historians of Mexico, the five suns, of which the last is only eight hundred years old.

The difference between a book accepted by a nation and one which makes a nation.

595. Mahomet was without authority. His reasons, then, should have been very strong, having only their own force. What does he say, then, that we must believe him?

596. The Psalms are chanted throughout the whole world.

Who renders testimony to Mahomet? Himself. Jesus Christ desires His own testimony to be as nothing.

The quality of witnesses necessitates their existence always and everywhere; and he, miserable creature, is alone.

597. *Against Mahomet.*—The Koran is not more of Mahomet than the Gospel is of Saint Matthew, for it is cited by many authors from age to age. Even its very enemies, Celsus and Porphyry, never denied it.

The Koran says Saint Matthew was an honest man. Therefore Mahomet was a false prophet for calling honest men wicked, or for not agreeing with what they have said of Jesus Christ.

598. It is not by that which is obscure in Mahomet, and which may be interpreted in a mysterious sense, that I would have him judged, but by what is clear, as his paradise and the rest. In that he is ridiculous. And since what is clear is ridiculous, it is not right to take his obscurities for mysteries.

It is not the same with the Scripture. I agree that there are in it obscurities as strange as those of Mahomet; but there are admirably clear passages, and the prophecies are manifestly fulfilled. The cases are, therefore, not on a par. We must not confound and put on one level things which only resemble each other in their obscurity, and not in the clearness, which requires us to reverence the obscurities.

599. *The difference between Jesus Christ and Mahomet.*—Mahomet was not foretold; Jesus Christ was foretold.

Mahomet slew; Jesus Christ caused His own to be slain.

Mahomet forbade reading; the Apostles ordered reading.

In fact, the two are so opposed that, if Mahomet took the way to succeed from a worldly point of view, Jesus Christ, from the same point of view, took the way to perish. And instead of concluding that, since Mahomet succeeded, Jesus Christ might well have succeeded, we ought to say that, since Mahomet succeeded, Jesus Christ should have failed.

600. Any man can do what Mahomet has done; for he performed no miracles, he was not foretold. No man can do what Christ has done.

601. The heathen religion has no foundation [at the present day. It is said once to have had a foundation by the oracles which spoke. But what are the books which assure us of this? Are they so worthy of belief on account of the virtue of their authors? Have they been preserved with such care that we can be sure that they have not been meddled with?]

The Mahometan religion has for a foundation the Koran and Mahomet. But has this prophet, who was to be the last hope of the world, been foretold? What sign has he that every other man has not who chooses to call himself a prophet? What miracles does he himself say that he has done? What mysteries has he taught, even according to his own tradition? What was the morality, what the happiness held out by him?

The Jewish religion must be differently regarded in the tradition of the Holy Bible and in the tradition of the people. Its morality and happiness are absurd in the tradition of the people, but are admirable in that of the Holy Bible. (And all religion is the same; for the Christian religion is very different in the Holy Bible and in the casuists.) The foundation is admirable; it is the most ancient book in the world, and the most authentic; and whereas Mahomet, in order to make his own book continue in existence, forbade men to read it, Moses, for the same reason, ordered every one to read his.

Our religion is so divine that another divine religion has only been the foundation of it.

602. *Order.*—To see what is clear and indisputable in the whole state of the Jews.

603. The Jewish religion is wholly divine in its authority, its duration, its perpetuity, its morality, its doctrine, and its effects.

604. The only science contrary to common sense and human nature is that alone which has always existed among men.

605. The only religion contrary to nature, to common sense, and to our pleasure, is that alone which has always existed.

606. No religion but our own has taught that man is born in sin. No sect of philosophers has said this. Therefore none have declared the truth.

No sect or religion has always existed on earth, but the Christian religion.

607. Whoever judges of the Jewish religion by its coarser forms will misunderstand it. It is to be seen in the Holy Bible, and in the tradition of the prophets, who have made it plain enough that they did not interpret the law according to the letter. So our religion is divine in the Gospel, in the Apostles, and in tradition; but it is absurd in those who tamper with it.

The Messiah, according to the carnal Jews, was to be a great temporal prince. Jesus Christ, according to carnal Christians, has come to dispense us from the love of God and to give us sacraments which shall do everything without our help. Such is not the Christian religion, nor the Jewish. True Jews and true Christians have always expected a Messiah who should make them love God and by that love triumph over their enemies.

608. The carnal Jews hold a midway place between Christians and heathens. The heathens know not God, and love the world only. The Jews know the true God, and love the world only. The Christians know the true God, and love not the world. Jews and heathens love the same good. Jews and Christians know the same God.

The Jews were of two kinds; the first had only heathen affections, the other had Christian affections.

609. There are two kinds of men in each religion: among the heathen, worshippers of beasts and the worshippers of the one only God of natural religion; among the Jews, the carnal, and the spiritual, who were the Christians of the old law; among Christians, the coarser-minded, who are the Jews of the new law. The carnal Jews looked for a carnal Messiah; the coarser Christians believe that the Messiah has dispensed them from the love of God; true Jews and true Christians worship a Messiah who makes them love God.

610. *To show that the true Jews and the true Christians have but the same religion.*— The religion of the Jews seemed to consist essentially in the fatherhood of Abraham, in circumcision, in sacrifices, in ceremonies, in the Ark, in the temple, in Jerusalem, and, finally, in the law, and in the covenant with Moses.

I say that it consisted in none of those things, but only in the love of God, and that God disregarded all the other things.

That God did not accept the posterity of Abraham.

That the Jews were to be punished like strangers, if they transgressed. Deut. 8. 19: "If thou do at all forget the Lord thy God, and walk after other gods, I testify against you this day that ye shall surely perish, as the nations which the Lord destroyeth before your face."

That strangers, if they loved God, were to be received by Him as the Jews. Isaiah 56.3: "Let not the stranger say, 'The Lord will not receive me.' The strangers who join themselves unto the Lord to serve Him and love Him, will I bring unto my holy mountain, and accept therein sacrifices, for mine house is a house of prayer."

That the true Jews considered their merit to be from God only, and not from Abraham. Isaiah 63.16: "Doubtless thou art our Father, though Abraham be ignorant of us, and Israel acknowledge us not. Thou art our Father and our Redeemer."

Moses himself told them that God would not accept persons. Deut. 10.17: "God," said he, "regardeth neither persons nor sacrifices."

The Sabbath was only a sign, Exod. 31.13; and in memory of the escape from Egypt, Deut. 5.19. Therefore it is no longer necessary, since Egypt must be forgotten.

Circumcision was only a sign, Gen. 17.11. And thence it came to pass that, being in the desert, they were not circumcised, because they could not be confounded with other peoples; and after Jesus Christ came, it was no longer necessary.

That the circumcision of the heart is commanded. Deut. 10.16; Jeremiah 4.4: "Be ye circumcised in heart; take away the superfluities of your heart, and harden yourselves not. For your God is a mighty God, strong and terrible, who accepteth not persons."

That God said He would one day do it. Deut. 30.6: "God will circumcise thine heart, and the heart of thy seed, that thou mayest love Him with all thine heart."

That the uncircumcised in heart shall be judged. Jeremiah 9.26: For God will judge the uncircumcised peoples, and all the people of Israel, because he is "uncircumcised in heart."

That the external is of no avail apart from the internal. Joel 2.13: *Scindite corda vestra*,[1] etc.; Isaiah 58.3, 4, etc.

The love of God is enjoined in the whole of Deuteronomy. Deut. 30.19: "I call heaven and earth to record that I have set before you life and death, that you should choose life, and love God, and obey Him, for God is your life."

That the Jews, for lack of that love, should be rejected for their offences, and the heathen chosen in their stead. Hosea 1.10; Deut. 32.20. "I will hide my face from them, I will see what their end shall be, for they are a very froward generation, children in whom is no faith. They have moved me to jealousy with that which is not God . . . and I will move them to jealousy with those which are not a people . . . and with a foolish nation." Isaiah 65.1.

That temporal goods are false, and that the true good is to be united to God. Psalm 143.15.

That their feasts are displeasing to God. Amos 5.21.

That the sacrifices of the Jews displeased God. Isaiah 66.1–3; 1.11; Jer. 6. 20; David, *Miserere*.[2] Even on the part of the good, *Expectavi*.[3] Psalm 49.8, 9, 10, 11, 12, 13 and 14.

That He has established them only for their hardness. Micah, admirably, 6; I Kings 15.22; Hosea 6.6.

[1] "Rend your heart."
[2] Ps. 9.14. "Have mercy."
[3] Is. 5.7. "He has looked for."

That the sacrifices of the Gentiles will be accepted of God, and that God will take no pleasure in the sacrifices of the Jews. Malachi 1.11.

That God will make a new covenant with the Messiah, and the old will be annulled. Jer. 31.31. *Mandata non bona*. Ezek.[1]

That the old things will be forgotten. Isaiah 43.18, 19; 65.17, 10.

That the Ark will no longer be remembered. Jer. 3.15, 16.

That the temple should be rejected. Jer 7.12, 13, 14.

That the sacrifices should be rejected, and other pure sacrifices established. Malachi 1.11.

That the order of Aaron's priesthood should be rejected, and that of Melchizedek introduced by the Messiah. Ps. *Dixit Dominus*.

That this priesthood should be eternal. *Ibid*.

That Jerusalem should be rejected, and Rome admitted, *Ibid*.

That the name of the Jews should be rejected, and a new name given. Isaiah 65.15.

That this last name should be more excellent than that of the Jews, and eternal. Isaiah 56.5.

That the Jews should be without prophets (Amos), without a king, without princes, without sacrifice, without an idol.

That the Jews should, nevertheless, always remain a people. Jer. 31.36.

611. *Republic*.—The Christian republic—and even the Jewish—has only had God for ruler, as Philo the Jew notices, *On Monarchy*.

When they fought, it was for God only; their chief hope was in God only; they considered their towns as belonging to God only, and kept them for God. I Chron. 19.13.

612. Gen. 17.7. *Statuam pactum meum inter me et te fœdere sempiterno . . . ut sim Deus tuus . . .*[2]

Et tu ergo custodies pactum meum.[3]

613. *Perpetuity*.—That religion has always existed on earth which consists in believing that man has fallen from a state of glory and of communion with God into a state of sorrow, penitence, and estrangement from God, but that after this life we shall be restored by a Messiah who should have come. All things have passed away, and this has endured, for which all things are.

Men have in the first age of the world been carried away into every kind of debauchery, and yet there were saints, as Enoch, Lamech, and others, who waited patiently for the Christ promised from the beginning of the world. Noah saw the wickedness of men at its height; and he was held worthy to save the world in his person, by the hope of the Messiah of whom he was the type. Abraham was surrounded by idolaters, when God made known to him the mystery of the Messiah, whom he welcomed from afar. In the time of Isaac and Jacob, abomination was spread over all the earth; but these saints lived in faith; and Jacob, dying and bless-

---

[1] 20.25. *Præcepta non bona*. "Statutes that were not good."

[2] "I will establish my covenant between me and Thee for an everlasting covenant, to be a God unto Thee."

[3] Gen. 17.9. "Thou shalt keep my covenant therefore."

ing his children, cried in a transport which made him break off his discourse, "I await, O my God, the Saviour whom Thou hast promised. *Salutare tuum expectabo, Domine.*"[1] The Egyptians were infected both with idolatry and magic; the very people of God were led astray by their example. Yet Moses and others believed Him whom they saw not, and worshipped Him, looking to the eternal gifts which He was preparing for them.

The Greeks and Latins then set up false deities; the poets made a hundred different theologies, while the philosophers separated into a thousand different sects; and yet in the heart of Judæa there were always chosen men who foretold the coming of this Messiah, which was known to them alone.

He came at length in the fullness of time, and time has since witnessed the birth of so many schisms and heresies, so many political revolutions, so many changes in all things; yet this Church, which worships Him who has always been worshipped, has endured uninterruptedly. It is a wonderful, incomparable, and altogether divine fact that this religion, which has always endured, has always been attacked. It has been a thousand times on the eve of universal destruction, and every time it has been in that state, God has restored it by extraordinary acts of His power. This is astonishing, as also that it has preserved itself without yielding to the will of tyrants. For it is not strange that a State endures, when its laws are sometimes made to give way to necessity, but that . . . (See the passage indicated in Montaigne.)[2]

614. States would perish if they did not often make their laws give way to necessity. But religion has never suffered this, or practised it. Indeed, there must be these compromises or miracles. It is not strange to be saved by yieldings, and this is not strictly self-preservation; besides, in the end they perish entirely. None has endured a thousand years. But the fact that this religion has always maintained itself, inflexible as it is, proves its divinity.

615. Whatever may be said, it must be admitted that the Christian religion has something astonishing in it. Some will say, "This is because you were born in it." Far from it; I stiffen myself against it for this very reason, for fear this prejudice bias me. But, although I am born in it, I cannot help finding it so.

616. *Perpetuity.*—The Messiah has always been believed in. The tradition from Adam was fresh in Noah and in Moses. Since then the prophets have foretold him, while at the same time foretelling other things, which, being from time to time fulfilled in the sight of men, showed the truth of their mission, and consequently that of their promises touching the Messiah. Jesus Christ performed miracles, and the Apostles also, who converted all the heathen; and all the prophecies being thereby fulfilled, the Messiah is for ever proved.

617. *Perpetuity.*—Let us consider that since the beginning of the world the expectation of worship of the Messiah has existed uninterruptedly; that there have been found men who said that God had revealed to them that a Redeemer was to be born, who should save His people; that Abraham came afterwards, saying that

[1] Gen. 49.18. "I have waited for thy salvation, O Lord."
[2] *Essays,* 1.22.

he had had a revelation that the Messiah was to spring from him by a son, whom he should have; that Jacob declared that, of his twelve sons, the Messiah would spring from Judah; that Moses and the prophets then came to declare the time and the manner of His coming; that they said their law was only temporary till that of the Messiah, that it should endure till then, but that the other should last for ever; that thus either their law, or that of the Messiah, of which it was the promise, would be always upon the earth; that, in fact, it has always endured; that at last Jesus Christ came with all the circumstances foretold. This is wonderful.

618. This is positive fact. While all philosophers separate into different sects, there is found in one corner of the world the most ancient people in it, declaring that all the world is in error, that God has revealed to them the truth, that they will always exist on the earth. In fact, all other sects come to an end, this one still endures, and has done so for four thousand years.

They declare that they hold from their ancestors that man has fallen from communion with God, and is entirely estranged from God, but that He has promised to redeem them; that this doctrine shall always exist on the earth; that their law has a double signification; that during sixteen hundred years they have had people, whom they believed prophets, foretelling both the time and the manner; that four hundred years after they were scattered everywhere, because Jesus Christ was to be everywhere announced; that Jesus Christ came in the manner, and at the time foretold; that the Jews have since been scattered abroad under a curse and, nevertheless, still exist.

619. I see the Christian religion founded upon a preceding religion, and this is what I find as a fact.

I do not here speak of the miracles of Moses, of Jesus Christ, and of the Apostles, because they do not at first seem convincing, and because I only wish here to put in evidence all those foundations of the Christian religion which are beyond doubt and which cannot be called in question by any person whatsoever. It is certain that we see in many places of the world a peculiar people, separated from all other peoples of the world and called the Jewish people.

I see then a crowd of religions in many parts of the world and in all times; but their morality cannot please me, nor can their proofs convince me. Thus I should equally have rejected the religion of Mahomet and of China, of the ancient Romans and of the Egyptians, for the sole reason that none having more marks of truth than another, nor anything which should necessarily persuade me, reason cannot incline to one rather than the other.

But, in thus considering this changeable and singular variety of morals and beliefs at different times, I find in one corner of the world a peculiar people, separated from all other peoples on earth, the most ancient of all, and whose histories are earlier by many generations than the most ancient which we possess.

I find, then, this great and numerous people, sprung from a single man, who worship one God and guide themselves by a law which they say that they obtained from His own hand. They maintain that they are the only people in the world to whom God has revealed His mysteries; that all men are corrupt and in disgrace with God; that they are all abandoned to their senses and their own imagination, whence come the strange errors and continual changes which happen among them, both of religions and of morals, whereas they themselves remain firm in their conduct; but that God will not leave other nations in this darkness for ever; that there will come a Saviour for all; that they are in the world to announce Him to men; that they are expressly formed to be forerunners and heralds of this great event and to summon all nations to join with them in the expectation of this Saviour.

To meet with this people is astonishing to me, and seems to me worthy of attention. I look at the law which they boast of having obtained from God, and I find it admirable. It is the first law of all and is of such a kind that, even before the term *law* was in currency among the Greeks, it had, for nearly a thousand years earlier, been uninterruptedly accepted and observed by the Jews. I likewise think it strange that the first law of the world happens to be the most perfect; so that the greatest legislators have borrowed their laws from it, as is apparent from the law of the Twelve Tables at Athens, afterwards taken by the Romans, and as it would be easy to prove, if Josephus and others had not sufficiently dealt with this subject.

620. *Advantages of the Jewish people.*—In this search the Jewish people at once attracts my attention by the number of wonderful and singular facts which appear about them.

I first see that they are a people wholly composed of brethren, and whereas all others are formed by the assemblage of an infinity of families, this, though so wonderfully fruitful, has all sprung from one man alone, and, being thus all one flesh, and members one of another, they constitute a powerful state of one family. This is unique.

This family, or people, is the most ancient within human knowledge, a fact which seems to me to inspire a peculiar veneration for it, especially in view of our present inquiry; since if God had from all time revealed Himself to men, it is to these we must turn for knowledge of the tradition.

This people are not eminent solely by their antiquity, but are also singular by their duration, which has always continued from their origin till now. For, whereas the nations of Greece and of Italy, of Lacedæmon, of Athens and of Rome, and others who came long after, have long since perished, these ever remain, and in spite of the endeavours of many powerful kings who have a hundred times tried to destroy them, as their historians testify, and as it is easy to conjecture from the natural order of things during so long a space of years, they have nevertheless been preserved (and this preservation has been foretold); and extending from the earliest times to the latest, their history comprehends in its duration all our histories [which it preceded by a long time].

The law by which this people is governed is at once the most ancient law in the world, the most perfect, and the only one which has been always observed without a break in a state. This is what Josephus admirably proves, *Against Apion*, and also Philo the Jew, in different places, where they point out that it is so ancient that the very name of *law* was only known by the oldest nation more than a thousand years afterwards; so that Homer, who has written the history of so many states, has never used the term. And it is easy to judge of its perfection by simply reading it; for we see that it has provided for all things with so great wisdom, equity, and judgement, that the most ancient legislators, Greek and Roman, having had some knowledge of it, have borrowed from it their principal laws; this is evident from what are called the Twelve Tables, and from the other proofs which Josephus gives.

But this law is at the same time the severest and strictest of all in respect to their religious worship, imposing on this people, in order to keep them to their duty, a thousand peculiar and painful observances, on pain of death. Whence it is very astonishing that it has been constantly preserved during many centuries by a people, rebellious and impatient as this one was; while all other states have changed their laws from time to time, although these were far more lenient.

The book which contains this law, the first of all, is itself the most ancient book in the world, those of Homer, Hesiod, and others, being six or seven hundred years later.

621. The creation of the deluge being past, and God no longer requiring to destroy the world, nor to create it anew, nor to give such great signs of Himself, He began to establish a people on the earth, purposely formed, who were to last until the coming of the people whom the Messiah should fashion by His spirit.

622. The creation of the world beginning to be distant, God provided a single contemporary historian, and appointed a whole people as guardians of this book, in order that this history might be the most authentic in the world, and that all men might thereby learn a fact so necessary to know, and which could only be known through that means.

623. [Japhet begins the genealogy.]
Joseph folds his arms, and prefers the younger.

624. Why should Moses make the lives of men so long, and their generations so few?

Because it is not the length of years, but the multitude of generations, which renders things obscure. For truth is perverted only by the change of men. And yet he puts two things, the most memorable that were ever imagined, namely, the creation and the deluge, so near that we reach from one to the other.

625. Shem, who saw Lamech, who saw Adam, saw also Jacob, who saw those who saw Moses; therefore the deluge and the creation are true. This is conclusive among certain people who understand it rightly.

626. The longevity of the patriarchs, instead of causing the loss of past history, conduced, on the contrary, to its preservation. For the reason why we are sometimes insufficiently instructed in the history of our ancestors is that we have never lived long with them, and that they are often dead before we have attained the age of reason. Now, when men lived so long, children lived long with their parents. They conversed long with them. But what else could be the subject of their talk save the history of their ancestors, since to that all history was reduced, and men did not study science or art, which now form a large part of daily conversation? We see also that in these days tribes took particular care to preserve their genealogies.

627. I believe that Joshua was the first of God's people to have this name, as Jesus Christ was the last of God's people.

628. *Antiquity of the Jews.*—What a difference there is between one book and another! I am not astonished that the Greeks made the *Iliad*, nor the Egyptians and the Chinese their histories.

We have only to see how this originates. These fabulous historians are not contemporaneous with the facts about which they write. Homer composes a romance, which he gives out as such, and which is received as such; for nobody doubted that Troy and Agamemnon no more existed than did the golden apple. Accordingly, he did not think of making a history, but solely a book to amuse; he is the only writer of his time; the beauty of the work has made it last, every one learns it and talks of it, it is necessary to know it, and each one knows it by heart. Four hundred years afterwards the witnesses of these facts are no longer alive, no one knows of his own knowledge if it be a fable or a history; one has only learnt it from his ancestors, and this can pass for truth.

Every history which is not contemporaneous, as the books of the Sibyls and Trismegistus, and so many others which have been believed by the world, are false, and found to be false in the course of time. It is not so with contemporaneous writers.

There is a great difference between a book which an individual writes and publishes to a nation, and a book which itself creates a nation. We cannot doubt that the book is as old as the people.

629. Josephus hides the shame of his nation.
Moses does not hide his own shame.
Quis mihi det ut omnes prophetent?[1]
He was weary of the multitude.

630. *The sincerity of the Jews.*—Maccabees, after they had no more prophets; the Masorah, since Jesus Christ.
This book will be a testimony for you.
Defective and final letters.
Sincere against their honour, and dying for it; this has no example in the world, and no root in nature.

631. *Sincerity of the Jews.*—They preserve lovingly and carefully the book in which Moses declares that they have been all their life ungrateful to God, and that he knows they will be still more so after his death; but that he calls heaven and earth to witness against them and that he has [*taught*] them enough.

He declares that God, being angry with them, shall at last scatter them among all the nations of the earth; that as they have offended Him by worshipping gods who were not their God, so He will provoke them by calling a people who are not His people; that He desires that all His words be preserved for ever, and that His book be placed in the Ark of the Covenant to serve for ever as a witness against them.

Isaiah says the same thing, 30.

632. *On Esdras.*—The story that the books were burnt with the temple proved false by Maccabees: "Jeremiah gave them the law."

[1]Num. 11.29 *Quis tribuat ut omnis populus prophetet.* "Would God that all the Lord's people were prophets."

The story that he recited the whole by heart. Josephus and Esdras point out *that he read the book*. Baronius, *Annales Ecclesiastici a Christo Nato ad Annum* 1198, 180: *Nullus penitus Hebræorum antiquorum reperitur qui tradiderit libros periisse et per Esdram esse restitutos, nisi in IV Esdræ*.

The story that he changed the letters.

Philo, in *Vita Mosis: Illa lingua ac character quo antiquitus scripta est lex sic permansit usque ad LXX.*

Josephus says that the Law was in Hebrew when it was translated by the Seventy.

Under Antiochus and Vespasian, when they wanted to abolish the books, and when there was no prophet, they could not do so. And under the Babylonians, when no persecution had been made, and when there were so many prophets, would they have let them be burnt?

Josephus laughs at the Greeks who would not hear . . .

Tertullian: *Perinde potuit abolefactam eam violentia cataclysmi in spiritu rursus reformare, quemadmodum et Hierosolymis Babylonia expugnatione deletis, omne instrumentum Judaicæ literaturæ per Esdram constat restauratum.*[1]

He says that Noah could as easily have restored in spirit the book of Enoch, destroyed by the Deluge, as Esdras could have restored the Scriptures lost during the Captivity.

(Θεὸς) ἐν τῇ ἐπὶ Ναβουχοδόνοσορ αἰχμαλωσίᾳ τοῦ λαοῦ, διαφθαρεισῶν τῶν Γραφῶν . . . ἐνέπνευσε Ἐσδρᾷ τῷ ἱερεῖ, ἐκ τῆς φυλῆς Λευὶ τοὺς τῶν προγεγονότων προφητῶν πάντας ἀνατάξασθαι λόγους, καὶ ἀποκαταστῆσαι τῷ λαῷ τὴν διὰ Μωυσέως νομοθεσίαν. He alleges this to prove that it is not incredible that the Seventy may have explained the Holy Scriptures with that uniformity which we admire in them. And he took that from Saint Irenæus.

Saint Hilary, in his preface to the Psalms, says that Esdras arranged the Psalms in order.

The origin of this tradition comes from the 14th chapter of the fourth book of Esdras. *Deus glorificatus est, et Scripturæ vere divinæ creditæ sunt, omnibus eandem et eisdem verbis et eisdem nominibus recitantibus ab initio usque ad finem, uti et præsentes gentes cognoscerent quoniam per inspirationem Dei interpretatæ sunt Scripturæ, et non esset mirabile Deum hoc in eis operatum: quando in ea captivitate populi quæ facta est a Nabuchodonosor, corruptis scripturis et post 70 annos Judæis descendentibus in regionem suam, et post deinde temporibus Artaxerxis Persarum regis, inspiravit Esdræ sacerdoti tribus Levi præteritorum prophetarum omnes rememorare sermones, et restituere populo eam legem quæ data est per Moysen.*[2]

---

[1] *De cultu feminarum*, i-3. "He could equally have renewed it, under the Spirit's inspiration, after it had been destroyed by the violence of the deluge, as, after the destruction of Jerusalem by the Babylonian storming of it, every document of the Jewish literature is generally agreed to have been restored through Ezra."

[2] Eusebius, *Ecclesiastical History*, V. viii.14. "God was glorified, and the Scriptures were recognized as truly divine, for they all rendered the same things in the same words and the same names, from beginning to end, so that even the heathen who were present knew that the Scriptures had been translated by the inspiration of God. And it is no marvel that God did this, for when the Scriptures had been destroyed in the captivity of the people in the days of Nebuchadnezzar, and the Jews had gone back to their country after seventy years, then in the times of Artaxerxes, the king of the Persians, he inspired Ezra, the priest of the tribe of Levi, to restore all the sayings of the prophets who had gone before, and to restore to the people the law given by Moses." This is Pascal's rendering into Latin of the passage from Eusebius of which the last lines are in Greek, above.

633. *Against the story in* Esdras, II Maccab. 2.; Josephus, *Antiquities*, II, i.—Cyrus took occasion from the prophecy of Isaiah to release the people. The Jews held their property in peace under Cyrus in Babylon; hence they could well have the Law.

Josephus, in the whole history of Esdras, does not say one word about this restoration. II Kings 17.27.

634. If the story in Esdras is credible, then it must be believed that the Scripture is Holy Scripture; for this story is based only on the authority of those who assert that of the Seventy, which shows that the Scripture is holy.

Therefore, if this account be true, we have what we want therein; if not, we have it elsewhere. And thus those who would ruin the truth of our religion, founded on Moses, establish it by the same authority by which they attack it. So by this providence it still exists.

635. *Chronology of Rabbinism.* (The citations of pages are from the book *Pugio*.)
Page 27. R. Hakadosch (*anno 200*), author of the *Mischna*, or vocal law, or second law.

Commentaries on the *Mischna* (*anno 340*):
The one *Siphra*.
Barajetot.
Talmud Hierosol.
Tosiphtot.

Bereschit Rabah, by R. Osaiah Rabah, commentary on the *Mischna*.

Bereschit Rabah, *Bar Naconi*, are subtle and pleasant discourses, historical and theological. This same author wrote the books called *Rabot*.

A hundred years after the *Talmud Hierosol* was composed the *Babylonian Talmud*, by R. Ase, A.D. 440, by the universal consent of all the Jews, who are necessarily obliged to observe all that is contained therein.

The addition of R. Ase is called the *Gemara*, that is to say, the *commentary* on the *Mischna*.

And the Talmud includes together the *Mischna* and the *Gemara*.

636. If does not indicate indifference: Malachi, Isaiah.
Isaiah, *Si volumus*, etc.
In quacumque die.[1]

637. *Prophecies.*—The sceptre was not interrupted by the captivity in Babylon, because the return was promised and foretold.

638. *Proofs of Jesus Christ.*—Captivity, with the assurance of deliverance within seventy years, was not real captivity. But now they are captives without any hope.

God has promised them that, even though He should scatter them to the ends of the earth, nevertheless, if they were faithful to His law, He would assemble them together again. They are very faithful to it and remain oppressed.

639. When Nebuchadnezzar carried away the people, for fear they should believe that the sceptre had departed from Judah, they were told beforehand that

[1]"Each time that."

they would be there for a short time, and that they would be restored. They were always consoled by the prophets; and their kings continued. But the second destruction is without promise of restoration, without prophets, without kings, without consolation, without hope, because the sceptre is taken away for ever.

640. It is a wonderful thing, and worthy of particular attention, to see this Jewish people existing so many years in perpetual misery, it being necessary as a proof of Jesus Christ both that they should exist to prove Him and that they should be miserable because they crucified Him; and though to be miserable and to exist are contradictory, they nevertheless still exist in spite of their misery.

641. They are visibly a people expressly created to serve as a witness to the Messiah (Isaiah 43.9; 44.8). They keep the books, and love them, and do not understand them. And all this was foretold; that God's judgments are entrusted to them, but as a sealed book.

SECTION X

TYPOLOGY

642. *Proof of the two Testaments at once.*—To prove the two at one stroke, we need only see if the prophecies in one are fulfilled in the other. To examine the prophecies, we must understand them. For if we believe they have only one meaning, it is certain that the Messiah has not come; but if they have two meanings, it is certain that He has come in Jesus Christ.

The whole problem then is to know if they have two meanings.

That the Scripture has two meanings, which Jesus Christ and the Apostles have given, is shown by the following proofs:

1. Proof by Scripture itself.

2. Proof by the Rabbis. Moses Maimonides says that it has two aspects and that the prophets have prophesied Jesus Christ only.

3. Proof by the Kabbala.

4. Proof by the mystical interpretation which the Rabbis themselves give to Scripture.

5. Proof by the principles of the Rabbis, that there are two meanings; that there are two advents of the Messiah, a glorious and an humiliating one, according to their desert; that the prophets have prophesied of the Messiah only—the Law is not eternal, but must change at the coming of the Messiah—that then they shall no more remember the Red Sea; that the Jews and the Gentiles shall be mingled.

[6. Proof by the key which Jesus Christ and the Apostles give us.]

643. Isaiah 51. The Red Sea an image of the Redemption. *Ut sciatis quod filius hominis habet potestatem remittendi peccata . . . tibi dico: Surge.*[1] God, wishing to show that He could form a people holy with an invisible holiness, and fill them with an

---

[1]Mark 2.10,11. "But that ye may know that the son of man hath power on earth to forgive sins . . . I say unto thee, Arise."

eternal glory, made visible things. As nature is an image of grace, He has done in the bounties of nature what He would do in those of grace, in order that we might judge that He could make the invisible, since He made the visible excellently.

Therefore He saved this people from the deluge; He has raised them up from Abraham, redeemed them from their enemies, and set them at rest.

The object of God was not to save them from the deluge, and raise up a whole people from Abraham, only in order to bring them into a rich land.

And even grace is only the type of glory, for it is not the ultimate end. It has been symbolised by the law, and itself symbolises [glory]. But it is the type of it, and the origin or cause.

The ordinary life of men is like that of the saints. They all seek their satisfaction and differ only in the object in which they place it; they call those their enemies who hinder them, etc. God has then shown the power which He has of giving invisible blessings, by that which He has shown Himself to have over things visible.

644. *Types.*—God, wishing to form for Himself an holy people, whom He should separate from all other nations, whom He should deliver from their enemies and should put into a place of rest, has promised to do so and has foretold by His prophets the time and the manner of His coming. And yet, to confirm the hope of His elect, He has made them see in it an image through all time, without leaving them devoid of assurances of His power and of His will to save them. For, at the creation of man, Adam was the witness, and guardian of the promise of a Saviour, who should be born of woman, when men were still so near the creation that they could not have forgotten their creation and their fall. When those who had seen Adam were no longer in the world, God sent Noah whom He saved, and drowned the whole earth by a miracle which sufficiently indicated the power which He had to save the world, and the will which He had to do so, and to raise up from the seed of woman Him whom He had promised. This miracle was enough to confirm the hope of men.

The memory of the Deluge being so fresh among men, while Noah was still alive, God made promises to Abraham, and, while Shem was still living, sent Moses, etc. . . . .

645. *Types.*—God, willing to deprive His own of perishable blessings, created the Jewish people in order to show that this was not owing to lack of power.

646. The Synagogue did not perish, because it was a type. But, because it was only a type, it fell into servitude. The type existed till the truth came, in order that the Church should be always visible, either in the sign which promised it, or in substance.

647. That the law was figurative.

648. Two errors: 1. To take everything literally. 2. To take everything spiritually.

649. To speak against too greatly figurative language.

650. There are some types clear and demonstrative, but others which seem some-

what far-fetched, and which convince only those who are already persuaded. These are like the Apocalyptics. But the difference is that they have none which are certain, so that nothing is so unjust as to claim that theirs are as well founded as some of ours; for they have none so demonstrative as some of ours. The comparison is unfair. We must not put on the same level and confound things, because they seem to agree in one point, while they are so different in another. The clearness in divine things requires us to revere the obscurities in them.

[It is like men, who employ a certain obscure language among themselves. Those who should not understand it would understand only a foolish meaning.]

651. *Extravagances of the Apocalyptics, Preadamites, Millenarians, etc.*—He who would base extravagant opinions on Scripture will, for example, base them on this. It is said that "this generation shall not pass till all these things be fulfilled." Upon that I will say that after that generation will come another generation, and so on ever in succession.

Solomon and the King are spoken of in the second book of Chronicles as if they were two different persons. I will say that they were two.

652. *Particular Types.*—A double law, double tables of the law, a double temple, a double captivity.

653. *Types.*—The prophets prophesied by symbols of a girdle, a beard, and burnt hair, etc.

654. Difference between dinner and supper.

In God the word does not differ from the intention, for He is true; nor the word from the effect, for He is powerful; nor the means from the effect, for He is wise. St. Bernard, *Ultimo Sermo in Missam.*

St. Augustine, *City of God*, v. 10. This rule is general. God can do everything, except those things which, if He could do, He would not be almighty, as dying, being deceived, lying, etc.

Several Evangelists for the confirmation of the truth; their difference useful.

The Eucharist after Lord's Supper. Truth after the type.

The ruin of Jerusalem, a type of the ruin of the world, forty years after the death of Jesus. "I know not," as a man, or as an ambassador (Mark 13.32; Matthew 24.36.)

Jesus condemned by the Jews and the Gentiles.

The Jews and the Gentiles typified by the two sons. St. Augustine *City of God*, xx. 29.

655. The six ages, the six Fathers of the six ages, the six wonders at the beginning of the six ages, the six mornings at the beginning of the six ages.

656. Adam *forma futuri.*[1] The six days to form the one, the six ages to form the other. The six days, which Moses represents for the formation of Adam, are only the picture of the six ages to form Jesus Christ and the Church. If Adam had not sinned, and Jesus Christ had not come, there had been only one covenant, only

[1]Rom. 5.14. "The figure of him that was to come."

one age of men, and the creation would have been represented as accomplished at one single time.

657. *Types.*—The Jewish and Egyptian peoples were plainly foretold by the two individuals whom Moses met; the Egyptian beating the Jew, Moses avenging him and killing the Egyptian, and the Jew being ungrateful.

658. The symbols of the Gospel for the state of the sick soul are sick bodies; but, because one body cannot be sick enough to express it well, several have been needed. Thus there are the deaf, the dumb, the blind, the paralytic, the dead Lazarus, the possessed. All this crowd is in the sick soul.

659. *Types.*—To show that the Old Testament is only figurative and that the prophets understood by temporal blessings other blessings, this is the proof:

First, that this would be unworthy of God.

Secondly, that their discourses express very clearly the promise of temporal blessings, and that they say nevertheless that their discourses are obscure, and that their meaning will not be understood. Whence it appears that this secret meaning was not that which they openly expressed, and that consequently they meant to speak of other sacrifices, of another deliverer, etc. They say that they will be understood only in the fullness of time (Jer. 30.24).

The third proof is that their discourses are contradictory, and neutralise each other; so that, if we think that they did not mean by the words *law* and *sacrifice* anything else than that of Moses, there is a plain and gross contradiction. Therefore they meant something else, sometimes contradicting themselves in the same chapter. Now, to understand the meaning of an author . . .

660. Lust has become natural to us and has made our second nature. Thus there are two natures in us—the one good, the other bad. Where is God? Where you are not, and the kingdom of God is within you. The Rabbis.

661. Penitence, alone of all these mysteries, has been manifestly declared to the Jews, and by Saint John, the Forerunner; and then the other mysteries; to indicate that in each man, as in the entire world, this order must be observed.

662. The carnal Jews understood neither the greatness nor the humiliation of the Messiah foretold in their prophecies. They misunderstood Him in His foretold greatness, as when He said that the Messiah should be lord of David, though his son, and that He was before Abraham, who had seen Him. They did not believe Him so great as to be eternal, and they likewise misunderstood Him in His humiliation and in His death. "The Messiah," said they, "abideth for ever, and this man says that he shall die." Therefore they believed Him neither mortal nor eternal; they only sought in Him for a carnal greatness.

663. *Typical.*—Nothing is so like charity as covetousness, and nothing is so opposed to it. Thus the Jews, full of possessions which flattered their covetousness, were very like Christians, and very contrary. And by this means they had the two qualities which it was necessary they should have, to be very like

the Messiah to typify Him, and very contrary not to be suspected witnesses.

664. *Typical.*—God made use of the lust of the Jews to make them minister to Jesus Christ, [who brought the remedy for their lust].

665. Charity is not a figurative precept. It is dreadful to say that Jesus Christ, who came to take away types in order to establish the truth, came only to establish the type of charity, in order to take away the existing reality which was there before.

"If the light be darkness, how great is that darkness!"

666. Fascination. *Somnum suum.*[1] *Figura hujus mundi.*[2]

The Eucharist. *Comedes panem tuum.*[3] *Panem nostrum.*[4]

Inimici Dei terram lingent.[5] Sinners lick the dust, that is to say, love earthly pleasures.

The Old Testament contains the types of future joy, and the New contains the means of arriving at it. The types were of joy; the means of penitence; and nevertheless the Paschal Lamb was eaten with bitter herbs, *cum amaritudinibus.*[6]

Singularis sum ego donec transeam.[7] Jesus Christ before His death was almost the only martyr.

667. *Typical.*—The expressions *sword, shield. Potentissime.*[8]

668. We are estranged only by departing from charity. Our prayers and our virtues are abominable before God, if they are not the prayers and the virtues of Jesus Christ. And our sins will never be the object of [*mercy*], but of the justice of God, if they are not [*those of*] Jesus Christ. He has adopted our sins, and has [*admitted*] us into union [*with Him*], for virtues are [*His own, and*] sins are foreign to Him; while virtues [*are*] foreign to us, and our sins are our own.

Let us change the rule which we have hitherto chosen for judging what is good. We had our own will as our rule. Let us now take the will of [*God*]; all that He wills is good and right to us, all that He does not will is [*bad*].

All that God does not permit is forbidden. Sins are forbidden by the general declaration that God has made, that He did not allow them. Other things which He has left without general prohibition, and which for that reason are said to be permitted, are nevertheless not always permitted. For when God removed some one of them from us, and when, by the event, which is a manifestation of the will of God, it appears that God does not will that we should have a thing, that is then forbidden to us as sin; since the will of God is that we should not have one more than another. There is this sole difference between these two things, that it is certain that God will never allow sin, while it is not certain that He will never allow

[1] Ps. 75.5. "They have slept their sleep."
[2] I Cor. 7.31. "The fashion of this world."
[3] Deut. 8.9. "Bread without scarceness."
[4] Luke 11.3. "Our daily bread."
[5] Ps. 71.9. "The enemies of the Lord shall lick the dust."
[6] Exod. 12.8. *Cum lacticibus agrestibus.* "With bitter herbs."
[7] Ps. 140.10. "Whilst that I withal escape."
[8] Ps. 44.4 "O most mighty."

the other. But so long as God does not permit it, we ought to regard it as sin; so long as the absence of God's will, which alone is all goodness and all justice, renders it unjust and wrong.

669. To change the type, because of our weakness.

670. *Types.*—The Jews had grown old in these earthly thoughts, that God loved their father Abraham, his flesh and what sprung from it; that on account of this He had multiplied them and distinguished them from all other nations, without allowing them to intermingle; that, when they were languishing in Egypt, He brought them out with all these great signs in their favour; that He fed them with manna in the desert, and led them into a very rich land; that He gave them kings and a well-built temple, in order to offer up beasts before Him, by the shedding of whose blood they should be purified; and that, at last, He was to send them the Messiah to make them masters of all the world, and foretold the time of His coming.

The world having grown old in these carnal errors, Jesus Christ came at the time foretold, but not with the expected glory; and thus men did not think it was He. After His death, Saint Paul came to teach men that all these things had happened in allegory; that the kingdom of God did not consist in the flesh, but in the spirit; that the enemies of men were not the Babylonians, but the passions; that God delighted not in temples made with hands, but in a pure and contrite heart; that the circumcision of the body was unprofitable, but that of the heart was needed; that Moses had not given them the bread from heaven, etc.

But God, not having desired to reveal these things to this people who were unworthy of them and having, nevertheless, desired to foretell them, in order that they might be believed, foretold the time clearly, and expressed the things sometimes clearly, but very often in figures, in order that those who loved symbols might consider them and those who loved what was symbolised might see it therein.

All that tends not to charity is figurative.

The sole aim of the Scripture is charity.

All which tends not to the sole end is the type of it. For since there is only one end, all which does not lead to it in express terms is figurative.

God thus varies that sole precept of charity to satisfy our curiosity which seeks for variety, by that variety which still leads us to the one thing needful. For one thing alone is needful, and we love variety; and God satisfies both by these varieties, which lead to the one thing needful.

The Jews have so much loved the shadows and have so strictly expected them that they have misunderstood the reality, when it came in the time and manner foretold.

The Rabbis take the breasts of the Spouse for types, and all that does not express the only end they have, namely, temporal good.

And Christians take even the Eucharist as a type of the glory at which they aim.

671. The Jews, who have been called to subdue nations and kings, have been the slaves of sin; and the Christians, whose calling has been to be servants and subjects, are free children.

672. *A formal point.*—When Saint Peter and the Apostles deliberated about abolishing circumcision, where it was a question of acting against the law of God, they did not heed the prophets, but simply the reception of the Holy Spirit in the persons uncircumcised.

They thought it more certain that God approved of those whom He filled with His Spirit than it was that the law must be obeyed. They knew that the end of the law was only the Holy Spirit; and that thus, as men certainly had this without circumcision, it was not necessary.

673. *Fac secundum exemplar quod tibi ostensum est in monte.*[1]—The Jewish religion then has been formed on its likeness to the truth of the Messiah; and the truth of the Messiah has been recognised by the Jewish religion, which was the type of it.

Among the Jews the truth was only typified; in heaven it is revealed.

In the Church it is hidden and recognised by its resemblance to the type.

The type has been made according to the truth, and the truth has been recognised according to the type.

Saint Paul says himself that people will forbid to marry, and he himself speaks of it to the Corinthians in a way which is a snare. For if a prophet had said the one, and Saint Paul had then said the other, he would have been accused.

674. *Typical.*—"Do all things according to the pattern which has been shown thee on the mount." On which Saint Paul says that the Jews have shadowed forth heavenly things.

675. . . . And yet this Covenant, made to blind some and enlighten others, indicated in those very persons, whom it blinded, the truth which should be recognised by others. For the visible blessings which they received from God were so great and so divine that He indeed appeared able to give them those that are invisible and a Messiah.

For nature is an image of Grace, and visible miracles are images of the invisible. *Ut sciatis . . . tibi dico: Surge.*[2]

Isaiah says that Redemption will be as the passage of the Red Sea.

God has, then, shown by the deliverance from Egypt, and from the sea, by the defeat of kings, by the manna, by the whole genealogy of Abraham, that He was able to save, to send down bread from heaven, etc.; so that the people hostile to Him are the type and the representation of the very Messiah whom they know not, etc.

He has, then, taught us at last that all these things were only types and what is "true freedom," a "true Israelite," "true circumcision," "true bread from heaven," etc.

In these promises each one finds what he has most at heart, temporal benefits or spiritual, God or the creatures; but with this difference, that those who therein seek the creatures find them, but with many contradictions, with a prohibition against loving them, with the command to worship God only, and to love Him only, which is the same thing, and, finally, that the Messiah came not for them; whereas those who therein seek God find Him, without any contradiction, with

[1] Exod. 25.40. "Make them after their pattern, which was showed thee on the mount."
[2] Mark 2.10,11. "That ye may know . . . I say unto thee: Arise."

the command to love Him only, and that the Messiah came in the time foretold, to give them the blessings which they ask.

Thus the Jews had miracles and prophecies, which they saw fulfilled, and the teaching of their law was to worship and love God only; it was also perpetual. Thus it had all the marks of the true religion; and so it was. But the Jewish teaching must be distinguished from the teaching of the Jewish law. Now the Jewish teaching was not true, although it had miracles and prophecy and perpetuity, because it had not this other point of worshipping and loving God only.

676. The veil, which is upon these books for the Jews, is there also for evil Christians and for all who do not hate themselves.

But how well disposed men are to understand them and to know Jesus Christ, when they truly hate themselves!

677. A type conveys absence and presence, pleasure and pain.

A cipher has a double meaning, one clear and one in which it is said that the meaning is hidden.

678. *Types.*—A portrait conveys absence and presence, pleasure and pain. The reality excludes absence and pain.

To know if the law and the sacrifices are a reality or a type, we must see if the prophets, in speaking of these things, confined their view and their thought to them, so that they saw only the old covenant; or if they saw therein something else of which they were the representation, for in a portrait we see the thing figured. For this we need only examine what they say of them.

When they say that it will be eternal, do they mean to speak of that covenant which they say will be changed; and so of the sacrifices, etc.?

A cipher has two meanings. When we find out an important letter in which we discover a clear meaning, and in which it is nevertheless said that the meaning is veiled and obscure, that it is hidden, so that we might read the letter without seeing it, and interpret it without understanding it, what must we think but that here is a cipher with a double meaning, and the more so if we find obvious contradictions in the literal meaning? The prophets have clearly said that Israel would be always loved by God and that the law would be eternal; and they have said that their meaning would not be understood and that it was veiled.

How greatly, then, ought we to value those who interpret the cipher and teach us to understand the hidden meaning, especially if the principles which they educe are perfectly clear and natural! This is what Jesus Christ did, and the Apostles. They broke the seal; He rent the veil, and revealed the spirit. They have taught us through this that the enemies of man are his passions; that the Redeemer would be spiritual, and His reign spiritual; that there would be two advents, one in lowliness to humble the proud, the other in glory to exalt the humble; that Jesus Christ would be both God and man.

679. *Types.*—Jesus Christ opened their mind to understand the Scriptures.

Two great revelations are these. (1) All things happened to them in types: *vere Israëlitæ, vere liberi,*[1] true bread from Heaven. (2) A God humbled to the Cross. It

[1]See note to 564.

was necessary that Christ should suffer in order to enter into glory, "that He should destroy death through death." Two advents.

680. *Types.*—When once this secret is disclosed, it is impossible not to see it. Let us read the Old Testament in this light, and let us see if the sacrifices were real; if the fatherhood of Abraham was the true cause of the friendship of God; and if the promised land was the true place of rest. No. They are therefore types. Let us in the same way examine all those ordained ceremonies, all those commandments which are not of charity, and we shall see that they are types.

All these sacrifices and ceremonies were then either types or nonsense. Now these are things too clear and too lofty to be thought nonsense.

To know if the prophets confined their view in the Old Testament, or saw therein other things.

681. *Typical.*—The key of the cipher. *Veri adoratores.*[1] *Ecce agnus Dei qui tollit peccata mundi.*[2]

682. Is. 1. 21. Change of good into evil, and the vengeance of God. Is. 10. 1; 26. 20; 28. 1. Miracles: Is. 33. 9; 40. 17; 41. 26; 43. 13.

Jer. 11. 21; 15. 12; 17. 9. *Pravum est cor omnium et incrustabile; quis cognoscet illud?*[3] that is to say, Who can know all its evil? For it is already known to be wicked. *Ego dominus,*[4] etc.—vii. 14, *Faciam domui huic,*[5] etc. Trust in external sacrifices—7. 22, *Quia non sum locutus,*[6] etc. Outward sacrifice is not the essential point—11. 13, *Secundum numerum,*[7] etc. A multitude of doctrines.

Is. 44. 20-24; 54. 8; 63. 12-17; 66. 17. Jer. 2. 35; 4. 22-24; 5. 4, 29-31; 6. 16; 22. 15-17.

683. *Types.*—The letter kills. All happened in types. Here is the cipher which Saint Paul gives us. Christ must suffer. An humiliated God. Circumcision of the heart, true fasting, true sacrifice, a true temple. The prophets have shown that all these must be spiritual.

Not the meat which perishes, but that which does not perish.

"Ye shall be free indeed." Then the other freedom was only a type of freedom.

"I am the true bread from Heaven."

684. *Contradiction.*—We can only describe a good character by reconciling all contrary qualities, and it is not enough to keep up a series of harmonious qualities, without reconciling contradictory ones. To understand the meaning of an author, we must make all the contrary passages agree.

Thus, to understand Scripture, we must have a meaning in which all the contrary passages are reconciled. It is not enough to have one which suits many con-

---

[1]John 4.23. "True worshippers."
[2]John 1.29. "Behold the Lamb of God, which taketh away the sin of the world."
[3]"The heart is deceitful above all things and desperately wicked: who can know it?"
[4]Is. 44.24. "I am the Lord."
[5]"I will do unto this house."
[6]"For I spoke not unto your fathers."
[7]"According to the number."

curring passages; but it is necessary to have one which reconciles even contradictory passages.

Every author has a meaning in which all the contradictory passages agree, or he has no meaning at all. We cannot affirm the latter of Scripture and the prophets; they undoubtedly are full of good sense. We must, then, seek for a meaning which reconciles all discrepancies.

The true meaning, then, is not that of the Jews; but in Jesus Christ all the contradictions are reconciled.

The Jews could not reconcile the cessation of the royalty and principality, foretold by Hosea, with the prophecy of Jacob.

If we take the law, the sacrifices, and the kingdom as realities, we cannot reconcile all the passages. They must then necessarily be only types. We cannot even reconcile the passages of the same author, nor of the same book, nor sometimes of the same chapter, which indicates copiously what was the meaning of the author. As when Ezekiel, chap. 20., says that man will not live by the commandments of God and will live by them.

685. *Types.*—If the law and the sacrifices are the truth, it must please God, and must not displease Him. If they are types, they must be both pleasing and displeasing.

Now in all the Scripture they are both pleasing and displeasing. It is said that the law shall be changed; that the sacrifice shall be changed; that they shall be without law, without a prince, and without a sacrifice; that a new covenant shall be made; that the law shall be renewed; that the precepts which they have received are not good; that their sacrifices are abominable; that God has demanded none of them.

It is said, on the contrary, that the law shall abide for ever; that this covenant shall be for ever; that sacrifice shall be eternal; that the sceptre shall never depart from among them, because it shall not depart from them till the eternal King comes.

Do all these passages indicate what is real? No. Do they then indicate what is typical? No, but what is either real or typical. But the first passages, excluding as they do reality, indicate that all this is only typical.

All these passages together cannot be applied to reality; all can be said to be typical; therefore they are not spoken of reality, but of the type.

Agnus occisus est ab origine mundi.[1] A sacrificing judge.

686. *Contradictions.*—The sceptre till the Messiah—without king or prince.
The eternal law—changed.
The eternal covenant—a new covenant.
Good laws—bad precepts. Ezekiel.

687. *Types.*—When the word of God, which is really true, is false literally, it is true spiritually. *Sede a dextris meis:*[2] this is false literally, therefore it is true spiritually.

In these expressions, God is spoken of after the manner of men; and this means nothing else but that the intention which men have in giving a seat at their right

[1]Rev. 13.8. "The Lambs slain from the foundation of the world."
[2]Ps. 109.1. "Sit then at my right hand."

hand, God will have also. It is then an indication of the intention of God, not of His manner of carrying it out.

Thus when it is said, "God has received the odour of your incense, and will in recompense give you a rich land," that is equivalent to saying that the same intention which a man would have, who, pleased with your perfumes, should in recompense give you a rich land, God will have towards you, because you have had the same intention as a man has towards him to whom he presents perfumes. So *iratus est*, a "jealous God," etc. For, the things of God being inexpressible, they cannot be spoken of otherwise, and the Church makes use of them even to-day: *Quia confortavit seras*,[1] etc.

It is not allowable to attribute to Scripture the meaning which is not revealed to us that it has. Thus, to say that the closed *mem* of Isaiah signifies six hundred, has not been revealed. It might be said that the final *tsade* and *he deficientes* may signify mysteries. But it is not allowable to say so, and still less to say this is the way of the philosopher's stone. But we say that the literal meaning is not the true meaning, because the prophets have themselves said so.

688. I do not say that the *mem* is mystical.

689. Moses (Deut. 30) promises that God will circumcise their heart to render them capable of loving Him.

690. One saying of David, or of Moses, as for instance that "God will circumcise the heart," enables us to judge of their spirit. If all their other expressions were ambiguous and left us in doubt whether they were philosophers or Christians, one saying of this kind would in fact determine all the rest, as one sentence of Epictetus decides the meaning of all the rest to be the opposite. So far ambiguity exists, but not afterwards.

691. If one of two persons, who are telling silly stories, uses language with a double meaning, understood in his own circle, while the other uses it with only one meaning, any one not in the secret, who hears them both talk in this manner, will pass upon them the same judgment. But, if, afterwards, in the rest of their conversation one says angelic things, and the other always dull commonplaces, he will judge that the one spoke in mysteries, and not the other; the one having sufficiently shown that he is incapable of such foolishness and capable of being mysterious; and the other that he is incapable of mystery and capable of foolishness.

The Old Testament is a cipher.

692. There are some that see clearly that man has no other enemy than lust, which turns him from God, and not God; and that he has no other good than God, and not a rich land. Let those who believe that the good of man is in the flesh, and evil in what turns him away from sensual pleasures, [*satiate*] themselves with them, and [*die*] in them. But let those who seek God with all their heart, who are only troubled at not seeing Him, who desire only to possess Him and have as enemies only those who turn them away from Him, who are grieved at seeing themselves surrounded and overwhelmed with such enemies, take comfort. I pro-

[1]Ps. 147.13. *Quoniam* not *quia*. "For he hath strengthened the bars."

claim to them happy news. There exists a Redeemer for them. I shall show Him to them. I shall show that there is a God for them. I shall not show Him to others. I shall make them see that a Messiah has been promised, who should deliver them from their enemies, and that One has come to free them from their iniquities, but not from their enemies.

When David foretold that the Messiah would deliver His people from their enemies, one can believe that in the flesh these would be the Egyptians; and then I cannot show that the prophecy was fulfilled. But one can well believe also that the enemies would be their sins; for indeed the Egyptians were not their enemies, but their sins were so. This word *enemies* is, therefore, ambiguous. But if he says elsewhere, as he does, that He will deliver His people from their sins, as indeed do Isaiah and others, the ambiguity is removed, and the double meaning of enemies is reduced to the simple meaning of iniquities. For if he had *sins* in his mind, he could well denote them as *enemies;* but if he thought of *enemies,* he could not designate them as *iniquities.*

Now Moses, David, and Isaiah used the same terms. Who will say, then, that they have not the same meaning and that David's meaning, which is plainly *iniquities* when he spoke of *enemies,* was not the same as [*that of*] Moses when speaking of *enemies?*

Daniel (ix) prays for the deliverance of the people from the captivity of their enemies. But he was thinking of *sins,* and, to show this, he says that Gabriel came to tell him that his prayer was heard, and that there were only seventy weeks to wait, after which the people would be freed from iniquity, sin would have an end, and the Redeemer, the Holy of Holies, would bring *eternal* justice, not legal, but eternal.

SECTION XI

THE PROPHECIES

693. When I see the blindness and the wretchedness of man, when I regard the whole silent universe and man without light, left to himself and, as it were, lost in this corner of the universe, without knowing who has put him there, what he has come to do, what will become of him at death, and incapable of all knowledge, I become terrified, like a man who should be carried in his sleep to a dreadful desert island and should awake without knowing where he is and without means of escape. And thereupon I wonder how people in a condition so wretched do not fall into despair. I see other persons around me of a like nature. I ask them if they are better informed than I am. They tell me that they are not. And thereupon these wretched and lost beings, having looked around them and seen some pleasing objects, have given and attached themselves to them. For my own part, I have not been able to attach myself to them, and, considering how strongly it appears that there is something else than what I see, I have examined whether this God has not left some sign of Himself.

I see many contradictory religions, and consequently all false save one. Each wants to be believed on its own authority, and threatens unbelievers. I do not therefore believe them. Every one can say this; every one can call himself a prophet.

But I see that Christian religion wherein prophecies are fulfilled; and that is what every one cannot do.

694. And what crowns all this is prediction, so that it should not be said that it is chance which has done it?

Whosoever, having only a week to live, will not find out that it is expedient to believe that all this is not a stroke of chance . . .

Now, if the passions had no hold on us, a week and a hundred years would amount to the same thing.

695. *Prophecies.*—Great Pan is dead.

696. *Susceperunt verbum cum omni aviditate, scrutantes Scripturas, si ita se haberent.*[1]

697. *Prodita lege. Impleta cerne. Implenda collige.*[2]

698. We understand the prophecies only when we see the events happen. Thus the proofs of retreat, discretion, silence, etc., are proofs only to those who know and believe them.

Joseph so internal in a law so external.

Outward penances dispose to inward, as humiliations to humility. Thus the . . .

699. The synagogue has preceded the church; the Jews, the Christians. The prophets have foretold the Christians; Saint John, Jesus Christ.

700. It is glorious to see with the eyes of faith the history of Herod and of Cæsar.

701. The zeal of the Jews for their law and their temple (Josephus, and Philo the Jew, *Ad Caïum*). What other people had such a zeal? It was necessary they should have it.

Jesus Christ foretold as to the time and the state of the world. The ruler taken from the thigh, and the fourth monarchy. How lucky we are to see this light amidst this darkness!

How fine it is to see, with the eyes of faith, Darius and Cyrus, Alexander, the Romans, Pompey and Herod working, without knowing it, for the glory of the Gospel!

702. Zeal of the Jewish people for the law, especially after there were no more prophets.

703. While the prophets were for maintaining the law, the people were indifferent. But, since there have been no more prophets, zeal has succeeded them.

---

[1] Acts 17.11. "They received the word with all readiness of mind, and searched the Scriptures daily, whether those things were so."

[2] "Read what has been announced. See what has been accomplished. Meditate on what is to be done."

704. The devil troubled the zeal of the Jews before Jesus Christ, because he would have been their salvation, but not since.

The Jewish people scorned by the Gentiles; the Christian people persecuted.

705. *Proof.*—Prophecies with their fulfilment; what has preceded and what has followed Jesus Christ.

706. The prophecies are the strongest proof of Jesus Christ. It is for them also that God has made most provision; for the event which has fulfilled them is a miracle existing since the birth of the Church to the end. So God has raised up prophets during sixteen hundred years, and, during four hundred years afterwards, He has scattered all these prophecies among all the Jews, who carried them into all parts of the world. Such was the preparation for the birth of Jesus Christ, and, as His Gospel was to be believed by all the world, it was not only necessary that there should be prophecies to make it believed, but that these prophecies should exist throughout the whole world, in order to make it embraced by the whole world.

707. But it was not enough that the prophecies should exist. It was necessary that they should be distributed throughout all places and preserved throughout all times. And, in order that this agreement might not be taken for an effect of chance, it was necessary that this should be foretold.

It is far more glorious for the Messiah that the Jews should be the spectators and even the instruments of His glory, besides that God had reserved them.

708. *Prophecies.*—The time foretold by the state of the Jewish people, by the state of the heathen, by the state of the temple, by the number of years.

709. One must be bold to predict the same thing in so many ways. It was necessary that the four idolatrous or pagan monarchies, the end of the kingdom of Judah, and the seventy weeks, should happen at the same time, and all this before the second temple was destroyed.

710. *Prophecies.*—If one man alone had made a book of predictions about Jesus Christ, as to the time and the manner, and Jesus Christ had come in conformity to these prophecies, this fact would have infinite weight.

But there is much more here. Here is a succession of men during four thousand years, who, consequently and without variation, come, one after another, to foretell this same event. Here is a whole people who announce it and who have existed for four thousand years, in order to give corporate testimony of the assurances which they have and from which they cannot be diverted by whatever threats and persecutions people may make against them. This is far more important.

711. *Predictions of particular things.*—They were strangers in Egypt, without any private property, either in that country or elsewhere. [There was not the least appearance, either of the royalty which had previously existed so long, or of that supreme council of seventy judges which they called the *Sanhedrin* and which, having been instituted by Moses, lasted to the time of Jesus Christ. All these things were as far removed from their state at that time as they could be], when Jacob,

dying, and blessing his twelve children, declared to them, that they would be proprietors of a great land, and foretold in particular to the family of Judah, that the kings, who would one day rule them, should be of his race; and that all his brethren should be their subjects; [and that even the Messiah, who was to be the expectation of nations, should spring from him; and that the kingship should not be taken away from Judah, nor the ruler and law-giver of his descendants, till the expected Messiah should arrive in his family].

This same Jacob, disposing of this future land as though he had been its ruler, gave a portion to Joseph more than to the others. "I give you," said he, "one part more than to your brothers." And blessing his two children, Ephraim and Man-asseh, whom Joseph had presented to him, the elder, Manasseh, on his right, and the young Ephraim on his left, he put his arms crosswise, and placing his right hand on the head of Ephraim, and his left on Manasseh, he blessed them in this manner. And, upon Joseph's representing to him that he was preferring the younger, he replied to him with admirable resolution: "I know it well, my son; but Ephraim will increase more than Manasseh." This has been indeed so true in the result that, being alone almost as fruitful as the two entire lines which com-posed a whole kingdom, they have been usually called by the name of Ephraim alone.

This same Joseph, when dying, bade his children carry his bones with them when they should go into that land to which they only came two hundred years afterwards.

Moses, who wrote all these things so long before they happened, himself as-signed to each family portions of that land before they entered it, as though he had been its ruler. [In fact he declared that God was to raise up from their nation and their race a prophet, of whom he was the type; and he foretold them exactly all that was to happen to them in the land which they were to enter after his death, the victories which God would give them, their ingratitude towards God, the punishments which they would receive for it, and the rest of their adventures.] He gave them judges who should make the division. He prescribed the entire form of political government which they should observe, the cities of refuge which they should build, and . . .

712. The prophecies about particular things are mingled with those about the Messiah, so that the prophecies of the Messiah should not be without proofs, nor the special prophecies without fruit.

713. *Perpetual captivity of the Jews.*—Jer. 11. 11: "I will bring evil upon Judah from which they shall not be able to escape."

Types.—Is. 5: "The Lord had a vineyard, from which He looked for grapes; and it brought forth only wild grapes. I will therefore lay it waste, and destroy it; the earth shall only bring forth thorns, and I will forbid the clouds from [*raining*] upon it. The vineyard of the Lord is the house of Israel, and the men of Judah His pleasant plant. I looked that they should do justice, and they bring forth only iniquities."

Is. 8: "Sanctify the Lord with fear and trembling; let Him be your only dread, and He shall be to you for a sanctuary, but for a stone of stumbling and a rock of offence to both the houses of Israel, for a gin and for a snare to the inhabitants of Jerusalem; and many among them shall stumble against that stone, and fall, and be broken, and be snared, and perish. Hide my words, and cover my law for my disciples.

"I will then wait in patience upon the Lord that hideth and concealeth Himself from the house of Jacob."

Is. 29: "Be amazed and wonder, people of Israel; stagger and stumble, and be drunken, but not with wine; stagger, but not with strong drink. For the Lord hath poured out upon you the spirit of deep sleep. He will close your eyes; He will cover your princes and your prophets that have visions." (Daniel xii: "The wicked shall not understand, but the wise shall understand." Hosea, the last chapter, the last verse, after many temporal blessings, says: "Who is wise, and he shall understand these things?" etc.) "And the visions of all the prophets are become unto you as a sealed book, which men deliver to one that is learned, and who can read; and he saith, I cannot read it, for it is sealed. And when the book is delivered to them that are not learned, they say, I am not learned.

"Wherefore the Lord said, Forasmuch as this people with their lips do honour me, but have removed their heart far from me,"—there is the reason and the cause of it; for if they adored God in their hearts, they would understand the prophecies, —"and their fear towards me is taught by the precept of man. Therefore, behold, I will proceed to do a marvellous work among this people, even a marvellous work and a wonder; for the wisdom of their wise men shall perish, and their understanding shall be [hid]."

Prophecies. Proofs of Divinity.—Is. 41: "Shew the things that are to come hereafter, that we may know that ye are gods: we will incline our heart unto your words. Teach us the things that have been at the beginning, and declare us things for to come.

"By this we shall know that ye are gods. Yea, do good or do evil, if you can. Let us then behold it and reason together. Behold, ye are of nothing, and only an abomination, etc. Who," (among contemporary writers), "hath declared from the beginning that we may know of the things done from the beginning and origin? that we may say, You are righteous. There is none that teacheth us, yea, there is none that declareth the future."

Is. 42: "I am the Lord, and my glory will I not give to another. I have foretold the things which have come to pass, and things that are to come do I declare. Sing unto God a new song in all the earth.

"Bring forth the blind people that have eyes and see not, and the deaf that have ears and hear not. Let all the nations be gathered together. Who among them can declare this, and shew us former things, and things to come? Let them bring forth their witnesses, that they may be justified; or let them hear, and say, It is truth.

"Ye are my witnesses, saith the Lord, and my servant whom I have chosen; that ye may know and believe me, and understand that I am He.

"I have declared, and have saved, and I alone have done wonders before your eyes: ye are my witnesses, said the Lord, that I am God.

"For your sake I have brought down the forces of the Babylonians. I am the Lord, your Holy One and Creator.

"I have made a way in the sea, and a path in the mighty waters. I am He that drowned and destroyed for ever the mighty enemies that have resisted you.

"Remember ye not the former things, neither consider the things of old.

"Behold, I will do a new thing; now it shall spring forth; shall ye not know it? I will even make a way in the wilderness, and rivers in the desert.

"This people have I formed for myself; I have established them to shew forth my praise, etc.

"I, even I, am He that blotteth out thy transgressions for mine own sake, and will not remember thy sins. Put in remembrance your ingratitude: see thou, if thou mayest be justified. Thy first father hath sinned, and thy teachers have transgressed against me."

Is. 44.: "I am the first, and I am the last, saith the Lord. Let him who will equal himself to me, declare the order of things since I appointed the ancient people, and the things that are coming. Fear ye not: have I not told you all these things? Ye are my witnesses."

Prophecy of Cyrus.—Is. 45. 4: "For Jacob's sake, mine elect, I have called thee by thy name."

Is. 45. 21: "Come and let us reason together. Who hath declared this from ancient time? Who hath told it from that time? Have not I, the Lord"?

Is. 46: "Remember the former things of old, and know there is none like me, declaring the end from the beginning, and from ancient times the things that are not yet done, saying, My counsel shall stand, and I will do all my pleasure."

Is. 42: "Behold, the former things are come to pass, and new things do I declare; before they spring forth I tell you of them."

Is. 48. 3: "I have declared the former things from the beginning; I did them suddenly; and they came to pass. Because I know that thou art obstinate, that thy spirit is rebellious, and thy brow brass; I have even declared it to thee before it came to pass: lest thou shouldst say that it was the work of thy gods, and the effect of their commands.

"Thou hast seen all this; and will not ye declare it? I have shewed thee new things from this time, even hidden things, and thou didst not know them. They are created now, and not from the beginning; I have kept them hidden from thee; lest thou shouldst say, Behold, I knew them.

"Yea, thou knewest not; yea, thou heardest not; yea, from that time that thine ear was not opened: for I knew that thou couldst deal very treacherously, and wast called a transgressor from the womb."

Reprobation of the Jews and conversion of the Gentiles.—Is. 65: "I am sought of them that asked not for me; I am found of them that sought me not; I said, Behold me, behold me, behold me, unto a nation that did not call upon my name.

"I have spread out my hands all the day unto an unbelieving people, which walketh in a way that was not good, after their own thoughts; a people that provoketh me to anger continually by the sins they commit in my face; that sacrificeth to idols, etc.

"These shall be scattered like smoke in the day of my wrath, etc.

"Your iniquities, and the iniquities of your fathers, will I assemble together, and will recompense you for all according to your works.

"Thus saith the Lord, As the new wine is found in the cluster, and one saith, Destroy it not, for a blessing is in it [and the promise of fruit]: for my servants' sake I will not destroy all Israel.

"Thus I will bring forth a seed out of Jacob and out of Judah, an inheritor of my mountains, and mine elect and my servants shall inherit it, and my fertile and abundant plains; but I will destroy all others, because you have forgotten your God to serve strange gods. I called, and ye did not answer; I spake, and ye did not hear; and ye did choose the thing which I forbade.

"Therefore thus saith the Lord, Behold, my servants shall eat, but ye shall be hungry; my servants shall rejoice, but ye shall be ashamed; my servants shall sing for joy of heart, but ye shall cry and howl for vexation of spirit.

"And ye shall leave your name for a curse unto my chosen: for the Lord shall slay thee, and call His servants by another name, that he who blesseth himself in the earth shall bless himself in God, etc., because the former troubles are forgotten.

"For, behold, I create new heavens and a new earth; and the former things shall not be remembered, nor come into mind.

"But be ye glad and rejoice for ever in that which I create; for, behold, I create Jerusalem a rejoicing, and her people a joy.

"And I will rejoice in Jerusalem and joy in my people; and the voice of weeping shall no more be heard in her, nor the voice of crying.

"Before they call, I will answer; and while they are yet speaking, I will hear. The wolf and the lamb shall feed together, and the lion shall eat straw like the bullock; and dust shall be the serpent's meat. They shall not hurt nor destroy in all my holy mountain."

Is. 56. 3: "Thus saith the Lord, Keep ye judgment, and do justice: for my salvation is near to come, and my righteousness to be revealed.

"Blessed is the man that doeth this, that keepeth the Sabbath, and keepeth his hand from doing any evil.

"Neither let the strangers that have joined themselves to me, say, God will separate me from His people. For thus saith the Lord: Whoever will keep my Sabbath, and choose the things that please me, and take hold of my covenant; even unto them will I give in mine house a place and a name better than that of sons and of daughters: I will give them an everlasting name, that shall not be cut off."

Is. 59. 9: "Therefore for our iniquities is justice far from us: we wait for light, but behold obscurity; for brightness, but we walk in darkness. We grope for the wall like the blind; we stumble at noonday as in the night: we are in desolate places as dead men.

"We roar all like bears, and mourn sore like doves; we look for judgment, but there is none; for salvation, but it is far from us."

Is. 66. 18: "But I know their works and their thoughts; it shall come that I will gather all nations and tongues, and they shall see my glory.

"And I will set a sign among them, and I will send those that escape of them unto the nations, to Africa, to Lydia, to Italy, to Greece, and to the people that have not heard my fame, neither have seen my glory. And they shall bring your brethren."

Jer. 7. *Reprobation of the Temple:* "Go ye unto Shiloth, where I set my name at the first, and see what I did to it for the wickedness of my people. And now, because ye have done all these works, saith the Lord, I will do unto this house, wherein my name is called upon, wherein ye trust, and unto the place which I gave to your priests, as I have done to Shiloth." (For I have rejected it, and made myself a temple elsewhere.)

"And I will cast you out of my sight, as I have cast out all your brethren, even the seed of Ephraim." (Rejected for ever.) "Therefore pray not for this people."

Jer. 7. 22: "What avails it you to add sacrifice to sacrifice? For I spake not unto your fathers, when I brought them out of the land of Egypt, concerning burnt offerings or sacrifices. But this thing commanded I them, saying, Obey and be faithful to my commandments, and I will be your God, and ye shall be my people." (It was only after they had sacrificed to the golden calf that I gave myself sacrifices to turn into good an evil custom.)

Jer. 7. 4: "Trust ye not in lying words, saying, The temple of the Lord, the temple of the Lord, the temple of the Lord, are these."

714. The Jews witnesses for God. Is. 43. 9; 44. 8.

Prophecies fulfilled.—I Kings 13. 2. I Kings 22. 16. Joshua 6. 26. I Kings 16. 34. Deut. 23.

Malachi i. 11. The sacrifice of the Jews rejected, and the sacrifice of the heathen, (even out of Jerusalem,) and in all places.

Moses, before dying, foretold the calling of the Gentiles, Deut. 32. 21 and the reprobation of the Jews.

Moses foretold what would happen to each tribe.

Prophecy.—"Your name shall be a curse unto mine elect, and I will give them another name."

"Make their heart fat," and how? by flattering their lust and making them hope to satisfy it.

715. *Prophecy.*—Amos and Zechariah. They have sold the just one, and therefore will not be recalled. Jesus Christ betrayed.

They shall no more remember Egypt. See Is. 43. 16, 17, 18, 19. Jer. 23. 6, 7.

Prophecy.—The Jews shall be scattered abroad. Is. 27. 6. A new law, Jerem. 31. 32.

Malachi. *Grotius.* The second temple glorious. Jesus Christ will come. Haggai 2. 7, 8, 9, 10.

The calling of the Gentiles. Joel 2. 28. Hosea 2. 24. Deut. 32. 21. Malachi 1. 11.

716. Hosea 3.—Is. 42. 48. 44. 60. 61. last verse. "I foretold it long since that they might know that it is I." Jaddus to Alexander.

717. [*Prophecies.*—The promise that David will always have descendants. Jer. 13. 13.]

718. The eternal reign of the race of David, II Chron., by all the prophecies, and with an oath. And it was not temporally fulfilled. Jer. 23. 20.

719. We might perhaps think that, when the prophets foretold that the sceptre should not depart from Judah until the eternal King came, they spoke to flatter the people and that their prophecy was proved false by Herod. But to show that this was not their meaning and that, on the contrary, they knew well that this

temporal kingdom should cease, they said that they would be without a king and without a prince, and for a long time. Hosea 3. 4.

720. *Non habemus regem nisi Cæsarem*.[1] Therefore Jesus Christ was the Messiah, since they had no longer any king but a stranger, and would have no other.

721. We have no king but Cæsar.

722. Daniel 2: "All thy soothsayers and wise men cannot shew unto thee the secret which thou hast demanded. But there is a God in heaven who can do so, and that hath revealed to thee in thy dream what shall be in the latter days." (This dream must have caused him much misgiving.)

"And it is not by my own wisdom that I have knowledge of this secret, but by the revelation of this same God, that hath revealed it to me, to make it manifest in thy presence.

"Thy dream was then of this kind. Thou sawest a great image, high and terrible, which stood before thee. His head was of gold, his breast and arms of silver, his belly and his thighs of brass, his legs of iron, his feet part of iron and part of clay. Thus thou sawest till that a stone was cut out without hands, which smote the image upon his feet, that were of iron and of clay, and brake them to pieces.

"Then was the iron, the clay, the brass, the silver, and the gold broken to pieces together, and the wind carried them away; but this stone that smote the image became a great mountain, and filled the whole earth. This is the dream, and now I will give thee the interpretation thereof.

"Thou who art the greatest of kings, and to whom God hath given a power so vast that thou art renowned among all peoples, art the head of gold which thou hast seen. But after thee shall arise another kingdom inferior to thee, and another third kingdom of brass, which shall bear rule over all the earth.

"But the fourth kingdom shall be strong as iron, and even as iron breaketh in pieces and subdueth all things, so shall this empire break in pieces and bruise all.

"And whereas thou sawest the feet and toes, part of clay and part of iron, the kingdom shall be divided; but there shall be in it of the strength of iron and of the weakness of clay.

"But as iron cannot be firmly mixed with clay, so they who are represented by the iron and by the clay, shall not cleave one to another though united by marriage.

"Now in the days of these kings shall God set up a kingdom, which shall never be destroyed, nor ever be delivered up to other people. It shall break in pieces and consume all these kingdoms, and it shall stand for ever, according as thou sawest that the stone was cut out of the mountain without hands, and that it fell from the mountain, and brake in pieces the iron, the clay, the silver, and the gold. God hath made known to thee what shall come to pass hereafter. This dream is certain, and the interpretation thereof sure.

"Then Nebuchadnezzar fell upon his face towards the earth," etc.

Daniel 8. 8. "Daniel having seen the combat of the ram and of the he-goat, who vanquished him and ruled over the earth, whereof the principal horn being broken four others came up toward the four winds of heaven, and out of one of them came forth a little horn, which waxed exceedingly great toward the south,

[1] John 19.15. "We have no king but Caesar."

and toward the east, and toward the land of Israel, and it waxed great even to the host of heaven; and it cast down some of the stars, and stamped upon them, and at last overthrew the prince, and by him the daily sacrifice was taken away, and the place of his sanctuary was cast down.

"This is what Daniel saw. He sought the meaning of it, and a voice cried in this manner, 'Gabriel, make this man to understand the vision.' And Gabriel said:

"The ram which thou sawest is the king of the Medes and Persians, and the he-goat is the king of Greece, and the great horn that is between his eyes is the first king of this monarchy.

"Now that being broken, whereas four stood up for it, four kingdoms shall stand up out of the nation, but not in his power.

"And in the latter time of their kingdom, when iniquities are come to the full, there shall arise a king, insolent and strong, but not by his own power, to whom all things shall succeed after his own will; and he shall destroy the holy people, and through his policy also he shall cause craft to prosper in his hand, and he shall destroy many. He shall also stand up against the Prince of princes, but he shall perish miserably, and nevertheless by a violent hand."

Daniel 9. 20. "Whilst I was praying with all my heart, and confessing my sin and the sin of all my people, and prostrating myself before my God, even Gabriel, whom I had seen in the vision at the beginning, came to me and touched me about the time of the evening oblation, and he informed me and said, O Daniel, I am now come forth to give thee the knowledge of things. At the beginning of thy supplications I came to shew that which thou didst desire, for thou are greatly beloved: therefore understand the matter, and consider the vision. Seventy weeks are determined upon thy people, and upon thy holy city, to finish the transgression, and to make an end of sins, and to abolish iniquity, and to bring in everlasting righteousness; to accomplish the vision and the prophecies, and to anoint the Most Holy. (After which this people shall be no more thy people, nor this city the holy city. The times of wrath shall be passed, and the years of grace shall come for ever.)

"Know therefore, and understand, that, from the going forth of the commandment to restore and to build Jerusalem unto the Messiah the Prince, shall be seven weeks, and three score and two weeks." (The Hebrews were accustomed to divide numbers, and to place the small first. Thus, 7 and 62 make 69. Of this 70 there will then remain the 70th, that is to say, the 7 last years of which he will speak next.)

"The street shall be built again, and the wall, even in troublous times. And after three score and two weeks," (which have followed the first seven. Christ will then be killed after the sixty-nine weeks, that is to say, in the last week), "the Christ shall be cut off, and a people of the prince that shall come shall destroy the city and the sanctuary, and overwhelm all, and the end of that war shall accomplish the desolation."

"Now one week," (which is the seventieth, which remains), "shall confirm the covenant with many, and in the midst of the week," (that is to say, the last three and a half years), "he shall cause the sacrifice and the oblation to cease, and for the overspreading of abominations he shall make it desolate, even until the consummation, and that determined shall be poured upon the desolate."

Daniel 11. "The angel said to Daniel: There shall stand up yet," (after Cyrus, under whom this still is), "three kings in Persia," (Cambyses, Smerdis, Darius);

"and the fourth who shall then come," (Xerxes) "shall be far richer than they all, and far stronger, and shall stir up all his people against the Greeks.

"But a mighty king shall stand up," (Alexander), "that shall rule with great dominion, and do according to his will. And when he shall stand up, his kingdom shall be broken, and shall be divided in four parts toward the four winds of heaven," (as he had said above, 7. 6; 8. 8), "but not his posterity; and his successors shall not equal his power, for his kingdom shall be plucked up, even for others besides these," (his four chief successors).

"And the king of the south," (Ptolemy, son of Lagos, Egypt), "shall be strong; but one of his princes shall be strong above him, and his dominion shall be a great dominion," (Seleucus, King of Syria. Appian says that he was the most powerful of Alexander's successors).

"And in the end of years they shall join themselves together, and the king's daughter of the south," (Berenice, daughter of Ptolemy Philadelphus, son of the other Ptolemy), "shall come to the king of the north," (to Antiochus Deus, King of Syria and of Asia, son of Seleucus Lagidas), "to make peace between these princes.

"But neither she nor her seed shall have a long authority; for she and they that brought her, and her children, and her friends, shall be delivered to death." (Berenice and her son were killed by Seleucus Callinicus.)

"But out of a branch of her roots shall one stand up," (Ptolemy Euergetes was the issue of the same father as Berenice), "which shall come with a mighty army into the land of the king of the north, where he shall put all under subjection, and he shall also carry captive into Egypt their gods, their princes, their gold, their silver, and all their precious spoils," (if he had not been called into Egypt by domestic reasons, says Justin, he would have entirely stripped Seleucus); "and he shall continue several years when the king of the north can do nought against him.

"And so he shall return into his kingdom. But his sons shall be stirred up, and shall assemble a multitude of great forces," (Seleucus Ceraunus, Antiochus the Great). "And their army shall come and overthrow all; wherefore the king of the south shall be moved with choler, and shall also form a great army, and fight him," (Ptolemy Philopator against Antiochus the Great at Raphia), "and conquer; and his troops shall become insolent, and his heart shall be lifted up," (this Ptolemy desecrated the temple; Josephus): "he shall cast down many ten thousands, but he shall not be strengthened by it. For the king of the north," (Antiochus the Great), "shall return with a greater multitude than before, and in those times also a great number of enemies shall stand up against the king of the south," (during the reign of the young Ptolemy Epiphanes); "also the apostates and robbers of thy people shall exalt themselves to establish the vision; but they shall fall." (Those who abandon their religion to please Euergetes, when he will send his troops to Scopas; for Antiochus will again take Scopas, and conquer them.) "And the king of the north shall destroy the fenced cities, and the arms of the south shall not withstand, and all shall yield to his will; he shall stand in the land of Israel, and it shall yield to him. And thus he shall think to make himself master of all the empire of Egypt," (despising the youth of Epiphanes, says Justin). "And for that he shall make alliance with him, and give his daughter" (Cleopatra, in order that she may betray her husband. On which Appian says that, doubting his ability to make himself master of Egypt by force, because of the protection of the Romans, he wished to attempt it by cunning). "He shall wish to corrupt her, but she shall not stand on his side, neither be for him. Then he shall turn his face to other designs, and shall think to make himself master of some isles," (that is to say, seaports), "and shall take many," (as Appian says).

"But a prince shall oppose his conquests," (Scipio Africanus, who stopped the progress of Antiochus the Great, because he offended the Romans in the person of their allies), "and shall cause the reproach offered by him to cease. He shall then return into his kingdom and there perish, and be no more." (He was slain by his soldiers.)

"And he who shall stand up in his estate," (Seleucus Philopator or Soter, the son of Antiochus the Great), "shall be a tyrant, a raiser of taxes in the glory of the kingdom," (which means the people), "but within a few days he shall be destroyed, neither in anger nor in battle. And in his place shall stand up a vile person, unworthy of the honour of the kingdom, but he shall come in cleverly by flatteries. All armies shall bend before him; he shall conquer them, and even the prince with whom he has made a covenant. For having renewed the league with him, he shall work deceitfully, and enter with a small people into his province, peaceably and without fear. He shall take the fattest places, and shall do that which his fathers have not done, and ravage on all sides. He shall forecast great devices during his time."

723. *Prophecies.*—The seventy weeks of Daniel are ambiguous as regards the term of commencement, because of the terms of the prophecy; and as regards the term of conclusion, because of the differences among chronologists. But all this difference extends only to two hundred years.

724. *Predictions.*—That in the fourth monarchy, before the destruction of the second temple, before the dominion of the Jews was taken away, in the seventieth week of Daniel, during the continuance of the second temple, the heathen should be instructed, and brought to the knowledge of the God worshipped by the Jews; that those who loved Him should be delivered from their enemies, and filled with His fear and love.

And it happened that in the fourth monarchy, before the destruction of the second temple, etc., the heathen in great number worshipped God, and led an angelic life. Maidens dedicated their virginity and their life to God. Men renounced their pleasures. What Plato could only make acceptable to a few men, specially chosen and instructed, a secret influence imparted by the power of a few words, to a hundred million ignorant men.

The rich left their wealth. Children left the dainty homes of their parents to go into the rough desert. (See Philo the Jew.) All this was foretold a great while ago. For two thousand years no heathen had worshipped the God of the Jews; and at the time foretold, a great number of the heathen worshipped this only God. The temples were destroyed. The very kings made submission to the cross. All this was due to the Spirit of God, which was spread abroad upon the earth.

No heathen, since Moses until Jesus Christ, believed according to the very Rabbis. A great number of the heathen, after Jesus Christ, believed in the books of Moses, kept them in substance and spirit, and only rejected what was useless.

725. *Prophecies.*—The conversion of the Egyptians (Isaiah 19. 19); an altar in Egypt to the true God.

726. *Prophecies.*—*In Egypt. Pugio Fidei*, p. 659. *Talmud:*
"It is a tradition among us, that, when the Messiah shall come, the house of God, destined for the dispensation of His Word, shall be full of filth and impurity; and that the wisdom of the scribes shall be corrupt and rotten. Those who shall be afraid to sin, shall be rejected by the people, and treated as senseless fools."

Is. xlix: "Listen, O isles, unto me, and hearken, ye people, from afar: The Lord hath called me by my name from the womb of my mother; in the shadow of His hand hath He hid me, and hath made my words like a sharp sword, and said unto me, Thou art my servant in whom I will be glorified. Then I said, Lord, have I laboured in vain? have I spent my strength for nought? yet surely my judgment is with Thee, O Lord, and my work with Thee. And now, saith the Lord, that formed me from the womb to be His servant, to bring Jacob and Israel again to Him, Thou shalt be glorious in my sight, and I will be thy strength. It is a light thing that thou shouldst convert the tribes of Jacob; I have raised thee up for a light to the Gentiles, that thou mayest be my salvation unto the ends of the earth. Thus saith the Lord to him whom man despiseth, to him whom the nation abhorreth, to a servant of rulers, Princes and kings shall worship thee, because the Lord is faithful that hath chosen thee.

"Again saith the Lord unto me, I have heard thee in the days of salvation and of mercy, and I will preserve thee for a covenant of the people, to cause to inherit the desolate nations, that thou mayest say to the prisoners: Go forth; to them that are in darkness show yourselves, and possess these abundant and fertile lands. They shall not hunger nor thirst, neither shall the heat nor sun smite them; for he that hath mercy upon them shall lead them, even by the springs of waters shall he guide them, and make the mountains a way before them. Behold, the peoples shall come from all parts, from the east and from the west, from the north and from the south. Let the heavens give glory to God; let the earth be joyful; for it hath pleased the Lord to comfort His people, and He will have mercy upon the poor who hope in Him.

"Yet Zion dared to say: The Lord hath forsaken me, and hath forgotten me. Can a woman forget her child, that she should not have compassion on the son of her womb? but if she forget, yet will not I forget thee, O Sion. I will bear thee always between my hands, and thy walls are continually before me. They that shall build thee are come, and thy destroyers shall go forth of thee. Lift up thine eyes round about, and behold; all these gather themselves together, and come to thee. As I live, saith the Lord, thou shalt surely clothe thee with them all, as with an ornament. Thy waste and thy desolate places, and the land of thy destruction shall even now be too narrow by reason of the inhabitants, and the children thou shalt have after thy barrenness shall say again in thy ears: The place is too strait for me: give place to me that I may dwell. Then shalt thou say in thy heart: Who hath begotten me these, seeing I have lost my children, and am desolate, a captive, and removing to and fro? and who brought up these? Behold, I was left alone; these, where had they been? And the Lord shall say to thee: Behold, I will lift up mine hand to the Gentiles, and set up my standard to the people; and they shall bring thy sons in their arms and in their bosoms. And kings shall be their nursing fathers, and queens their nursing mothers; they shall bow down to thee with their face toward the earth, and lick up the dust of thy feet; and thou shalt know that I am the Lord; for they shall not be ashamed that wait for me. Shall the prey be taken from the mighty? But even if the captives be taken away from the strong, nothing shall hinder me from saving thy children, and from destroying thy enemies; and all flesh shall know that I am the Lord, thy Saviour and thy Redeemer, the mighty One of Jacob.

"Thus saith the Lord: What is the bill of this divorcement, wherewith I have put away the synagogue? and why have I delivered it into the hand of your enemies? Is it not for your iniquities and for your transgressions that I have put it away?

"For I came, and no man received me; I called and there was none to hear. Is my arm shortened, that I cannot redeem?

"Therefore I will show the tokens of mine anger; I will clothe the heavens with darkness, and make sackcloth their covering.

"The Lord hath given me the tongue of the learned that I should know how to speak a word in season to him that is weary. He hath opened mine ear, and I have listened to Him as a master.

"The Lord hath revealed His will, and I was not rebellious.

"I gave my body to the smiters, and my cheeks to outrage; I hid not my face from shame and spitting. But the Lord hath helped me; therefore I have not been confounded.

"He is near that justifieth me; who will contend with me? who will be mine adversary, and accuse me of sin, God himself being my protector?

"All men shall pass away, and be consumed by time; let those that fear God hearken to the voice of His servant; let him that languisheth in darkness put his trust in the Lord. But as for you, ye do but kindle the wrath of God upon you; ye walk in the light of your fire and in the sparks that ye have kindled. This shall ye have of mine hand; ye shall lie down in sorrow.

"Hearken to me, ye that follow after righteousness, ye that seek the Lord: look unto the rock whence ye are hewn, and to the hole of the pit whence ye are digged. Look unto Abraham, your father, and unto Sarah that bare you: for I called him alone, when childless, and increased him. Behold, I have comforted Zion, and heaped upon her blessings and consolations.

"Hearken unto me, my people, and give ear unto me; for a law shall proceed from me, and I will make my judgment to rest for a light of the Gentiles."

Amos viii. The prophet, having enumerated the sins of Israel, said that God had sworn to take vengeance on them.

He says this: "And it shall come to pass in that day, saith the Lord, that I will cause the sun to go down at noon, and I will darken the earth in the clear day; and I will turn your feasts into mourning, and all your songs into lamentation.

"You all shall have sorrow and suffering, and I will make this nation mourn as for an only son, and the end therefore as a bitter day. Behold, the days come, saith the Lord, that I will send a famine in the land, not a famine of bread, nor a thirst for water, but of hearing the words of the Lord. And they shall wander from sea to sea, and from the north even to the east; they shall run to and fro to seek the word of the Lord, and shall not find it.

"In that day shall the fair virgins and young men faint for thirst. They that have followed the idols of Samaria, and sworn by the god of Dan, and followed the manner of Beersheba, shall fall, and never rise up again."

Amos 3. 2: "Ye only have I known of all the families of the earth for my people."

Daniel 12. 7. Having described all the extent of the reign of the Messiah, he says: "All these things shall be finished, when the scattering of the people of Israel shall be accomplished."

Haggai 2. 4: "Ye who, comparing this second house with the glory of the first, despise it, be strong, saith the Lord, be strong, O Zerubbabel, and O Jesus, the high priest, be strong, all ye people of the land, and work. For I am with you, saith the Lord of hosts; according to the word that I covenanted with you when ye came out of Egypt, so my spirit remaineth among you. Fear ye not. For thus saith the Lord of hosts: Yet one little while, and I will shake the heavens, and the earth, and the sea, and the dry land," (a way of speaking to indicate a great and an extraordinary change); "and I will shake all nations, and the desire of all the Gentiles shall come; and I will fill this house with glory, saith the Lord.

"The silver is mine, and the gold is mine, saith the Lord," (that is to say, it is not by that that I wish to be honoured; as it is said elsewhere: All the beasts of the field are mine, what advantages me that they are offered me in sacrifice?). "The glory of this latter house shall be greater than of the former, saith the Lord of hosts; and in this place will I establish my house, saith the Lord.

"According to all that thou desiredst in Horeb in the day of the assembly, saying, Let us not hear again the voice of the Lord, neither let us see this fire any more, that we die not. And the Lord said unto me, Their prayer is just. I will raise them up a prophet from among their brethren, like unto thee, and will put my words in his mouth; and he shall speak unto them all that I shall command him. And it shall come to pass, that whosoever will not hearken unto my words which he will speak in my name, I will require it of him."

Genesis 49: "Judah, thou art he whom thy brethren shall praise, and thou shalt conquer thine enemies; thy father's children shall bow down before thee. Judah is a lion's whelp: from the prey, my son, thou art gone up, and art couched as a lion, and as a lioness that shall be roused up.

"The sceptre shall not depart from Judah, nor a lawgiver from between his feet, until Shiloh come; and unto him shall the gathering of the people be."

727. *During the life of the Messiah. Ænigmatis.* Ezek. 17.

His forerunner. Malachi 3.

He will be born an infant. Is. 9.

He will be born in the village of Bethlehem. Micah 5. He will appear chiefly in Jerusalem and will be a descendant of the family of Judah and of David.

He is to blind the learned and the wise, Is. 6. 8. 29. etc.; and to preach the Gospel to the lowly, Is. 29; to open the eyes of the blind, give health to the sick, and bring light to those that languish in darkness. Is. 61.

He is to show the perfect way, and be the teacher of the Gentiles. Is. 55; 43.1—7.

The prophecies are to be unintelligible to the wicked, Dan. 12; Hosea 14. 10; but they are to be intelligible to those who are well informed.

The prophecies, which represent Him as poor, represent Him as master of the nations. Is. 52. 14, etc.; 53; Zech. 9. 9.

The prophecies, which foretell the time, foretell Him only as master of the nations and suffering, and not as in the clouds nor as judge. And those, which represent Him thus as judge and in glory, do not mention the time. When the Messiah is spoken of as great and glorious, it is as the judge of the world, and not its Redeemer.

He is to be the victim for the sins of the world. Is. 39. 53. etc.

He is to be the precious corner-stone. Is. 28. 16.

He is to be a stone of stumbling and offence. Is. viii. Jerusalem is to dash against this stone.

The builders are to reject this stone. Ps. 117. 22.

God is to make this stone the chief corner-stone.

And this stone is to grow into a huge mountain and fill the whole earth. Dan. 2.

So He is to be rejected, despised, betrayed (Ps. 108. 8), sold (Zech. 11. 12), spit upon, buffeted, mocked, afflicted in innumerable ways, given gall to drink (Ps. 68), pierced (Zech. 12), His feet and His hands pierced, slain, and lots cast for His raiment.

He will rise again (Ps. 15) the third day (Hosea 6. 3).

He will ascend to heaven to sit on the right hand. Ps. 110.

The kings will arm themselves against Him. Ps. 2.

Being on the right hand of the Father, He will be victorious over His enemies.

The kings of the earth and all nations will worship Him. Is. lx.

The Jews will continue as a nation. Jeremiah.

They will wander, without kings, etc. (Hosea 3), without prophets (Amos), looking for salvation and finding it not (Isaiah).

Calling of the Gentiles by Jesus Christ. Is. 52. 15; 55. 5; 60. etc. Ps. 81.

Hosea 1. 9: "Ye are not my people, and I will not be your God, when ye are multiplied after the dispersion. In the places where it was said, Ye are not my people, I will call them my people."

728. It was not lawful to sacrifice outside of Jerusalem, which was the place that the Lord had chosen, nor even to eat the tithes elsewhere. Deut. 12. 5, etc.; Deut. 14. 23, etc.; 15. 20; 16. 2, 7, 11, 15.

Hosea foretold that they should be without a king, without a prince, without a sacrifice, and without an idol; and this prophecy is now fulfilled, as they cannot make a lawful sacrifice out of Jerusalem.

729. Predictions.—It was foretold that, in the time of the Messiah, He should come to establish a new covenant, which should make them forget the escape from Egypt (Jer. 23. 5; Is. 43. 10); that He should place His law not in externals, but in the heart; that He should put His fear, which had only been from without, in the midst of the heart. Who does not see the Christian law in all this?

730. . . . That then idolatry would be overthrown; that this Messiah would cast down all idols and bring men into the worship of the true God.

That the temples of the idols would be cast down, and that among all nations and in all places of the earth. He would be offered a pure sacrifice, not of beasts.

That He would be king of the Jews and Gentiles. And we see this king of the Jews and Gentiles oppressed by both, who conspire His death; and ruler of both, destroying the worship of Moses in Jerusalem, which was its centre, where He made His first Church; and also the worship of idols in Rome, the centre of it, where He made His chief Church.

731. *Prophecies.*—That Jesus Christ will sit on the right hand, till God has subdued His enemies.

Therefore He will not subdue them Himself.

732. "... Then they shall teach no more every man his neighbour, saying, Here is the Lord, *for God shall make Himself known to all.*"

"... Your sons shall prophesy." "I will put my spirit and my fear *in your heart.*"

All that is the same thing. To prophesy is to speak of God, not from outward proofs, but from an inward and immediate feeling.

733. That He would teach men the perfect way.

And there has never come, before Him nor after Him, any man who has taught anything divine approaching to this.

734. ... That Jesus Christ would be small in His beginning, and would then increase. The little stone of Daniel.

If I had in no wise heard of the Messiah, nevertheless, after such wonderful predictions of the course of the world which I see fulfilled, I see that He is divine. And, if I knew that these same books foretold a Messiah, I should be sure that He would come; and seeing that they place His time before the destruction of the second temple, I should say that He had come.

735. *Prophecies.*—That the Jews would reject Jesus Christ, and would be rejected of God, for this reason, that the chosen vine brought forth only wild grapes. That the chosen people would be fruitless, ungrateful, and unbelieving, *populum non credentem et contradicentem.*[1] That God would strike them with blindness, and in full noon they would grope like the blind; and that a forerunner would go before Him.

736. *Transfixerunt.*[2] Zech. 12. 10.

That a deliverer should come, who would crush the demon's head, and free His people from their sins, *ex omnibus iniquitatibus;*[3] that there should be a New Covenant, which would be eternal; that there should be another priesthood after the order of Melchisedek, and it should be eternal; that the Christ should be glorious, mighty, strong, and yet so poor that He would not be recognised, nor taken for what He is, but rejected and slain; that His people who denied Him should no longer be His people; that the idolaters should receive Him, and take refuge in Him; that He should leave Zion to reign in the centre of idolatry; that nevertheless the Jews should continue for ever; that He should be of Judah, and when there should be no longer a king.

[1]Is. 65. 2. "A rebellious people, which walketh in a way that was not good."
[2]"They have pierced."
[3]Ps. 130. 8. "from all his iniquities."

SECTION XII

PROOFS OF JESUS CHRIST

737. Therefore I reject all other religions. In that way I find an answer to all objections. It is right that a God so pure should only reveal Himself to those whose hearts are purified. Hence this religion is lovable to me, and I find it now sufficiently justified by so divine a morality. But I find more in it.

I find it convincing that, since the memory of man has lasted, it was constantly announced to men that they were universally corrupt, but that a Redeemer should come; that it is not one man who said it, but innumerable men, and a whole nation expressly made for the purpose and prophesying for four thousand years. This is a nation which is more ancient than every other nation. Their books, scattered abroad, are four thousand years old.

The more I examine them, the more truths I find in them: an entire nation foretell Him before His advent, and an entire nation worship Him after His advent; what has preceded and what has followed; in short, people without idols and kings, this synagogue which was foretold, and these wretches who frequent it and who, being our enemies, are admirable witnesses of the truth of these prophecies, wherein their wretchedness and even their blindness are foretold.

I find this succession, this religion, wholly divine in its authority, in its duration, in its perpetuity, in its morality, in its conduct, in its doctrine, in its effects. The frightful darkness of the Jews was foretold. *Eris palpans in meridie.*[1] *Dabitur liber scienti literas . . . et dicet: Non possum legere.*[2] While the sceptre was still in the hands of the first foreign usurper, there is the report of the coming of Jesus Christ.

So I hold out my arms to my *Redeemer*, who, having been foretold for four thousand years, has come to suffer and to die for me on earth, at the time and under all the circumstances foretold. By His grace, I await death in peace, in the hope of being eternally united to Him. Yet I live with joy, whether in the prosperity which it pleases Him to bestow upon me, or in the adversity which He sends for my good, and which He has taught me to bear by His example.

738. The prophecies having given different signs which should all happen at the advent of the Messiah, it was necessary that all these signs should occur at the same time. So it was necessary that the fourth monarchy should have come, when the seventy weeks of Daniel were ended; and that the sceptre should have then departed from Judah. And all this happened without any difficulty. Then it was necessary that the Messiah should come; and Jesus Christ then came, who was called the Messiah. And all this again was without difficulty. This indeed shows the truth of the prophecies.

739. The prophets foretold, and were not foretold. The saints again were foretold, but did not foretell. Jesus Christ both foretold and was foretold.

[1]Deut.28. 29. *Et palpes in meridie.* "And thou shalt grope at noonday."
[2]Is. 29. 11. *Quem (librum) cum dederint scienti litteras et respondebit: Non possum.* "Which men deliver to one that is learned . . . and he saith, I cannot."

740. Jesus Christ, whom the two Testaments regard, the Old as its hope, the New as its model, and both as their centre.

741. The two oldest books in the world are those of Moses and Job, the one a Jew and the other a Gentile. Both of them look upon Jesus Christ as their common centre and object: Moses in relating the promises of God to Abraham, Jacob, etc., and his prophecies; and Job, *Quis mihi det ut*, etc. *Scio enim quod redemptor meus vivit*, etc.[1]

742. The Gospel only speaks of the virginity of the Virgin up to the time of the birth of Jesus Christ. All with reference to Jesus Christ.

743. *Proofs of Jesus Christ.*
Why was the book of Ruth preserved?
Why the story of Tamar?

744. "Pray that ye enter not into temptation." It is dangerous to be tempted; and people are tempted because they do not pray.
Et tu conversus confirma fratres tuos. But before, *conversus Jesus respexit Petrum.*[2]
Saint Peter asks permission to strike Malchus and strikes before hearing the answer. Jesus Christ replies afterwards.
The word, *Galilee*, which the Jewish mob pronounced as if by chance, in accusing Jesus Christ before Pilate, afforded Pilate a reason for sending Jesus Christ to Herod. And thereby the mystery was accomplished, that He should be judged by Jews and Gentiles. Chance was apparently the cause of the accomplishment of the mystery.

745. Those who have a difficulty in believing seek a reason in the fact that the Jews do not believe. "Were this so clear," say they, "why did the Jews not believe"? And they almost wish that they had believed, so as not to be kept back by the example of their refusal. But it is their very refusal that is the foundation of our faith. We should be much less disposed to the faith, if they were on our side. We should then have a more ample pretext. The wonderful thing is to have made the Jews great lovers of the things foretold, and great enemies of their fulfilment.

746. The Jews were accustomed to great and striking miracles, and so, having had the great miracles of the Red Sea and of the land of Canaan as an epitome of the great deeds of their Messiah, they therefore looked for more striking miracles, of which those of Moses were only the patterns.

747. The carnal Jews and the heathen have their calamities, and Christians also. There is no Redeemer for the heathen, for they do not so much as hope for one. There is no Redeemer for the Jews; they hope for Him in vain. There is a Redeemer only for Christians. (See *Perpetuity*.)

[1]Job 19. 23-25. "for I know that my redeemer liveth."
[2]Luke 22. 32,61. "And when thou art converted, strengthen thy brother." "And the Lord turned, and looked upon Peter."

748. In the time of the Messiah the people divided themselves. The spiritual embraced the Messiah, and the coarser-minded remained to serve as witnesses of Him.

749. "If this was clearly foretold to the Jews, how did they not believe it, or why were they not destroyed for resisting a fact so clear?"

I reply: in the first place, it was foretold both that they would not believe a thing so clear and that they would not be destroyed. And nothing is more to the glory of the Messiah; for it was not enough that there should be prophets; their prophets must be kept above suspicion. Now, etc.

750. If the Jews had all been converted by Jesus Christ, we should have none but questionable witnesses. And if they had been entirely destroyed, we should have no witnesses at all.

751. What do the prophets say of Jesus Christ? That He will be clearly God? No; but that He is a God truly hidden; that He will be slighted; that none will think that it is He; that He will be a stone of stumbling, upon which many will stumble, etc. Let people then reproach us no longer for want of clearness, since we make profession of it.

But, it is said, there are obscurities. And without that, no one would have stumbled over Jesus Christ, and this is one of the formal pronouncements of the prophets: Excæca . . .[1]

752. Moses first teaches the Trinity, original sin, the Messiah.

David: a great witness; a king, good, merciful, a beautiful soul, a sound mind, powerful. He prophesies, and his wonder comes to pass. This is infinite.

He had only to say that he was the Messiah, if he had been vain; for the prophecies are clearer about him than about Jesus Christ. And the same with Saint John.

753. Herod was believed to be the Messiah. He had taken away the sceptre from Judah but he was not of Judah. This gave rise to a considerable sect.

Curse of the Greeks upon those who count three periods of time.

In what way should the Messiah come, seeing that through Him the sceptre was to be eternally in Judah and at His coming the sceptre was to be taken away from Judah?

In order to effect that seeing they should not see, and hearing they should not understand, nothing could be better done.

754. *Homo existens te Deum facit.*[2]
Scriptum est, Dii estis, et non potest solvi Scriptura.[3]
Hæc infirmitas non est ad vitam et est ad mortem.[4]
Lazarus dormit, et deinde dixit: Lazarus mortuus est.[5]

[1] Is. 6.10. "Shut their eyes."
[2] "The man who exists makes you God."
[3] "It is written: 'You are Gods' (Ps. 80.6), and the Scripture cannot be made naught of."
[4] "This weakness is not for life; it is for death."
[5] John 11.11 and 14. "'Lazarus sleeps,' and later it says: 'Lazarus is dead.'"

755. The apparent discrepancy of the Gospels.

756. What can we have but reverence for a man who foretells plainly things which come to pass, and who declares his intention both to blind and to enlighten, and who intersperses obscurities among the clear things which come to pass?

757. The time of the first advent was foretold; the time of the second is not so; because the first was to be obscure, and the second is to be brilliant and so manifest that even His enemies will recognise it. But, as He was first to come only in obscurity and to be known only of those who searched the Scriptures . . .

758. God, in order to cause the Messiah to be known by the good and not to be known by the wicked, made Him to be foretold in this manner. If the manner of the Messiah had been clearly foretold, there would have been no obscurity, even for the wicked. If the time had been obscurely foretold, there would have been obscurity, even for the good. For their [goodness of heart] would not have made them understand, for instance, that the closed *mem* signifies six hundred years. But that time has been clearly foretold, and the manner in types.

By this means, the wicked, taking the promised blessings for material blessings, have fallen into error, in spite of the clear prediction of the time; and the good have not fallen in error. For the understanding of the promised blessings depends on the heart, which calls *good* that which it loves; but the understanding of the promised time does not depend on the heart. And thus the clear prediction of the time, and the obscure prediction of the blessings, deceive the wicked alone.

759. [Either the Jews or the Christians must be wicked.]

760. The Jews reject Him, but not all. The saints receive Him, and not the carnal-minded. And so far is this from being against His glory, that it is the last touch which crowns it. For their argument, the only one found in all their writings, in the Talmud and in the Rabbinical writings, amounts only to this, that Jesus Christ has not subdued the nations with sword in hand, *gladium tuum, potentissime*.[1] (Is this all they have to say? Jesus Christ has been slain, say they. He has failed. He has not subdued the heathen with His might. He has not bestowed upon us their spoil. He does not give riches. Is this all they have to say? It is in this respect that He is lovable to me. I would not desire Him whom they fancy.) It is evident that it is only His life which has prevented them from accepting Him; and through this rejection they are irreproachable witnesses, and, what is more, they thereby accomplish the prophecies.

[By means of the fact that this people have not accepted Him, this miracle here has happened. The prophecies were the only lasting miracles which could be wrought, but they were liable to be denied.]

761. The Jews, in slaying Him in order not to receive Him as the Messiah, have given Him the final proof of being the Messiah.

And in continuing not to recognise Him, they made themselves irreproachable

[1]Ps. 44.4. Gladio tuo—"Thy sword, O most mighty."

witnesses. Both in slaying Him and in continuing to deny Him, they have fulfilled the prophecies (Is. 60; Ps. 71).

762. What could the Jews, His enemies, do? If they receive Him, they give proof of Him by their reception; for then the guardians of the expectation of the Messiah receive Him. If they reject Him, they give proof of Him by their rejection.

763. The Jews, in testing if He were God, have shown that He was man.

764. The Church has had as much difficulty in showing that Jesus Christ was man, against those who denied it, as in showing that He was God; and the probabilities were equally great.

765. *Source of contradictions.*—A God humiliated, even to the death on the cross; a Messiah triumphing over death by his own death. Two natures in Jesus Christ, two advents, two states of man's nature.

766. *Types.*—Saviour, father, sacrificer, offering, food, king, wise, law-giver, afflicted, poor, having to creat a people whom He must lead and nourish and bring into His land . . .
Jesus Christ. Offices.—He alone had to create a great people, elect, holy, and chosen; to lead, nourish, and bring it into the place of rest and holiness; to make it holy to God; to make it the temple of God; to reconcile it to, and save it from, the wrath of God; to free it from the slavery of sin, which visibly reigns in man; to give laws to this people, and engrave these laws on their heart; to offer Himself to God for them, and sacrifice Himself for them; to be a victim without blemish, and Himself the sacrificer, having to offer Himself, His body, and His blood, and yet to offer bread and wine to God . . .
Ingrediens mundum.[1]
"Stone upon stone."
What preceded and what followed. All the Jews exist still and are wanderers.

767. Of all that is on earth, He partakes only of the sorrows, not of the joys. He loves His neighbours, but His love does not confine itself within these bounds, and overflows to His own enemies, and then to those of God.

768. Jesus Christ typified by Joseph, the beloved of his father, sent by his father to see his brethren, etc., innocent, sold by his brethren for twenty pieces of silver, and thereby becoming their lord, their saviour, the saviour of strangers and the saviour of the world; which had not been but for their plot to destroy him, their sale and their rejection of him.
In prison, Joseph innocent between two criminals; Jesus Christ on the cross between two thieves. Joseph foretells freedom to the one, and death to the other, from the same omens. Jesus Christ saves the elect, and condemns the outcast for the same sins. Joseph foretells only; Jesus Christ acts. Joseph asks him who will be saved to remember him, when he comes into his glory; and he whom Jesus Christ saves asks that He will remember him, when He comes into His kingdom.

[1]Heb. 10.5. "When he cometh into the world."

769. The conversion of the heathen was only reserved for the grace of the Messiah. The Jews have been so long in opposition to them without success; all that Solomon and the prophets said has been useless. Sages, like Plato and Socrates, have not been able to persuade them.

770. After many persons had gone before, Jesus Christ at last came to say: "Here am I, and this is the time. That which the prophets have said was to come in the fullness of time, I tell you my apostles will do. The Jews shall be cast out. Jerusalem shall be soon destroyed. And the heathen shall enter into the knowledge of God. My apostles shall do this after you have slain the heir of the vineyard."

Then the apostles said to the Jews: "You shall be accursed," (*Celsus laughed at it*); and to the heathen, "You shall enter into the knowledge of God." And this then came to pass.

771. Jesus Christ came to blind those who saw clearly, and to give sight to the blind; to heal the sick, and leave the healthy to die; to call to repentance, and to justify sinners, and to leave the righteous in their sins; to fill the needy, and leave the rich empty.

772. *Holiness.—Effundam spiritum meum.*[1] All nations were in unbelief and lust. The whole world now became fervent with love. Princes abandoned their pomp; maidens suffered martyrdom. Whence came this influence? The Messiah was come. These were the effect and sign of His coming.

773. Destruction of the Jews and heathen by Jesus Christ: *Omnes gentes venient et adorabunt eum.*[2] *Parum est ut,*[3] etc. *Postula a me.*[4] *Adorabunt eum omnes reges.*[5] *Testes iniqui.*[6] *Dabit maxillam percutienti.*[7] *Dederunt fel in escam.*[8]

774. Jesus Christ for all, Moses for a nation.

The Jews blessed in Abraham: "I will bless those that bless thee." But: "All nations blessed in his seed." *Parum est ut,*[3] etc.

Lumen ad revelationem gentium.[9]

Non fecit taliter omni nationi, said David, in speaking of the Law. But, in speaking of Jesus Christ, we must say: *Fecit taliter omni nationi.*[10] *Parum est ut,*[3] etc., Isaiah. So it belongs to Jesus Christ to be universal. Even the Church offers sacrifice only for the faithful. Jesus Christ offered that of the cross for all.

775. There is heresy in always explaining *omnes* by *all*, and heresy is not explain-

[1] Joel. 2.28. "I will pour out my spirit."
[2] Ps. 21.28. "All peoples shall come and worship him."
[3] Is. 49.6. "It is a light thing that thou shouldst be my servant," etc.
[4] Ps. 2.8. "Ask of me."
[5] Ps. 71.11. "All kings shall fall down before him."
[6] Ps. 34.11. "Witnesses rise up."
[7] Lam. 3.30. "He giveth his cheek to him that smiteth him."
[8] Ps. 68.22. *Dederunt in escam meam fel.* "They gave me also gall for my meat."
[9] Luke 2.32. "A light to lighten the Gentiles."
[10] Ps. 167.20. "He hath not dealt so with any nation."

ing it sometimes by *all*. *Bibite ex hoc omnes;*[1] The Huguenots are heretics in explaining it by *all*. *In quo omnes peccaverunt;*[2] the Huguenots are heretics in excepting the children of true believers. We must, then, follow the Fathers and tradition in order to know when to do so, since there is heresy to be feared on both sides.

776. *Ne timeas pusillus grex.*[3] *Timore et tremore.*[4]—*Quid ergo? Ne timeas [modo] timeas.* Fear not, provided you fear; but if you fear not, then fear.

Qui me recipit, non me recipit, sed eum qui me misit.[5]

Nemo scit, neque Filius.[6]

Nubes lucida obumbravit.[7]

Saint John was to turn the hearts of the fathers to the children, and Jesus Christ to plant division. There is not contradiction.

777. The effects *in communi* and *in particulari*. The semi-Pelagians err in saying of *in communi* what is true only *in particulari;* and the Calvinists in saying *in particulari* what is true *in communi*. (Such is my opinion.)

778. *Omnis Judæa regio, et Jerosolmymi universi, et baptizabantur.*[8] Because of all the conditions of men who came there.

From these stones there *can* come children unto Abraham.

779. If men knew themselves, God would heal and pardon them. *Ne convertantur et sanem eos, et dimittantur eis peccata.*[9]

780. Jesus Christ never condemned without hearing. To Judas: *Amice, ad quid venisti?*[10] To him that had not on the wedding garment, the same.

781. The types of the completeness of the Redemption, as that the sun gives light to all, indicate only completeness; but [*the types*] of exclusions, as of the Jews elected to the exclusion of the Gentiles, indicate exclusion.

"Jesus Christ the Redeemer of all." Yes, for He has offered, like a man who has ransomed all those who were willing to come to Him. If any die on the way, it is their misfortune; but, so far as He was concerned, He offered them redemption. That holds good in this example, where he who ransoms and he who prevents death are two persons, but not of Jesus Christ, who does both these things. No, for Jesus Christ, in the quality of Redeemer, is not perhaps Master of all; and thus, in so far as it is in Him, He is the Redeemer of all.

When it is said that Jesus Christ did not die for all, you take undue advantage

---

[1]Matt. 26.27. "Drink ye all of it."

[2]Rom. 5.12. "for that all have sinned."

[3]Luke 12.32. "Fear not little flock."

[4]Phil. 2.12. "With fear and trembling."

[5]Mark 9. 37. "Whosoever receiveth me, receiveth not me, but him that sent me."

[6]Mark 13.32. "No one knows, neither the Son, but the Father."

[7]"Clouds shadowed over the light."

[8]Mark 1.5. "All the land of Judaea, and they of Jerusalem, and were all baptized of him."

[9]Mark 4.12. "Lest they should be converted, and their sins should be forgiven them."

[10]Matt. 26.50. "Friend, wherefore art thou come?"

of a fault in men who at once apply this exception to themselves; and this is to favour despair, instead of turning them from it to favour hope. For men thus accustom themselves in inward virtues by outward customs.

782. The victory over death. "What is a man advantaged if he gain the whole world and lose his own soul? Whosoever will save his soul, shall lose it."

"I am not come to destroy the law, but to fulfil."

"Lambs took not away the sins of the world, but I am the lamb which taketh away the sins."

"Moses hath not led you out of captivity, and made you truly free."

783. . . . Then Jesus Christ comes to tell men that they have no other enemies but themselves; that it is their passions which keep them apart from God; that He comes to destroy these, and give them His grace, so as to make of them all one Holy Church; that He comes to bring back into this Church the heathen and Jews; that He comes to destroy the idols of the former and the superstition of the latter. To this all men are opposed, not only from the natural opposition of lust; but, above all, the kings of the earth, as had been foretold, join together to destroy this religion at its birth. (*Proph.: Quare fremuerunt gentes . . . reges terræ . . . adversus Christum.*)[1]

All that is great on earth is united together; the learned, the wise, the kings. The first write; the second condemn; the last kill. And notwithstanding all these oppositions, these men, simple and weak, resist all these powers, subdue even these kings, these learned men and these sages, and remove idolatry from all the earth. And all this is done by the power which had foretold it.

784. Jesus Christ would not have the testimony of devils, nor of those who were not called, but of God and John the Baptist.

785. I consider Jesus Christ in all persons and in ourselves: Jesus Christ as a Father in His Father, Jesus Christ as a Brother in His Brethren, Jesus Christ as poor in the poor, Jesus Christ as rich in the rich, Jesus Christ as Doctor and Priest in priests, Jesus Christ as Sovereign in princes, etc. For by His glory He is all that is great, being God; and by His mortal life He is all that is poor and abject. Therefore He has taken this unhappy condition, so that He could be in all persons and the model of all conditions.

786. Jesus Christ is an obscurity (according to what the world calls obscurity), such that historians, writing only of important matters of states, have hardly noticed Him.

787. *On the fact that neither Josephus, nor Tacitus, nor other historians have spoken of Jesus Christ.*—So far is this from telling against Christianity that, on the contrary, it tells for it. For it is certain that Jesus Christ has existed; that His religion has made a great talk; and that these persons were not ignorant of it. Thus it is plain that they purposely concealed it, or that, if they did speak of it, their account has been suppressed or changed.

[1] Ps. 2.1,2. "Why do the heathen rage . . . and the rulers of the earth . . . against the Lord."

788. "I have reserved me seven thousand." I love the worshippers unknown to the world and to the very prophets.

789. As Jesus Christ remained unknown among men, so His truth remains among common opinions without external difference. Thus the Eucharist among ordinary bread.

790. Jesus would not be slain without the forms of justice; for it is far more ignominious to die by justice than by an unjust sedition.

791. The false justice of Pilate only serves to make Jesus Christ suffer; for he causes Him to be scourged by his false justice, and afterwards puts Him to death. It would have been better to have put Him to death at once. Thus it is with the falsely just. They do good and evil works to please the world, and to show that they are not altogether of Jesus Christ; for they are ashamed of Him. And at last, under great temptation and on great occasions, they kill Him.

792. What man ever had more renown? The whole Jewish people foretell Him before His coming. The Gentile people worship Him after His coming. The two peoples, Gentile and Jewish, regard Him as their centre.

And yet what man enjoys this renown less? Of thirty-three years, He lives thirty without appearing. For three years He passes as an impostor; the priests and the chief people reject Him; His friends and His nearest relatives despise Him. Finally, He dies, betrayed by one of His own disciples, denied by another, and abandoned by all.

What part, then, has He in this renown? Never had man so much renown; never had man more ignominy. All that renown has served only for us, to render us capable of recognising Him; and He had none of it for Himself.

793. The infinite distance between body and mind is a symbol of the infinitely more infinite distance between mind and charity; for charity is supernatural.

All the glory of greatness has no lustre for people who are in search of understanding.

The greatness of clever men is invisible to kings, to the rich, to chiefs, and to all the worldly great.

The greatness of wisdom, which is nothing if not of God, is invisible to the carnal-minded and to the clever. These are three orders differing in kind.

Great geniuses have their power, their glory, their greatness, their victory, their lustre, and have no need of worldly greatness, with which they are not in keeping. They are seen, not by the eye, but by the mind; this is sufficient.

The saints have their power, their glory, their victory, their lustre, and need no worldly or intellectual greatness, with which they have no affinity; for these neither add anything to them, nor take away anything from them. They are seen of God and the angels, and not of the body, nor of the curious mind. God is enough for them.

Archimedes, apart from his rank, would have the same veneration. He fought no battles for the eyes to feast upon; but he has given his discoveries to all men. Oh! how brilliant he was to the mind!

Jesus Christ, without riches and without any external exhibition of knowledge, is in His own order of holiness. He did not invent; He did not reign. But He was humble, patient, holy, holy to God, terrible to devils, without any sin. Oh! in what great pomp and in what wonderful splendour He is come to the eyes of the heart, which perceive wisdom!

It would have been useless for Archimedes to have acted the prince in his books on geometry, although he was a prince.

It would have been useless for our Lord Jesus Christ to come like a king, in order to shine forth in His kingdom of holiness. But He came there appropriately in the glory of His own order.

It is most absurd to take offence at the lowliness of Jesus Christ, as if His lowliness were in the same order as the greatness which He came to manifest. If we consider this greatness in His life, in His passion, in His obscurity, in His death, in the choice of His disciples, in their desertion, in His secret resurrection, and the rest, we shall see it to be so immense that we shall have no reason for being offended at a lowliness which is not of that order.

But there are some who can only admire worldly greatness, as though there were no intellectual greatness; and others who only admire intellectual greatness, as though there were not infinitely higher things in wisdom.

All bodies, the firmament, the stars, the earth and its kingdoms, are not equal to the lowest mind; for mind knows all these and itself; and these bodies nothing.

All bodies together, and all minds together, and all their products, are not equal to the least feeling of charity. This is of an order infinitely more exalted.

From all bodies together, we cannot obtain one little thought; this is impossible and of another order. From all bodies and minds, we cannot produce a feeling of true charity; this is impossible and of another and supernatural order.

794. Why did Jesus Christ not come in a visible manner, instead of obtaining testimony of Himself from preceding prophecies? Why did He cause Himself to be foretold in types?

795. If Jesus Christ had only come to sanctify, all Scripture and all things would tend to that end; and it would be quite easy to convince unbelievers. If Jesus Christ had only come to blind, all His conduct would be confused; and we would have no means of convincing unbelievers. But as He came *in sanctificationem et in scandalum*,[1] as Isaiah says, we cannot convince unbelievers, and they cannot convince us. But by this very fact we convince them; since we say that in His whole conduct there is no convincing proof on one side or the other.

796. Jesus Christ does not say that He is not of Nazareth, in order to leave the wicked in their blindness; nor that He is not Joseph's son.

797. *Proofs of Jesus Christ.*—Jesus Christ said great things so simply that it seems as though He had not thought them great; and yet so clearly that we easily see what He thought of them. This clearness, joined to this simplicity, is wonderful.

798. The style of the gospel is admirable in so many ways, and among the rest

[1] Is. 8.14. "For a sanctuary and for a rock of offence."

in hurling no invectives against the persecutors and enemies of Jesus Christ. For there is no such invective in any of the historians against Judas, Pilate, or any of the Jews.

If this moderation of the writers of the Gospels had been assumed, as well as many other traits of so beautiful a character, and they had only assumed it to attract notice, even if they had not dared to draw attention to it themselves, they would not have failed to secure friends who would have made such remarks to their advantage. But as they acted thus without pretence and from wholly disinterested motives, they did not point it out to any one; and I believe that many such facts have not been noticed till now, which is evidence of the natural disinterestedness with which the thing has been done.

799. An artisan who speaks of wealth, a lawyer who speaks of war, of royalty, etc.; but the rich man rightly speaks of wealth, a king speaks indifferently of a great gift he has just made, and God rightly speaks of God.

800. Who has taught the evangelists the qualities of a perfectly heroic soul, that they paint it so perfectly in Jesus Christ? Why do they make Him weak in His agony? Do they not know how to paint a resolute death? Yes, for the same Saint Luke paints the death of Saint Stephen as braver than that of Jesus Christ.

They make Him, therefore, capable of fear, before the necessity of dying has come, and then altogether brave.

But when they make Him so troubled, it is when He afflicts Himself; and when men afflict Him, He is altogether strong.

801. *Proof of Jesus Christ.*—The supposition that the apostles were impostors is very absurd. Let us think it out. Let us imagine those twelve men, assembled after the death of Jesus Christ, plotting to say that He was risen. By this they attack all the powers. The heart of man is strangely inclined to fickleness, to change, to promises, to gain. However little any of them might have been led astray by all these attractions, nay more, by the fear of prisons, tortures, and death, they were lost. Let us follow up this thought.

802. The apostles were either deceived or deceivers. Either supposition has difficulties; for it is not possible to mistake a man raised from the dead . . .

While Jesus Christ was with them, He could sustain them. But, after that, if He did not appear to them, who inspired them to act?

SECTION XIII

THE MIRACLES

803. *The beginning.*—Miracles enable us to judge of doctrine, and doctrine enables us to judge of miracles.

There are false miracles and true. There must be a distinction, in order to know them; otherwise they would be useless. Now they are not useless; on the contrary, they are fundamental. Now the rule which is given to us must be such that it does not destroy the proof which the true miracles give of the truth, which is the chief end of the miracles.

Moses has given two rules: that the prediction does not come to pass (Deut. 18.), and that they do not lead to idolatry (Deut. 13.); and Jesus Christ one.

If doctrine regulates miracles, miracles are useless for doctrine.

If miracles regulate . . .

Objection to the rule.—The distinction of the times. One rule during the time of Moses, another at present.

804. *Miracle.*—It is an effect, which exceeds the natural power of the means which are employed for it; and what is not a miracle is an effect, which does not exceed the natural power of the means which are employed for it. Thus, those who heal by invocation of the devil do not work a miracle; for that does not exceed the natural power of the devil. But . . .

805. The two fundamentals; one inward, the other outward; grace and miracles; both supernatural.

806. Miracles and truth are necessary, because it is necessary to convince the entire man, in body and soul.

807. In all times, either men have spoken of the true God, or the true God has spoken to men.

808. Jesus Christ has verified that He was the Messiah, never in verifying His doctrine by Scripture and the prophecies, but always by His miracles.

He proves by a miracle that He remits sins.

Rejoice not in your miracles, said Jesus Christ, but because your names are written in heaven.

If they believe not Moses, neither will they believe one risen from the dead.

Nicodemus recognises by His miracles that His teaching is of God. *Scimus quia venisti a Deo magister; nemo enim potest hæc signa facere quæ tu facis nisi Deus fuerit cum eo.*[1] He does not judge of the miracles by the teaching, but of the teaching by the miracles.

The Jews had a doctrine of God as we have one of Jesus Christ, and confirmed by miracles. They were forbidden to believe every worker of miracles; and they were further commanded to have recourse to the chief priests and to rely on them.

And thus, in regard to their prophets, they had all those reasons which we have for refusing to believe the workers of miracles.

And yet they were very sinful in rejecting the prophets and Jesus Christ because of their miracles; and they would not have been culpable, if they had not seen the miracles. *Nisi fecissem . . . peccatum non haberent.*[2] Therefore all belief rests upon miracles.

Prophecy is not called miracle; as Saint John speaks of the first miracle in Cana

[1]John 3.2. "We know that thou art a teacher come from God; for no man can do these miracles that thou doest, except God be with him."
[2]John. 15.24. "If I had not done . . . they had not had sin."

and then of what Jesus Christ says to the woman of Samaria, when He reveals to her all her hidden life. Then He heals the centurion's son; and Saint John calls this "the second miracle."

809. The combinations of miracles.

810. The second miracle can suppose the first, but the first cannot suppose the second.

811. Had it not been for the miracles, there would have been no sin in not believing in Jesus Christ.

812. "I should not be a Christian, but for the miracles," said Saint Augustine.

813. *Miracles.*—How I hate those who make men doubt of miracles! Montaigne speaks of them as he should in two places. In one, we see how careful he is; and yet, in the other, he believes and makes sport of unbelievers.

However it may be, the Church is without proofs if they are right.

814. Montaigne against miracles.
Montaigne for miracles.

815. It is not possible to have a reasonable belief against miracles.

816. Unbelievers the most credulous. They believe the miracles of Vespasian, in order not to believe those of Moses.

817. *Title: How it happens that men believe so many liars, who say that they have seen miracles, and do not believe any of those who say that they have secrets to make men immortal, or restore youth to them.*—Having considered how it happens that so great credence is given to so many impostors, who say they have remedies, often to the length of men putting their lives into their hands, it has appeared to me that the true cause is that there are true remedies. For it would not be possible that there should be so many false remedies and that so much faith should be placed in them, if there were none true. If there had never been any remedy for any ill, and all ills had been incurable, it is impossible that men should have imagined that they could give remedies, and still more impossible that so many others should have believed those who boasted of having remedies; in the same way as did a man boast of preventing death, no one would believe him, because there is no example of this. But as there were a number of remedies found to be true by the very knowledge of the greatest men, the belief of men is thereby induced; and, this being known to be possible, it has been therefore concluded that it was. For people commonly reason thus: "A thing is possible, therefore it is"; because the thing cannot be denied generally, since there are particular effects which are true, the people, who cannot distinguish which among these particular effects are true, believe them all. In the same way, the reason why so many false effects are credited to the moon is that there are some true, as the tide.

It is the same with prophecies, miracles, divination by dreams, sorceries, etc.

For if there had been nothing true in all this, men would have believed nothing of them; and thus, instead of concluding that there are no true miracles because there are so many false, we must, on the contrary, say that there certainly are true miracles, since there are false, and that there are false miracles only because some are true. We must reason in the same way about religion; for it would not be possible that men should have imagined so many false religions, if there had not been a true one. The objection to this is that savages have a religion; but the answer is that they have heard the true spoken of, as appears by the Deluge, circumcision, the cross of Saint Andrew, etc.

818. Having considered how it comes that there are so many false miracles, false revelations, sorceries, etc., it has seemed to me that the true cause is that there are some true; for it would not be possible that there should be so many false miracles, if there were none true, nor so many false revelations, if there were none true, nor so many false religions, if there were not one true. For if there had never been all this, it is almost impossible that men should have imagined it, and still more impossible that so many others should have believed it. But as there have been very great things true, and as they have been believed by great men, this impression has been the cause that nearly everybody is rendered capable of believing also the false. And thus, instead of concluding that there are no true miracles, since there are so many false, it must be said, on the contrary, that there are true miracles, since there are so many false; and that there are false ones only because there are true; and that in the same way there are false religions because there is one true.—Objection to this: savages have a religion. But this is because they have heard the true spoken of, as appears by the cross of Saint Andrew, the Deluge, circumcision, etc. This arises from the fact that the human mind, finding itself inclined to that side by the truth, becomes thereby susceptible of all the falsehoods of this . . .

819. Jeremiah 23. 32. The *miracles* of the false prophets. In the Hebrew and Vatable they are the *tricks*.

Miracle does not always signify miracle. I Sam. 14. 15; *miracle* signifies *fear*, and is so in the Hebrew. The same evidently in Job 33. 7; and also Isaiah 21. 4; Jeremiah 44. 12. *Portentum* signifies *simulacrum*, Jeremiah 50. 38; and it is so in the Hebrew and Vatable. Isaiah 8. 18. Jesus Christ says that He and His will be in *miracles*.

820. If the devil favoured the doctrine which destroys him, he would be divided against himself, as Jesus Christ said. If God favoured the doctrine which destroys the Church, He would be divided against Himself. *Omne regnum divisum*.[1] For Jesus Christ wrought against the devil, and destroyed his power over the heart, of which exorcism is the symbolisation, in order to establish the kingdom of God. And thus He adds, *Si in digito Dei . . . regnum Dei ad vos*.[2]

821. There is a great difference between tempting and leading into error. God tempts, but He does not lead into error. To tempt is to afford opportunities,

[1]Matt. 12.25; Luke 11.17. "Every kingdom divided against itself."
[2]Luke 11.20. "If with the finger of God . . . the kingdom of God is come upon you."

which impose no necessity; if men do not love God, they will do a certain thing. To lead into error is to place a man under the necessity of inferring and following out what is untrue.

822. Abraham and Gideon are above revelation. The Jews blinded themselves in judging of miracles by the Scripture. God has never abandoned His true worshippers.

I prefer to follow Jesus Christ than any other, because He has miracle, prophecy, doctrine, perpetuity, etc.

The Donatists. No miracle which obliges them to say it is the devil.

The more we particularise God, Jesus Christ, the Church . . .

823. If there were no false miracles, there would be certainty. If there were no rule to judge of them, miracles would be useless and there would be no reason for believing.

Now there is, humanly speaking, no human certainty, but we have reason.

824. Either God has confounded the false miracles, or He has foretold them; and in both ways He has raised Himself above what is supernatural with respect to us, and has raised us to it.

825. Miracles serve not to convert, but to condemn. Part I-II (Q. 113, A. 10, *Ad.* 2.)[1]

826. *Reasons why we do not believe.*

John xii. 37. *Cum autem tanta signa fecisset, non credebant in eum, ut sermo Isayæ impleretur . . . Excæcavit,*[2] etc.

Hæc dixit Isaias, quando vidit gloriam ejus et locutus est de eo.[3]

Judæi signa petunt et Græci sapientiam quærunt, nos autem Jesum crucifixum.[4] (*Sed plenum signis, sed plenum sapientia; vos autem Christum non crucifixum et religionem sine miraculis et sine sapientia.*)[5]

What makes us not believe in the true miracles is want of love. John: *Sed vos non creditis, quia non estis ex ovibus.*[6] What makes us believe the false is want of love. II Thess. 2.

The foundation of religion. It is the miracles. What then? Does God speak against miracles, against the foundations of the faith which we have in Him?

If there is a God, faith in God must exist on earth. Now the miracles of Jesus Christ are not foretold by Antichrist, but the miracles of Antichrist are foretold by Jesus Christ. And so, if Jesus Christ were not the Messiah, He would have indeed led into error. When Jesus Christ foretold the miracles of Antichrist, did He think of destroying faith in His own miracles?

---

[1]St. Thomas Aquinas, *Summa Theologica.*

[2]"But though he had done so many miracles before them, yet they believed not on him: that the saying of Esaias the prophet might be fulfilled . . . He hath blinded their eyes."

[3]John 12.41. "These things said Esaias, when he saw his glory, and spake of him."

[4]I Cor. 1.22,23. "For the Jews require a sign, and the Greeks seek after wisdom: but we preach Christ crucified."

[5]"But full of signs, full of wisdom; you [the Jesuits], what you wish is a Christ not crucified, a religion without miracles and without wisdom."

[6].10.26 "But ye believe not, because ye are not of my sheep."

Moses foretold Jesus Christ and bade to follow Him. Jesus Christ foretold Antichrist and forbade to follow him.

It was impossible that in the time of Moses men should keep their faith for Antichrist, who was unknown to them. But it is quite easy, in the time of Antichrist, to believe in Jesus Christ, already known.

There is no reason for believing in Antichrist, which there is not for believing in Jesus Christ. But there are reasons for believing in Jesus Christ, which there are not for believing in the other.

827. Judges 13. 23: "If the Lord were pleased to kill us, He would not have shewed us all these things."

Hezekiah, Sennacherib.

Jeremiah. Hananiah, the false prophet, dies in seven months.

II Macc. 3. The temple, ready for pillage, miraculously succoured.—II Macc. 15.

I Kings 17. The widow to Elijah, who had restored her son, "By this I know that thy words are true."

I Kings 18. Elijah with the prophets of Baal.

In the dispute concerning the true God and the truth of religion, there has never happened any miracle on the side of error, and not of truth.

828. *Opposition.*—Abel, Cain; Moses, the Magicians; Elijah, the false prophets: Jeremiah, Hananiah; Micaiah, the false prophets; Jesus Christ, the Pharisees; Saint Paul, Bar-jesus; the Apostles, the Exorcists; Christians, unbelievers; Catholics, heretics; Elijah, Enoch, Antichrist.

829. Jesus Christ says that the Scriptures testify of Him. But He does not point out in what respect.

Even the prophecies could not prove Jesus Christ during His life; and so men would not have been culpable for not believing in Him before His death had the miracles not sufficed without doctrine. Now those who did not believe in Him, when He was still alive, were sinners, as He said Himself, and without excuse. Therefore they must have had proof beyond doubt, which they resisted. Now, they had not the prophecies, but only the miracles. Therefore the latter suffice, when the doctrine is not inconsistent with them; and they ought to be believed.

John 7. 40. *Dispute among the Jews as among the Christians of to-day.* Some believed in Jesus Christ; others believed Him not, because of the prophecies which said that He should be born in Bethlehem. They should have considered more carefully whether He was not. For His miracles being convincing, they should have been quite sure of these supposed contradictions of His teaching to Scripture; and this obscurity did not excuse, but blinded them. Thus those who refuse to believe in the miracles in the present day on account of a supposed contradiction, which is unreal, are not excused.

The Pharisees said to the people, who believed in Him, because of His miracles: "This people who knoweth not the law are cursed. But have any of the rulers or of the Pharisees believed in him? For we know that out of Galilee ariseth no prophet." Nicodemus answered: "Doth our law judge any man before it hear him, [and specially such a man who works such miracles]"?

830. The prophecies were ambiguous; they are no longer so.

831. The five propositions were ambiguous; they are no longer so.

832. Miracles are no longer necessary, because we have had them already. But when tradition is no longer minded; when the Pope alone is offered to us; when he has been imposed upon; and when the true source of truth, which is tradition, is thus excluded; and the Pope, who is its guardian, is biased; the truth is no longer free to appear. Then, as men speak no longer of truth, truth itself must speak to men. This is what happened in the time of Arius. (Miracles under Diocletian and under Arius.)

833. *Miracle.*—The people concluded this of themselves; but if the reason of it must be given to you . . .

It is unfortunate to be in exception to the rule. The same must be strict, and opposed to exception. But yet, as it is certain that there are exceptions to a rule, our judgment must though strict, be just.

834. John 6. 26: *Non quia vidisti signum, sed quia saturati estis.*[1]
Those who follow Jesus Christ because of His miracles honour His power in all the miracles which it produces. But those who, making profession to follow Him because of His miracles, follow Him in fact only because He comforts them and satisfies them with worldly blessings, discredit His miracles, when they are opposed to their own comforts.

John 9: *Non est hic homo a Deo, quia sabbatum non custodit. Alii: Quomodo potest homo peccator hæc signa facere?*[2]
Which is the most clear?

This house is not of God; for they do not there believe that the five propositions are in Jansenius. Others: This house is of God; for in it there are wrought strange miracles.

Which is the most clear?

Tu quid dicis? Dico quia propheta est. Nisi esset hic a Deo, non poterat facere quidquam.[3]

835. In the Old Testament, when they will turn you from God. In the New, when they will turn you from Jesus Christ. These are the occasions for excluding particular miracles from belief. No others need be excluded.

Does it, therefore, follow that they would have the right to exclude all the prophets who came to them? No; they would have sinned in not excluding those who denied God, and would have sinned in excluding those who did not deny God.

So soon, then, as we see a miracle, we must either assent to it or have striking proofs to the contrary. We must see if it denies a God, or Jesus Christ, or the Church.

836. There is a great difference between not being for Jesus Christ and saying

---

[1]"Not because ye saw the miracles, but because ye . . . were filled."

[2]16. "This man is not of God, because he keepeth not the Sabbath day. Others said: How can a man that is a sinner do such miracles?"

[3]John 9.17,33. "What sayest thou of him? He said, He is a prophet. If this man were not of God, he could do nothing."

so, and not being for Jesus Christ and pretending to be so. The one party can do miracles, not the others. For it is clear of the one party that they are opposed to the truth, but not of the others; and thus miracles are clearer.

837. That we must love one God only is a thing so evident that it does not require miracles to prove it.

838. Jesus Christ performed miracles, then the apostles, and the first saints in great number; because the prophecies not being yet accomplished, but in the process of being accomplished by them, the miracles alone bore witness to them. It was foretold that the Messiah should convert the nations. How could this prophecy be fulfilled without the conversion of the nations? And how could the nations be converted to the Messiah, if they did not see this final effect of the prophecies which prove Him? Therefore, till He had died, risen again, and converted the nations, all was not accomplished; and so miracles were needed during all this time. Now they are no longer needed against the Jews; for the accomplished prophecies constitute a lasting miracle.

839. "Though ye believe not Me, believe at least the works." He refers them, as it were, to the strongest proof.

It had been told to the Jews, as well as to Christians, that they should not always believe the prophets; but yet the Pharisees and Scribes are greatly concerned about His miracles and try to show that they are false, or wrought by the devil. For they must needs be convinced, if they acknowledge that they are of God.

At the present day we are not troubled to make this distinction. Still it is very easy to do: those who deny neither God nor Jesus Christ do no miracles which are not certain. *Nemo facit virtutem in nomine meo, et cito possit de me male loqui.*[1]

But we have not to draw this distinction. Here is a sacred relic. Here is a thorn from the crown of the Saviour of the world, over whom the prince of this world has no power, which works miracles by the peculiar power of the blood shed for us. Now God Himself chooses this house in order to display conspicuously therein His power.

These are not men who do miracles by an unknown and doubtful virtue, which makes a decision difficult for us. It is God Himself. It is the instrument of the Passion of His only Son, who, being in many places, chooses this, and makes men come from all quarters there to receive these miraculous alleviations in their weaknesses.

840. The Church has three kinds of enemies: the Jews, who have never been of her body; the heretics, who have withdrawn from it; and the evil Christians, who rend her from within.

These three kinds of different adversaries usually attack her in different ways. But here they attack her in one and the same way. As they are all without miracles, and as the Church has always had miracles against them, they have all had the same interest in evading them; and they all make use of this excuse, that doctrine must not be judged by miracles, but miracles by doctrine. There were two parties

[1]Mark 9.39. *Nemo est enim qui faciat.* "There is no man which shall do a miracle in my name, that can lightly speak evil of me."

among those who heard Jesus Christ: those who followed His teaching on account of His miracles; others who said . . . There were two parties in the time of Calvin . . . There are now the Jesuits, etc.

841. Miracles furnish the test in matters of doubt, between Jews and heathens, Jews and Christians, Catholics and heretics, the slandered and slanderers, between the two crosses.

But miracles would be useless to heretics; for the Church, authorised by miracles which have already obtained belief, tells us that they have not the true faith. There is no doubt that they are not in it, since the first miracles of the Church exclude belief of theirs. Thus there is miracle against miracle, both the first and greatest being on the side of the Church.

These nuns, astonished at what is said—that they are in the way of perdition; that their confessors are leading them to Geneva; that they suggest to them that Jesus Christ is not in the Eucharist, nor on the right hand of the Father—know that all this is false and, therefore, offer themselves to God in this state. *Vide si via iniquitatis in me est.*[1] What happens thereupon? This place, which is said to be the temple of the devil, God makes His own temple. It is said that the children must be taken away from it. God heals them there. It is said that it is the arsenal of hell. God makes of it the sanctuary of His grace. Lastly, they are threatened with all the fury and vengeance of heaven; and God overwhelms them with favours. A man would need to have lost his senses to conclude from this that they are therefore in the way of perdition.

(We have without doubt the same signs as Saint Athanasius.)

842. *Si tu es Christus, dic nobis.*[2]

Opera quæ ego facio in nomine patris mei, hæc testimonium perhibent de me. Sed vos non creditis quia non estis ex ovibus meis. Oves meæ vocem meam audiunt.[3]

John 6. 30. *Quod ergo tu facis signum ut videamus et credamus tibi? (Non dicunt: Quam doctrinam prædicas?)*[4]

Nemo potest facere signa quæ tu facis nisi Deus.[5]

II Macc. 14. 15. *Deus qui signis evidentibus suam portionem protegit.*[6]

Volumus signum videre de cœlo, tentantes eum.[7] Luke 11. 16.

Generatio prava signum quærit; et non dabitur.[8]

Et ingemiscens ait: Quid generatio ista signum quærit?[9] (Mark 8. 12.) They asked a sign with an evil intention.

Et non poterat facere.[10] And yet he promises them the sign of Jonah, the great and wonderful miracle of his resurrection.

[1]Ps. 138.24. "And see if there be any wicked way in me."
[2]Luke 22.66. "Art thou the Christ? tell us."
[3]John 5.36. "The works which the father hath given me to finish . . . bear witness of me." John 10.26-27. "But ye believe not, because ye are not of my sheep . . . My sheep hear my voice."
[4]"What sign shewest thou then, that we may see, and believe thee. (They do not say: What doctrine do you preach?)"
[5]John 3.2. "No man can do these miracles that thou doest, except God be with him."
[6]"The Lord, making manifest his presence, upholdeth them that are his own portion."
[7]"And others, tempting him, sought of him a sign from heaven."
[8]Matt. 12.39. "An evil generation seeketh after a sign; and there shall no sign be given to it."
[9]"And he sighed deeply in his spirit, and saith, why doth this generation seek after a sign?"
[10]Mark 6.5. "And he could there do no mighty work."

Nisi videritis, non creditis.[1] He does not blame them for not believing unless there are miracles, but for not believing unless they are themselves spectators of them.

Antichrist *in signis mendacibus,*[2] says Saint Paul, II Thess. 2.

Secundum operationem Satanæ, in seductione iis qui pereunt eo quod charitatem veritatis non receperunt ut salvi fierent, ideo mittet illis Deus optationes erroris ut credant mendacio.[3]

As in the passage of Moses: *Tentat enim vos Deus, utrum diligatis eum.*[4]

Ecce prædixi vobis: vos ergo videte.[5]

843. Here is not the country of truth. She wanders unknown amongst men. God has covered her with a veil, which leaves her unrecognised by those who do not hear her voice. Room is opened for blasphemy, even against the truths that are at least very likely. If the truths of the Gospel are published, the contrary is published too, and the questions are obscured, so that the people cannot distinguish. And they ask, "What have you to make you believed rather than others? What sign do you give? You have only words, and so have we. If you had miracles, good and well." That doctrine ought to be supported by miracles is a truth, which they misuse in order to revile doctrine. And if miracles happen, it is said that miracles are not enough without doctrine; and this is another truth, which they misuse in order to revile miracles.

Jesus Christ cured the man born blind and performed a number of miracles on the Sabbath day. In this way He blinded the Pharisees, who said that miracles must be judged by doctrine.

"We have Moses: but, as for this fellow, we know not from whence he is." It is wonderful that you know not whence He is, and yet He does such miracles.

Jesus Christ spoke neither against God, nor against Moses.

Antichrist and the false prophets, foretold by both Testaments, will speak openly against God and against Jesus Christ. Who is not hidden . . . God would not allow him, who would be a secret enemy, to do miracles openly.

In a public dispute where the two parties profess to be for God, for Jesus Christ, for the Church, miracles have never been on the side of the false Christians, and the other side has never been without a miracle.

"He hath a devil." John 10. 21. And others said, "Can a devil open the eyes of the blind?"

The proofs which Jesus Christ and the apostles draw from Scripture are not conclusive; for they say only that Moses foretold that a prophet should come. But they do not thereby prove that this is He; and that is the whole question. These passages, therefore, serve only to show that they are not contrary to Scripture and that there appears no inconsistency, but not that there is agreement. Now this is enough, namely, exclusion of inconsistency, along with miracles.

[1]John 4.48. "Except ye see . . . ye will not believe."

[2]9. "In signs and lying wonders."

[3]IIThess. 2.9-11 "After the working of Satan . . . and with all deceivableness of unrighteousness in them that perish, because they received not the love of the truth, that they might be saved. And for this cause God shall send them strong delusion, that they should believe a lie."

[4]Deut. 13.3 "for the Lord your God proveth you, to know whether ye love the Lord."

[5]Matt. 24.25-26. "Behold, I have told you before. Wherefore if they shall say unto you, Behold."

There is a mutual duty between God and men. We must pardon Him this saying: *Quid debui?*[1] "Accuse me," said God in Isaiah.

"God must fulfil His promises," etc.

Men owe it to God to accept the religion which He sends. God owes it to men not to lead them into error. Now, they would be led into error, if the workers of miracles announced a doctrine which should not appear evidently false to the light of common sense, and if a greater worker of miracles had not already warned men not to believe them.

Thus, if there were divisions in the Church, and the Arians, for example, who declared themselves founded on Scripture just as the Catholics, had done miracles, and not the Catholics, men should have been led into error.

For, as a man, who announces to us the secrets of God, is not worthy to be believed on his private authority, and that is why the ungodly doubt him; so when a man, as a token of the communion which he has with God, raises the dead, foretells the future, removes the seas, heals the sick, there is none so wicked as not to bow to him, and the incredulity of Pharaoh and the Pharisees is the effect of a supernatural obduracy.

When, therefore, we see miracles and a doctrine not suspicious, both on one side, there is no difficulty. But when we see miracles and suspicious doctrine on the same side, we must then see which is the clearest. Jesus Christ was suspected.

Bar-jesus blinded. The power of God surpasses that of His enemies.

The Jewish exorcists beaten by the devils, saying, "Jesus I know, and Paul I know; but who are ye"?

Miracles are for doctrine, and not doctrine for miracles.

If the miracles are true, shall we be able to persuade men of all doctrine? No; for this will not come to pass. *Si angelus . . .*[2]

Rule: we must judge of doctrine by miracles; we must judge of miracles by doctrine. All this is true, but contains no contradiction.

For we must distinguish the times.

How glad you are to know the general rules, thinking thereby to set up dissension and render all useless! We shall prevent you, my father; truth is one and constant.

It is impossible, from the duty of God to men, that a man, hiding his evil teaching, and only showing the good, saying that he conforms to God and the Church, should do miracles so as to instil insensibly a false and subtle doctrine. This cannot happen.

And still less that God, who knows the heart should perform miracles in favour of such a one.

844. The three marks of religion: perpetuity, a good life, miracles. They destroy perpetuity by their doctrine of probability; a good life by their morals, miracles by destroying either their truth or the conclusions to be drawn from them.

If we believe them, the Church will have nothing to do with perpetuity, holiness, and miracles. The heretics deny them, or deny the conclusions to be drawn from them; they do the same. But one would need to have no sincerity in order

[1] Is. 5.4. *Quis est quod debui ultra facere vineæ meæ, et non faci ei?* "What could have been done more to my vineyard, that I have not done in it?"

[2] Gal. 1.8. "But though an angel."

to deny them, or again to lose one's senses in order to deny the conclusions to be drawn from them.

Nobody has ever suffered martyrdom for the miracles which he says he has seen; for the folly of men goes perhaps to the length of martyrdom, for those which the Turks believe by tradition, but not for those which they have seen.

845. The heretics have always attacked these three marks, which they have not.

846. *First objection:* "An angel from heaven. We must not judge of truth by miracles, but of miracles by truth. Therefore the miracles are useless."

Now they are of use, and they must not be in opposition to the truth. Therefore what Father Lingende has said that "God will not permit that a miracle may lead into error . . ."

When there shall be a controversy in the same Church, miracle will decide.

Second objection: "But Antichrist will do miracles."

The magicians of Pharaoh did not entice to error. Thus we cannot say to Jesus respecting Antichrist, "You have led me into error." For Antichrist will do them against Jesus Christ, and so they cannot lead into error. Either God will not permit false miracles, or He will procure greater.

[Jesus Christ has existed since the beginning of the world: this is more impressive than all the miracles of Antichrist.]

If in the same Church there should happen a miracle on the side of those in error, men would be led into error. Schism is visible; a miracle is visible. But schism is more a sign of error than a miracle is a sign of truth. Therefore a miracle cannot lead into error.

But, apart from schism, error is not so obvious as a miracle is obvious. Therefore a miracle could lead into error.

Ubi est Deus tuus?[1] Miracles show Him, and are a light.

847. One of the anthems for Vespers at Christmas: *Exortum est in tenebris lumen rectis corde.*[2]

848. If the compassion of God is so great that He instructs us to our benefit, even when He hides Himself, what light ought we not to expect from Him when He reveals Himself?

849. Will *Est et non est.*[3] be received in faith itself as well as in miracles? And if it is inseparable in the others . . .

When Saint Xavier works miracles. [Saint Hilary. "Ye wretches, who oblige us to speak of miracles."]

Unjust judges, make not your own laws on the moment; judge by those which are established, and by yourselves. *Væ qui conditis leges iniquas.*[4]

Miracles endless, false.

In order to weaken your adversaries, you disarm the whole Church.

[1]Ps. 41.4. "Where is thy God?"
[2]Ps. 111.4. "Unto the upright there ariseth light in the darkness."
[3]"The *yes* and the *no*."
[4]Is. 10.1. "Woe unto them that decree unrighteous decrees."

If they say that our salvation depends upon God, they are "heretics." If they say that they are obedient to the Pope, that is "hypocrisy." If they are ready to subscribe to all the articles, that is not enough. If they say that a man must not be killed for an apple, "they attack the morality of Catholics." If miracles are done among them, it is not a sign of holiness, and is, on the contrary a symptom of heresy.

This way in which the Church has existed is that truth has been without dispute, or, if it has been contested, there has been the Pope, or, failing him, there has been the Church.

850. The five propositions condemned, but no miracle; for the truth was not attacked. But the Sorbonne . . . but the bull . . .

It is impossible that those who love God with all their heart should fail to recognise the Church; so evident is she. It is impossible that those who do not love God should be convinced of the Church.

Miracles have such influence that it was necessary that God should warn men not to believe in them in opposition to Him, all clear as it is that there is a God. Without this they would have been able to disturb men.

And thus so far from these passages, Deut. 13, making against the authority of the miracles, nothing more indicates their influence. And the same in respect of Antichrist. "To seduce, if it were possible, even the elect."

851. The history of the man born blind.

What says Saint Paul? Does he continually speak of the evidence of the prophecies? No, but of his own miracle. What says Jesus Christ? Does He speak of the evidence of the prophecies? No; His death had not fulfilled them. But he says, *Si non fecissem*.[1] Believe the works.

Two supernatural foundations of our wholly supernatural religion; one visible, the other invisible; miracles with grace, miracles without grace.

The synagogue, which had been treated with love as a type of the Church, and with hatred, because it was only the type, has been restored, being on the point of falling when it was well with God, and thus a type.

Miracles prove the power which God has over hearts, by that which He exercises over bodies.

The Church has never approved a miracle among heretics.

Miracles a support of religion: they have been the test of Jews; they have been the test of Christians, saints, innocents, and true believers.

A miracle among schismatics is not so much to be feared; for schism, which is more obvious than a miracle, visibly indicates their error. But, when there is no schism and error is in question, miracle decides.

Si non fecissem quæ alius non fecit.[2] The wretches who have obliged us to speak of miracles.

Abraham and Gideon confirm faith by miracles.

Judith. God speaks at last in their greatest oppression.

If the cooling of love leaves the Church almost without believers, miracles will rouse them. This is one of the last effects of grace.

If one miracle were wrought among the Jesuits!

[1] John 15.24. "If he had not done."
[2] John 15.24. "If he had not done among them the works which none other man did."

When a miracle disappoints the expectation of those in whose presence it happens, and there is a disproportion between the state of their faith and the instrument of the miracle, it ought then to induce them to change. But with you it is otherwise. There would be as much reason in saying that, if the Eucharist raised a dead man, it would be necessary for one to turn a Calvinist rather than remain a Catholic. But when it crowns the expectation, and those, who hoped that God would bless the remedies, see themselves healed without remedies . . .

The ungodly.—No sign has ever happened on the part of the devil without a stronger sign on the part of God, or even without it having been foretold that such would happen.

852. Unjust persecutors of those whom God visibly protects. If they reproach you with your excesses, "they speak as the heretics." If they say that the grace of Jesus Christ distinguishes us, "they are heretics." If they do miracles, "it is the mark of their heresy."

Ezekiel. They say: These are the people of God who speak thus.

It is said, "Believe in the Church"; but it is not said, "Believe in miracles"; because the last is natural, and not the first. The one had need of a precept, not the other. Hezekiah.

The synagogue was only a type, and thus it did not perish; and it was only a type, and so it is decayed. It was a type which contained the truth, and thus it has lasted until it no longer contained the truth.

My reverend father, all this happened in types. Other religions perish; this one perishes not.

Miracles are more important than you think. They have served for the foundation, and will serve for the continuation of the Church till Antichrist, till the end.

The two witnesses.

In the Old Testament and the New, miracles are performed in connection with types. Salvation, or a useless thing, if not to show that we must submit to the Scriptures: type of the sacrament.

853. [We must judge soberly of divine ordinances, my father. Saint Paul in the isle of Malta.]

854. The hardness of the Jesuits, then, surpasses that of the Jews, since those refused to believe Jesus Christ innocent only because they doubted if His miracles were of God. Whereas the Jesuits, though unable to doubt that the miracles of Port-Royal are of God, do not cease to doubt still the innocence of that house.

855. I suppose that men believe miracles. You corrupt religion either in favour of your friends or against your enemies. You arrange it at your will.

856. *On the miracle.*—As God has made no family more happy, let it also be the case that He find none more thankful.

SECTION XIV

APPENDIX: POLEMICAL FRAGMENTS

857. *Clearness, obscurity.*—There would be too great darkness, if truth had not visible signs. This is a wonderful one, that it has always been preserved in one Church and one visible assembly [of men]. There would be too great clearness, if there were only one opinion in this Church. But in order to recognise what is true, one has only to look at what has always existed; for it is certain that truth has always existed, and that nothing false has always existed.

858. The history of the Church ought properly to be called the history of truth.

859. There is a pleasure in being in a ship beaten about by a storm, when we are sure that it will not founder. The persecutions which harass the Church are of this nature.

860. In addition to so many other signs of piety, they are also persecuted, which is the best sign of piety.

861. The Church is in an excellent state when it is sustained by God only.

862. The Church has always been attacked by opposite errors, but perhaps never at the same time, as now. And if she suffer more because of the multiplicity of errors, she derives this advantage from it, that they destroy each other.

She complains of both, but far more of the Calvinists, because of the schism.

It is certain that many of the two opposite sects are deceived. They must be disillusioned.

Faith embraces many truths which seem to contradict each other. *There is a time to laugh, and a time to weep*, etc. *Responde. Ne respondeas,*[1] etc.

The source of this is the union of the two natures in Jesus Christ; and also the two worlds (the creation of a new heaven and a new earth; a new life and a new death; all things double, and the same names remaining); and finally the two natures that are in the righteous (for they are the two worlds, and a member and image of Jesus Christ. And thus all the names suit them: righteous, yet sinners; dead, yet living; living, yet dead; elect, yet outcast, etc.).

There are then a great number of truths, both of faith and of morality, which seem contradictory and which all hold good together in a wonderful system. The source of all heresies is the exclusion of some of these truths; and the source of all the objections which the heretics make against us is the ignorance of some of our truths. And it generally happens that, unable to conceive the connection of two opposite truths, and believing that the admission of one involves the exclusion of the other, they adhere to the one, exclude the other, and think of us as opposed to them. Now exclusion is the cause of their heresy; and ignorance that we hold the other truth causes their objections.

[1]Prov. 26.4-5. "Answer . . . Answer not."

1st example: Jesus Christ is God and man. The Arians, unable to reconcile these things, which they believe incompatible, say that He is man; in this they are Catholics. But they deny that He is God; in this they are heretics. They allege that we deny His humanity; in this they are ignorant.

2nd example: On the subject of the Holy Sacrament. We believe that, the substance of the bread being changed, and being consubstantial with that of the body of our Lord, Jesus Christ is therein really present. That is one truth. Another is that this Sacrament is also a type of the cross and of glory, and a commemoration of the two. That is the Catholic faith, which comprehends these two truths which seem opposed.

The heresy of to-day, not conceiving that this Sacrament contains at the same time both the presence of Jesus Christ and a type of Him, and that it is a sacrifice and a commemoration of a sacrifice, believes that neither of these truths can be admitted without excluding the other for this reason.

They fasten to this point alone, that this Sacrament is typical; and in this they are not heretics. They think that we exclude this truth; hence it comes that they raise so many objections to us out of the passages of the Fathers which assert it. Finally, they deny the presence; and in this they are heretics.

3rd example: Indulgences.

The shortest way, therefore, to prevent heresies is to instruct in all truths; and the surest way to refute them is to declare them all. For what will the heretics say?

In order to know whether an opinion is a Father's . . .

863. All err the more dangerously, as they each follow a truth. Their fault is not in following a falsehood, but in not following another truth.

864. Truth is so obscure in these times, and falsehood so established, that, unless we love the truth, we cannot know it.

865. If there is ever a time in which we must make profession of two opposite truths, it is when we are reproached for omitting one. Therefore the Jesuits and Jansenists are wrong in concealing them, but the Jansenists more so, for the Jesuits have better made profession of the two.

866. Two kinds of people make things equal to one another, as feasts to working days, Christians to priests, all things among them, etc. And hence the one party conclude that what is then bad for priests is also so for Christians, and the other that what is not bad for Christians is lawful for priests.

867. If the ancient Church was in error, the Church is fallen. If she should be in error to-day, it is not the same thing; for she has always the superior maxim of tradition from the hand of the ancient Church; and so this submission and this conformity to the ancient Church prevail and correct all. But the ancient Church did not assume the future Church and did not consider her, as we assume and consider the ancient.

868. That which hinders us in comparing what formerly occurred in the Church with what we see there now is that we generally look upon Saint Athanasius,

Saint Theresa, and the rest, as crowned with glory and acting towards us as gods. Now that time has cleared up things, it does so appear. But at the time when he was persecuted, this great saint was a man called Athanasius; and Saint Theresa was a nun. "Elias was a man subject to like passions as we are," says Saint James, to disabuse Christians of that false idea which makes us reject the example of the saints as disproportioned to our state. "They were saints," say we, "they are not like us." What then actually happened? Saint Athanasius was a man called Athanasius, accused of many crimes, condemned by such and such a council for such and such a crime. All the bishops assented to it, and finally the Pope. What said they to those who opposed this? That they disturbed the peace, that they created schism, etc.

Zeal, light. Four kinds of persons: zeal without knowledge; knowledge without zeal; neither knowledge nor zeal; both zeal and knowledge. The first three condemned him. The last acquitted him, were excommunicated by the Church and yet saved the Church.

869. If Saint Augustine came at the present time and was as little authorised as his defenders, he would accomplish nothing. God directs His Church well, by having sent him before with authority.

870. God has not wanted to absolve without the Church. As she has part in the offence, He desires her to have part in the pardon. He associates her with this power, as kings their parliaments. But if she absolves or binds without God, she is no longer the Church. For, as in the case of parliament, even if the king have pardoned a man, it must be ratified; but if parliament ratifies without the king, or refuses to ratify on the order of the king, it is no longer the parliament of the king, but a rebellious assembly.

871. *The Church, the Pope. Unity, plurality.*—Considering the Church as a unity, the Pope, who is its head, is as the whole. Considering it as a plurality, the Pope is only a part of it. The Fathers have considered the Church now in the one way, now in the other. And thus they have spoken differently of the Pope. (Saint Cyprian: *Sacerdos Dei*.)[1] But in establishing one of these truths, they have not excluded the other. Plurality which is not reduced to unity is confusion; unity which does not depend on plurality is tyranny. There is scarcely any other country than France in which it is permissible to say that the Council is above the Pope.

872. The Pope is head. Who else is known of all? Who else is recognised by all, having power to insinuate himself into all the body, because he holds the principal shoot, which insinuates itself everywhere? How easy it was to make this degenerate into tyranny! That is why Christ has laid down for them this precept: *Vos autem non sic.*[2]

873. The Pope hates and fears the learned, who do not submit to him at will.

874. We must not judge of what the Pope is by some words of the Fathers—as

[1] Epistle 63. "Priest of the Lord."
[2] Luke 22.26. "But ye shall not be so."

the Greeks said in a council, important rules—but by the acts of the Church and the Fathers, and by the canons.

Duo[1] *aut tres.*[2] *In unum.* Unity and plurality. It is an error to exclude one of the two, as the papists do who exclude plurality, or the Huguenots who exclude unity.

875. Would the Pope be dishonoured by having his knowledge from God and tradition; and is it not dishonouring him to separate him from this holy union?

876. God does not perform miracles in the ordinary conduct of His Church. It would be a strange miracle if infallibility existed in one man. But it appears so natural for it to reside in a multitude, since the conduct of God is hidden under nature, as in all His other works.

877. Kings dispose of their own power; but the Popes cannot dispose of theirs.

878. *Summum jus, summa injuria.*[3]
The majority is the best way, because it is visible and has strength to make itself obeyed. Yet it is the opinion of the least able.

If men could have done it, they would have placed might in the hands of justice. But as might does not allow itself to be managed as men want, because it is a palpable quality, whereas justice is a spiritual quality of which men dispose as they please, they have placed justice in the hands of might. And thus that is called just which men are forced to obey.

Hence comes the right of the sword, for the sword gives a true right. Otherwise we should see violence on one side and justice on the other (end of the twelfth *Provincial Letter*). Hence comes the injustice of the Fronde, which raises its alleged justice against power. It is not the same in the Church, for there is a true justice and no violence.

879. *Injustice.*—Jurisdiction is not given for the sake of the judge, but for that of the litigant. It is dangerous to tell this to the people. But the people have too much faith in you; it will not harm them and may serve you. It should, therefore, be made known. *Pasce oves meas,* not *tuas.*[4] You owe me pasturage.

880. Men like certainty. They like the Pope to be infallible in faith, and grave doctors to be infallible in morals, so as to have certainty.

881. The Church teaches, and God inspires, both infallibly. The work of the Church is of use only as a preparation for grace or condemnation. What it does is enough for condemnation, not for inspiration.

882. Every time the Jesuits may impose upon the Pope, they will make all Christendom perjured.

[1]John 10.30. "I and my father are one."
[2]I John 5.7. "And these three agree in one."
[3]"The strictest law is the greatest injustice." Terrence, *Heauton Timorumenus*, iv.5.47; and Cicero, *De officiis*, i.10.
[4]John 21.17 "Feed my sheep." Not "yours."

The Pope is very easily imposed upon, because of his occupations, and the confidence which he has in the Jesuits; and the Jesuits are very capable of imposing upon him by means of calumny.

883. The wretches who have obliged me to speak of the basis of religion.

884. Sinners purified without penitence; the righteous justified without love; all Christians without the grace of Jesus Christ; God without power over the will of men; a predestination without mystery; a redemption without certitude!

885. Any one is made a priest, who wants to be so, as under Jeroboam.

It is a horrible thing that they propound to us the discipline of the Church of to-day as so good that it is made a crime to desire to change it. Formerly it was infallibly good, and it was thought that it could be changed without sin; and now, such as it is, we cannot wish it changed! It has indeed been permitted to change the custom of not making priests without such great circumspection that there were hardly any who were worthy; and it is not allowed to complain of the custom which makes so many who are unworthy!

886. *Heretics.*—Ezekiel. All the heathen, and also the Prophet, spoke evil of Israel. But the Israelites were so far from having the right to say to him, "You speak like the heathen," that he is most forcible upon this, that the heathen say the same as he.

887. The Jansenists are like the heretics in the reformation of morality; but you are like them in evil.

888. You are ignorant of the prophecies, if you do not know that all this must happen; princes, prophets, Pope, and even the priests. And yet the Church is to abide. By the grace of God we have not come to that. Woe to these priests! But we hope that God will bestow His mercy upon us that we shall not be of them.

Saint Peter, Epistle ii: false prophets in the past, the image of future ones.

889. . . . So that if it is true, on the one hand, that some lax monks and some corrupt casuists, who are not members of the hierarchy, are steeped in these corruptions, it is, on the other hand, certain that the true pastors of the Church, who are the true guardians of the Divine Word, have preserved it unchangeably against the efforts of those who have attempted to destroy it.

And thus true believers have no pretext to follow that laxity, which is only offered to them by the strange hands of these casuists, instead of the sound doctrine which is presented to them by the fatherly hands of their own pastors. And the ungodly and heretics have no ground for publishing these abuses as evidence of imperfection in the providence of God over His Church; since, the Church consisting properly in the body of the hierarchy, we are so far from being able to conclude from the present state of matters that God has abandoned her to corruption, that it has never been more apparent than at the present time that God visibly protects her from corruption.

For if some of these men, who, by an extraordinary vocation, have made profession of withdrawing from the world and adopting the monks' dress, in order to live in a more perfect state than ordinary Christians, have fallen into excesses which horrify ordinary Christians, and have become to us what the false prophets were among the Jews; this is a private and personal misfortune, which must indeed be deplored, but from which nothing can be inferred against the care which God takes of His Church; since all these things are so clearly foretold, and it has been so long since announced that these temptations would arise from people of this kind; so that when we are well instructed, we see in this rather evidence of the care of God than of His forgetfulness in regard to us.

890. Tertullian: *Nunquam Ecclesia reformabitur.*[1]

891. Heretics, who take advantage of the doctrine of the Jesuits, must be made to know that it is not that of the Church, and that our divisions do not separate us from the altar.

892. If in differing we condemned, you would be right. Uniformity without diversity is useless to others; diversity without uniformity is ruinous for us. The one is harmful outwardly; the other inwardly.

893. By showing the truth, we cause it to be believed; but by showing the injustice of ministers, we do not correct it. Our mind is assured by a proof of falsehood; our purse is not made secure by proof of injustice.

894. Those who love the Church lament to see the corruption of morals; but laws at least exist. But these corrupt the laws. The model is damaged.

895. Men never do evil so completely and cheerfully as when they do it from religious conviction.

896. It is in vain that the Church has established these words, anathemas, heresies, etc. They are used against her.

897. The servant knoweth not what his lord doeth, for the master tells him only the act and not the intention. And this is why he often obeys slavishly, and defeats the intention. But Jesus Christ has told us the object. And you defeat that object.

898. They cannot have perpetuity, and they seek universality; and therefore they make the whole Church corrupt, that they may be saints.

899. *Against those who misuse passages of Scripture, and who pride themselves in finding one which seems to favour their error.*—The chapter for Vespers, Passion Sunday, the prayer for the king.
Explanation of these words: "He that is not with me is against me." And of these others: "He that is not against you is for you." A person who says: "I am neither for nor against"; we ought to reply to him . . .

[1]"The Church will never be reformed."

900. He who will give the meaning of Scripture, and does not take it from Scripture, is an enemy of Scripture. (St. Augustine, *Of Christian Doctrine*.)

901. *Humilibus dat gratiam;*[1] *an ideo non dedit humilitatem?*[2]
Sui eum non receperunt; quotquot autem non receperunt,[3] *an non erant sui?*[4]

902. "It must indeed be," says Feuillant, "that this is not so certain; for controversy indicates uncertainty (Saint Athanasius, Saint Chrysostom, morals, unbelievers)."

The Jesuits have not made the truth uncertain, but they have made their own ungodliness certain.

Contradiction has always been permitted, in order to blind the wicked; for all that offends truth or love is evil. This is the true principle.

903. All religions and sects in the world have had natural reason for a guide. Christians alone have been constrained to take their rules from without themselves, and to acquaint themselves with those which Jesus Christ bequeathed to men of old to be handed down to true believers. This constraint wearies these good Fathers. They desire, like other people, to have liberty to follow their own imaginations. It is in vain that we cry to them, as the prophets said to the Jews of old: "Enter into the Church; acquaint yourselves with the precepts which the men of old left to her, and follow those paths." They have answered like the Jews: "We will not walk in them; but we will follow the thoughts of our hearts"; and they have said, "We will be as the other nations."

904. They make a rule of exception.

Have the men of old given absolution before penance? Do this as exceptional. But of the exception you make a rule without exception, so that you do not even want the rule to be exceptional.

905. *On confessions and absolutions without signs of regret.*

God regards only the inward; the Church judges only by the outward. God absolves as soon as He sees penitence in the heart; the Church when she sees it in works. God will make a Church pure within, which confounds, by its inward and entirely spiritual holiness, the inward impiety of proud sages and Pharisees; and the Church will make an assembly of men whose external manners are so pure as to confound the manners of the heathen. If there are hypocrites among them, but so well disguised that she does not discover their venom, she tolerates them; for, though they are not accepted of God, whom they cannot deceive, they are of men, whom they do deceive. And thus she is not dishonoured by their conduct, which appears holy. But you want the Church to judge neither of the inward, because that belongs to God alone, nor of the outward, because God dwells only upon the inward; and thus, taking away from her all choice of men, you retain in the Church the most dissolute and those who dishonour her so greatly that the

---

[1] Jas. 4.6. "God giveth grace unto the humble."
[2] "But did he not give them humility?"
[3] John 1.11-12. "The world knew him not; and his own received him not."
[4] "And were they not his?"

synagogues of the Jews and sects of philosophers would have banished them as unworthy and have abhorred them as impious.

906. The easiest conditions to live in according to the world are the most difficult to live in according to God, and vice versa. Nothing is so difficult according to the world as the religious life; nothing is easier than to live it according to God. Nothing is easier, according to the world, than to live in high office and great wealth; nothing is more difficult than to live in them according to God, and without acquiring an interest in them and a liking for them.

907. The casuists submit the decision to the corrupt reason, and the choice of decisions to the corrupt will, in order that all that is corrupt in the nature of man may contribute to his conduct.

908. But is it *probable* that *probability* gives assurance?
Difference between rest and security of conscience. Nothing gives certainty but truth; nothing gives rest but the sincere search for truth.

909. The whole society itself of their casuists cannot give assurance to a conscience in error, and that is why it is important to choose good guides.
Thus they will be doubly culpable, both in having followed ways which they should not have followed, and in having listened to teachers to whom they should not have listened.

910. Can it be anything but compliance with the world which makes you find things probable? Will you make us believe that it is truth and that, if duelling were not the fashion, you would find it probable that they might fight, considering the matter in itself?

911. Must we kill to prevent there being any wicked? This is to make both parties wicked instead of one. *Vince in bono malum.*[1] (Saint Augustine.)

912. *Universal.*—Ethics and language are special, but universal sciences.

913. *Probability.*—Each one can employ it; no one can take it away.

914. They allow lust to act, and check scruples; whereas they should do the contrary.

915. *Montalte.*—Lax opinions please men so much, that it is strange that theirs displease. It is because they have exceeded all bounds. Again, there are many people who see the truth, and who cannot attain to it; but there are few who do not know that the purity of religion is opposed to our corruptions. It is absurd to say that an eternal recompense is offered to the morality of Escobar.

916. *Probability.*—They have some true principles; but they misuse them. Now,

[1]Rom. 12.21. "But overcome evil with good."

the abuse of truth ought to be as much punished as the introduction of falsehood.

As if there were two hells, one for sins against love, the other for those against justice!

917. *Probability.*—The earnestness of the saints in seeking the truth was useless, if the probable is trustworthy. The fear of the saints who have always followed the surest way. (Saint Theresa having always followed her confessor.)

918. Take away *probability*, and you can no longer please the world; give *probability*, and you can no longer displease it.

919. These are the effects of the sins of the peoples and of the Jesuits. The great have wished to be flattered. The Jesuits have wished to be loved by the great. They have all been worthy to be abandoned to the spirit of lying, the one party to deceive, the others to be deceived. They have been avaricious, ambitious, voluptuous. *Coacervabunt tibi magistros.*[1] Worthy disciples of such masters, they have sought flatterers, and have found them.

920. If they do not renounce their doctrine of probability, their good maxims are as little holy as the bad, for they are founded on human authority; and thus, if they are more just, they will be more reasonable, but not more holy. They take after the wild stem on which they are grafted.

If what I say does not serve to enlighten you, it will be of use to the people.

If these are silent, the stones will speak.

Silence is the greatest persecution; the saints were never silent. It is true that a call is necessary; but it is not from the decrees of the Council that we must learn whether we are called, it is from the necessity of speaking. Now, after Rome has spoken, and we think that she has condemned the truth, and that they have written it, and after the books which have said the contrary are censured; we must cry out so much the louder, the more unjustly we are censured, and the more violently they would stifle speech, until there come a Pope who hears both parties, and who consults antiquity to do justice. So the good Popes will find the Church still in outcry.

The Inquisition and the Society are the two scourges of the truth.

Why do you not accuse them of Arianism? For, though they have said that Jesus Christ is God, perhaps they mean by it not the natural interpretation, but, as it is said, *Dii estis.*[2]

If my *Letters* are condemned at Rome, that which I condemn in them is condemned in heaven. *Ad tuum, Domine Jesu, tribunal appello.*[3]

You yourselves are corruptible.

I feared that I had written ill, seeing myself condemned; but the example of so many pious writings makes me believe the contrary. It is no longer allowable to write well, so corrupt or ignorant is the Inquisition!

"It is better to obey God than men."

I fear nothing; I hope for nothing. It is not so with the bishops. Port-Royal

[1] IITim. 4.3. "Shall they heap to themselves teachers."
[2] Ps. 81.6. "Ye are gods."
[3] "To your tribunal, Lord Jesus, I call."

fears, and it is bad policy to disperse them; for they will fear no longer and will cause greater fear. I do not even fear your like censures, if they are not founded on those of tradition. Do you censure all? What! Even my respect? No. Say then what, or you will do nothing, if you do not point out the evil, and why it is evil. And this is what they will have great difficulty in doing.

Probability.—They have given a ridiculous explanation of certitude; for, after having established that all their ways are sure, they have no longer called that sure which leads to heaven without danger of not arriving there by it, but that which leads there without danger of going out of that road.

921. . . . The saints indulge in subtleties in order to think themselves criminals and impeach their better actions. And these indulge in subtleties in order to excuse the most wicked.

The heathen sages erected a structure equally fine outside, but upon a bad foundation; and the devil deceived men by this apparent resemblance based upon the most different foundation.

Man never had so good a cause as I; and others have never furnished so good a capture as you . . .

The more they point out weakness in my person, the more they authorise my cause.

You say that I am a heretic. Is that lawful? And if you do not fear that men do justice, do you not fear that God does justice?

You will feel the force of the truth, and you will yield to it . . .

There is something supernatural in such a blindness. *Digna necessitas.*[1] *Mentiris impudentissime* . . .[2]

Doctrina sua noscetur vir . . .[3]

False piety, a double sin.

I am alone against thirty thousand. No. Protect you, the court; protect, you, deception; let me protect the truth. It is all my strength. If I lose it, I am undone. I shall not lack accusations, and persecutions. But I possess the truth, and we shall see who will take it away.

I do not need to defend religion, but you do not need to defend error and injustice. Let God, out of His compassion, having no regard to the evil which is in me, and having regard to the good which is in you, grant us all grace that truth may not be overcome in my hands, and that falsehood . . .

922. *Probable.*—Let us see if we seek God sincerely, by comparison of the things which we love. It is *probable* that this food will not poison me. It is *probable* that I shall not lose my action by not prosecuting it . . .

923. It is not absolution only which remits sins by the sacrament of penance, but contrition, which is not real if it does not seek the sacrament.

924. People who do not keep their word, without faith, without honour, without truth, deceitful in heart, deceitful in speech; for which that amphibious ani-

[1]Wisd. of Sol. 19.4. "Doom which they deserved."
[2]"Most impudent Liars." See *Provincial Letter* xvi.
[3]Prov. 12.8. "A man shall be commended according to his wisdom."

mal in fable was once reproached, which held itself in a doubtful position between the fish and the birds . . .

It is important to kings and princes to be considered pious; and therefore they
must confess themselves to you.

CONTENTS
SCIENTIFIC TREATISES

SCIENTIFIC TREATISES

PREFACE TO THE TREATISE ON THE VACUUM

WE have carried our respect for antiquity so far today, in matters in which it should have less influence, that we treat all its ideas as revelations and even its obscurities as mysteries; we can no longer advance new opinions without danger, and an author's text is enough to destroy the strongest arguments. . .

Not that my intention is to correct one vice by another, and to have no esteem for the ancients because they are too much esteemed. I do not want to banish their authority to set up reason alone, although there is an attempt to establish their authority alone to the prejudice of reason. . .

To make this important distinction with care we must consider that one group depend exclusively on memory and are purely historical, having as their only object to know what the authors have written; the other group depend exclusively on reason and are wholly dogmatic, having as their object to seek and discover hidden truths. Those of the first kind have the same limits as the books containing them. . .

It is in accordance with this distinction that we should regulate differently the extent of our respect. The respect that we should have for. . .

In matters in which we seek to know only what authors have written, as in history, geography, jurisprudence, languages, and above all in theology, and in short wherever either the simple fact or an institution, human or divine, is the starting point, we must necessarily have recourse to books, since all that can be known about such matters is contained there. Whence it is evident that we can have the whole of that knowledge and that it is not possible to add anything to it.

If it is a question of knowing who was the first king of France, where the geographers put the first meridian, what words are used in a dead language, and everything of this sort, how could we find it out except from books? And who can add anything new to what they tell us about it, since we desire to know only what they contain? Authority alone can give us light on such matters. But it is in theology that authority has its chief weight because there it is inseparable from truth, which we know only through it; so that to give absolute certainty to things which reason can least grasp, it is sufficient to point them out in Holy Scripture (as, to show the uncertainty of the most probable things, we need only point out that they are not included there); because the principles of theology are above nature and reason, and the mind of man, too feeble to reach them by its own efforts, can arrive at this highest knowledge only if carried there by an all-powerful and supernatural force.

It is quite otherwise with subjects accessible to sense or reasoning: here author-ity is useless, only reason can know them. Authority and reason have their sepa-rate rights: a moment ago one had all the advantage; here the other is queen in her turn. But since subjects of this kind are suited to the mind's reach, it has perfect freedom to concern itself with them; its inexhaustible fertility produces continually, and its discoveries can be at once without end and without inter-ruption. . .

Thus it is that geometry, arithmetic, music, physics, medicine, architecture, and all the sciences subject to experiment and reason must be added to if they are to become perfect. The ancients found them merely sketched by their predeces-sors, and we shall leave them to our successors in a more perfected state than we received them. Since their perfection depends upon time and effort, it is evident that even if our effort and time had gained us less than the labors of the ancients, separated from ours, the two together nevertheless must have more effect than either alone.

The clearing up of this difference should make us pity the blindness of those who advance authority alone as proof in physics instead of reason or experiment, and should fill us with horror at the wickedness of others who use reason alone in theology instead of the authority of Scripture and the Fathers. We must strengthen the courage of those timid souls who dare discover nothing in physics, and con-found the insolence of that temerity which introduces novelty into theology. Meanwhile the misfortune of the age is such that we see many new opinions in theology altogether unknown to antiquity maintained with obstinacy and re-ceived with applause; whereas those put forward in physics, though few in num-ber, must be convicted of error, it seems, as soon as they shock, however little, received opinions. As if respect for the philosophers of antiquity were a duty but for the most ancient of the Fathers only decorum! I leave it to the judicious to observe the importance of this abuse which perverts the order of the sciences so unjustly, and I think there will be few who do not wish this . . . to be applied to other subjects, since new discoveries are inevitably errors in those matters we profane with impunity, whereas they are absolutely necessary for the perfection of so many other subjects incomparably lower, which however we would be afraid to touch.

Let us make a more just distribution of our credulity and our doubt, and set limits to our respect for the ancients. Since reason is its source, reason should also be its measure. Let us consider that if the ancients had kept to this deference of daring to add nothing to the knowledge transmitted to them and if their con-temporaries had been as much opposed to accepting anything new, they would have deprived both themselves and their posterity of the fruit of their discoveries. Just as they used the discoveries handed down to them only as the means of making new ones, and that happy daring had opened the road for them to great achievements, so we should take the discoveries won for us by them in the same spirit, and following their example make these discoveries the means and not the end of our study, and thus by imitating the ancients try to surpass them. For what is more unfair than to treat our predecessors with more respect than they treated those who preceded them, and to have for them that inviolable respect they have deserved from us only because they did not themselves have it for those who had the same advantage over them? . . .

The secrets of nature are hidden. Although she is always at work, her effects are not always discovered: time reveals them from generation to generation, and although always the same in herself, she is not always equally known. The experiments which give us our knowledge of nature multiply continually; and since they are the only principles of physics, the consequences multiply in proportion. It is in this way that we can today have other ideas and new opinions without scorn and without ingratitude, since the first knowledge given us by the ancients has served as steps to our own, and since we are indebted to them for the advantage of a position higher than theirs; because placed by them part way up the ladder, we are carried higher by our slightest effort, and with less labor and less glory we find ourselves above them. It is from that height we can discover things it was impossible for them to see. Our view has a wider range, and although they knew as well as we do everything they could observe of nature, they nevertheless did not know so much and we see more than they did.

However it is a strange thing how we reverence their opinions. To contradict them counts as a crime and to add to them is an outrage, as if they had left no more truths to know. Is not this to treat man's reason with indignity and to put it on a level with animal instinct, since we thereby take away the main difference, which consists in this that the effects of reason increase continually whereas instinct always remains in the same state? Beehives were as well laid out a thousand years ago as today, and each bee forms that hexagon as exactly the first time as the last. It is the same with everything animals make by that hidden motion. Nature teaches them in response to the pressure of necessity; but this frail knowledge dies with its need: as they receive it without study, they do not have the happiness of preserving it; and every time they are given it, they find it new, because nature, whose object is merely to maintain animals in an order of limited perfection, infuses in them this necessary knowledge, always the same, lest they perish, and does not allow them to add to it lest they go beyond the boundaries prescribed to them. It is different with man, made only for infinity. He is ignorant in his life's first age, but he never ceases to learn as he goes forward, for he has the advantage not only of his own experience but also of his predecessors', because he always keeps in his memory the knowledge he has once acquired, and that of the ancients is always at hand in the books they have left. And since he keeps his knowledge, he can also easily increase it, so that men today are in a certain sense in the same condition in which those ancient philosophers would be if they could have prolonged their old age until now, adding to the knowledge they had what their studies might have won for them by the grace of so many centuries. Hence it is that by a special prerogative not only does each man advance from day to day in the sciences, but all men together make a continual progress as the universe grows old, because the same thing happens in the succession of men as in the different ages of an individual man. So that the whole series of men during the course of so many centuries should be considered as one self-same man, always in existence and continually learning. Whence it is seen with what injustice we respect antiquity in the persons of its philosophers; for since old age is the age furthest removed from childhood, who does not see that the old age of this universal man should be sought not in the times near his birth but in those which are most distant from it? Those whom we call ancients were in truth new in every respect, and actually formed the childhood of man; and since we have added to their knowledge the experience of the succeeding centuries, it is in ourselves that that antiquity can be found which we revere in others.

The ancients should be admired for the consequences they drew correctly from the little stock of principles they had, and they should be excused for those in which they lacked the advantage of experiment rather than force of reason.

For were they not excusable for their opinion about the Milky Way when, the weakness of their eyes as yet unaided by artifice, they attributed its color to a greater density in that part of the sky, which would more powerfully reflect the light? But would we not be inexcusable for holding to the same opinion now that with the help of the telescope we have discovered an infinity of little stars there, whose more abundant light has made us recognize the true cause of that whiteness?

Did they not also have cause to say that all corruptible bodies were contained within the sphere of the moon's heaven, when during the course of so many centuries they had never yet observed corruption or generation beyond this space? But should we not give contrary assurance when the whole earth has seen with its eyes comets burst into flame and vanish far beyond that sphere?

Thus it is that concerning the vacuum the ancients were right to say that nature did not permit it, because all their experiments had always led to the observation that she abhorred it and could not endure it. But if the new experiments had been known to them, perhaps they would have found reason to affirm what they had reason to deny because the vacuum had not yet appeared. Therefore in making the judgment that nature did not permit a vacuum, they meant to speak of nature only as they knew her; since to make the judgment in general it would not be enough to have seen it true in a hundred instances or in a thousand or in any other number however great, for if there remained a single case to examine, it alone would suffice to prevent the general definition, and if a single case were opposed, it alone. . . . For in all matters whose proof is by experiment and not by demonstration no universal assertion can be made except by the general enumeration of all the parts and all the different cases. Thus when we say the diamond is the hardest of all bodies, we mean of all bodies we know, and we neither can nor should include those we do not know. And when we say that gold is the heaviest of all bodies, it would be rash of us to include in this general proposition bodies not yet in our knowledge, although it is not impossible they are in nature. Similarly when the ancients asserted that nature did not permit a vacuum, they meant she did not permit a vacuum in all the experiments they had seen, and they could not without rashness include experiments they did not know. But if they had known them, undoubtedly they would have drawn the same consequences as we do and would by their avowal have given them the authority of that antiquity which men today want to make the sole principle of the sciences.

Thus without contradicting the ancients we can assert the opposite of what they said; and finally whatever the weight of antiquity, truth should always have the advantage, even when newly discovered, since it is always older than every opinion men have held about it, and only ignorance of its nature could imagine it began to be at the time it began to be known.

NEW EXPERIMENTS CONCERNING THE VACUUM

DONE IN TUBES, SYRINGES, BELLOWS, AND SIPHONS OF VARIOUS LENGTHS, SIZES, AND SHAPES, WITH DIVERS FLUIDS, SUCH AS QUICKSILVER, WATER, WINE, OIL, AIR, ETC.

WITH A DISCOURSE ON THE SAME SUBJECT, IN WHICH IT IS SHOWN THAT A VESSEL AS LARGE AS CAN BE PROCURED MAY BE EMPTIED OF ALL SUBSTANCES KNOWN IN NATURE WHICH ARE CAPABLE OF BEING PERCEIVED BY THE SENSES, AND WHAT FORCE IS NECESSARY FOR THE CREATION OF THIS VACUUM.

DEDICATED TO M. PASCAL, PRIVY COUNCILOR AND COUNCILOR OF STATE TO THE KING, BY B. P., HIS SON, THE WHOLE HAVING BEEN REDUCED TO A SUMMARY AND PUBLISHED IN ADVANCE OF A LARGER TREATISE ON THE SAME SUBJECT.

TO THE READER

My dear reader, since certain considerations prevent my publishing at this time in its entirety a treatise in which I have reported many new experiments I have made concerning the vacuum together with the conclusions I have drawn from them, I decided to give an account of the chief of them in this summary, where you will see in advance the plan of the whole work.

The occasion of these experiments was as follows: *About four years ago in Italy it was found that a glass tube four feet in height, with one end open and the other hermetically sealed, having been filled with quicksilver and the open end then stopped by a finger or in some other way and the tube placed vertically with the stopped end down and plunged two or three fingers' breadths into some more quicksilver contained in a vessel half full of quicksilver and half full of water; if the stopper is removed, the tube remaining plunged in the quicksilver of the vessel, the quicksilver of the tube descends part way, leaving at the top of the tube an apparently empty space, the bottom of the tube remaining full of quicksilver up to a certain height. And if the tube is lifted a little until its open end, which had been dipped in the quicksilver of the vessel, leaving this quicksilver, reaches the region of water, the quicksilver of the tube rises to the top with the water and these two liquids are mingled in the tube, but finally all the quicksilver falls, and the tube is found to be entirely filled with water.*

An account of this experiment having been sent from Rome to the Rev. Father Mersenne, Minim, at Paris, he made it public in France in the year 1644, to the admiration of all the learned and curious, through whose intercourse it became famous on all sides. I heard about it from M. Petit, Superintendent of Fortifications and skilled in all good learning, who had heard about it from the Rev. Father Mersenne himself. We did the experiment together at Rouen, the said M. Petit and I, in the same way it had been done in Italy, and we found every detail just as it had been reported from that country, without noticing at that time anything new.

Afterwards, reflecting on the consequences of these experiments, I was confirmed in the opinion I had always held that the vacuum was not a thing impossible in nature and that she did not flee it with such horror as many imagine.

I was forced to this opinion by seeing how slight was the foundation of the maxim so widely accepted that nature does not permit a vacuum, a maxim based only on experiments of which the greater number are false though considered most certain; and of the rest, some are so far from contributing to its proof that they show nature abhors too much fulness rather than flees a vacuum, and the most favorable do not bring anything more to light than that nature abhors a vacuum; they do not show that she cannot suffer it to be.

To the weakness of this principle I added our daily observations of the rare-faction and condensation of the air, which, as some have found, can be con-densed to the thousandth part of the place it seemed to occupy before and which can become so rare that I thought there must be either a large vacuum between its parts or penetration of dimensions. But since everyone did not accept that as proof, I believed this Italian experiment might convince even those who were the most obsessed with the impossibility of the vacuum.

However prejudice was strong enough again to invent objections which robbed the experiment of the belief it deserved. Some said that the top of the tube was filled with spirits of mercury, others with a rarefied and imperceptible particle of air, others with a kind of matter which only existed in their imagination; and all, in a conspiracy to banish the vacuum, vied with each other in the exercise of that power of the mind called subtlety in the schools, which for the solution of real difficulties gives only empty words without foundation. I resolved therefore to devise such convincing experiments that they should be proof against all possible objections; and at the beginning of this year I performed a great many, of which some are related to the Italian experiment and others are entirely different, having nothing in common with it. These experiments were so accurate and so success-ful that I showed by means of them that the largest vessel procurable can be emptied of every substance perceived by sense and known in nature, and what force is necessary for the creation of this vacuum. In this way I also tested the height a siphon must have if it is to do what is expected of it, beyond which height it ceases to act, contrary to the opinion universally accepted by the world for so many centuries, as also the slight force required to draw up the piston of a syringe, without any matter taking its place, and many other things that you will find in the complete work, in which it is my intention to show what force nature exerts to avoid a vacuum and that she actually admits it and suffers its existence in a large space which can easily be emptied of every substance perceptible to sense. Accordingly I have divided the complete treatise into two parts, of which the first contains a detailed account of all my experiments, with accompanying figures, and a summary of the results, divided into a number of maxims. And the second part contains the consequences I have drawn from the experiments, divided into several propositions, in which I have shown that the apparently empty space which appeared in the experiments is actually empty of every sub-stance perceptible to sense and known in nature. And in the conclusion I give my opinion on the subject of the vacuum, and reply to the objections that can be made. Thus I am content to show a large empty space, and I leave it to the learned and curious to find out what goes on in such a space (as whether animals live there, whether the refraction of glass is diminished by it, and whatever can be done there), making no mention of it in this treatise, a summary of which I have thought it appropriate to give you in advance; because having made these experiments with much expense, effort, and time, I was afraid that someone else who had spent neither time, money, nor effort might anticipate me and make public things he had not seen and which consequently he could not report with the exactness and order necessary for their proper deduction; for there is no one who has had tubes and siphons so long as mine, and there are few who would be willing to take the necessary trouble to get them.

And since honest men add to the common desire of all men to maintain themselves in their rightful possessions the desire to refuse the honor which is not their due, you will undoubtedly approve of my defending myself equally against those who would take from me some of the experiments which I report to you here and which I promise you in the complete treatise, since they are of my own invention, and against those who would attribute to me the Italian experiment I have spoken to you about, since it is not mine. For although I have performed it in more ways than anyone else and with tubes twelve and even fifteen feet long, nevertheless I shall not even speak of it in these writings because I am not its discoverer and because it is my intention to give only those experiments which are of my own invention and altogether mine.

Summary of the first part, in which the experiments are reported

EXPERIMENTS

1. A glass syringe with a carefully fitted piston having been completely immersed in water and its opening closed by a finger touching the bottom of the piston (thus obliging the hand and arm to be in the water), only a moderate force is required to draw the piston up and make it separate from the finger, without any water coming in (which the philosophers believed could not be done with any finite force); and thereby the finger is felt to be strongly and painfully pulled, and the piston leaves an apparently empty space, into which it does not appear any body can have entered, since it is entirely surrounded by water which could have had no access to it because the opening had been closed; and if the piston is drawn higher, the apparently empty space becomes greater, but the finger is not felt to be more pulled. And if the syringe is lifted almost entirely out of the water so that only its opening and the covering finger remain in it, then upon the finger's being removed the water, contrary to its nature, rises with violence and entirely fills all the space left by the piston.

2. A bellows carefully closed on every side produces the same effect, with a similar preparation, contrary to the opinion of the same philosophers.

3. A glass tube forty-six feet long, open at one end and hermetically sealed at the other, having been filled with water or rather with very red wine, for greater visibility, then stoppered and lifted in this condition and placed vertically, the stoppered end down, in a vessel full of water, with about one foot of the tube below the surface of the water; if the stopper is removed, the wine in the tube descends to a certain height, which is about thirty-two feet above the surface of the water in the vessel, and runs out and mingles with the water in the vessel, to which it gives a tinge of color, and separating from the top of the glass leaves a space of about thirteen feet apparently empty, where again it does not appear any body can have taken its place. And if the tube is inclined, as then the height of the wine in the tube is decreased by this inclination, the wine ascends until it

reaches the height of thirty-two feet. And finally if the tube is inclined to the height of thirty-two feet, it is entirely refilled, thus drawing back as much water as it had rejected wine, so that it is seen to be full of wine from the top to about thirteen feet from the bottom and filled with slightly colored water in the thirteen feet remaining.

4. A scalene siphon, of which the longer leg is fifty feet long and the shorter leg is forty-five, having been filled with water and the two stoppered openings immersed about a foot in two vessels filled with water so that the siphon is vertical and the surface of the water of one vessel is five feet higher than the surface of the other; if the stoppers of the openings are removed with the siphon in the position described, the longer leg does not attract the water in the shorter leg nor consequently that in the vessel in which the shorter leg dips, contrary to the opinion of all philosophers and artisans, but the water descends from both legs into the two vessels until it reaches the same height as in the afore-mentioned tube, measuring the height from the surface of the water of each vessel. But when the siphon is inclined at a height less than about thirty-one feet, the longer leg attracts the water in the vessel of the shorter leg, and when the siphon is drawn up again toward the vertical, the attraction stops and water flows from both sides into their respective vessels. And when the siphon is lowered again, the water in the longer leg attracts the water in the shorter as before.

5. If a cord about fifteen feet long with a thread fastened to the end (having been left in water for a long time in order that whatever air may have been enclosed in the cord might be expelled by the gradual absorption of moisture) is put in a tube fifteen feet long, sealed at one end as above and filled with water, so that outside the tube there is only the thread attached to the cord to pull it with, and the opening of the tube is placed in quicksilver; when the cord is pulled little by little, the quicksilver rises in proportion until the height of the quicksilver, added to the fourteenth part of the height of the water remaining, is two feet, three inches. For afterwards, when the cord is pulled, the water quits the top of the glass and leaves an apparently empty space, which increases in proportion as the cord is pulled. But if the tube is inclined, the quicksilver of the vessel rises in it, so that if it is inclined enough, it is completely filled with quicksilver and water, which strikes the top of the tube with violence, making the same noise and the same sharp sound as if it were breaking the glass, which does in fact run the risk of being broken. And lest it be suspected that some air may have remained in the cord, the same experiment may be performed with a number of little wooden cylinders fastened together with brass wire.

6. A syringe with an accurately fitted piston having been placed in quicksilver so that its opening is immersed at least an inch and the rest of the syringe stands vertically outside, if the piston is drawn up, the syringe remaining as described, the quicksilver, entering by the opening of the syringe, rises and remains in contact with the piston until it has been drawn up in the syringe two feet, three inches. But after this height if the piston is drawn up more, it does not attract the quicksilver higher, which continuing to remain at this height of two feet, three inches quits the piston, so that an apparently empty space is formed, which increases in proportion as the piston is drawn up more. *It is probable that the same thing happens in a suction pump, and that the water rises only to a height of thirty-one feet, which corresponds to that of two feet, three inches of quicksilver.* And what is more remarkable is

that the syringe, weighed as it is without being taken from the quicksilver or moved in any way, weighs just as much (although the apparently empty space be as small as we please) as when, the piston having been drawn up more, the apparently empty space is made as great as we please, and that it always weighs the same as the body of the syringe with the two feet, three inches of quicksilver it contains when there is not yet any apparently empty space, that is, when the piston has not yet quit the quicksilver in the syringe, but is ready to separate from it at the slightest pull. So that the apparently empty space, although all the bodies surrounding it tend to fill it, does not change its weight, and however these spaces may differ in size, they differ not at all in weight.

7. A siphon with one leg ten feet long and the other nine and a half, having been filled with quicksilver and the two openings having been immersed about an inch each in two vessels of quicksilver so that the surface of the quicksilver in one vessel is half a foot higher than in the other; when the siphon is vertical, the longer leg does not attract the quicksilver of the shorter, but the quicksilver, breaking at the top, descends in each of the legs and pours into the vessels, falling to the ordinary height of two feet, three inches from the surface of the quicksilver in each vessel. But if the siphon is inclined, the quicksilver in the vessels rises again in the legs, fills them and begins to run from the shorter leg into the longer leg and thus empties the shorter leg's vessel; for the inclining of tubes containing an apparent vacuum, when they are in a fluid, always attracts the fluids in the vessels if the openings of the tubes are not closed, or attracts the finger if it closes these openings.

8. The same siphon having been entirely filled with water and afterwards with a cord as above and the two openings having also been put in the same two vessels of quicksilver, when the cord is drawn through one of the openings, the quicksilver rises from the vessels into both of the legs, so that the fourteenth part of the height of the water in one leg, together with the height of the quicksilver which has risen, is equal to the fourteenth part of the height of the water in the other, added to the height of the quicksilver which has risen; which will be the case as long as the fourteenth part of the height of the water, added to the height of the quicksilver in each leg, is two feet, three inches high, for afterwards the water will divide at the top and there will be an apparent vacuum.

From these experiments and from several others reported in the complete book, in which are seen tubes of all lengths, sizes, and shapes, filled with different fluids, immersed in divers ways in different fluids, carried from one to another, weighed in several ways, and in which are observed the different attractions felt by the finger stopping the mouths of tubes containing an apparent vacuum, it is clear that we may deduce the following maxims:

MAXIMS

1. That it is repugnant to all bodies to separate from each other and to admit an apparent vacuum between them; that is, nature abhors an apparent vacuum.

2. That this abhorrence or repugnance on the part of all bodies is not greater for a large apparent vacuum than for a small one, that is, for a wide interval of separation than for a narrow one.

3. That the force of this abhorrence is limited, and equal to that with which water at a certain height, which is about thirty-one feet, tends to flow downward.

4. That the bodies forming the boundaries of an apparent vacuum tend to fill it.

5. That this tendency is not greater for a large apparent vacuum than for a small one.

6. That the force of this tendency is limited, and always equal to that with which water at a certain height, which is about thirty-one feet, tends to flow downward.

7. That a force greater by however little than that with which water at a height of about thirty-one feet tends to flow downward is sufficient to cause an apparent vacuum, and as great as we please, that is, to separate bodies by as great an interval as we please, provided there is no other obstacle to their separation and going apart than nature's horror of an apparent vacuum.

Summary of the second part, in which are reported the consequences of these experiments, concerning the matter that might fill this apparently empty space, divided into several propositions with their demonstrations.

PROPOSITIONS

1. That the apparently empty space is not filled with the outside air surrounding the tube and that air has not come in through the pores of the glass.

2. That it is not filled with the air which some philosophers say is enclosed in the pores of all bodies, air which would be in this way in the liquid filling the tubes.

3. That it is not filled with the air which some consider to be between the tube and the liquid which fills it, and enclosed in the interstices or atoms of the small bodies constituting these liquids.

4. That it is not filled with an imperceptible particle of air, remaining by chance between the liquid and the glass, either carried by the finger acting as a stopper or introduced in some other way, which would become extraordinarily rarefied, and which some, rather than admit a vacuum, would maintain could become sufficiently rarefied to fill the whole world.

5. That it is not filled with a bit of quicksilver or water, which, drawn in one direction by the walls of the glass and in the other by the force of the liquid, becomes rarefied and transformed into vapor, so that this reciprocal attraction has the same effect as heat, which transforms these liquids into vapor and makes them volatile.

6. That it is not filled with the spirits of the liquid contained in the tube.

7. That it is not filled with a finer air mixed with the outside air, which, separated from it and having entered through the pores of the glass, would always tend to return or would be continually attracted back.

8. That the apparently empty space is not filled by any substance known in nature and perceptible to any sense.

SUMMARY OF THE CONCLUSION, IN WHICH I GIVE MY OPINION

After having demonstrated that none of the substances perceived by our senses and known by us fills this apparently empty space, I shall think, until I am shown the existence of a substance filling it, that it is really empty and void of all matter.

Therefore I shall say of the real vacuum what I have shown of the apparent vacuum, and I shall consider the above maxims as true when now enunciated of the absolute vacuum as before of the apparent.

MAXIMS

1. That it is repugnant to all bodies to separate from each other and to admit a vacuum between them; that is, nature abhors a vacuum.

2. That this abhorrence or repugnance on the part of all bodies is not greater for a large vacuum than for a small one, that is, for a wide interval of separation than for a narrow one.

3. That the force of this abhorrence is limited, and equal to that with which water at a certain height, which is about thirty-one feet, tends to flow downward.

4. That the bodies forming the boundaries of a vacuum tend to fill it.

5. That this tendency is not greater for a large vacuum than for a small one.

6. That the force of this tendency is limited, and always equal to that with which water at a certain height, which is about thirty-one feet, tends to flow downward.

7. That a force greater by however little than that with which water at a height of about thirty-one feet tends to flow downward is sufficient to cause a vacuum, and as great as we please, that is, to separate bodies by as great an interval as we please, provided there is no other obstacle to their separation and going apart than nature's horror of a vacuum.

AFTERWARDS I REPLY TO THE OBJECTIONS THAT COULD BE MADE, OF WHICH THE CHIEF ARE:

OBJECTIONS

1. That this proposition, a space is empty, is repugnant to common sense.

2. That this proposition, nature abhors a vacuum and nevertheless permits it to exist, accuses her of impotence or implies contradiction.

3. That many experiments, and even our everyday experience, show that nature cannot suffer the existence of a vacuum.

4. That an imperceptible matter, unheard of and unknown to any sense, fills this space.

5. That since light is either an accident or a substance, it is not possible for it to exist in a vacuum if it is an accident, and that it fills the apparently empty space if it is a substance.

PASCAL'S ANSWER

To the Very Good Reverend Father Noël, Rector, of the Society of Jesus, Paris
MY VERY REVEREND FATHER,

The honor you have done me in writing to me obliges me to give up my intention of resolving none of the difficulties mentioned in my *abridgement* except in the complete work on which I am at present engaged; for since the civilities of your letter are joined to the objections you raise against me, I cannot divide my answer nor acknowledge the former without satisfying the latter.

But to proceed with more order, permit me to remind you of a universal rule which is applicable to all the particular subjects in which our concern is with establishing truth. I do not doubt your acceptance of it since it is generally admitted by all who consider things with an open mind and since it constitutes the chief part of the method of the schools in dealing with the sciences and that used by seekers after what is really solid, filling and fully satisfying the mind. The rule is never to make a decisive judgment, affirming or denying a proposition, unless what one affirms or denies satisfies one of the two following conditions: either that of itself it appear so clearly and distinctly to sense or to reason, according as it is subject to one or the other, that the mind cannot doubt its certainty, and this is what we call a *principle* or *axiom*, as, for example, *if equals are added to equals, the results are equal;* or that it be deduced as an infallible and necessary consequence from such principles or axioms, upon whose certainty entirely depends that of the consequences correctly drawn from them, as this proposition, *the three angles of a triangle are equal to two right angles,* "which not being self-evident," is evidently demonstrated as an infallible consequence of such axioms. Everything satisfying one of these two conditions is certain and true, and everything satisfying neither is considered doubtful and uncertain. We pass decisive judgment on things of the first kind and leave the rest undecided, calling them, according to their deserts, now a *vision*, now a *caprice*, occasionally a *fancy*, sometimes an *idea*, and at the most a *happy thought;* and since it is rash to affirm them, we incline rather to the negative, ready however to return to the affirmative if a convincing demonstration brings their truth to light. And we reserve for the mysteries of the faith, revealed by the Holy Spirit Himself, that submission of mind which leads us to believe in mysteries hidden from sense and reason.

This principle having been laid down, I turn to your letter, in whose first lines, to prove that the space in question is a body, you make use of the following words: *I say that it is a body since it acts like a body, transmitting light with refraction and reflection, and retarding the motion of another body.* Upon which I observe that you base your claim that it is a body upon two principles: the first is that it transmits light with refraction and reflection; the second, that it retards the motion of a body. Of these two principles the first has seemed true to none of those who have tried to get experimental evidence of it, and we have always found on the contrary that the ray penetrating the glass and the apparently empty space has no refraction other than that caused by the glass, and that therefore if some matter fills this space, either it in nowise bends the ray or the refraction is not perceptible; so that since you have undoubtedly experienced nothing to the contrary, I perceive that the meaning of your words is that the ray reflected or refracted by the glass passes through this space. From that and from the fact that bodies take time to fall there, you wish to conclude that it is filled by a material substance which transmits the light and causes the retardation of motion.

But, Reverend Father, if we refer this to the method of reasoning we have spoken of, we shall find that we should first have to agree upon the definition of empty space, of light, and of motion, and to show from the nature of these things a manifest contradiction in the propositions: "Light penetrates empty space, and it takes time for a body to move there." Until then your proof cannot hold, and since moreover the nature of light is unknown both to you and to me, since of all those who have tried to define it not one has satisfied any seeker after experienceable truths, and since it will perhaps remain eternally unknown to us, I foresee that it will be a long time before this argument acquires enough strength to be convincing.

For I beg you to consider how it is possible to conclude infallibly that the nature of light is such that it cannot exist in the void when we do not know what the nature of light is. But if our knowledge of it were as complete as is our ig-

norance, we should know perhaps that it would exist in the void with more brilliance than in any other *medium* since we perceive that it increases its strength
according as the *medium* in which it is becomes rarer, and so somehow closer to
nothingness. And if we knew the nature of motion, I do not at all doubt that it
would appear to us that motion ought to take almost as much time in a vacuum
as in air, whose non-resistance is apparent in the equal falling-time of bodies of
different weights.

This is why, with our slight knowledge of the nature of these things, if by a
similar liberty I conceive a thought which I offer as a principle, I can say with as
much show of reason: light subsists in a vacuum and it takes time for a body to
move there; but light penetrates this apparently empty space and it takes time
for a body to move there; hence it may be really empty.

Therefore let us put off this proof until such time as we shall know the nature
of light. Until then I cannot admit your principle, and it will be hard for you to
prove it. And let us not, I beg you, draw infallible consequences from the nature
of a thing when we do not know it; otherwise I should be afraid that you were
not in agreement with me on the conditions necessary for a perfect demonstration, and that you would call certain what we only call doubtful.

In the rest of your letter, as if you had invincibly established that this void
space is a body, you concern yourself only with finding what body it is, and to
decide positively what kind of matter fills it you begin as follows: "Let us assume
that, just as blood is made up of several liquids mingled together, so air is made
up of air and fire and the (remaining) four elements which enter into the composition of all natural bodies." You then *assume* that this fire can be separated
from the air, and that once separated it can penetrate the pores of the glass; you
again *assume* that once separated it has an inclination to return and again that it is
incessantly drawn back; and you explain these statements, intelligible enough in
themselves, by bringing in certain analogies.

But I think you offer this as an idea, Father, and not as a demonstration, and
however hard it is for me to reconcile this belief with the end of your letter, I
believe that if you wanted to give proofs, they would not be so unfounded. For
in these times when so many learned men are trying with such care to find what
matter fills this space, when this problem is agitating so many minds, it would be
hard for me to believe you would offer as the longed-for solution of a question
so justly doubtful nothing but a substance of which you suppose not only the
properties but the very existence itself, so that if anyone will make the contrary
assumption, he will draw a contrary consequence just as necessarily. If this kind of
proof is acceptable, there will no longer be any difficulty in solving the greatest
difficulties. And the ocean tides and the magnet's attraction will become easy to
understand, if it is permissible to make substances and properties for the purpose.

For all things of this kind whose existence is not manifest to sense are as hard
to believe as they are easy to invent. Many persons, even among the most learned
men of the day, have opposed me with this same substance before you (but simply as an idea and not as a certain truth), and that is why I mentioned it among
my propositions. Others, to fill empty space with some kind of matter, have
imagined one with which they have filled the entire universe, because imagination has this peculiarity that it produces the greatest things with as little time
and trouble as little things; some have considered this matter as of the same sub-

stance as the sky and the elements, and others of a different substance, as their fancy dictated, for they disposed of it as of their own work.

But if we ask of them, as of you, that they show us this matter, they answer that it cannot be seen; if we ask that it make a sound, they say it cannot be heard, and so with all the remaining senses; and they think they have done much when they have convicted others of powerlessness to show that it does not exist by depriving themselves of all power to show that it does.

But we find more cause to deny its existence on account of our inability to prove it than to believe it for the sole reason that it cannot be shown not to be.

For we cannot believe in all these substances at once without making nature a monster, and since reason cannot incline more toward one than toward another because she finds them equally remote, she rejects them all to avoid an unjust choice.

I know you can say that you have not made this matter of yours all by yourself and that many physicists had already worked at it. But in this matter we base nothing on authority; when we cite authors, we cite their demonstrations and not their names; we respect them only in historical matters, so that if the authors you cite said they saw those little fiery bodies mingled with the air, I should sufficiently defer to their sincerity and to their accuracy to believe they were telling the truth and I should believe them as historians; but since they only say they think these particles are constituents of the air, you will permit me to remain in my first doubt.

Finally, Father, consider, I beg you, that all the men there are put together could not demonstrate that any body succeeds that which leaves the apparent vacuum, and again that it is impossible for all the men there are to show that when the water refills it some body has left. Should not that be sufficient, following your maxims, to assure the emptiness of the space? However I simply say that my opinion is that it is empty. Judge whether those who speak with so much restraint about something they have a right to speak about with so much assurance will find it possible to make a decisive judgment on the existence of this fiery matter, so doubtful and so little established.

After having supposed this substance with all the properties you wanted it to have, you explain some of my experiments. It is not a very difficult thing to explain how an effect can be produced if we suppose the substance, the nature, and the qualities of its cause; however it is hard for those who imagine them to resist an idle satisfaction and a secret charm which they find in their invention, especially when they have worked them out so well that from the imaginations they have supposed they necessarily infer truths already evident.

But I feel obliged to say a word or two to you in this connection. Every time to find the cause of several known phenomena we frame an hypothesis, this hypothesis can be of three kinds.

For sometimes an obvious absurdity follows from its negation, and then the hypothesis is true and certain; or an obvious absurdity follows from its affirmation, and then the hypothesis is considered false; and when we have not yet been able to draw an absurdity either from its negation or from its affirmation, the hypothesis remains doubtful. So that to establish the truth of an hypothesis it is not enough that all the phenomena should follow from it, whereas if there follows from it something opposed to a single phenomenon, that is enough to make certain its falsity.

For example, if someone finds a hot stone without knowing why it is hot, would he who should reason as follows be thought to have found the true cause: Let us assume that this stone has been put in a big fire, from which it has very recently been removed; therefore this stone should still be hot; but it is hot; consequently it had been put in the fire? For that, fire would have to be the only cause of a stone's being hot; but since such heat can come from the sun or from friction, this inference would have no cogency. For just as the same cause can produce several different effects, so the same effect can be produced by several different causes. Thus in the discourse of natural reason on the motion or the stability of the earth all the phenomena of the motions and retrogradations of the planets follow perfectly from the hypotheses of Ptolemy, of Tycho, of Copernicus and from many others that could be framed, of all of which only one can be true. But who will venture to discern so far, and who can without risk of error support one to the prejudice of the others, as in the analogy of the stone who can with insistence maintain it is hot because of fire without making himself ridiculous?

You see from this that even if all the phenomena of my experiments followed from your hypothesis, it would still be like the rest; and that always remaining in terms of probability, it would never reach those of demonstration. But I hope one day to make you see more at length that the necessary consequences of its affirmation are opposed to the experiments. And to touch upon one of them in a few words here: If it is true, as you suppose, that the apparent vacuum is filled with that more subtle and fiery air, and that it has the inclination you suppose to return to the air it left, and that the outside air has the force to draw it back *like a squeezed sponge*, and that it is by this mutual attraction that the quicksilver is held suspended and is even made to rise again when the tube is inclined; it necessarily follows that when the apparent vacuum is greater, a larger column of quicksilver should be suspended (contrary to what is seen in the experiments). For since all the parts of the inside and outside air have this power of attraction, it is certain by all the laws of mechanics that their quantity, increased directly as the space, must necessarily increase their effect, as a large sponge when squeezed absorbs more water than a small one.

But if to resolve this difficulty you make a second supposition; and if you make another quality on purpose to save this awkwardness, which, still not accurate enough, obliges you to imagine a third supposition to save the other two, without any proof, any support; I shall never have anything to say except what I have already said, or rather I shall think I have already answered you.

But when I say this, Father, and when I anticipate in some sort these last suppositions, I myself make a false supposition, for I do not doubt that if you give us something, it will be supported by convincing arguments, since otherwise you would be imitating those who wish only to show that they have no lack of words.

Finally, Father, to restate the whole of my answer, if it should be true that this apparently empty space where a body (which I am very far from granting you), and the air were filled with fiery spirits (which I do not even find probable), and that they had the qualities you assign them (which is only a mere idea, evident neither to you nor to anyone); it would not follow that this space was filled with them. And again if it should be true that by supposing it were filled with them (which is in no way apparent) we could deduce everything in the experiments, the most favorable judgment we could make of this opinion would be that it is probable. But since we necessarily infer from it things opposed to the experiments, judge what place it should have among the three kinds of hypotheses we spoke of above.

Toward the end of your letter, to define body, you only mention a few accidents, and those relative, as *top, bottom, right, left,* which actually constitute the definition of space, and which apply to a body only in so far as it occupies space. For according to your own authors body is defined as *what is composed of form and matter;* and what we call a *void space* is a space having length, breadth, and depth, motionless and capable of receiving and containing a body of the same size and shape; this is what we call a *solid* in geometry, where we consider only abstract and immaterial things. So that the essential difference between empty space and body, which has length, breadth, and depth, is that one is immobile and the other is mobile, and that one can receive within itself a body which penetrates its dimensions, whereas the other cannot; for the maxim on the impenetrability of dimensions is to be understood only of the dimensions of two material bodies; otherwise it would not be universally accepted. Whence it can be seen that there is as much difference between nothingness and empty space as there is between empty space and material body, and that thus empty space is a mean between material body and nothingness. That is why the maxim of Aristotle you mention, *that non-beings do not have differences,* is to be understood of true nothingness and not of empty space.

I take leave of your letter where you say that you do not recognize as *being held by any physicist* the fourth of my objections, namely, that a matter unheard of and not known to any sense fills this space. To which I answer that I can assure you of the contrary, since it is held by one of the most celebrated physicists of our time, whom you could have found in his works filling the whole universe with a universal matter, imperceptible and unheard of, of the same substance as the sky and the elements; and moreover that in examining your own matter I have found it to be so imperceptible and to have qualities so unheard of, that is, never considered as belonging to it, that I find it to be of the same nature.

The sentence preceding your final civilities defines light as follows: *Light is a luminary motion of rays composed of lucid, that is, luminous bodies;* with respect to which I must say that it seems to me you should first have defined *luminary,* and *lucid* or *luminous body,* for until that is done I cannot understand what light is. And since we never use in definitions the term *defined,* I should have difficulty in accepting yours, which says that *light* (lumière) is a *luminary* motion of *luminous* bodies. There you have my views, Father, which I shall always submit to yours.

For the rest, you cannot be denied the glory of having maintained Peripatetic physics as well as it can be maintained; and I find your letter not less a mark of the weakness of the opinion you defend than of the vigor of your mind.

Certainly the skill with which you have defended the impossibility of a vacuum in the decline of its strength makes it easy to see that with an equal effort you would invincibly have established the opposed opinion in the advantages given it by the experiments.

The same indisposition that has deprived me of the honor of seeing you has kept me from writing with my own hand. It is for this reason I beg you to excuse the mistakes of my letter, especially in spelling.

I am with all my heart, Very Reverend Father, your very humble and very obedient servant,

PASCAL

Paris, *October 29*, 1647.

LETTER FROM PASCAL TO M. LE PAILLEUR, CONCERNING FATHER NOËL, JESUIT.

SIR,

Since you wish to know why I broke off the correspondence which the Reverend Father Noël had done me the honor of engaging me in, I want to give you prompt satisfaction; and I do not doubt that if you blamed my conduct before knowing its cause, you will approve it when you know the reasons that have held me back.

The strongest is that the Reverend Father Talon, when he took the trouble to bring me Father Noël's last letter, informed me in the presence of three of your good friends that Father Noël was distressed by my illness, that he feared my first letter had affected my health, and that he begged me not to run the risk of a second; in a word, not to answer; that we could clear up by word of mouth any remaining difficulties, and that moreover he begged me not to show his letter to anyone, that since he had written it only for me, he wished it to be seen by no one else, and that to make letters public was to violate their nature, addressed, as they are, to particular persons.

I confess that if this proposal had come from anyone except these good fathers, I should have been suspicious and I should have feared that its author wished to take advantage of my silence after having secured it by trickery. But I had so little doubt of their sincerity that I promised everything without reservation or fear. Afterwards I was especially careful to keep Father Noël's letter to myself and not to answer it. Whereupon several persons and even some Jesuit fathers who were not well informed of the wishes of Father Noël took occasion to say that, having found in his letter the overthrow of my opinions, I concealed its beauties lest my shame be discovered, and that it was by my weakness alone I was prevented from replying.

You see, Sir, how unfortunate for me this circumstance was, since I could not conceal the letter without disadvantage nor make it public without breach of faith, and that my honor was equally threatened both by a reply and by silence in that one betrayed my promise and the other my interest.

However I religiously kept my word, and I was saving my reply to his letter for the treatise in which I have to make specific answers to all the objections made against the proposition advanced in my abridgement, "that this space is not filled with any substance perceptible to sense and known in nature." Accordingly I thought I was not at all obliged to be in a hurry with my reply, which I wished to make more exact by postponing it for a while. To these considerations I added this, that since all differences of this kind go on forever unless someone breaks them off and since they cannot be concluded unless one of the two parties begins to make an end, I thought that the age, distinction, and calling of Father Noël obliged me to yield him the advantage of having had the last word in the matter. But besides all these reasons, I confess that his letter alone was enough to give me a dispensation from answering, and I am sure you will find that it seems to have been expressly conceived in terms that would not put upon me the obligation of a reply.

To make this clear I shall put before you the points Father Noël takes up, but in a different order such as he undoubtedly would have followed in a more elaborate work but did not judge necessary in the artlessness of a letter; for each of these points is scattered throughout the whole body of his discourse and lodged in almost every part of it.

It is his intention to state that he was led by my letter to give up his first opinion without being able however to fall in with mine. So that we may consider his letter as having two parts, of which one contains the things that prevent him from agreeing with me and the other those that support his second view. With respect to each of these parts I hope to show you how little I was obliged to reply.

As to the first, concerning the things that keep him from my view, his first difficulties are that the apparently empty space can only be a body since it receives and transmits light, and since it retards the motion of another body. But I thought I had sufficiently shown him in my letter the weakness of these same objections as contained in his first letter; for I told him in tolerably clear words that even if it takes time for bodies to fall in this space and even if it is penetrated by light, these effects should not necessarily be attributed to a substance filling it, since it is possible that they belong to the nature of motion and of light, and that as long as we remain in our present ignorance of the nature of these things, we should make no inferences from it since they would be based merely on uncertainty; and that, just as Father Noël infers from the appearance of these effects that this space is filled by a substance receiving light and retarding motion, it is possible with as much reason to infer from these effects that light subsists and motion requires time in a vacuum, in view of the fact that so many other things were favorable to this latter view that it was, in the opinion of the learned, incomparably more probable than the other even before it received the support of these experiments.

But if Father Noël has shown here that he paid little attention to that part of my letter, he gives evidence of not having understood another part by the second thing shocking him in my view; for he imputes to me an opinion contrary to the terms both of my letter and of my printed statement and entirely opposed to the foundation of all my maxims. He imagines that I decisively asserted the real existence of the vacuum, and on the basis of this imagination, which he takes as certain truth, he exercises his pen to show the weakness of the assertion.

However he could have seen I wrote in my printed statement that my conclusion is simply that I shall think "this space is empty until I have been shown that some substance fills it," which is not an assertion of the reality of the vacuum; and he could also have seen that I wrote in my letter the following words, which seem to me sufficiently clear: "Finally, Father, consider, I beg you, that all the men there are put together could not demonstrate that any body succeeds that which leaves the apparent vacuum, and again that it is impossible for all the men there are to show that when the water refills it some body has left. Should not that be sufficient, following your maxims, to assure the emptiness of the space? However I simply say that my opinion is that it is empty. Judge whether those who speak with so much restraint about something they have a right to speak about with so much assurance will find it possible to make a decisive judgment on the existence of this fiery matter, so doubtful and so little established."

Accordingly I should never have guessed what gave rise to this idea in Father Noël if he had not revealed it to me himself in the first page, where he faithfully repeats the definition of void space I gave in my letter, which is as follows: "What we call a void space is a space having length, breadth, and depth, motionless and capable of receiving and containing a body of the same size and shape; this is what we call a *solid* in geometry, where we consider only abstract and immaterial things." After having repeated this definition word for word he immediately derives from it this consequence: "There, Sir, is your notion of void space, very clearly stated; I am willing to believe that all this is obvious to you and that your mind is convinced and fully satisfied by it, since you affirm it."

If he had not repeated my own words, I should have supposed he had misread them or that they had been badly written, and that instead of the first words, *I call*, he must have found, *I assert*. But since he quoted my entire sentence, I can only suppose he believes one of these terms necessarily implies the other, and that he does not distinguish between defining a thing and asserting its existence.

Therefore he believed that I asserted the real existence of the vacuum by the very terms with which I defined it. I know that those who are not accustomed to seeing things handled in the true order imagine that we cannot define a thing unless we are assured of its existence; but they should notice that we ought always to define things before investigating their possibility, and that the steps leading to the knowledge of truths are definition, axiom, and proof. For first we conceive the idea of a thing; then we give a name to this idea, that is, we define it; and finally we try to discover the truth or falsity of the thing. If we find it is impossible, it passes for error; if we demonstrate its truth, it passes for truth; and as long as we can demonstrate neither its possibility nor its impossibility, it passes for imagination. Whence it is evident that there is no necessary connection between the definition of a thing and the assertion of its existence, and that we can just as well define an impossible thing as a true thing. Thus we can call rectilinear and rectangular a triangle we should imagine as having two right angles, and afterwards show that such a triangle is impossible; thus Euclid first defines parallels and shows afterwards that they can be, and the definition of the circle precedes the *postulate* which lays down its possibility; thus the astronomers have given names to the concentric and eccentric circles and to the epicycles they have imagined in the heavens, without possessing any certainty that the stars actually describe such figures by their motions; thus the Peripatetics have given a name to that fiery sphere whose truth it would be difficult to demonstrate.

This is why when I wished to oppose Father Noël's decision, which excluded the vacuum from nature, I thought that I could not enter upon this attempt or even say a word about the matter until I had declared what I understand by the word *vacuum*, to which I felt myself the more obliged by certain passages in Father Noël's first letter from which I judged that his notion of the vacuum was not in conformity with mine. I saw that he was unable to distinguish between dimensions and matter, between immateriality and non-being; and that this confusion made him conclude that when I attributed to the apparently empty space length, breadth, and depth, I committed myself to saying that it was a body, and that from the moment I made it immaterial, I reduced it to nothing. To untangle all these ideas, I stated this definition for him, in which he can see that what we conceive and express by the words *empty space* holds the mean position between material substance and nothingness, without participating in either; that it differs from non-being by having dimensions, and that its non-resistance and immobility distinguish it from matter, so that it keeps between these two extremes without losing itself in either.

Toward the end of his letter Father Noël gathers together into one sentence all his objections to make them stronger by uniting them. His words are: *this space which is neither God nor creature, neither mind nor body, neither substance nor accident, which transmits light without being transparent, which resists without resistance, which though immobile is moved with the tube, which is everywhere and nowhere, which does everything and nothing. These are the wonderful qualities of void space: as space it exists and performs miracles, as void it is nothing and does nothing; as space it has length, breadth, and depth, as void it excludes length, breadth, and depth. If desired, I shall show that all these fine properties follow necessarily from a void space.*

Since a long series of fine things is fatiguing in the end by its very length, I think Father Noël grew weary on this occasion from having given birth to so many; and that, foreseeing a like fatigue on the part of his readers, he wanted to descend from a graver to a less serious style, to refresh them with a little raillery in order that, after having supplied them with so many things calling for the effort of admiration, he might give them, of his charity, something for amusement. I was the first to feel the effect of this benevolence and whoever reads his letter afterwards will experience it too; for no one, reading what I wrote, but will laugh at the inferences Father Noël draws from it and at those antitheses opposed with so nice a care that it is easy to see he was more concerned with making his terms antithetical to each other than conformable to reason and truth.

For to take up these objections one by one: *this space, he says, is neither God nor creature.* Mysteries having to do with the Divine Nature are too holy for us to profane with our disputes; they should be an object of worship for us and not a subject of discourse. So that without discussing them in any way I submit my judgment entirely to what they shall decide who have the right to decide.

Neither mind nor body. It is true that space is neither mind nor body but is space; just as time is neither mind nor body but is time; and just as time does not cease to be although it is neither of these things, so void space may perfectly well be, without having to be either mind or body.

Neither substance nor accident. True, if we understand by the word *substance* what is either mind or body. For in this sense space will be neither substance nor accident but will be space; just as in this same sense time is neither substance nor accident, but is time; because in order to be, it is not necessary to be either substance or accident certain of the Jesuits maintaining that God is neither one nor the other although he is the Supreme Being.

Which transmits light without being transparent. These words are so lacking in light that they are dark to me. For I do not understand what meaning the word *transparent* has for Father Noël, since he finds that it cannot be said of void space. For if like all opticians he understands by transparence the absence of any hindrance to the passage of light, I do not see why he denies it to our space, which lets light pass freely. So that speaking on this subject with my small knowledge, I should have said to him that the words *transmit light*, which belong only to his way of imagining light, mean the same as *let light pass* and *it is transparent*, that is, offers no obstacle to light, in which I find neither absurdity nor contradiction.

It resists without resistance. Since he judges of the resistance of this space only by the fact that it takes time for bodies to move in it, and since we have had so much to say on the nullity of this inference, it will be seen that he is wrong in saying it resists; and it will be found on the contrary that this space does not resist or that it is without resistance, in which I see nothing but what is perfectly conformable to reason.

Which though immobile is moved with the tube. Here Father Noël shows how little he understands the opinion he wishes to refute; and I should have to beg him to observe in this connection that when an opinion is embraced by a number of learned men, we should not attach importance to objections that appear fatal when they are very easy to anticipate, because we should suppose that those who maintain this opinion are already aware of them, and that since they stick to their opinion in spite of the obviousness of the objections, they have found an answer to them. But to examine this difficulty in particular, if these antitheses or contraries had not dazzled his mind as much as they charmed his fancy, he would undoubtedly have noticed that, whatever may seem to be the case, the vacuum is not moved with the tube, and that immobility is as natural to space as motion is to body. To make this truth evident we must observe that space in general comprehends all natural bodies, each one of which individually occupies a certain part of it, but that although they are all mobile, the space they fill is not. For when a body is moved from one position to another, it merely changes place, without carrying with it the place it occupied while at rest. In fact what does it do except leave its first immobile place, successively to take up others equally immobile? But the place it quits remains still firm and unshakeable, so that either it is filled by another body succeeding that which has gone or it is left empty if no successor presents itself; but whether void or filled, ever equally at rest, this vast space, whose immensity embraces the universe, is as stable and immobile in each of its parts as in its totality. Therefore I cannot see how Father Noël could maintain that the tube communicates its motion to the void space, which, offering neither consistency for pushing nor a hold for pulling and without susceptibility to weight or to any attractive force, obviously cannot be made to change. Father Noël was led astray by the fact that when the tube was carried from one place to another, he saw no change inside it, and so he thought the space continued to be the same since it was always like itself. But he should observe that the space enclosed by the tube in one position is not the same as the space enclosed by it in the following position, and that the tube in the course of its motion continually acquires new spaces; so that the space that was empty in its first position is filled with air when it quits it to take the second, in which it makes void the space encountered whereas this space was filled with air before; but both of these spaces, alternately filled and void, always remain equally immobile. Whence it is evident that it is out of the question to believe that the void space changes place; and what is strangest is that the substance with which Father Noël fills it is such that according to his own hypothesis it could not be carried by the moving tube; for since it would enter and leave the glass through its pores with perfect ease without in any way adhering to it, like water in a sieve, it is obvious that it would not be carried along with it, just as we see that this same tube does not transport light, which penetrates it easily and freely, and that our space itself, when exposed to sunlight, changes rays when it changes place without carrying with it to its second place the light which filled it in the first, and in different positions it receives different rays as well as divers spaces.

Finally Father Noël is amazed that *it should do everything and nothing, that it should be everywhere and nowhere, that it should exist and perform miracles though not existing, that it should have dimensions without having them.* If these words have any meaning, I confess that I do not understand it; therefore I do not consider myself obliged to answer them.

There you have, Sir, Father Noël's objections and the things that shock him in my view. But since they are evidence rather of his not understanding my opinion than of his gainsaying it and since he seems to find obscurity rather than error in it, I thought he would find its clarification in my letter if he would take the trouble to read it more carefully; and that therefore I was under no obligation to answer him since a second reading would sufficiently resolve the doubts arising from the first.

With reference to the second part of his letter, which is taken up with the changing of his first opinion and the establishing of his second opinion, he first states why he denies the vacuum. The reason he gives is that the vacuum cannot be perceived by any of the senses; whence he takes occasion to say that just as I deny the existence of matter [in the top of the tube] for this reason alone that it gives no sensible indication of its presence and that the mind conceives no necessity for it, he can with as much force and more deny the vacuum because it has this in common with the matter, that it is perceived by no sense. His words are: *We say that there is water because we see and touch it; we say that there is air in an inflated balloon because we feel its resistance; that there is fire because we feel the heat; but the true vacuum touches none of our senses.*

But I am surprised that Father Noël should compare things so dissimilar, and that he should not have observed that, as there is nothing so opposed to being as non-being or to affirmation as negation, we proceed to their demonstration by opposed methods, and that what establishes one overthrows the other. For what is needed for the knowledge of non-being except to know the utter lack of every kind of quality and effect; whereas if a single one appeared, we would infer on the contrary the real existence of a cause producing it? And then he says: *Consider, Sir, which of us two is the more to be believed, you who assert the existence of a space hidden to sense and serving neither art nor nature, which you make use of only to decide a very doubtful question,* etc.

But I leave it to you to decide, Sir, when we see nothing and the senses perceive nothing in a place, which is on firmer ground, he who asserts that there is something although he perceives nothing or he who thinks there is nothing because he does not see anything.

After Father Noël has declared, as we have just seen, his reason for excluding the vacuum, and has found grounds for denying it in that very privation of qualities which so justly gives occasion to others to believe in it and is the only sensible means of proving its existence, he now undertakes to show that it is a body. To this end he thought up a definition of body expressly conceived to fit our space that he might easily draw his inference from it. His words are: *I define body as that which is composed of separate parts, and I say that every body is space when it is considered between its boundaries, and that every other space is body because it is composed of separate parts.*

But to show that our space is not void it is not a question here of giving it the name of body, as Father Noël has done, but of showing that it is a body, as he claims to have done. Not that it is not permissible for him to give to what has separate parts any name that pleases him; but he will win small advantage from this liberty, for the word *body* as a result of his use of it becomes equivocal. So that there will be two kinds of things, entirely different and even heterogeneous, called *body*: one, that which has separate parts, for we shall call that *body*, following Father Noël; the other, a material substance, mobile and impenetrable, for we shall call that *body* in common parlance. But he will not be able to conclude from this nominal resemblance a resemblance of real properties or to show in this way that what has separate parts is the same thing as a material, immobile, impenetrable substance, because it is not in his power to make them agree in nature as well as in name. Just as, if he had given to what has separate parts the name *water*, *mind*, or *light*, which he could have done as easily as give it that of *body*, he could not have drawn the conclusion that our space was any of these things. Thus when he has called *body* what has separate parts and says as a consequence of that definition, *I say that every space is body*, we should take the word *body* in the sense he has just given it; so that if we substitute the definition in place of the thing defined, which can always be done without changing the meaning of a proposition, it will be found that the conclusion, *every space is body*, is nothing but *every space has separate parts*, but not *every space is material*, as Father Noël fancied. I shall not dwell longer on an inference so patently weak, since I am speaking to an excellent mathematician and since you have as much skill in discovering defects in reasoning as you have strength to avoid them.

The Reverend Father Noël, going further, wishes to show what this body is; and to establish his view he begins with a long discourse, in which he claims to prove the continual and necessary mixture of the elements, but shows nothing except that some parts of one element are found among those of another, and that they are confounded rather by accident than by nature; so that it might come about that they would separate without violence and return of themselves to their original unmixed state. For the natural mingling of two bodies occurs when their separation makes them change both their name and their nature. Such is the mingling of all metals and of all things made up of different elements, because when the mercury which enters into the composition of gold has been removed, what remains is no longer gold. But in the mixture Father Noël imagines for us we see only a violent confusion of certain vapors scattered in the air, which remains there like dust, without appearing to enter into the composition of the air, and similarly for the other mixtures. And as for that of water and air, which he offers as the best demonstrated and which he says is peremptorily proved by those bellows made by water falling into a chamber almost entirely closed (which you see explained at length in his letter), it is strange that Father Noël has not noticed that the air which he says emerges from the water is nothing but the outside air carried with it by the falling water, which air is completely free to go in by the same opening (wider than the opening from which the water comes), so that the water, spreading out as it falls into this opening, carries in with it all the air it meets and envelops, preventing its escape by the violence of its fall and the impact of its motion; so that air, continually entering through this opening and unable ever to leave by it, escapes with violence through the opening it finds free. Since it is by this experiment alone that Father Noël proves the mixture of water and air and since the experiment in no way shows it, he is found not at all to have proved it.

The mixture he least proves and is most concerned with is the mixture of fire with the other elements; for all that can be concluded from the experiments of the handkerchief and the cat is that certain of their greasiest and most oily particles catch fire from the friction, since they are already so disposed by the heat. He then declares it to be his opinion that our space is filled with this fiery matter, spread out and intermingled, as he supposes without proof, in all the elements and extended over the whole universe. This is the matter he puts in the tube. As for the suspension of the liquid, he attributes it to the weight of the outside air. In this I was delighted to see him adopting the view of those who have the most penetratingly examined these experiments; for you know that the letter written by the great Torricelli to Ricci more than four years ago shows that at that time he already held this opinion, and that more and more all our men of science are in agreement and support each other on this point. However we are waiting for the confirmation of the experiment which is to be performed on one of our high mountains. But I do not hope to hear the results for some time because, in answer to letters I wrote more than six months ago, I have always been told that the tops of the mountains are inaccessible because of the snow.

This then is Father Noël's second opinion; and although there seems to be little difference between this matter and the matter he puts in the tube in his first letter, it is nevertheless greater than appears, as I shall show.

In his first view nature abhorred a vacuum and made that horror felt; in his second view nature gives no indication of the horror she has of the vacuum and does nothing to prevent it. In the first he attributed an attractive faculty to this subtle matter and to all other bodies; in the second he does away with all attraction both active and passive. Finally he attributed many properties to it in the first of which he deprives it in the second. So that if there are several steps in the descent to nothingness, this matter is now on the last, and it seems there is only some remnant of prejudice that prevents him from throwing it headlong in.

But I should like to know from Father Noël how he comes to have such an ascendancy over nature and to exercise so absolute an empire over the subservient elements that they change their properties as he changes his mind, and that the universe accommodates its effects to the inconstancy of his intentions. I do not understand what blindness can be proof against such light or how any faith can be placed in what oneself causes to be or not to be with such ease.

But the chief difference I find between the two opinions is that Father Noël affirmatively asserted the truth of the first and that he proposes the second simply as an opinion. This is the influence of my first letter and the chief effect it had on his mind; so that, just as I had replied to his first opinion that I did not believe it met the conditions necessary for the affirmation of a thing, so I shall say to the second opinion that since he offers it only as an idea and since neither reason nor sense bears witness to the matter he establishes, I leave him in his opinion, as I leave in their opinion those who think there are dwellers in the moon and that in the inaccessible regions about the poles there are men entirely different from ourselves.

Thus you see, Sir, that Father Noël puts in the tube a subtle matter spread throughout the whole universe, and that he gives to the outer air the force to suspend the liquid. Whence it is easy to see that this idea is in no respect different from M. Descartes', since Father Noël concurs in the cause of the suspension of the quicksilver as well as in the matter which fills the apparently empty space, as is seen by his own words on page 6 where he says that this matter, which he calls *subtle air*, is the same as that M. Descartes calls *subtle matter*. Therefore I have believed myself less obliged to answer him, since I should make my answer to the father of this opinion.

As I was writing these last lines Father Noël did me the honor of sending me his book on another subject, bearing the title, *The Plenum of the Vacuum*. He charged the person who took the trouble to deliver it to assure me there was nothing in it against myself, and that any words that seemed to be harsh were addressed not to me but to the Reverend Father Valerianus Magni, Capuchin. And the reason he gave is that Father Magni affirms the existence of the vacuum, whereas I only profess to oppose those who speak dogmatically on this subject. But Father Noël would have acquitted me of this charge better if he had made his testimony as public as the suspicion he had given rise to.

I glanced through this book, and I found he has a different idea there, that he puts in our tube a matter close to his first, but attributes the suspension of the quicksilver to a quality he assigns to it which he calls *moving levity*, and not to the weight of the outside air, as in his letter.

To make a little survey of the book in brief compass, the title promises in the first place to demonstrate the plenum by new experiments and to confirm it by mine. At the beginning of the book Father Noël sets himself up as the defender of nature, and by an allegory, perhaps a little drawn out, he conducts a suit-at-law in which he makes her complain of the belief in the void as of a calumny; and without her having imparted to him her resentment or having charged him to defend her, he assumes the office of her advocate. And in this capacity he asserts that he will expose the imposture and false depositions of the witnesses against her—this is how he refers to our experiments—and promises to produce witness for witness, that is, experiment for experiment, and to show that ours have been badly understood and worse verified. But in the body of the book, when it is a question of carrying out these large promises, he speaks only to doubt; and having given hopes of so high a vengeance, he but brings in guesses instead of convictions. For in the third chapter, when he wishes to establish that the apparent vacuum is a body, he simply says he finds it much more reasonable to say that it is a body. When it is a question of showing the mixture of the elements, he only adds some very weak things to those he had mentioned in his letter. When it is a question of showing that the world is a plenum, he gives no proof. It is on such empty appearances he establishes his *ether*, imperceptible to sense, with the imaginary levity he attributes to it.

What is strange is that Father Noël, after having given doubts to support his view, confirms it by false experiments. However he proposes them with such boldness that they would be accepted as true by everyone who has not seen the opposite; for he says that the eyes show, that all this cannot be denied, that we see it with our eyes (although our eyes show us the opposite). Thus it is evident he has seen none of the experiments he talks about, and it is strange he should have spoken with so much assurance of things he did not know and of which he had been given anything but a faithful account. For I prefer to believe that he was himself deceived and not that he wanted to deceive others, and the esteem I have for him makes me judge that he was too credulous rather than lacking in sincerity. Certainly he has reason to complain of those who told him that a bellows full of this apparent vacuum, when quickly opened and closed, emits a substance sensible as air; and that when a tube filled with quicksilver and this same vacuum is turned upside down, the quicksilver falls as slowly in the vacuum as in the air, the vacuum retarding its natural motion as much as the air, and in short many other things he reports. For I assure him on the contrary that the air enters and the quicksilver falls in this vacuum with the utmost impetuosity, etc.

Finally, that you may see Father Noël does not understand the experiments recorded in my printed statement, I draw your attention to this point among others: I said in the first experiments of mine he gave an account of, "that a glass syringe with a carefully fitted piston having been completely immersed in water and its opening closed by a finger touching the bottom of the piston (thus obliging the hand and arm to be in the water), only a moderate force is required to draw the piston up and make it separate from the finger, without any water coming in (which the philosophers believed could not be done with any finite force); and thereby the finger is felt to be strongly and painfully pulled, and the piston leaves an apparently empty space, into which it does not appear any body can have entered, since it is entirely surrounded by water which could have had no access to it because the opening had been closed; and if the piston is drawn higher, the apparently empty space becomes greater, but the finger is not felt to be more pulled." Father Noël thought that the words, *is not felt to be more pulled,* have the same meaning as *is no more felt to be pulled;* whereas according to all the rules of grammar they mean that the finger does not feel a greater pull. And since he knows the experiments only through reading them, he thought the finger actually no longer felt any pull, which is absolutely false, for the pull continues to be felt just as before. But Father Noël's hypothesis is so accommodating that he demonstrates, as a necessary consequence of his principles, why the finger no longer feels any pull, although it is absolutely false that it does not. I think he will be able to give as easily the reason for the opposite by the same principles. But I do not know what esteem the judicious will have for his method of demonstration if he proves with equal force the affirmative and the negative of the same proposition.

From which you see, Sir, that Father Noël bases this invisible matter on false experiments in order to explain other experiments he has imperfectly understood. And so it was right and proper that he should make use of a matter we would be unable to see and cannot understand to reply to experiments he has not seen and has not understood. When he is better informed about them, I do not doubt that he will change his mind, especially with respect to his moving levity. Therefore the reply to this book should be postponed until Father Noël has corrected it and has recognized the falsity of the facts and the imposture of the witnesses he offers in opposition and until he no longer bases his charges against the belief in the vacuum on experiments badly understood and worse verified.

While writing these words I have just received a printed notice from Father Noël which overthrows the greater part of his book: he withdraws the moving levity of the *ether* and calls back the weight of the outside air to suspend the quicksilver. So that I find it rather hard to refute Father Noël's opinions, since he is more prompt in changing them than one can be in replying to him; and I begin to see that his conduct is very different from mine because he makes his opinions public as fast as they occur to him; but the very fact that they contradict each other is sufficient to show their want of solidity, since the power with which he disposes of this matter is evidence enough that he is its author and consequently that it exists only in his imagination.

All who resist truth suffer from a like inconstancy of thought and they who fall into such variableness are to be suspected of denying truth. Accordingly it is curious to see among the defenders of the plenum the great number of opinions clashing with each other; one supports *ether* (and excludes every other substance); another, the spirits of the liquid [in the tube] to the prejudice of *ether;* another, the air contained in the bodies' pores (and banishes everything else); another, rarefied air void of every other body. Finally there are those who, not having dared to place the immensity of God there, have chosen among men a person so illustrious by birth and merit that his mind could be placed there and made to fill the universe. So each of them has all the rest for enemies; and as all conspire to destroy one alone, he necessarily succumbs. But since they only triumph over each other, they are all victorious without a single one of them being able to profit by his victory, because all this advantage comes from their own confusion. So that it is not necessary to fight with them to destroy them, since it is enough to abandon them to themselves, for they make up a body divided against itself, whose members opposed to each other rend themselves within, whereas the friends of the vacuum remain in a unity always the same, which by this very fact is so related to truth that it should be followed until truth appears to us openly. For it is not in entanglement and tumult that truth should be sought; it cannot be found apart from that maxim which permits us to decide only about evident things, and which forbids us to affirm or to deny those which are not. This is the just mean and perfect balance that you keep to with such advantage and that I, by a good fortune I can never acknowledge enough, was always brought up in with singular method and more than paternal care.

There you have, Sir, the reasons that have restrained me, reasons I did not think I ought longer to conceal from you. And although it may seem that I write this rather for my own interest than for your curiosity, I hope this doubt will not go so far as yourself, since you know that I have much less uneasiness about these fantastic points of honor than passion to converse with you, and that I find much less charm in defending my opinions than in assuring you that I am with all my heart, Sir, your very humble and very obedient servant,

PASCAL

ACCOUNT OF THE GREAT EXPERIMENT CONCERNING THE EQUILIBRIUM OF FLUIDS

Devised by M. Pascal

TO COMPLETE THE TREATISE PROMISED BY HIM IN HIS ABRIDGMENT ON THE VACUUM AND CARRIED OUT BY M. PERIER ON ONE OF THE HIGHEST MOUNTAINS IN AUVERGNE.

WHEN I published my abridgment under the title: *New experiments concerning the vacuum*, etc., in which I had made use of the maxim on the horror of the vacuum because it was universally accepted and because I did not yet have convincing proofs to the contrary, I continued to feel certain difficulties which made me seriously doubt the truth of that maxim; to clear up these difficulties I thought at that time of the experiment here recorded, which would make it possible for me to know with certainty what I ought to believe. I have called it the *great experiment on the equilibrium of fluids* because it is the most significant of all the experiments that can be made on this subject in that it shows the equilibrium of air and quicksilver, which are the lightest and the heaviest of all fluids known in nature. But because it was impossible to carry out the experiment here in Paris, because there are only a very few places in France suited to this purpose, and because Clermont in Auvergne is one of the most convenient, I asked my brother-in-law, M. Perier, councilor on the Board of Excise of Auvergne, to be at the trouble of doing it there. It will be seen from the letter I wrote him at that time what my difficulties were and just what this experiment is.

COPY OF THE LETTER OF M. PASCAL THE YOUNGER TO M. PERIER, *November 15, 1647*

SIR,

I would not interrupt the official duties with which you are constantly occupied in order to discuss physical speculations with you if I did not know that they will help to refresh you in your leisure hours and that whereas they would be a burden to others, you will find amusement in them. I have the less hesitation in doing this as I know the pleasure you take in such conversations. This one will be only a continuation of those we have had together about the vacuum. You know what the philosophers have thought on this subject: all have held as a maxim that nature abhors a vacuum, and almost all, going further, have maintained that she cannot permit it and that she would destroy herself sooner than suffer it. Thus opinions have been divided: some have been content to say only that she abhorred it, and others have maintained she could not suffer it. I tried in my abridgment of the *Treatise on the Vacuum* to destroy this latter opinion, and I think the experiments I give there are sufficient to make it manifestly clear that nature can and actually does suffer a space as large as we please, void of every substance known to us and perceptible to sense. I am now trying to examine the truth of the former opinion and to find experiments which will show whether the effects attributed to the horror of the vacuum should really be attributed to it, or whether they should be attributed to the weight and pressure of the air; for, to tell you frankly what I think, it is hard for me to believe that nature, which is not animate or sensitive, is capable of horror, since the passions presuppose a soul capable of feeling them, and I incline much more to impute all these effects to the weight and pressure of the air, because I consider them only as particular cases of a universal proposition on the equilibrium of fluids, which is to constitute the larger part of the treatise I have promised. Not that I did not have these same thoughts at the time I wrote my abridgment; but through lack of convincing experiments I did not then dare (and I do not yet dare) depart from the maxim of the horror of the vacuum, and I even used it as a maxim in my abridgment, having then no further design than to combat the opinion of those who maintain that the vacuum is absolutely impossible, and that nature would suffer her own destruction rather than the least void space. Indeed I do not consider it permissible for us lightly to depart from the maxims we hold from antiquity unless we are constrained by proofs indubitable and invincible. But in this case I hold it would be an extreme weakness to have the slightest scruple, and that in fine we should have more veneration for evident truths than obstinate attachment to received opinions. I could not give you better evidence of how circumspect I am before giving up ancient maxims than to remind you of the experiment I recently made in your presence with two tubes, one inside the other, which demonstrates a vacuum in a vacuum. You saw that the quicksilver in the inner tube remained suspended at the same height as in the ordinary experiment, when it was counterbalanced and pressed by the weight of the whole mass of the air, and that on the contrary it all fell down without height or suspension when because of the surrounding vacuum it was no longer at all pressed or counterbalanced by any air, which had been removed on all sides. You saw afterwards that this height or suspension of the quicksilver increased or diminished as the pressure of the air increased or diminished, and finally that all the different heights or suspensions of the quicksilver were always proportional to the pressure of the air.

Certainly after this experiment one might well be persuaded that it is not the abhorrence of a vacuum, as we suppose, which causes the suspension of the quicksilver in the ordinary experiment, but the weight and pressure of the air which counterbalances the weight of the quicksilver. But because all the effects of this last experiment with the two tubes, which are explained so naturally by the pressure and weight of the air alone, can yet be explained with some probability by the abhorrence of a vacuum, I hold to that ancient maxim, resolved however to seek the complete clearing up of this difficulty by a decisive experiment. I have thought of one which can of itself suffice to give us the light we seek if it can be carried out accurately. It is to perform the ordinary vacuum experiment several times on the same day, in the same tube, with the same quicksilver, now at the bottom and now at the top of a mountain at least 500 or 600 fathoms high, to find out whether the height of the quicksilver suspended in the tube will be the same or different in the two situations. Doubtless you already see that this experiment will decide the question, and that if it should happen that the height of the quicksilver is less at the top than at the bottom of the mountain (as I have many reasons for believing it will be, although all who have considered this matter are against me), it will follow necessarily that the weight and pressure of the air is the only cause of the quicksilver's suspension and not the horror of the vacuum, since it is perfectly certain that there is much more air pressing down on the foot of the mountain than on its summit; whereas it could hardly be said that nature abhors a vacuum at the foot of the mountain more than at its summit.

But as great things are ordinarily found to be accompanied by difficulty, I anticipate much of it in the carrying out of this plan, which requires that an unusually high mountain be picked out near a city in which there is a person capable of bringing to this test all the necessary accuracy. For if the mountain were distant, it would be difficult to carry to it the vessels, the quicksilver, the tubes, and many other necessary things, and to undertake troublesome journeys as many times as might be required for finding on the mountain tops clear and suitable weather, which is not often met with there. And since it is as rare to find persons outside of Paris with such qualities as it is to find places satisfying the conditions, I counted myself happy on this occasion to have fallen in with both, since our town of Clermont is at the foot of the high mountain of the Puy de Dôme, and since I hope that you will grant me of your goodness the favor of being willing to make the experiment yourself. In this assurance I have led all our natural philosophers in Paris to hope that the experiment will be performed, and among others the Rev. Father Mersenne, who has already pledged himself, in letters he has written to Italy, Poland, Sweden, Holland, etc., to communicate the results to the friends he has acquired there by his merit. I do not specify the means of carrying out the experiment, because I well know that you will omit none of the circumstances necessary for doing it with precision.

Only I beg you to do it as soon as you possibly can and to excuse the liberty I am taking, which is due to my impatience to learn the outcome of the experiment, without which I cannot complete the treatise I have promised the public or satisfy the desire of so many persons who are waiting to hear it and who will be infinitely obliged to you. Not that I wish to diminish my gratitude by the number of those who share it with me, since I want on the contrary to participate in theirs and thus remain so much the more, Sir,

Your very humble and very obedient servant,

PASCAL

M. Perier received this letter at Moulins, where he was kept by the king's business, so that however great his desire to perform the experiment promptly he was unable to do it until last September.

You will see the reasons for this delay, the account of the experiment, and the precision he brought to it, in the following letter which I had the honor of receiving from him.

COPY OF THE LETTER OF M. PERIER TO M. PASCAL
THE YOUNGER, *September* 22, 1648

SIR,

At last I have made the experiment you have so long been desiring. I would have given you this satisfaction sooner; I was prevented, as much by the official business I was on in Bourbonnais as because since my arrival snow or mist has so covered the Puy de Dôme, on which I was to make the experiment, that even in this season, which is the finest of the year here, I had difficulty in finding a day on which it was possible to see the summit of this mountain, which is usually in the midst of clouds and sometimes above them although at the same time it is fine weather on the plain; so that my own and the season's convenience did not meet until the 19th of this month. But the success with which I performed the experiment on that day amply consoled me for the petty annoyance of so many delays I had been unable to avoid.

I am sending you a full and faithful account, wherein you will see with what precision and care I performed the experiment, to which I also added the precaution of having for witnesses certain persons as learned as irreproachable, that the sincerity of their testimony might leave no doubt of the certainty of the experiment.

Copy of the account of the experiment by M. Perier

Last Saturday, the 19th of this month, was very unsettled; nevertheless since the weather seemed pretty good at 5 o'clock in the morning and the summit of the Puy de Dôme was fully visible, I decided to ascend the mountain to make the experiment. To this end I gave notice of my intention to several persons of condition in the town of Clermont who had asked me to let them know the day when I would go up, of whom some are churchmen and others laymen. Among the churchmen were the Very Rev. Father Bannier, Minim of this city, who has several times been Superior, and M. Mosnier, Canon of the Cathedral of this city; and among the laymen, M. Laville and M. Begon, councilors on the Board of Excise, and M. La Porte, doctor of medicine and practitioner in the city, all very capable men not only in their professions but also in all good learning, with whom I was delighted to carry out this fine project. Accordingly on that day at 8 o'clock in the morning we were all together in the garden of the Minim Fathers, which is almost the lowest place in the town, where the experiment was begun as follows:

First I poured into a vessel sixteen pounds of quicksilver, which I had rectified during the three preceding days; and having taken two glass tubes of the same size, each four feet long, hermetically sealed at one end and open at the other, I performed with each of them the ordinary vacuum experiment in the above mentioned vessel, and having brought the two tubes together and placed them one against the other without lifting them out of the vessel, I found that the quicksilver left in each of them was at the same level, 26 inches, 3½ lines above the surface of the quicksilver in the vessel. I did the experiment in the same place, in the same two tubes, with the same quicksilver, and in the same vessel two more times; it was always found that the quicksilver in the two tubes was at the same level and had the same height as the first time.

That done, I fixed one of the tubes in its vessel as a continuous experiment. I marked on the glass the height of the quicksilver, and leaving the tube in the same place it had been, I asked the Rev. Father Chastin, one of the religious of the house, a man as pious as he is capable, who talks very well on these matters, to be at the pains of observing from time to time during the whole day whether any change came about. And with the other tube and a part of the same quicksilver I went with the above-mentioned gentlemen to perform the same experiments on the top of the Puy de Dôme, about 500 fathoms above the Minims, where it was found that there was left in the tube only 23 inches, 2 lines of quicksilver, whereas there had been found at the Minims, in the same tube, 26 inches,

3½ lines, and that thus there was a difference of 3 inches, 1½ lines; which overcame us all with wonder and astonishment, and so surprised us that for our own satisfaction we wanted to repeat the experiment. This is why I did it five times very accurately, at different places on the summit of the mountain, now inside in the little chapel, now outside, now in a sheltered spot, now exposed to the wind, now in fine weather, now during the rain and mists which occasionally visited us, each time having very carefully eliminated all air from the tube; the quicksilver was always found to be at the same height of 23 inches, 2 lines, which when subtracted from the 26 inches, 3½ lines found at the Minims makes the difference of 3 inches, 1½ lines. Which fully satisfied us.

Afterwards while descending the mountain I repeated the same experiment on the way, always with the same tube, the same quicksilver, and the same vessel, at a place called *Lafon de l' Arbre*, much higher than the Minims yet nearer to them than to the summit of the mountain; and there I found that the height of the quicksilver left in the tube was 25 inches. I did it a second time in the same place, and the said M. Mosnier, mentioned above, had the curiosity to want to perform the experiment himself. Accordingly he did it in this same place, and the same height of 25 inches was always found, which is less than that observed at the Minims by 1 inch, 3½ lines and greater than that we had just observed on top of the Puy de Dôme by 1 inch, 10½ lines, a circumstance which increased our satisfaction not a little, since we saw that the height of the quicksilver decreased as the height of the places increased.

Finally on our return to the Minims I found the vessel I had left as a continuous experiment with its quicksilver suspended at the same height at which I had left it, 26 inches, 3½ lines, in which height the Rev. Father Chastin, who had remained there to observe, reported there had been no change during the entire day, although the weather had been extremely variable, now clear, now rainy, now dank with mists, and now windy.

I repeated the experiment with the tube I had taken to the Puy de Dôme, in the same vessel with the tube of the continuous experiment; I found the quicksilver was at the same level in both tubes and at the same height of 26 inches, 3½ lines, as had been found that morning in this same tube and as it had remained the whole day in the tube of the continuous experiment.

I repeated the experiment again for the last time, not only in the same tube I had used on the Puy de Dôme, but also with the same quicksilver and in the same vessel I had carried up there, and I always found the quicksilver at the same height of 26 inches, 3½ lines which had been found in the morning. And now we were completely confirmed in the certainty of the experiment.

The next day the Very Rev. Father Delamare, priest of the Oratory and Canon Theologian of the Cathedral, who had been present at what had taken place on the morning of the preceding day in the garden of the Minims, and to whom I had reported what had happened on the Puy de Dôme, invited me to perform the same experiment at the foot and on top of the highest tower of Notre Dame de Clermont to find out if there would be a difference. To satisfy the curiosity of a man of such distinguished merit, who has given all France proofs of his ability, I performed on the same day the usual vacuum experiment in a private house, situated in the most elevated part of the city, 6 or 7 fathoms above the garden of the Minims and on a level with the foot of the tower. We found the height of the quicksilver there was about 26 inches, 3 lines, which is less than that found at the Minims by about ½ line.

Afterwards I did the experiment on top of the tower, 20 fathoms above its foot and about 26 or 27 fathoms above the garden of the Minims; I found the height of the quicksilver to be about 26 inches, 1 line, which is less than that found at the foot of the tower by about 2 lines and less than that found at the Minims by about 2½ lines.

So that, to repeat and to compare the different elevations of the places where the experiments were performed with the different heights of the quicksilver left in the tubes, it is found:

That in the experiment performed in the lowest of the places the quicksilver remained at the height of 26 inches, 3½ lines.

In that performed in a place about 7 fathoms higher the height of the quicksilver was 26 inches, 3 lines.

In that performed in a place about 27 fathoms higher the height of the quicksilver was 26 inches, 1 line.

In that performed in a place about 150 fathoms higher the height of the quicksilver was 25 inches.

In that performed in a place about 500 fathoms higher the height of the quicksilver was 23 inches, 2 lines.

And consequently it is found that an elevation of about 7 fathoms makes a difference in the height of the quicksilver: ½ line.

About 27 fathoms: 2½ lines.

About 150 fathoms: 15½ lines, i.e., 1 inch, 3½ lines.

And about 500 fathoms: 37½ lines, i.e., 3 inches, 1½ lines.

There you have the true account of all the details of this experiment, which all the gentlemen who were present will sign whenever you wish them to.

For the rest, I must tell you that the heights of the quicksilver were very accurately measured; but those of the places where the experiments were performed were much less so.

If I had had the leisure and the facilities, I would have taken the altitudes more precisely, and I would even have marked a place on the mountain for each 100 fathoms of elevation and performed the experiment there and marked the differences found in the height of the quicksilver at each of these stations, in order to give you the exact difference due to the first 100 fathoms, that due to the second 100 fathoms, and similarly of the rest; in this way a table could be drawn up which, if anyone would go to the trouble of carrying it further, might finally lead to certain knowledge of the true size of the diameter of the whole sphere of the air.

I do not give up hope of sending you some day these differences for every 100 fathoms, as much for our own satisfaction as for their usefulness to the public.

If you find any parts of this account obscure, I shall be able to clear them up for you by word of mouth in a few days since I am on the point of making a little trip to Paris, where I shall assure you that I am, Sir,

Your very humble and very affectionate servant,

PERIER

This account having cleared up all my difficulties, I do not conceal the extreme satisfaction it gave me; and having seen there that a difference in elevation of 20 fathoms made a difference in the height of the quicksilver of 2 lines, and that a difference of 6 or 7 fathoms made a difference of about ½ line, differences which it was easy for me to test in this city, I performed the ordinary vacuum experiment at the top and at the bottom of the Tower of Saint-Jacques de la Boucherie, whose height is 24 or 25 fathoms; I found a difference of more than 2 lines in the height of the quicksilver; and afterwards I performed the experiment in a private house 90 steps up, where I found an evident difference of ½ line; results which agree perfectly with what is said in M. Perier's account.

All students of nature can make the test for themselves at their leisure.

Many consequences can be drawn from this experiment, such as:

A way of knowing whether two places are at the same level, that is, equidistant from the center of the earth, or which of the two has the greater altitude, however far apart they may be, even if they should be each other's antipodes; which would be all but impossible by any other means.

The little certainty there is in the thermometer's indication of degrees of heat (contrary to common opinion), and that its water sometimes rises with increasing heat and sometimes falls with decreasing heat, though the thermometer has always remained in the same place.

The unequal pressure of the air, which at the same degree of heat is always much greater in the lowest places.

All these consequences will be unfolded at length in the *Treatise on the Vacuum*, along with many others as useful as they are interesting to students.

To the Reader

My dear reader, the universal consensus of nations and the crowd of philosophers agree in establishing the principle that nature would rather suffer her own destruction than the least void space. Some of the most enlightened minds have adopted a more moderate principle: for although they have believed that nature abhors the vacuum, they have nevertheless thought that this repugnance had limits, and that with some violence it could be overcome; but no one has yet been found to advance the third principle: that nature has no repugnance for the vacuum, that she makes no effort to avoid it, and that she admits it without difficulty and without resistance. The experiments I placed before you in my abridgment do away, in my opinion, with the first of these principles, and I do not see how the second can hold up against the present experiment; so that I no longer make any difficulty about adopting the third: that nature has no repugnance for the vacuum, that she makes no effort to avoid it, that all the effects that have been attributed to her horror have their origin in the weight and pressure of the air, that it is their sole and true cause, and that through ignorance of it this imaginary horror of the vacuum had been made to order in an attempt to account for them. It is not on this occasion only that, when the weakness of men has been unable to find the true causes, their subtlety has substituted imaginary causes, to which they have given specious names filling the ears and not the mind. Thus it is said that the sympathy and antipathy of natural bodies are efficient causes, responsible for many effects, as if inanimate bodies were capable of sympathy and antipathy; it is the same with antiperistasis and with many other chimerical causes, which but give a vain solace to man's hunger to know hidden truths, and which, far from revealing them, serve only to cover up the ignorance of such inventors and to feed that of their followers.

It is not however without regret that I depart from opinions so generally received; I only do it constrained by truth, to whose force I yield. I resisted these new views as long as I had any excuse for following the old; the maxims I made use of in my abridgment sufficiently witness that. But at last the evidence of experiments forces me to quit opinions to which respect for antiquity had held me. Accordingly I but quitted them little by little, and only gradually did I give them up, for from the first of these three principles, that nature has an invincible horror of the void, I passed to the second, that she feels horror but not invincibly; and thence I finally came to believe in the third, that nature has no horror of the void.

Thus far have I been brought by this last experiment on the equilibrium of fluids, which I would not think I had imparted to you in its entirety if I did not reveal my motives for wanting it tried; this is why I am publishing my letter of last November 15th, addressed to M. Perier, who undertook the labor of carrying out the experiment with all the accuracy and precision one could wish. It is to him alone that all those who have so long been wanting to know the results are indebted.

As by a particular good fortune this universal desire had made the experiment famous before its appearance, I am sure it will not become less celebrated after having been performed, and that it will give as much satisfaction as the expectation of it caused impatience.

It would not be right to prolong this impatience; and that is why I could not refrain from giving out the experiment in advance, against my earlier intention of not publishing it until the complete treatise (which I promised you in my abridgment), in which I shall unfold the consequences I have drawn from it and which I had put off finishing until this last experiment, because it is to complete my demonstrations. But since the treatise cannot appear at this time, I have been unwilling to withhold the experiment longer, as much to deserve more gratitude from you for being in haste as to avoid blame for the wrong I should think I was doing you by a longer delay.

TREATISES ON THE EQUILIBRIUM OF LIQUIDS AND ON THE WEIGHT OF THE MASS OF THE AIR

CONTAINING THE EXPLANATION OF THE CAUSES OF DIVERS EFFECTS OF NATURE WHICH HAD NOT BEEN WELL UNDERSTOOD UNTIL NOW AND ESPECIALLY OF THOSE THAT HAD BEEN ATTRIBUTED TO THE HORROR OF THE VACUUM.

TREATISE ON THE EQUILIBRIUM OF LIQUIDS

CHAPTER I. *That liquids weigh in proportion to their height*

If we fasten to a wall several vessels, one as in the first figure, another inclined as in the second, another very wide as in the third, another narrow as in the fourth, another only a little tube ending at the bottom in a vessel which is wide but has almost no depth as in the fifth figure, and if we fill them all with water up to the same height and make openings of the same size in their bases, which we close with stoppers to keep the water in, experiment shows that the same force is required to prevent the stoppers from coming out, for although the amount of water in each vessel is entirely different, its height is the same in all; and the measure of the force required is the weight of the water contained in the first vessel, which is uniform throughout, for if this water weighs 100 pounds, a force of 100 pounds will be required to hold in each of the stoppers, even that in the fifth vessel, though the water in it should not weigh an ounce.

To make an exact test of this we must stop the opening of the fifth vessel with a round piece of wood, cased in tow like the plunger of a pump, which fits the opening and slides in it with such nicety that it does not stick and yet keeps the water in; and we must attach to the center of this piston a cord, which is then passed through the small tube and attached to one arm of a balance, on the other arm of which we hang a weight of 100 pounds; we shall find a perfect equilibrium between this 100 pound weight and the water in the small tube, weighing an ounce; and however little we take away from the 100 pounds, the weight of the water will lower the piston, and consequently lower the arm of the balance to which it is attached and lift that from which hangs the weight of a little less than 100 pounds.

If the water should freeze and the ice not stick to the vessel (as in fact it ordinarily does not), the other arm of the balance will need only an ounce to counterbalance the weight of the ice; but if we apply heat to the vessel so as to melt the ice, a weight of 100 pounds will be required to counterbalance the weight of the ice melted to water, although we are supposing it to be only an ounce.

The same thing would happen if the openings we stop were at the side or even at the top; and it would even be easier to make the test that way.

Plate I, *Figure* VI. We must have an entirely closed vessel and make two openings in the top, one very narrow, the other wider, and solder to each a tube of the same size as the opening; and we shall see that if we put a piston in the large tube and pour water in the small tube, it will be necessary to put a heavy weight on the

PLATE I

piston to prevent the weight of the water in the small tube from pushing it up, just as in the first examples a weight of 100 pounds was required to prevent the weight of the water from pushing the pistons down, since the opening was beneath; and if it were at the side, an equal force would be required to prevent the weight of the water from pushing the piston toward that side.

And if the tube filled with water should be a hundred times wider or a hundred times narrower, provided the water were always at the same height, the same weight would always be required to counterbalance the water; and however little the weight is diminished, the water will fall and cause the diminished weight to rise.

Rule for the force required to make the water stand

But if we poured water in the tube to twice the height, twice the weight would be required on the piston to counterbalance the water; and similarly if we made the opening into which the piston fits twice as big, it would be necessary to double the force in order to hold down the double piston; whence we see that the force required to prevent the water from flowing out is proportional to the height of the water in the tube and not to the area of its base; and that the measure of this force is always the weight of all the water contained in a column having the height of the water in the tube and the base of the opening into which the piston fits.

What I have said of water is to be understood of every other kind of liquid.

Chapter 2. *Why liquids weigh in proportion to their height*

It is seen from all these examples that a mere thread of water can counterbalance a great weight; it remains to show the cause of this multiplication of force; that is what we shall do in the following experiment.

Plate I, Figure VII. New kind of machine to multiply forces

If a vessel full of water, closed on all sides, has two openings, one a hundred times larger than the other, with a piston carefully fitted to each, a man pressing the small piston will match the strength of a hundred men pressing the piston in the hundredfold greater opening, and will overmaster ninety-nine.

And whatever be the ratio of the openings, if the forces applied to the pistons are as the openings, there will be equilibrium. Whence it is apparent that a vessel full of water is a new mechanical principle and a new machine for multiplying forces to any amount desired, since a man by this means will be able to lift any burden proposed.

And we must find it wonderful to meet again in this new machine that fixed order which is found in all the old machines, such as the lever, the wheel, the endless screw, etc., which is that the distance covered is increased in the same ratio as the force. For it is obvious that since one of these openings is a hundred times the other, if the man who pushes the small piston drove it down one inch, he would push the other up only the hundredth part of an inch; for since this pressure is transmitted because of the continuity of the water, which joins the two pistons amd makes it impossible for one to move without pushing the other, it is obvious that when the small piston moves one inch, the water which it has pushed, pushing the other piston, since it finds this opening a hundred times greater, occupies only a hundredth part of the height, so that distance covered is to distance covered as force to force. Which can even be taken as the true cause of this effect, it being clear that to move a hundred pounds of water one inch is the same thing as to move a pound of water a hundred inches, and that thus when a pound of water is so placed with respect to a hundred pounds of water that the hundred pounds cannot move one inch without making the pound move a hundred inches, they must remain in equilibrium, one pound having as much force to make a hundred pounds move one inch as a hundred pounds have to make one pound move a hundred inches.

We can also add for greater clarity that the water under these two pistons is equally pressed; for if one piston is a hundred times heavier than the other, it is also in contact with a hundred times as many parts of water, and so each part is equally pressed; therefore all must be at rest because there is not more reason why one part should give way than another; so that if a vessel filled with water has only one opening, an inch in area, for example, in which we put a piston carrying a weight of one pound, this weight acts against all the parts of the vessel generally because of the continuity and fluidity of the water. But to determine how much of this action is felt by each part, the rule is as follows: each part an inch in area, like the opening, is acted against as if pushed by the weight of one pound (without counting the weight of the water, which I do not mention here for I am considering only the weight of the piston), because the pound weight presses the piston in the opening, and each part of the vessel, more or less great, is acted upon more or less, exactly in proportion to its size, whether this part is over against the opening or to the side, near or far, for the continuity and fluidity of the water makes all those things equal and indifferent; so that the material of which the vessel is made must have enough resistance in all its parts to hold up against all these pressures; if its resistance is anywhere less, it breaks; if it is greater, the vessel supplies what is necessary, and the rest, on this occasion, remains useless; so that if a new opening is made in the vessel, there will be required to keep the water from spurting out a force equal to the resistance this part should have, that is, a force which is to that of one pound as this new opening is to the original opening.

Here is another proof which only geometers will be able to follow, and which may be passed over by others.

I lay down as a principle that a body never moves by its own weight without downward displacement of its center of gravity. Whence I prove that the two pistons represented in *Plate* I, *Figure* VII are in equilibrium, as follows: for their common center of gravity is at the point which divides the line joining their individual centers of gravity in the ratio of their weights; let them move now if possible; therefore the distances covered will be to each other inversely as the weights, as we have shown; but if we take their common center of gravity in this second position, we shall find it precisely in the same place as before; for it will always be found at the point which divides the line joining their individual centers of gravity in the ratio of their weights; therefore, because of the parallelism of the lines of their motions, it will be found at the intersection of the two lines joining the centers of gravity in the two positions; therefore the common center of gravity will be at the same point as before; therefore the two pistons, considered as a single body, have moved without any lowering of the common center of gravity, which is against the principle; therefore they cannot move; therefore they will be at rest, that is, in equilibrium. Q.E.D.

By this method I have demonstrated in a little treatise on mechanics the reason for all the multiplications of forces found in all the other mechanical instruments so far invented. For I show in all of them that the unequal weights which are in equilibrium by mechanical advantage are so disposed by the construction of the machines that their common center of gravity could never descend, no matter what positions they took; whence it follows they must remain at rest, that is, in equilibrium.

Let us accept then as certainly true that if in a vessel filled with water and having openings there are forces at these openings proportional to them, the forces are in equilibrium; this is the foundation and the reason of the equilibrium of liquids, of which we are going to give several examples.

By this new device of mechanics we understand why liquids weigh according to their height.

This device of mechanics for multiplying forces, when once understood, gives the reason why liquids weigh in accordance with their height and not in accordance with their expanse in all the effects we have recorded.

For it is obvious that in *Plate* I, *Figure* VI the water in a small tube counterpoises a piston carrying a hundred pounds because the vessel beneath is itself a vessel filled with water, having two openings, at one of which is the large piston and at the other the water in the tube, which is actually a piston carrying its own weight, which must counterbalance the other piston if their weights are as the openings.

Also in *Plate* I, *Figure* V the water in the fine tube is in equilibrium with a weight of one hundred pounds, because the vessel at the bottom, which is wide and shallow, is a closed vessel filled with water having two openings, one wide, at the bottom, where the piston is, the other small, on top, where the fine tube is, whose water is actually a piston carrying its own weight and counterbalancing the other because the weights are proportional to the openings; for it makes no difference whether the openings are opposite each other or not, as has already been said.

Wherein we see that the water of these tubes does nothing that copper pistons equally heavy would not do; since a copper piston weighing an ounce would be as much in equilibrium with the hundred pound weight as the thread of water weighing an ounce; so that the cause of the equilibrium of a small weight with a greater, as in all these examples, is not that these bodies weighing so little and yet counterpoising much heavier bodies are liquid, for that is not common to all the examples, since those in which little copper pistons counterbalance such heavy ones show the same thing; but it is that the substance in the bottom of the vessels extending from one opening to the other is liquid, for that is common to all and is the true cause of the multiplication.

Also in the example of *Plate* I, *Figure* V if the water in the little tube should freeze and that in the wide vessel beneath remained liquid, a hundred pounds would be required to sustain the weight of this ice; but if the water in the bottom freezes, whether that in the upper tube freezes or remains liquid, only an ounce is required to counterbalance it.

Whence it is clearly apparent that it is the fluidity of the body joining the two openings which causes this multiplication of forces, because its foundation is, as we have already said, that a vessel filled with water is a mechanical instrument for multiplying forces.

Let us pass to other effects whose explanation is discovered by this machine.

CHAPTER 3. *Examples of the equilibrium of liquids with their explanation.*

Plate I, *Figure* VIII. If a vessel filled with water has two openings, in each of which a tube has been soldered, and if we pour water in both up to the same height, it will be in equilibrium.

For since the heights are the same, the water will be proportional to the surface, that is, to the opening; therefore the water in each tube is really a piston whose weight varies as the opening; therefore there will be equilibrium by the preceding demonstrations.

Thence it is that if we pour water in one of these tubes only, it will make the water in the other rise until the same height has been reached in both, and then there will be equilibrium; for then they will be two pistons whose weights are proportional to the openings.

Why water rises as high as its source.

This is the reason why water rises as high as its source.

(The following experiments require that the vessel be filled up to the mouth of the tubes with the heavier of the liquids.)

But if we put different liquids in the tubes, as water in one and quicksilver in the other, the two liquids will be in equilibrium when their heights are proportional to their weights; that is to say, when the water is fourteen times higher than the quicksilver, because quicksilver as such is fourteen times heavier than water, for they will be two pistons, one of water, the other of quicksilver, whose weights will be proportional to the openings.

And even if the tube filled with water should be a hundred times finer than the tube filled with quicksilver, this thread of water would hold in equilibrium all that great mass of quicksilver, provided the water were fourteen times higher.

All that I have heretofore said of tubes should be understood of any vessel whatsoever, regular or not, for we meet with the same equilibrium; so that if, instead of the two tubes we have represented at the two openings, we should attach two vessels also emptying into these openings, but wide in some places, narrow in others, and in short entirely irregular in their whole length, and pour liquids in them until they had the specified height, these liquids would be as much in equilibrium in these irregular tubes as in the uniform tubes, because liquids weigh only according to their height and not according to their expanse.

This could easily be demonstrated by inscribing in both vessels many regular small tubes; for it would be shown by what we have demonstrated that two of these inscribed tubes, corresponding to each other, one in each vessel, are in equilibrium; therefore all those in one vessel would be in equilibrium with all those in the other. Those who are used to the inscriptions and circumscriptions of geometry will have no trouble in understanding this; and it would be very difficult to demonstrate it to others, at least geometrically.

Plate I, *Figure* IX. If we place in a river a tube curved back at its lower end, filled with quicksilver, in such a way that its upper end is always out of the water, the quicksilver will fall part way until it has reached a certain height, when it will fall no lower, but will remain suspended at this point, so that its height is the fourteenth part of the height of the water above the recurved end; so that if the distance from the top of the water to the recurved end is fourteen feet, the quicksilver will fall until it is only one foot higher than the recurved end, at which height it will remain suspended; for the weight of the quicksilver which weighs inside the tube will be in equilibrium with the weight of the water weighing outside the tube, because the heights of these liquids are proportional to their weights, and their areas do not count for equilibrium; for the same reason it is also a matter of indifference whether the recurved end is wide or not and whether accordingly little or much water weighs upon it.

Also if we lower the tube, the quicksilver rises, for the weight of the water is greater; and if on the contrary we raise it, the quicksilver falls, for its weight is greater than that of the water; and if we incline the tube, the quicksilver rises until it has again reached the required height, which the inclining of the tube had diminished, for an inclined tube has less height than a vertical tube.

Plate I, *Figure* X. The same thing happens in a plain tube, that is, not recurved; for in such a tube open at both ends, filled with quicksilver and plunged into a river, provided that the upper end emerges from the water, if the lower end is fourteen feet from the surface, the quicksilver will fall until what is left has a height of only one foot; and there it will hang suspended by the weight of the water; which is easy to understand; for the water, in contact with the quicksilver from beneath and not from above, tries to push it up, as if it were a piston, and with so much the greater force as the water has greater depth; so that since the weight of the quicksilver makes the same effort to fall that the weight of the water makes to push it up, everything remains counterpoised.

Also if the quicksilver were not there, it is obvious that the water would enter the tube and rise to a height of fourteen feet, which is that of its level; therefore, the foot of quicksilver weighing as much as the fourteen feet of water whose place it takes, it is natural that it keep the water in the same equilibrium in which the fourteen feet of water would keep it.

But if the tube were thrust so far down in the water that the upper end was submerged, then the water would enter the tube and the quicksilver would fall; for the water weighing inside as well as outside the tube, the quicksilver would lack the necessary counterpoise for its suspension.

CHAPTER 4. *On the equilibrium of a liquid with a solid.*

I am now going to give examples of the equilibrium of water with solid bodies, such as a cylinder of solid copper, which can be suspended in the water as follows.

Plate I, *Figure* XI. A very long tube is required, say twenty feet, which widens at the lower end like a funnel; if this lower end is round and has fitted into it a copper cylinder so accurately turned that it can enter and leave the opening of the funnel, sliding back and forth there without allowing any water to escape and thus acting as a piston, we shall see that if we put the funnel with the cylinder in it in a river, making sure that the end of the tube emerges from the water, and if, holding the tube with the hand, we abandon the copper cylinder to its fate, this solid cylinder will not fall, but will remain suspended because the water is in contact with it from beneath and not from above (for it cannot get into the tube); and thus the water pushes it up in the same way it pushed the quicksilver in the preceding example, making the same effort as the weight of the copper makes to fall; and thus the opposed forces are in equilibrium. To be sure, for this result the cylinder must be far enough beneath the surface of the water to give the water the depth necessary for counterbalancing the copper; so that if the cylinder is a foot in height, there must be nine feet from the surface of the water to the bottom of the cylinder, because copper as such has nine times the weight of water; accordingly if the water is too shallow, as would be the case if the tube were drawn up toward the top of the water, the cylinder's weight wins out and it falls; but if the tube is thrust further down than is required, say twenty feet, so far is the cylinder from being able to fall by its own weight that on the contrary we should have to employ a great force to separate it and pull it away from the funnel, for the weight of the water pushes it up with a force of twenty feet. But if we pierce the tube and the water, entering, weighs upon the cylinder from above as well as from below, then the cylinder will fall of its own weight, like the quicksilver in the other example, because it no longer has the counterweight needed for its suspension.

Plate I, *Figure* XII. If this tube which we have just described is curved over and a wooden cylinder is introduced and the whole is put into water, but in such a way that the upper end emerges, the wood will not rise, although it is surrounded by water, but on the contrary it will sink down into the tube because the water is in contact with it from above and not from below; for the water cannot enter the tube, and thus it pushes the cylinder down with all its weight and not at all up, for it is not in contact with it from below.

Plate I, *Figure* XIII. But if the cylinder were flush with the water, that is, if it were only sunk in such a way that there was no water above it but also none of it above the water, then it would be pushed neither up nor down by the weight of the water, which would be in contact with it neither from above nor from below (since it cannot enter the tube), but only on all sides; accordingly the cylinder would not rise for nothing lifts it, and on the contrary it would fall, but by its own weight only.

But if the lower end of the tube were bent to one side like a crutch and a cylinder were put in and the whole immersed, still in such a way that the upper end is out of the water, the weight of the water will push the cylinder laterally into the tube, because the water is not in contact with it on the opposite side, and the water will act in this way with so much the more force as it has more depth.

CHAPTER 5. *Of bodies entirely immersed in water.*

Plate I, *Figure* XV. We see from the above that water pushes up bodies it is in contact with from below, that it pushes down those it is in contact with from above, and that it pushes to one side those it is in contact with on the opposite side; whence it is easily concluded that when a body is entirely immersed in water, since the water is in contact with it from above, from below, and on every side, it tries to push it up, down, and sideways in every direction; but since its depth is the measure of the force it exerts in all these efforts, it is easy to see which of them must prevail.

For it is apparent at once that since the water has the same depth with respect to all the lateral surfaces, it will push them equally; and accordingly the body will receive no lateral impulsion in any direction, any more than a weathervane between two winds of equal strength. But since the water is deeper at the lower surface of the body than at the upper, it is obvious that it will push it more up than down, and since the difference between the two levels of the water is the height of the body itself, it is easy to understand that the water pushes it more up than down with a force equal to the weight of a volume of water equal to the body.

A body in water is counterpoised by an equal volume of water.

So that a body in water is carried there as if in the pan of a balance whose other pan carried an equal volume of water.

Hence it comes about that some bodies sink.

Whence it is apparent that if the body is of copper or some other substance heavier than an equal volume of water, it sinks; for its weight wins out against that counterbalancing it.

Others rise.

If the body is of wood or some other substance lighter than an equal volume of water, it rises with as much force as its weight is exceeded by the weight of water.

Others neither rise nor sink.

And if the body has the same weight as water, it neither sinks nor rises, like wax, which stays in water almost where it is put.

This is the reason why a well bucket is not hard to pull up so long as it is in the water, and why we do not feel its weight until it begins to come out, just as a bucket filled with wax would not be more difficult to pull up while it was in the water; but when they are in the water, they have a counterpoise which they no longer have when they have been drawn out, just as a balance pan carrying a hundred pounds is not hard to lift if the other pan is equally laden.

Copper weighs more in air than in water.

This is why when copper is in water we find that it is less heavy precisely by the weight of a volume of water equal to its own; so that if it weighs nine pounds in air, it weighs but eight in water because the equal volume of water counterbalancing it weighs a pound; and in sea water it weighs less because sea water is almost one forty-fifth heavier.

Two bodies which are in equilibrium in air are not in equilibrium in water.

For the same reason two bodies, one copper, the other lead, of equal weight and consequently of different volume (since the same weight requires more copper), will be found to balance each other in the scales; but if the scales are put in water, the equilibrium is lost, for each body being counterbalanced by a volume of water equal to its own, and the volume of the copper being greater than that of the lead, the copper has a greater counterpoise, and accordingly the weight of the lead is the master.

Nor even in moist air.

Thus two weights of different material having been perfectly balanced with the greatest precision to which men can attain, if they are in equilibrium when the air is very dry, they are no longer so when the air is moist.

All bodies in water are pushed up by its weight, not down.

By the same principle when a man is in water, so far is the weight of the water from pushing him down that on the contrary it pushes him up, but he weighs more than it; and that is why he nonetheless goes down, but with much less violence than in air because he is counterpoised by a volume of water equal to his own, which weighs almost as much as he does; and if it weighed the same, he would float. And so by kicking the ground or making the slightest effort against the water, he rises and floats; and in mud baths a man could not sink, and if he is pushed down, he rises of himself.

For the same reason a man bathing in a tub lifts his arm without effort as long as it is in the water; but when he thrusts it out of the water, he feels that it is heavy because it is no longer counterbalanced by a volume of water equal to its own, as it was in the water.

How it is that bodies float.

Finally bodies which float on the water weigh exactly as much as the water whose place they occupy; for the water, in contact with them from below and not from above, only pushes them up.

And this is why a lead plate convex in shape floats, because it occupies a large place in the water because of this shape; whereas if it were a solid mass, it would never occupy more than the place of a volume of water equal to the volume of its matter, which would not suffice to balance it.

CHAPTER 6. *On compressible bodies in water.*

It is seen from everything I have shown how water acts against all bodies in it, pressing them on every side; whence it is easy to judge that if a compressible body is submerged, the water should compress it inward toward the center; and that is exactly what it does, as will be seen in the following examples.

Plate I, *Figure* XIV. If a bellows with a very long tube, say twenty feet, is placed in water in such a way that the nozzle emerges, it will be hard to open, if the little holes which are in one of the wings have been stopped, whereas it would be opened without any trouble if it were in the air, because the water compresses it from every side with its weight; but if all the necessary force is employed and it is opened, however little this force is relaxed, the bellows closes again with violence (whereas it would remain wide open if it were in air) because of the weight of the mass of water pressing against it. Also the deeper it is in the water the more difficult it is to open because there is a greater depth of water to support.

Plate I, *Figure* XVI. Similarly if we put a tube in the opening of a balloon and bind the balloon about the end of the tube, which is twenty feet long, pouring quicksilver in the tube until the balloon is full and putting the entire apparatus in a cistern of water, so that the end of the tube emerges from the water, we shall see the quicksilver rise from the balloon into the tube, up to a certain height, because since the weight of the water presses the balloon from all sides, the quicksilver it contains, being pressed equally at every point except where the tube enters (for the water has no access there since the mouth of the tube is above the surface of the water), is pushed from the places where it is pressed toward the place where it is not pressed; and thus it rises in the tube up to a certain height at which it weighs as much as the water outside the tube.

Wherein the same thing happens as if we pressed the balloon between the hands; for we should without difficulty make the liquid in it rise in the tube, and it is obvious that the surrounding water presses it in the same way.

Plate I, *Figure* XVII. It is for the same reason that if a man puts the end of a glass tube twenty feet long on his thigh, and if, holding it there, he seats himself in a tank filled with water so that the upper end of the tube emerges from the water, his flesh will swell where the mouth of the tube is and a large and painful tumor will be formed, as if the flesh were sucked and drawn by a cupping glass; because the weight of the water compressing his body from all sides except the place where the mouth of the tube is (which the water cannot reach because the tube, into which it cannot enter, prevents its getting there), the flesh is pushed from the places where it is compressed to the place where it is not; and the greater the depth of water, the larger the swelling, and when the water is withdrawn, the swelling goes down; and similarly if water is poured into the tube, for the weight of the water affecting this part of the body as well as the others, there is no more swelling there than elsewhere.

This effect is perfectly conformable to the preceding one, for the quicksilver in the one case and the man's flesh in the other, since they are everywhere pressed except at the mouth of the tube, are pushed into the tube as much as the force of the water's weight can push them.

If we put in the bottom of a tank filled with water a balloon in which the air is not under much pressure, we shall see that it will be noticeably compressed; and in proportion as the water is removed, the balloon will gradually expand, because the weight of the mass of the water which is above it presses it on all sides toward the center, until the spring of this compressed air is as strong as the weight of the water pressing the balloon.

If we put at the bottom of the same tank of water a balloon filled with air at high pressure, we shall not notice any compression; not that the water does not press it; for the contrary is apparent from the other balloon and from the one containing quicksilver, from the bellows and from all the other examples, but the water has not enough force to compress it noticeably, because it was already very much compressed; just as when a spring is very stiff, like that of a crossbow, it cannot be noticeably bent by a moderate force which would bend a weaker spring perfectly noticeably.

We must not be surprised that the weight of the water does not noticeably compress this balloon and that nevertheless we very considerably compress it merely by laying our finger on it, although we press it then with a force less than that of water. The reason for this difference is that when the balloon is in the water, the water presses it on all sides, whereas when we press it with the finger, it is pressed in one place only; but when we press it with the finger in one place only, we make a large dent inasmuch as the neighboring parts are not pressed and thus easily accommodate what is expelled from the part that is pressed; so that since the matter driven from the one place that is pressed is distributed to all the rest, each place has little to take care of; and thus there is a dent in that place which becomes very noticeable by comparison with all the surrounding parts, which are without it.

But if we succeeded in pressing all the other parts as well as that one, each part giving back what it had received from the first, the first would return to its original state because the rest would themselves be pressed as well as it; and as there would now be only a general compression of all parts towards the center, we should no longer see a compression in any particular place; and we should not be able to judge of the general compression except by a comparison of the two spaces occupied by the balloon; and as they would differ very little, it would be impossible to notice it. Whence we see how much difference there is between pressing one part only and pressing all the parts generally.

It is the same with a body every part of which is pressed save one; for a swelling occurs there from the emptying, as it were, of the others, as could be seen in the example of the man in the water with a tube on his thigh. Also if we press the same balloon between the hands, although we try to touch each of its parts, there will always be one which escapes between the fingers and swells out into a tumor; but if it were possible to press the balloon everywhere equally, we should never be able noticeably to compress it, whatever effort we made, provided the air in the balloon were already under considerable pressure; this is what happens when it is in the water, for the water is in contact with it on all sides.

CHAPTER 7. *Of animals in water. Why they are not noticeably compressed by the weight of the water*

All this reveals to us why water does not compress the animals in it, although it presses generally all bodies it surrounds, as we have shown by so many examples. For it is not that the water does not press them but as we have already said, since it is in contact with them on all sides, it can cause neither swelling nor depression in any particular part but only a general condensation of all the parts toward the center, which would not be noticeable unless great and which can only be extremely slight because flesh is very compact.

For if the water were in contact with a body in one part only or if it were in contact with it in all but one, provided the body were at a considerable depth, the result would be very noticeable, as we have shown; but since all parts are equally pressed, nothing is seen.

Why the weight of the water is not felt.

It is easy to pass from this to the reason why animals in water do not feel its weight.

For the pain we feel when something presses us is great if the compression is great; because the part compressed is drained of blood, and the flesh, the nerves, and the other parts composing it are pushed out of their natural place, and this violence cannot occur without pain. But if the compression is slight, as when the skin is grazed by the finger with such delicacy that the blood is not driven from the part touched and that neither the flesh nor the nerves are displaced or in any way altered, there can also be no sensible pain; and if we are touched in this way in every part of the body, we should feel no pain from so slight a compression.

And this is what happens to animals in water; for the weight compresses them, to be sure, but so little that it is by no means noticeable, for the reason we have given; so that no part being pressed or drained of blood, no nerve or vein or fleshy part being displaced (for since the whole body is equally pressed, there is no more reason why they should be pressed toward one part than toward another) and everything remaining in short without change, everything should remain without pain and without awareness.

And we should not be surprised that these animals do not feel the weight of the water and that nevertheless they would certainly feel the weight of our finger if we only rested it on them, although they were thereby pressed with less force than by the water; for the reason for this difference is that when they are in water, they are pressed on all sides generally, whereas when they are pressed with the finger, they are pressed in one place only. But we have shown that this difference is the reason why they are quite noticeably compressed by the tip of the finger and are not noticeably compressed by the weight of the water, even if it should be increased a hundredfold; and as sensation is always proportional to compression, this difference is the reason why animals feel the pressure of the finger and not the weight of the water.

And thus the true reason why animals in water do not feel its weight is that they are equally pressed from all sides.

Also if we put a worm in dough, even though we should press the dough between our hands, we could never crush the worm or even injure it or compress it, because we would be pressing it in all its parts. The following experiment will serve as proof. We must have a glass tube, closed at the lower end and half filled with water, into which we put three things: a little balloon half filled with air, a second balloon entirely filled with air, and a fly (for it lives in lukewarm water as well as in air); and we must put a piston into the tube which will go as far as the water. If we press the piston with whatever force we like, as by putting a large number of weights on top of it, the water thus pressed will press everything it contains; accordingly the soft balloon will be quite noticeably compressed, but the hard balloon will be no more compressed than if there were nothing pressing it, nor the fly either, which will feel no pain under this great weight; for we shall see it, free and lively, walking along the glass and even flying away as soon as it is released from this prison.

No special brilliance is needed to draw out of this experiment everything we had already demonstrated.

We see the weight presses all these bodies as much as it can.

We see that it compresses the soft balloon; consequently it also presses the one beside it, for the same reason holds for both. But we see that no compression appears.

Whence then comes this difference? Whence could it come except from the single thing in which the two balloons differ, which is that one is filled with compressed air, which has been forcibly pumped into it, whereas the other is only half full; and thus the slack air which is in one is capable of great compression, but not the air in the other, because it is very compact and the water which presses it, surrounding it on all sides, can make no perceptible impression on the balloon, which makes an arch against it on all sides?

We also see that the fly is not compressed. Why, except for the same reason the balloon filled with air is not? And finally we see it feels no pain for the same reason.

But if we put dough instead of water in the bottom of the tube, and the balloon and the fly in the dough, and put the piston on top and pressed it, the same thing would happen.

Therefore since the condition of being pressed on all sides makes it impossible for the compression to be either noticeable or painful, must we not agree that this is the sole reason why the weight of the water cannot be felt by animals in it?

Let it no longer be said then that the reason is that water does not weigh upon itself, for it weighs everywhere the same; or that it weighs in a different fashion from solid bodies, for all weights are of the same nature; and here is a solid weight that a fly supports without feeling it.

And if anyone is still not satisfied, let the piston be removed and let water be poured into the tube until the water taking the piston's place weighs as much as the piston itself; it cannot be doubted that the fly will no more feel the weight of the water than that of the piston. Whence comes then this insensibility to so great a weight in these two examples? Is it because the weight is water? No, for when the weight is solid, there is the same insensibility. Let us say then that it is only because the fly is surrounded by water, for that alone is common to the two examples; accordingly it is the true reason.

Also if it happened that all the water above the fly should freeze, provided there was left a little above it unfrozen and that thus it was entirely surrounded by water, it would no more feel the weight of this ice than it did the weight of the water before.

And if all the water in the river should freeze except for about a foot at the bottom, the fish swimming there would no more feel the weight of that ice than the weight of the water into which it would later melt.

And thus animals in water do not feel its weight, not because it is only water that weighs down on them but because it is water that surrounds them.

TREATISE ON THE WEIGHT OF THE MASS OF THE AIR

CHAPTER 1. *That the mass of the air has weight, and that it presses with its weight all the bodies it surrounds.*

No one denies today that the air is heavy. We know that a balloon weighs more when inflated than when empty, which is sufficient proof; for if the air were light, the more of it we put in the balloon the more levity the whole would have, for the whole would have more than a part would have; but since on the contrary the more air we put in the heavier the whole is, it follows that each part is itself heavy and consequently that the air is heavy.

Those who want longer proofs have only to look them up in the authors who have expressly dealt with this matter.

If it be objected that air is light when it is pure but that the air which surrounds us is not pure air because it is mixed with vapors and gross bodies, and that it is only because of these foreign bodies that it is heavy, I reply in a word that I do not know pure air and that it might be hard to find; but I speak in this treatise only of the air as it exists in the state in which we breathe it, without considering whether it be composite or not; and it is that body, simple or composite, which I call air and of which I say that it is heavy: a fact which cannot be denied, and that is all I require in what follows.

This principle laid down, I shall stop only to draw certain consequences.

1. Since each part of the air is heavy, it follows that the whole mass of the air (that is, the whole sphere of the air) is heavy; and since the sphere of the air is not infinite in its extent, since it has limits, so also the weight of the mass of all the air is not infinite.

2. Just as the mass of the water of the sea presses with its weight the earth beneath it, and just as, if it covered the whole earth instead of a part of it only, it would press with its weight the whole surface of the earth; so since the mass of the air covers the entire surface of the earth, this weight presses its every part.

3. Just as the bottom of a bucket containing water is more pressed by the weight of the water when the bucket is full than when it is half full, and is the more pressed the deeper the water; so high places like mountain tops are not so pressed by the weight of the mass of the air as are low places like valleys, because there is more air above the valleys than above the mountain tops; for all the air

alongside the mountain weighs on the valley and not on the summit, because it is above the one and below the other.

4. Just as bodies in water are pressed on all sides by the weight of the water above, as I have shown in the *Treatise on the equilibrium of liquids*, so bodies in the air are pressed on all sides by the weight of the mass of the air above.

5. As animals in water do not feel its weight, so for the same reason we do not feel the weight of the air; and as we could not conclude that water has no weight from our not feeling it when we are immersed in it, so we cannot conclude that air is not heavy because we do not feel it to be so. We have shown the reason for this in the *Equilibrium of liquids*.

6. Just as if we had got together a great heap of wool twenty or thirty fathoms high, this mass would be compressed by its own weight, and the bottom part would be much more compressed than the middle part or the part near the top because it would be pressed by a greater amount of wool; so the mass of the air, which like wool is a compressible and heavy body, is compressed by its own weight; and the air on the bottom, that is, in low-lying places, is much more compressed than that higher up, as on mountain tops, because it carries a greater weight of air.

7. Just as if we took a handful of that mass of wool from the bottom in its compressed state and keeping it still compressed in the same way, put it in the middle of the mass, it would of itself increase in size since it was nearer the top, because it would have to carry the weight of a lesser amount of wool there; so if we contrived in some way to take air, as it is down here and compressed as it is, to the top of a mountain, it would have to increase in size of itself and attain to the condition of the air surrounding it on the mountain top, because it would carry a lesser weight of air in this place than below. Consequently if we took a balloon only half filled with air, and not entirely inflated as they usually are, and carried it up a mountain, it should be more inflated on the mountain top and should increase in size in proportion to its being less pressed; and the difference should be perceptible if the weight of the quantity of air alongside the mountain from which it is freed is considerable enough to cause a sensible effect and difference.

These consequences are so necessarily bound up with their principle that the one cannot be true without the others being equally so; and since it is certain that the air reaching from the earth to the top of its sphere has weight, all our conclusions therefrom are equally true.

But however certain we find these conclusions, it seems to me that everyone, even though accepting them, would want to see the last consequence confirmed by experiment, because it contains both all the rest and its own principle; for it is certain that if we saw a balloon, as described above, expand as it is carried higher, we could not possibly doubt that this expansion came from the fact that the air in the balloon was more pressed below than above, since there is nothing else that could cause it to expand, it being even colder on the mountain tops than in the valleys; and this compression of the air in the balloon could have no other cause than the weight of the mass of the air, for the air was taken as it was in the low altitude and was not compressed, since the balloon was even soft and only half filled. Consequently this would absolutely prove that the air is heavy; that the mass of the air is heavy; that it presses with its weight all the bodies it surrounds; that it presses low-lying places more than high places; that it is itself compressed by its own weight; that the air is more compressed below than above. And since in physics experiments have much more force of persuasion than arguments have, I do not doubt that everyone would want to see the latter confirmed by the former.

But if the experiment were made, I should have this advantage that in case there occurred no difference in the inflation of the balloon on the highest mountains, that would not invalidate my conclusion, because I could say they are not yet sufficiently high to cause a perceptible difference; whereas if there should be a very considerable difference, as of one-eighth or one-ninth, certainly the experiment would be decisive in my favor, and there could no longer be any doubt of the truth of everything I have established.

But I must say at once without further delay that the test has been made, and successfully, as follows.

Experiment made in two places, differing in altitude by about 500 fathoms.

If we take a balloon half filled with air, flaccid and soft, and carry it at the end of a string up a mountain 500 fathoms high, it will expand of itself as we go up, and when we are at the top, it will be entirely full and rounded out as if we had blown in more air; and as we go down again, it will little by little lose its roundness, passing through the same degrees, so that when we reach the bottom, the balloon will have returned to its original state.

This experiment proves conclusively everything I have said about the mass of the air; and it was necessary to establish that firmly, since it is the foundation of the whole discourse.

It only remains to point out that the mass of the air is heavier at one time than at another, namely, when it carries more vapor or is more compressed by cold.

Let us observe then, 1. that the mass of the air is heavy; 2. that its weight is limited; 3. that it is heavier at one time than at another; 4. that it is heavier in certain places than in others, as in valleys; 5. that it presses with its weight all the bodies it surrounds, and presses the more the heavier it is.

CHAPTER 2. That the weight of the mass of the air produces all the effects hitherto attributed to the horror of a vacuum.

This chapter is divided into two sections: in the first is an account of the principal effects attributed to the horror of the vacuum; and in the second it is shown that they come from the weight of the air.

FIRST SECTION. Account of the effects attributed to the horror of a vacuum.

There are certain effects which it is claimed nature produces because of her horror of a vacuum. The chief are:

1. It is hard to open a bellows whose apertures have been carefully stopped; and if we try to do it, we feel resistance as if its sides were glued together. And the piston of a sealed syringe resists when we try to pull it up, as if it were stuck to the bottom.

It is claimed that this resistance comes from nature's horror of the vacuum which would be made in the bellows if it could be opened up; which is confirmed by the fact that the resistance ceases as soon as the stoppers are removed and the air can get in to fill the bellows when it is opened.

PLATE II

2. Two polished bodies when placed together are hard to separate and seem to adhere.

Similarly a hat when put on a table is hard to snatch up.

Similarly a piece of leather when put on a paving stone and suddenly lifted, loosens and lifts up the stone.

It is claimed that this adhesion comes from nature's horror of the vacuum which would exist during the time it would take the air to get from the edges to the center.

3. When a syringe is dipped in water, if the piston is pulled up, the water follows and rises as if it adhered to the piston.

Similarly the water rises in a suction pump, which is actually nothing but a long syringe, and follows the piston when it is lifted, as if it adhered to it.

It is claimed that the rising of the water comes from nature's horror of the vacuum which would be made in the place left by the piston if the water did not rise, because the air cannot get in; which is confirmed by this, that if holes are made through which the air can get in, the water no longer rises.

In the same way if we put the nozzle of a bellows in water and suddenly open the bellows, the water rises to fill it because the air cannot get in, and especially if we stop the air holes in the wing.

Similarly when we put our mouth in water and suck, we draw up the water for the same reason; for the lungs are like a bellows, of which the mouth would be the nozzle.

Similarly in breathing we draw in the air as a bellows in opening draws in the air to fill up its capacity.

Similarly when we put lighted wicks in a saucer filled with water and a glass over them, as the flame of the wicks dies down, the water rises in the glass because the air in the glass, which had been rarefied by the flame, is now condensed by the cold and draws the water up and makes it rise along with itself as it contracts, in order to fill the place it is leaving; just as the piston of a syringe draws the water up with it when we lift it.

Similarly cupping glasses draw the flesh and cause a swelling, because the air inside the glass, rarefied by the candle flame, is now condensed by the cold when the flame is extinguished and draws the flesh with it to fill the place it leaves, as it drew the water in the preceding example.

4. If we put a bottle filled with water mouth down in a vessel filled with water, the water in the bottle remains suspended without falling.

It is claimed that the water does not fall because of nature's horror of the vacuum which would be made in the place left by the water in falling, for the air could not get in; this explanation is confirmed by the fact that if a hole is made through which the air can get in, all the water falls immediately.

We can make the same test with a tube, ten feet long say, stopped at the upper end and open at the bottom; for if it is filled with water and the lower end is dipped in a vessel of water, all the water in the tube remains suspended, whereas it would fall at once if the top of the tube had been opened.

We can do the same thing with a like tube, stopped at the top and recurved at the bottom, without putting it in a vessel of water as was done with the other one; for if it is filled with water, this water too will remain suspended, whereas if the top were opened, the water would at once spurt out with violence from the recurved end as from a fountain.

Finally the same thing can be done with a plain tube, without its being recurved, provided it be very narrow at the bottom; for if it is stopped at the top, the water will remain suspended, whereas it would fall with violence if we opened the upper end.

It is for the same reason that a cask filled with wine does not give up a drop of it, though the spigot be open, unless we make an opening in the top to admit air.

5. If we fill with water a tube in the shape of an inverted crescent (which is ordinarily called a siphon), and let each leg dip in a vessel filled with water, then unless the two vessels are at exactly the same level, all the water in the higher vessel will rise in the leg dipping in it to the top of the siphon and will pass through the other leg into the lower vessel; so that if water is constantly supplied to the higher vessel, the flow will be continuous.

It is claimed that this rising of the water comes from nature's horror of the vacuum which would be made in the siphon if the water in the two legs fell from each into the corresponding vessels, as it actually does fall when an opening is made in the top of the siphon through which the air can get in.

There are several other like effects I omit because they are all similar to those of which I have spoken and because in all there appears only this, that all the contiguous bodies resist the effort made to separate them when air cannot get in between them, whether this effort comes from their own weight, as in the examples in which water rises and remains suspended in spite of its weight, or whether it comes from forces we use to separate them, as in the first examples.

These are the effects commonly attributed to the horror of the vacuum; I am going to show that they come from the weight of the air.

SECOND SECTION. *That the weight of the mass of the air produces all the effects that have been attributed to the horror of the vacuum.*

If we have clearly understood in the *Treatise on the equilibrium of liquids* how liquids act with their weight against all bodies in them, we shall have no difficulty in understanding how the weight of the mass of air, acting upon all bodies, produces all the effects that had been attributed to the horror of the vacuum, for they are exactly alike, as we shall show in each instance.

1. *That the weight of the mass of the air causes the difficulty in opening a bellows with all its apertures stopped.*

That it may be understood how the weight of the mass of the air causes the difficulty we experience in opening a bellows when the air cannot get in, I shall point out a like resistance caused by the weight of water. All that is needed is to recall what I said in the *Equilibrium of liquids* (*Plate* I, *Figure* XIV), that a bellows with a tube of twenty feet or more, placed in a tank of water in such a way that the end of the tube emerges from the water, is hard to open, and so much the harder as the water is deeper; which comes obviously from the weight of the water above, for when there is no water, the bellows opens very easily; and in proportion as water is poured in, the resistance increases and is always equal to the weight of the water carried by the bellows, because since the water cannot get in because the tube is outside, we could not open the bellows without lifting and holding up the whole mass of the water; for the water displaced by opening the bellows, not being able to enter it, is forced to go elsewhere and thus to raise the level of the water, which cannot be done without effort; whereas if the bellows were broken and the water could get in, we could open and close it without resistance because the water would go in through the breaks as fast as the bellows was opened, and so we could open it without having to lift up the water.

I do not think anyone will be tempted to say that this resistance comes from the horror of the vacuum, and it is absolutely certain that it comes from the weight of the water alone.

But what I say of water should be understood of any other fluid; for if we put the bellows in a tank filled with wine, we shall feel a like resistance to opening it, and likewise if we put it in milk, in oil, in quicksilver, and in short in any fluid whatsoever. It is then a general rule and a necessary effect of the weight of fluids: that if a bellows is put in any fluid whatsoever in such a way that it cannot get into the body of the bellows, the weight of the fluid above prevents our opening the bellows without feeling resistance, because we could not do it without holding up the fluid; and consequently, applying this general rule to the particular case of the air, it will be true that when the air is kept from entering a bellows, the weight of the mass of the air above prevents our opening the bellows without feeling resistance, because we could not open it without lifting the whole mass of the air; but as soon as we make an opening in it, we open and close it without resistance because the air can get in and out, and so when we open the bellows, we do not have to lift the mass of the air; which is entirely conformable to the example of the bellows in water.

Whence we see that the difficulty in opening a sealed bellows is only a particular case of the general rule concerning the difficulty of opening a bellows in any fluid whatsoever when the fluid has no access to it.

What I have said of this effect I shall say of each of the others, but more succinctly.

2. *That the weight of the mass of the air is the cause of the difficulty we experience in separating two polished bodies when placed together.*

That it may be understood how the weight of the mass of the air causes the resistance we feel when we want to separate two polished bodies that have been placed together, I shall give an example of an altogether similar resistance caused by the weight of the water, which will leave no room for doubt that the air causes this effect.

We must here again recall what was set forth in the *Equilibrium of liquids* (Plate I, Figure XI):

That if we put a copper cylinder, turned on a lathe, in the opening of a funnel, also turned on a lathe, so that they fit so perfectly that the cylinder easily enters and slides back and forth in the funnel but without letting any water escape between, and if we put this machine in a tank of water in such a way that the stem of the funnel emerges from the water (which stem may have a length of twenty feet if necessary); if with the cylinder at a depth of fifteen feet in the water, holding the funnel with the hand, we let loose the cylinder and abandon it to its fate, we shall see that not only will it not fall although it seems there is nothing to hold it up, but even that it will be difficult to pull it out of the funnel although it is in no way stuck to it; whereas it would fall by its own weight with violence if it were at a depth of only four feet in the water, and still more violently if it were entirely outside the water. I have also shown the reason for this, which is that the water, in contact with the cylinder from below and not from above (for it does not touch its upper surface because the funnel keeps it from getting there), pushes it from the side it touches toward the side it does not touch, and thus pushes it up and presses it against the funnel.

The same thing should be understood of every other fluid; and consequently if two bodies are polished and placed together and if we hold the upper one with the hand and let the other go, the lower one remains suspended because the air is in contact with it from beneath and not from above, for it cannot get in between the two bodies and consequently it cannot reach the surfaces in contact; whence it follows by a necessary effect of the weight of all fluids in general that the weight of the air must push this body up and press it against the other, so that if we try to separate them, we meet with great resistance; which is entirely conformable to the effect of the weight of water.

Whence we see that the difficulty in separating two polished bodies is only a particular case of the general rule concerning the pressure of all fluids in general when they are in contact with a body on one of its surfaces and not on the opposite surface.

3. *That the weight of the mass of the air is the cause of the rise of water in syringes and pumps.*

To explain how the weight of the mass of the air makes water rise in pumps as the plunger is lifted, I shall show an entirely similar effect of the weight of water, which will make the reason perfectly clear as follows:

If we fit a syringe with a long piston, ten feet say, hollow throughout its length, with a valve at the lower end so arranged that it opens downward but not upward, so that the syringe is incapable of lifting water or any liquid above the level of the liquid because the air can enter it perfectly freely through the hollow piston; if now we put the opening of the syringe in a vessel filled with quicksilver and the whole in a tank of water in such a way that the top of the piston emerges from the water, when we lift the piston, the quicksilver will rise and follow it as if it adhered to it; whereas it would not rise at all if there were no water in the tank, because the air is entirely free to enter the body of the syringe through the hollow piston.

So the fear of the vacuum is not the cause; for if the quicksilver did not rise to fill the place left by the piston, there would be no vacuum since the air may freely enter; but it is only because the mass of the water weighing upon the quicksilver in the vessel and pressing it in all its parts except where the opening of the syringe is (for the water cannot reach there since it is kept away by the body of the syringe and by the piston), the quicksilver, pressed in every place but one, is pushed by the weight of the water toward that one as soon as the piston by being lifted leaves it a free place to enter, and balances in the syringe the weight of the water which weighs on the quicksilver outside.

But if holes are made in the syringe so the water can get in, the quicksilver will no longer rise because the water enters and is as much in contact with the quicksilver at the mouth of the syringe as elsewhere, and thus since all of it is equally pressed, none of it rises. All this was clearly demonstrated in the *Equilibrium of liquids.*

We see in this example how the weight of the water makes the quicksilver rise; and we could produce a similar effect with the weight of sand by removing the water from the tank; if instead of water we pour in sand, the weight of the sand will make the quicksilver rise in the syringe because it presses, just as the water did, everywhere except at the mouth of the syringe, and thus it pushes the quicksilver and forces it to rise in the syringe.

And if we put our hands on the sand and press it, we shall make the quicksilver rise higher inside the syringe and keep on rising to a height at which it can counterpoise the pressure outside.

The explanation of these effects makes it very easy to understand why the weight of the air causes water to rise in ordinary syringes as the piston is drawn up; for since the air is in contact with the water in the vessel everywhere except at the opening of the syringe (from which it is kept away by the syringe and the piston), it is obvious that the weight of the air, pressing the water in every place but that one, must push it thither and make it rise, as the piston by being lifted leaves room for it to come in, and counterbalance within the syringe the weight of the air which weighs outside, for the same reason and by the same necessity as the quicksilver rose, pressed by the weight of the water and by the weight of the sand, in the example we have just given.

It is then obvious that the rising of water in syringes is only a particular case of the general rule that when a fluid is pressed in every place but one by the weight of some other fluid, this weight pushes it toward the place where it is not being pressed.

4. *That the weight of the mass of the air causes water to be suspended in tubes stopped at the upper end.*

To make it understood how the weight of the air holds water suspended in tubes stopped at the upper end, I shall point out an entirely similar example of a like suspension caused by the weight of water, which will make the reason perfectly clear.

And first it may be said at once that this effect is entirely comprehended in the preceding; for just as I have shown that the weight of the air makes water rise in syringes and holds it suspended there, so the same weight of the air holds water suspended in a tube. That this effect may not lack, any more than the rest, another entirely like it to which it may be compared, I shall say that nothing is needed to this end but to remember what was said in the *Equilibrium of liquids* (*Plate* I, *Figure* IX), namely, that a tube ten feet long or more, recurved at the bottom and filled with mercury, having been put in a tank of water so that the upper end emerges from the water, part of the mercury remains suspended inside the tube, that is, at the height where it can counterbalance the water which weighs outside; and that a like suspension takes place even in a tube not recurved, simply open at both ends, with the upper end emerging from the water.

Now it is obvious that this suspension does not come from the horror of a vacuum, but only from this, that the water, weighing outside and not inside the tube and in contact with the mercury on one side and not on the other, holds it suspended by its weight at a certain height; therefore if the tube is pierced so that the water can get in, straightway all the mercury falls, because since the water is in contact with it everywhere and acting within as well as without, the mercury no longer has a counterpoise. All this was said in the *Equilibrium of liquids*.

Since this is a necessary effect of the equilibrium of fluids, it is not strange that when a tube is filled with water, stopped at the top and recurved at the bottom, the water remains suspended in it; for the air, weighing on the part of the water at the recurved end and not on the part in the tube (since it is prevented by the stopper), must of necessity hold the water suspended inside to counterbalance its own weight outside, exactly as the weight of the water held the mercury in equilibrium in the example we just gave.

And similarly when the tube is not recurved; for because the air is in contact with the water from below and not from above (since the stopper prevents contact there), it is absolutely necessary that the weight of the air hold up the water, exactly as the water held up the mercury in the example just given, and as the water pushes up and holds suspended a copper cylinder it is in contact with from below and not from above; but if the stopper is removed, the water falls, for the air is in contact with the water below and above and weighs inside and outside the tube.

Whence we see that the action of the air in holding liquids suspended with which it is in contact on one side and not on the other is a case of the general rule that fluids contained in any kind of tube whatsoever, immersed in another fluid which presses them from one side and not from the other, are suspended by the equilibrium of the fluids.

5. *That the weight of the mass of the air makes water rise in siphons.*

To explain how the weight of the air makes water rise in siphons I am going to show that the weight of water makes quicksilver rise in a siphon open at the top so that it is freely accessible to the air; whence we shall see how the weight of the air produces this effect. This I shall do as follows.

If one leg of a siphon is about one foot high and the other about one foot, one inch, and if we make an opening in the top of the siphon in which we insert a tube twenty feet long and carefully soldered to the opening, and if, having filled the siphon with quicksilver, we put each of its legs in a vessel also filled with quicksilver and the whole in a tank of water, fifteen or sixteen feet deep in the water, with the end of the tube therefore out of the water, then if there is any difference at all in level between the two vessels, say an inch, all the quicksilver in the higher vessel will rise in the siphon to the top and will pass through the other leg into the lower vessel in a continuous flow; and if we keep the higher vessel supplied with quicksilver, the flow will never cease; but if we make an opening in the siphon through which the water can get in, immediately the quicksilver will fall from each leg into the vessels and water will take its place.

This rising of quicksilver does not come from the horror of the vacuum, for the air has perfectly free access to the siphon; accordingly if we emptied the tank of water, the quicksilver would fall from each leg into the corresponding vessel, and the air would take its place, coming in through the open tube.

It is then obvious that the weight of the water causes the quicksilver to rise, because the water weighs upon the quicksilver in the vessels and not upon that in the siphon; and for this reason the water by its weight forces the quicksilver to rise and to flow as it does; but as soon as the siphon has been pierced and the water can enter, it no longer makes the quicksilver rise, because it weighs inside as well as outside the siphon.

But for the same reason and by the same necessity as the water thus makes the quicksilver rise in a siphon when it weighs on the vessels and has no access to the interior of the siphon, so also the weight of the air makes water rise in ordinary siphons, because it weighs on the vessels in which the legs of the siphon dip and has no access to the body of the siphon, which is entirely closed; and as soon as an opening is made in the siphon, the water no longer rises, but on the contrary falls into each vessel, and air takes its place because then the air weighs inside as well as outside the siphon.

It is obvious that this last effect is only a case of the general rule, and that if we really understand why the weight of the water makes the quicksilver rise in the example we gave, we shall see at the same time why the weight of the air makes water rise in ordinary siphons; this is the reason it must be made perfectly clear why the weight of the water produces this effect, and why it is the higher vessel which empties into the lower vessel rather than the other way around.

To this end it must be observed that, the water weighing on the quicksilver in each of the vessels and not at all on that in the legs of the siphon dipping in the vessels, the quicksilver in the vessels is urged by the weight of the water to rise in each leg of the siphon all the way up and still higher, if that were possible, because the water is sixteen feet deep and the siphon is only one foot high, and one foot of quicksilver is equal in weight to only fourteen feet of water; whence it is seen that the weight of the water pushes the quicksilver in each leg all the way up and still has some force left; whence the quicksilver in each leg being pushed up by the weight of the water, they contend at the top of the siphon, pushing each other, so that the one having the greater force must prevail.

Now that will be easy to calculate; for it is clear that since the water has greater depth above the vessel which is an inch lower, it pushes up the quicksilver in the longer leg more forcibly than that in the other leg by the force which an inch of depth gives it; whence it seems at first the result should be that the quicksilver should be pushed from the longer leg into the shorter; but we must consider that the weight of the quicksilver in each leg resists the effort made by the water to push it up, but they do not resist equally, for since the quicksilver of the long leg has an inch more of height, it resists more forcibly by the force given it by the height of one inch; therefore the mercury in the longer leg is more pushed up by the weight of the water by the force of an inch of water, but it is more pushed down by its own weight by the force of an inch of quicksilver; but an inch of quicksilver weighs more than an inch of water; therefore the quicksilver in the shorter leg is pushed up with more force, and consequently it must rise and continue to rise as long as there is any quicksilver in the vessel in which it dips.

Whence it is apparent that the reason why the higher vessel empties into the lower is that quicksilver is a heavier liquid than water. The opposite would happen if the siphon were filled with oil and the whole were in the same tank of water, for then the oil in the lower vessel would rise and flow through the top of the siphon into the higher vessel for the same reasons just given; for the water still pushing the oil in the lower vessel with more force because it has an inch more of depth and the oil in the long leg resisting and weighing more by its extra inch of height, since an inch of oil weighs less than an inch of water, the oil in the long leg would be pushed up with more force than the oil in the other leg, and consequently it would flow and would pass from the lower vessel to the higher vessel.

And finally if the siphon were filled with a liquid which had the same weight as the water in the tank, then neither would the water in the higher vessel pass into the other vessel nor that in the lower pass into the higher, but everything would remain at rest, for by calculating all the forces we shall see that they are all equal.

That is what had to be firmly grasped if we were to have a thorough understanding of why liquids rise in siphons; after which it is too easy to see why the weight of the air makes water rise in ordinary siphons and pass from the higher vessel into the lower for us to give more time to it, since it is only a case of the general rule we have just given.

6. *That the weight of the mass of the air causes the swelling of the flesh when a cupping glass is applied.*

To explain how the weight of the mass of the air makes the flesh swell where a cupping glass is applied, I shall cite an entirely similar effect caused by the weight of water, which will leave no doubt in the mind.

It is the effect recorded in the *Equilibrium of liquids* (*Plate* I, *Figure* XVII), where I showed that a man applying to his thigh the end of a glass tube twenty feet long and seating himself in this condition at the bottom of a tank of water in such a way that the upper end of the tube emerges from the water, his flesh swells at the opening of the tube as if there were suction in that place.

Now it is evident that this swelling does not come from the horror of the vacuum, for the tube is completely open and the swelling would not occur if there were only a little water in the tank; and it is altogether certain that it comes from the weight of the water only, because the water, pressing the flesh everywhere except at the entrance of the tube (for it finds no access there), drives the blood and the flesh there to make the swelling.

And what I say of the weight of the water is to be understood of the weight of any other liquid; for if our man seats himself in a tank of oil, the same thing will happen as long as that liquid is in contact with every part of his body but one. But if the tube is removed, the swelling goes down because the water now exerting its action upon that part as well as on the others, there will be no more effect there than elsewhere.

This being understood, we shall see that when we put a candle on the flesh and a cupping glass over it, as soon as the flame is extinguished, the flesh necessarily swells; for the air in the cupping glass, which was highly rarefied by the flame, having become condensed by the cold following upon the extinction of the flame, the weight of the air is in contact with the body everywhere except beneath the cupping glass (for there is no access there); and consequently the flesh must swell there, and the weight of the air must drive the adjacent blood and flesh, which it presses, into that part which it does not press, for the same reason and by the same necessity that the weight of the water did in the example I gave, when it was in contact with the body in every place but one; whence it is apparent that the behavior of the cupping glass is only a particular case of the general rule concerning the action of all fluids upon a body with all parts of which they are in contact save one.

7. *That the weight of the mass of the air is the cause of the attraction that takes place in suction.*

Only a word is now required to explain why when we apply our mouth to water and suck, the water comes in; for we know that the weight of the air presses the water everywhere except where the mouth is, for it is in contact with it everywhere except there; and thence it is that when the respiratory muscles, lifting the chest, enlarge the capacity of the interior of the body, the air inside, having more space to fill than before, has less force to prevent the water from entering the mouth than the air outside, which weighs on the water everywhere except in this one place, has force to make it enter.

That is the cause of this attraction, which differs in no respect from the attraction of syringes.

8. *That the weight of the mass of the air is the cause of the drawing of milk by infants from their nurses' breasts.*

Similarly a baby with its lips about the nipple of its nurse's breast, when it sucks, draws in milk, because the breast is pressed on all sides by the weight of the surrounding air except in the part which is in the child's mouth; and that is why as soon as the respiratory muscles make more room in the child's body, as has just been said, and nothing is in contact with the nipple of the breast but the air inside, the air outside, which has more force and compresses the breast, pushes the milk through this opening where there is less resistance; which is as necessary and as natural as for the milk to come out when the nipple is pressed between the hands.

9. *That the weight of the mass of the air is the cause of the drawing in of air in breathing.*

And for the same reason when we breathe, air enters the lungs, because when the lungs open and the nose and all the passages are free and open, the air which is in contact with these passages, pushed by the weight of all its mass, enters and falls by the natural and necessary action of its weight; which is so understandable, so easy, and so simple that it is strange recourse should have been had to the horror of the vacuum, to occult qualities, and to causes so remote and so chimerical, to find a reason, since it is as natural for air to enter and to fall in this way into the lungs when they open as for wine to fall into a bottle when it is poured in.

This is the way in which the weight of the air produces all the effects hitherto attributed to the horror of the vacuum. I have explained the chief of them; if any remain, it is so easy to understand them after these that I should think I was being both superfluous and tedious if I sought out others to treat in detail; and it may even be said they had all been seen already, as in their source, in the preceding treatise, since all these effects are only particular cases of the general rule concerning the equilibrium of fluids.

CHAPTER 3. *That as the weight of the mass of the air is limited, so the effects it produces are limited.*

Since the weight of the air produces all the effects hitherto attributed to the horror of the vacuum, it should be the case that since this weight is not infinite but has limits, its effects too should be limited; which is confirmed by experiment, as what follows will show.

As soon as we raise the piston of a suction pump or of a syringe, the water follows, and if we continue to raise it, the water will keep on following, but not to any height whatsoever, for there is a certain point it does not pass, which is approximately at the height of thirty-one feet; so that as long as we only raise the piston to this height, the water rises and remains always in contact with the piston, but as soon as we raise the piston higher, it no longer draws the water with it, but the water remains motionless and suspended at that height without rising further, and to whatever height we raise the piston beyond, the water lets it go without following it.

The cause of which is that the mass of the air weighs approximately as much as water at a depth of thirty-one feet; so that as it makes the water rise in the syringe because it weighs outside and not inside, in order to counterbalance the water it makes it rise to the height at which it has the same weight as itself, and then the water in the syringe and the air outside weighing equally, the whole is in equilibrium, just as water and quicksilver are in equilibrium when their heights are to each other [reciprocally] as their weights, as we have so often shown in the *Equilibrium of liquids;* and as the water rose only for the reason that the weight of the air forced it to, when it has arrived at that height at which the weight of the air can no longer make it rise, no other cause moving it, it remains at that point.

And whatever the size of the pump, the water always rises to the same height, because liquids do not weigh according to their bulk but according to their height, as we have shown in the *Equilibrium of liquids.*

But if we draw up quicksilver in a syringe, it will rise to a height of two feet, three inches, and five lines, which is precisely the height at which it weighs as much as thirty-one feet of water, because it will weigh as much then as the mass of the air.

And if we draw up oil in a pump, it will rise to about thirty-four feet and no more; because it weighs as much at this height as water at thirty-one feet, and consequently as much as the air; and similarly with all other liquids.

A tube stopped at the top and open at the bottom, having been filled with water, if it has any length we please less than thirty-one feet, all the water will remain suspended in it; because the weight of the mass of the air is capable of holding it there.

But if it is longer than thirty-one feet, the water will fall part way, that is, until it has a height of only thirty-one feet; and then it will remain suspended at this height without falling lower, just as in the *Equilibrium of liquids* we saw that the quicksilver in a tube placed in a tank of water fell part way until it came to rest at the height at which it weighed as much as the water.

But if we were to put in the tube quicksilver instead of water, the quicksilver would fall until it came to rest at the height of two feet, three inches, and five lines, which exactly corresponds to thirty-one feet of water.

And if we slant a little these tubes in which water and quicksilver remain suspended, these liquids will rise until they have returned to their former height, which was diminished by the slanting, because the weight of the air prevails as long as they are below that height and is in equilibrium when they have reached it; which is exactly like what is recorded in the *Treatise on the equilibrium of liquids* of a tube of quicksilver immersed in a tank of water; and if the tube is straightened, the liquids fall again, always to return to the same height.

Thus in a siphon all the water in the higher vessel rises and passes into the lower vessel as long as the leg of the siphon dipping in it is of any length we please less than thirty-one feet; because, as I have said elsewhere, the weight of the air is quite capable of lifting water to this height and holding it suspended there; but as soon as the leg dipping in the higher vessel exceeds this length, the siphon no longer works (that is, the water in the higher vessel no longer rises to the top of the siphon to pass into the other vessel, because the weight of the air cannot lift it higher than thirty-one feet); so that the water divides at the top of the siphon and falls in each leg into the corresponding vessel until it comes to rest at the height of thirty-one feet above each vessel, and remains suspended at this height by the weight of the air which counterbalances it.

If we slant the siphon a little, the water will rise in both legs until it has again reached the height which the slanting had diminished; and if we slant it until the top of the siphon has an elevation of only thirty-one feet above the surface of the higher vessel, the water in the leg dipping in that vessel will be at the top of the siphon, so that it will fall into the other leg; and thus the water in the higher vessel always taking its place, there will be a continuous flow, but in a thin trickle only; and if we slant the siphon more, the water will flow at the full capacity of the tube.

The same thing must be understood of all other liquids, allowance being made for the ratio of their weights.

Thus if we try to open a bellows. as long as we do not use more than a certain amount of force, we shall be unable to do it; but if we pass that point, we shall open it. Now the required force is as follows: if the wings of the bellows are a foot in diameter, there will be needed to open it a force able to lift a vessel filled with water one foot in diameter, like the wings, and thirty-one feet high, which is the height to which water rises in a pump. If the wings are only six inches in diameter, there will be needed to open the bellows a force equal to the weight of the water in a vessel six inches in diameter and thirty-one feet high, and similarly of the rest; so that by hanging to one of the wings a weight equal to that of the water just specified we shall open the bellows, and a lesser weight could not do it, because the weight of the air pressing it is exactly equal to that of thirty-one feet of water.

The same weight will raise the piston of a sealed syringe, and the same weight will separate two polished bodies placed together; so that if they are an inch in diameter, by applying to them a force equal to the weight of thirty-one feet of water one inch in diameter we shall separate them.

CHAPTER 4. *That as the weight of the mass of the air increases when it is more laden with moisture and diminishes when it is less laden, so the effects it produces increase and diminish proportionally.*

Since the weight of the air causes all the effects we are considering and since that weight is not always the same for the same place but constantly varies according to the humidity, its effects should not be always uniform but on the contrary constantly variable; this is confirmed by experiment, which shows that the measure of thirty-one feet of water, which we gave to serve as an example, is not a precise measure always accurate; for water does not rise in pumps exactly to this height and always remain suspended there; on the contrary sometimes it rises to thirty-one and a half feet, then returns to thirty-one feet, then falls again three inches more, then suddenly rises a foot, following the variations of the air, and all that with the same freakishness with which the air passes from murky to clear.

And experiment shows that the same pump lifts water higher at one time than at another by one foot, eight inches. So that a pump, and for the same reason a siphon, can be made of such a height that at one time they will work and at another time they will not, according as the air is more or less laden with moisture or for some other reason weighs more or less; which would make a rather interesting experiment and not too hard if we used quicksilver instead of water, for in that way such long tubes would not be needed.

Hence we are to understand that water remains suspended in tubes at a lesser height at one time than at another and that a bellows is easier to open at one time than at another precisely in the same ratio, and similarly with the other effects; for what is said of one applies exactly to all the rest, each in accordance with its own nature.

CHAPTER 5. *That since the weight of the mass of the air is greater over low places than over high places, so the effects produced by it there are proportionately greater.*

Since the weight of the mass of the air produces all the effects we are considering and since that mass is not the same over every place on the earth because it is greater over the lower places, the effects should be different there too; as indeed experiment confirms, showing that the measure of thirty-one feet I had taken as an example is not the height to which water rises in pumps everywhere in the world; for it rises to different heights in all places not at the same level (the lower the altitude the higher the water rises and the higher the altitude the lower the water rises); so that by experiments made in places differing in altitude by five or six hundred fathoms a difference of four feet, three inches has been found, so that the same pump which lifts water in one place to a height of thirty feet, four inches lifts it, under the same atmospheric conditions, in another place some five hundred fathoms higher only to a height of twenty-six feet, one inch, which constitutes a difference of one-sixth.

The same thing should be understood of all the other effects, each in its own fashion; that is to say, for example, that two polished bodies are more difficult to separate in a valley than on a mountain top, and so on.

But as five hundred fathoms of altitude cause four feet, three inches difference in the height of the water, lesser altitudes make proportionately lesser differences; one hundred fathoms about ten inches, twenty fathoms about two inches, and so on.

The best instrument for observing such variations is a glass tube, stopped at the top, recurved at the bottom, three or four feet long, to which a strip of paper has been pasted, divided into inches and lines; for if we fill it with quicksilver, we shall see that part of the quicksilver will fall and part of it will remain suspended, and we shall be able to notice exactly the point at which it will be suspended; and it will be easy to observe the variations which will take place there because of the varying humidity following upon changes in the weather, and those which will take place through the tube's being carried to a higher altitude; for leaving it in the same place, we shall see that as the weather changes the quicksilver will rise and fall, and we shall see that it will vary from one time to another by one inch, six lines, which correspond exactly to one foot, eight inches of water, which I gave in another chapter for the difference caused by changes in weather.

And carrying the tube from the foot of a mountain to the summit, we shall see that when we have gone up ten fathoms the quicksilver will have fallen close to a line, when we have gone up twenty fathoms it will have fallen two lines, when we have gone up a hundred fathoms it will have fallen nine lines. And as we go down, the quicksilver will rise again by the same amounts.

All this was tested on the Puy de Dôme in Auvergne, as can be seen in the account of that experiment; and these measurements of quicksilver correspond exactly to those we have just given of water.

The same thing is to be understood with respect to the difficulty in opening a bellows, and of the rest.

Wherein we see that exactly the same thing happens in the effects produced by the weight of the air as in those produced by the weight of water; for we saw that a bellows immersed in water and hard to open because of the weight of the water, is the less so the nearer we bring it to the surface; and that the quicksilver in a tube immersed in water remains suspended at a greater or lesser height according as it is more or less deep in the water; and all these effects, whether of the weight of the air or of that of water, are such necessary consequences of the equilibrium of fluids that there is nothing clearer in the world.

CHAPTER 6. *That as the effects of the weight of the mass of the air increase or diminish according as that weight increases or diminishes, they would cease entirely if we were above the air or in a place where there were none.*

Having now seen that the effects hitherto attributed to the horror of the vacuum but actually due to the weight of the air always depend upon its quantity and that as it increases, they increase and as it diminishes, they diminish; and that for this reason we see in the tube filled with quicksilver the quicksilver remains suspended at a height so much the lower as the tube is carried to a higher altitude, because less air is left above it, just as the quicksilver in a tube immersed in water falls as the tube is lifted toward the surface of the water, because less water is left to counterbalance it; we may conclude with assurance that if we carried the tube to the top of the extreme limit of the air and lifted it entirely out of the air's sphere, the quicksilver would fall entirely since there would no longer be any air to counterbalance it, just as the quicksilver in the tube immersed in water falls entirely when we draw the tube entirely out of the water.

The same thing would happen if we could remove all the air from the room in which the experiment was made; for if there were no longer any air weighing upon the recurved end of the tube, we must believe that the quicksilver would fall, no longer having a counterpoise.

But because both of these experiments are impossible, since we cannot go above the air and since we could not live in a room entirely emptied of air, it is sufficient to remove the air, not from the entire room, but only from about the tube's recurved end to keep the air away from it, in order to see if all the quicksilver will fall when there is no longer any air to counterbalance it; and this can easily be done as follows:

We must have a tube recurved at the bottom, closed at the end *A* and open at the end *B*, and another tube, straight throughout, open at both ends, *M* and *N*, but with the end *M* inserted and soldered into the recurved end of the other tube, as in the figure.

We must stop *B*, which is the opening of the recurved end of the first tube, with the finger or otherwise, as with a pig's bladder, and invert the whole tube (that is to say, the two tubes, which actually make only one, since they open into each other), fill it with quicksilver and then put the end A at the top again and the end N in a basin of quicksilver; what will happen is that the quicksilver of the upper tube will fall in its entirety and all of it will be caught in the curved end, unless a part of it flows into the lower tube by the opening at M; but only part of the quicksilver in the lower tube will fall and part of it will remain suspended at a height of from twenty-six to twenty-seven inches, according to the place and time of the experiment. Now the reason for this difference is that the air weighs upon the quicksilver in the basin at the bottom of the lower tube, and accordingly it holds the quicksilver inside suspended and in equilibrium; but it does not weigh on the quicksilver at the recurved end of the upper tube (for the finger or the pig's bladder closing it keeps the air out); so that as there is no air weighing on this part, the quicksilver in the tube is free to fall since nothing holds it up and opposes its falling.

But since nothing is lost in nature, if the quicksilver in the curved end does not feel the weight of the air because the finger stopping the opening keeps it away, the finger itself, by compensation, suffers much pain, for it endures all the weight of the air pressing down from above and nothing holds it up from below; therefore it feels itself pressed against the glass and, as it were, drawn and sucked inside the tube, and a swelling forms, as if under a cupping glass, because the weight of the air pressing our finger, our hand, and our whole body everywhere except at the end of the finger (where it has no access), that part swells and feels pain for the reason just given.

And if we remove our finger from the opening, the quicksilver in the recurved end will suddenly rise in the tube to a height of from twenty-six to twenty-seven inches, because the air suddenly falling on the quicksilver will immediately lift it to the height capable of counterbalancing it, and even, because of the violence of its fall, it lifts the quicksilver a little beyond the limit; but the quicksilver will afterwards fall a little lower and then it will rise again, and after some goings and comings, as of a weight suspended at the end of a string, it will come to rest at a certain height, at which it exactly counterbalances the air.

Whence we see that when the air does not weigh on the quicksilver at the recurved end, all the quicksilver in the tube falls, and that consequently if we had taken the tube to a place where there was no air or, if possible, beyond the air's sphere, all the quicksilver would fall.

Conclusion of the last three chapters.

Whence it may be concluded that as the weight of the air is great, small, or null, so the height to which water rises in the pump is great, small, or null, and that the height is always exactly in proportion to the weight, as effect to cause.

The same thing must be understood with respect to the difficulty of opening a sealed bellows, and so on.

CHAPTER 7. *How far water rises in pumps everywhere on the earth.*

From everything we know it follows that there are as many different measures of the height to which water rises in pumps as there are different conditions of place and weather for taking the measurement; and that thus if we are asked to what height suction pumps lift water in general, we could not give an exact answer to the question, or even to this other: to what height pumps lift water at Paris, unless the state of the air is also specified, since they lift water higher when the air is more laden with moisture; but it is quite possible to say to what height pumps lift water at Paris when the air is most laden, for everything is specified. But without stopping at the different heights to which water is lifted in each place according as the air is more or less laden, I shall take the height of the water when the air carries its mean burden of moisture as the natural height of that place, because it is midway between the two extremes and by knowing that measurement we shall know the other two, because we have only to add or subtract ten inches. Accordingly I shall give the height to which water rises everywhere in the world, whatever the altitude, when the air has its average moisture.

But first it must be understood that in all pumps at the same altitude water rises to exactly the same height (I always mean in the same state of the atmosphere), for since the air has the same height there and consequently the same weight, the weight produces like effects.

And that is why I shall first give the height to which water is raised in places at sea level, because the sea is all exactly at the same level (that is to say, equally distant at all points from the center of the earth), for liquids cannot otherwise come to rest since the higher parts would flow down; and so the height to which we find water rises in pumps at any place whatever on the coast will be common to all places in the world on the coast, and it will be easy to infer from that the height to which water will rise in places higher or lower by ten, twenty, one hundred, two hundred, or five hundred fathoms, since we have given the differences caused by such differences in altitude.

At sea level suction pumps lift water to the height of approximately thirty-one feet, two inches (that is, when the air has its average moisture).

This is the measure common to all places in the world at sea level; whence it follows that a siphon lifts water in those places as long as its shorter leg is less than thirty-one feet, two inches, and that a sealed bellows is opened by the weight of water having that height and the width of its wings; which is in conformity with the general rule. It is easy to know from this to what height water is raised by pumps in places ten fathoms higher; for since I have said that ten fathoms of altitude cause a decrease of one inch in the height to which water rises, it follows that at those places the water rises only to thirty-one feet, one inch.

And in the same way we find that in places twenty fathoms above sea level water rises to only thirty-one feet.

In those one hundred fathoms above sea level water rises to only thirty feet, four inches.

In those with an altitude of two hundred fathoms water rises to twenty-nine feet, six inches.

In those with an altitude of about five hundred fathoms water rises to almost twenty-seven feet.

Similarly we could make observations for the rest. And for places lower than sea level we shall find in the same way the heights to which the water rises by adding, instead of subtracting, the differences caused by these differences in altitude.

Consequences

1. From all this it is easy to see that a pump never lifts water at Paris to thirty-two feet and never lifts it to less than twenty-nine and a half feet.

2. We also see that a siphon whose short leg is thirty-two feet long never works at Paris.

3. That a siphon whose short leg is twenty-nine feet long or less always works at Paris.

4. That at Paris a siphon whose short leg is exactly thirty-one feet long sometimes works and sometimes does not work, depending on the humidity of the air.

5. That a siphon with a short leg twenty-nine feet long always works at Paris and never works in a higher place, such as Clermont in Auvergne.

6. That a siphon ten feet high works everywhere in the world, for there is no mountain high enough to keep it from working; and that a siphon fifty feet long works nowhere in the world, for there is no cave deep enough to make a sufficient depth of air to raise water thus high.

7. That water rises in the pumps at Dieppe, when the air has its average moisture, to thirty-one feet, two inches, as I have said, and when the air is most laden to thirty-two feet; that it rises in pumps on mountains five hundred fathoms above the sea, when the air has its mean burden of moisture, to twenty-six feet, eleven inches, and when it is least laden to twenty-six feet, one inch; so that there is a difference between this height and that occurring at Dieppe when the air is most laden of five feet, eleven inches, which is almost one-fourth of the height occurring on mountains.

8. Just as we see that in all places at the same level water rises to the same height and that it rises less in those of greater elevation, so, conversely, if we see that water rises to the same height in two different places, we can conclude they have the same altitude, and if it does not rise to the same height, we can judge by the difference how much higher one place is than the other; which is a way of finding the altitudes of places, however far apart, quite exactly and very easily; since instead of using a suction pump, which would be hard to make thus long, we need only take a tube three or four feet in length, filled with quicksilver and stopped at the top, such as we have often spoken of, and see at what height the quicksilver remains suspended, for its height corresponds perfectly to the height to which water rises in pumps.

9. We also see from this that the degrees of heat are not accurately marked in the best thermometers; since all the different heights at which the water remains suspended have always been attributed to the rarefaction or condensation of the air inside the tube, but we learn from these experiments that changes in the outside air, that is, in the mass of the air, have a great deal to do with them.

I pass over a large number of other consequences which follow from this new knowledge, as for example the means it gives us of finding out the exact extent of the air's sphere and of the vapors called the atmosphere; since by taking exact observations for every hundred fathoms and noting the differences caused by the first hundred, by the second hundred, and by all the remaining hundreds we would be able to determine accurately the entire height of the air. But I leave all that to devote myself to what is essential to the subject.

CHAPTER 8. *How much each place in the world is pressed by the weight of the mass of the air.*

We learn from these experiments that since the weight of the air and the weight of the water in pumps are in equilibrium, they weigh exactly the same, and that by thus knowing the height to which water rises everywhere in the world we know at the same time how much each place is pressed by the weight of the air above it, and consequently:

That places beside the sea are pressed by the weight of the air above them, up to the top of its sphere, exactly as much as if instead of this air there were substituted a column of water thirty-one feet, two inches in height.

Places with an altitude of ten fathoms as much as if they carried thirty-one feet, one inch of water.

Places with an altitude of five hundred fathoms as much as if they carried twenty-six feet, eleven inches of water, and similarly of the rest.

CHAPTER 9. *How much the entire mass of all the air in the world weighs.*

We learn from these experiments that the air at sea level has the same weight as water at a height of thirty-one feet, two inches; but because the air weighs less on places above sea level and therefore does not weigh the same on all places on the earth, and even weighs everywhere differently, we cannot calculate a fixed measure which will show how much all places in the world, reduced to an average altitude, are pressed by the air; but we can arrive at a measure by conjecture approaching very closely to the true measure, as for example we may assume that all places on the earth in general, reduced to an average altitude and considered as equally pressed by the air, are as much pressed as if they carried thirty-one feet of water; and it is certain that the error in this assumption is not half a foot of water.

Now we have seen that the air over mountains five hundred fathoms high weighs as much as water at the height of twenty-six feet, eleven inches.

And consequently all the air from sea level to the mountain tops five hundred fathoms high weighs as much as water at the height of four feet, one inch, and since that is about one-seventh of the entire height, it is obvious that the air lying between the sea and these mountains is about one-seventh of the entire mass of the air.

We learn from these same experiments that the heavy vapors in the air, when it is most charged with them, weigh as much as water at a height of one foot, eight inches, since to counterbalance themselves, they raise the water in the pumps to this height above the height at which the water already counterbalanced the weight of the air; so that if all the vapors above a region were reduced to water, as happens when they are converted to rain, they could produce only one foot, eight inches of water over that region. And if storms sometimes occur in which the rainfall comes to a greater height, it is because the wind carries vapor there from neighboring regions.

We also see from this that if the whole sphere of the air were pressed and compressed against the earth by a force which, pushing it from above, reduced it to the smallest possible compass below and reduced it to water, it would then have a height of only thirty-one feet.

And consequently that we must consider the whole mass of the air, in its present free state, as if it had formerly been like a mass of water thirty-one feet deep about the entire earth, which should have been extremely rarefied and dilated and converted into this state we call air, in which it occupies more space, to be sure, but keeps exactly the same weight as thirty-one feet of water.

And as there would be nothing easier than to calculate how many pounds all the water surrounding the earth to a height of thirty-one feet would weigh and as a child who knows addition and subtraction could do it, we should find by the same calculation how many pounds all the air there is weighs, since it is the same thing; and if we work it out, we shall find the weight of the mass of the air is approximately eight millions of millions of millions of pounds.

I wanted to give myself this pleasure, and this is how I did the reckoning.

I supposed that the diameter of a circle is to its circumference as 7 is to 22.

I supposed that when the diameter of a sphere is multiplied by the circumference of its great circle, the product is the area of the spherical surface.

We know that the circumference of the earth has been divided into 360 degrees. This division was arbitrary, for it could have been divided into more or less than 360, if desired, as could also the celestial circles.

It has been found that each of the degrees contains 50,000 fathoms.

Leagues in the neighborhood of Paris are 2,500 fathoms, and consequently there are 20 leagues to a degree; some count 25, but they also give only 2,000 fathoms to the league, which comes to the same thing.

Each fathom has 6 feet.

A cubic foot of water weighs 72 pounds.

Whereupon it is very easy to make the desired calculation.

For since the great circle, or circumference, of the earth is 360 degrees,

The distance around it is, therefore, 7,200 leagues.

And by the ratio of the circumference to the diameter its diameter will be 2,291 leagues.

Therefore multiplying the diameter of the earth by the circumference of its great circle, we shall find that its spherical surface has 16,495,200 square leagues.

That is to say 103,095,000,000,000 square fathoms.

That is to say 3,711,420,000,000,000 square feet.

And since a cubic foot of water weighs 72 pounds

It follows that a prism of water with a base of 1 square foot and 31 feet high weighs 2,232 pounds.

Therefore if the earth were covered with water to a height of thirty-one feet, there would be as many prisms of water thirty-one feet high as there are square feet in its surface (I know full well they would not be prisms but sectors of a sphere, and I purposely neglect to be precise).

And consequently the earth would carry as many units of water, each weighing 2,232 pounds, as it has square feet in its surface.

Therefore all this mass of water would weigh 8,283,889,440,000,000,000 pounds.

Therefore the mass of all the air there is has this same weight of 8,238,889,440,000,000,000 pounds.

That is to say, eight million million million, two hundred eighty-three thousand eight hundred eighty-nine million million, four hundred forty thousand million pounds.

Conclusion of the two preceding treatises

I have recorded in general in the preceding treatises all the effects which it has hitherto been believed nature produces to avoid a vacuum; wherein I have shown it is absolutely false that they occur for this imaginary reason. And I have demonstrated on the contrary by arguments and experiments absolutely convincing that the weight of the mass of the air is their true and only cause. So that it is now certain there is no effect in the whole of nature produced by her to avoid a vacuum.

After that it will not be difficult to show that nature does not abhor a vacuum, for this way of speaking is improper, since created nature, which is here in question, being inanimate is not capable of passion; accordingly such speech is metaphorical, and nothing more is meant by it than that nature makes the same efforts to avoid the vacuum that she would make if she abhorred it; so that in the opinion of those who speak in this fashion it is the same thing to say that nature abhors a vacuum and to say that nature makes great efforts to prevent a vacuum. Therefore, since I have shown she does nothing to avoid the vacuum, it follows that she does not abhor it, for to go on with the same figure, as we say of a man that he is indifferent to a thing if we never observe in any of his actions a movement of desire or aversion for this thing, so we must say of nature that she is perfectly indifferent to the vacuum since we never see her doing anything either to seek it or to avoid it (I always mean by the word *vacuum* a space empty of all bodies perceptible to sense).

It is perfectly true (and this is what led the ancients astray) that water rises in a pump when there is no opening for the air to get in and there would therefore be a vacuum if the water did not follow the plunger, and also that water no longer rises as soon as there are cracks through which the air can enter to fill the pump; whence it seems the water rises only to prevent a vacuum since it rises only when there would be a vacuum.

It is certain likewise that a bellows is hard to open when its apertures are so carefully stopped that the air cannot get in and that therefore if it were opened, there would be a vacuum, whereas this resistance ceases when the air can enter to fill the bellows, so that resistance is met only when there would be a vacuum; whence it seems that resistance occurs only from fear of a vacuum.

Finally it is certain that all bodies in general make great efforts to follow each other and to keep united whenever there would be a vacuum between them if they were separated, and never otherwise; and that is why the conclusion has been drawn that their adhesion comes from the fear of the vacuum.

But to show the weakness of this inference I shall make use of the following example: when a bellows is in the water in the way I have often described so that the tip of the tube, which I suppose to be twenty feet long, is out of the water and exposed to the air and the apertures which are in one of the wings are carefully stopped to keep the water out, we know that the bellows is opened with difficulty, and with the greater difficulty the more water there is above it, and that if we remove the stoppers from the airholes and the water is free to come in, the resistance ceases.

If we wanted to argue in the same way about this effect as about the others, we should say: when the apertures are stopped and therefore, if the bellows were opened, air would come in by the tube, it is opened with difficulty, and when the water can get in to fill the bellows instead of air, the resistance ceases. Therefore since the bellows resists when air would enter and not otherwise, the resistance comes from its horror of the air.

Everybody would laugh at this inference because there can be another cause for the bellows' resistance. And indeed it is obvious that we could not open it without raising the water since the water we would displace in opening it could not enter the body of the bellows, and therefore it would have to find room for itself elsewhere and would have to raise the whole mass, and that is what causes the resistance; which does not occur when the bellows has apertures through which the water may enter, for then, whether we open or close the bellows, the water neither rises nor falls, because the water displaced enters the bellows as fast as it is displaced; accordingly the bellows is opened without resistance.

That is perfectly clear, and consequently we must consider that the bellows cannot be opened without two things happening: one, that air certainly does enter, the other, that the mass of the water is lifted; and it is the latter which causes the resistance and the former is quite unrelated to it, although it takes place at the same time.

Let us speak in the same way about the difficulty experienced in opening in the air a bellows with all its apertures stopped; if it were forcibly opened, two things would happen: one, that there certainly would be a vacuum, the other, that it would be necessary to lift and hold up the whole mass of the air; and it is the latter which causes the resistance encountered and the former has nothing to do with it; accordingly the resistance increases and diminishes in proportion to the weight of the air, as I have shown.

The same thing must be understood of the resistance encountered in separating all bodies between which there would be a vacuum; for the air cannot get in, otherwise there would not be a vacuum. And so we could not separate them without lifting and holding up the entire mass of the air, and that is what causes the resistance.

There you have the true cause of the adhesion of bodies between which there would be a vacuum, which we have remained so long without knowing because we have remained so long in false opinions, from which we have only gradually emerged; so that there have been three different periods in which different views have been held.

There were three errors in the world which absolutely prevented our knowing the true cause of the adhesion of bodies.

The first error is that almost from the beginning the air was believed to have levity, because the ancient authors said so and because those whose profession it is to believe them followed them blindly and would have remained eternally of that opinion if abler persons had not freed them from it by the force of experiment; so that it was not possible to think the weight of the air was the cause of the adhesion of bodies when the air was thought not to have any weight.

The second error is that it was imagined that the elements do not weigh when in themselves, for no other reason than that we do not feel the weight of water when we are in it and that a bucket of water is easy to lift as long as it is still there and only begins to make its weight felt when it leaves the water; as if these effects could come from no other cause or rather as if this cause were not out of the question, there being no reason to believe that the water we draw in a bucket has weight when it is taken out of the water and no longer has any when it is poured back in, that it loses its weight when confounded with the rest and regains it when it quits the level of the water. Strange ways that men seek to conceal their ignorance! Because they could not understand why we do not feel the weight of the water and were unwilling to admit it, they said it has no weight in water, to satisfy their vanity by the overthrow of truth, and in this way it became an accepted opinion; and that is why as long as men clung to this fancy it was impossible to believe that the weight of the air was the cause of these effects; since even if they had known that the air is heavy, they would still have said that it does not weigh when in itself, and therefore they would not have believed that it produced any effect by its weight.

This is why I showed in the *Equilibrium of liquids* that water weighs when in itself as much as when outside, and I explained there why in spite of that weight a bucket is easy to lift in water and why we do not feel its weight; and in the *Treatise on the weight of the mass of the air* I showed the same thing with respect to the air in order to clear up all doubts.

The third error is of a different sort; it is not with respect to the air, but has to do with the effects they attributed to the horror of the vacuum, about which they had completely false ideas.

For they imagined that a pump lifts water not only to ten or twenty feet, which is perfectly true, but even to fifty, a hundred, a thousand, and to any height desired, without limit.

They also believed that it is not only hard to separate two polished bodies placed together, but absolutely impossible, that an angel could not do it, nor any created force, with a hundred exaggerations too idle to mention; and similarly of the rest.

This is an error of fact so ancient that we do not know its origin; even Heron, one of the first and most excellent authors to write on the raising of water, expressly states, as a thing that may not be doubted, that the water of a river can be carried over a mountain to be poured into the valley on the other side, provided it be a little lower, by means of a siphon placed on the summit with its legs extending down the sides, one in the river, the other in the next valley; and he asserts that the water will rise from the river to the mountain to redescend into the other valley, whatever the height of the mountain.

All those who have written of these matters have said the same thing; and even all our fountain builders still claim today that they can make suction pumps which will raise water sixty feet, if desired.

Not that either Heron or these authors or these artisans, and still less the philosophers, carried their experiments very far, for if they had tried to raise water only forty feet, they would have found it impossible; but they had seen suction pumps and siphons six feet, ten feet, twelve feet long, which did not fail to work, and they had never seen the water fail to rise in all the experiments they had happened to make. So that they did not imagine there was a certain point beyond which it would be otherwise. They thought they were dealing with a necessity of nature, whose order could not be changed; and since they believed the water rose because of an invincible horror of the vacuum, they were sure it would continue to rise, as it had begun, without ever ceasing; and in this way inferring from what they did see to what they did not see, they gave out both as equally true.

And it was believed with such certainty that the philosophers have made of it one of the chief principles of their science and the foundation of their treatises on the vacuum. It is laid down every day in the classroom and everywhere in the world, and as far back as our written records go all men have held to this opinion, without anyone's ever having opposed it until now.

Perhaps this example will open the eyes of those who dare not think an opinion doubtful if it has from all time been universally accepted by all men, since simple artisans have been capable of convicting of error all the great men called philosophers. For Galileo declares in his *Dialogues*[1] that he learned from the Italian fountain makers that pumps lift water only to a certain height, after which he tested it himself; and others afterwards made the experiment in Italy, and since then in France with quicksilver, more conveniently, but only showing the same thing in several different ways.

Before this was known, it could not be demonstrated that the weight of the air was what raised water in pumps, for that weight, since it is limited, could not produce an infinite effect.

But all these experiments did not suffice to show that the air produces these effects, because although they freed us from one error, they left us in another. For certainly it was learned from all these experiments that water rises only to a certain height, but it was not learned that water rose higher in places of lower altitude. It was thought on the contrary that it always rose to the same height, that is was everywhere invariable; and since the weight of the air never occurred to anyone, it was imagined that the nature of the pump is such that it lifts water to a certain limited height and no further. Accordingly Galileo considered it as the pump's natural height, and called it *la altessa limitatissima* [the fixed elevation].

How then could it have been imagined that this height was variable according to the variety of places? Certainly that was not likely; and yet this last error made it still impossible to prove that the weight of the air is the cause of these effects, for since that weight is greater at the foot of a mountain than at the top, it is manifest that the effects will be proportionately greater there.

That is why I came to the conclusion that we could arrive at the proof only by making the experiment in two places differing from each other in altitude by four or five hundred fathoms. And I selected for this purpose the Puy de Dôme in Auvergne for the reason I gave in a little pamphlet I had printed as early as the year 1648, as soon as the experiment had been successfully made.

This experiment, having revealed that water rises in pumps to quite different heights according to the variety of place and weather and that its height is always proportional to the weight of the air, perfected our knowledge of these effects; it put all doubts to rest; it showed their true cause; it established that it is not the horror of the vacuum; and in short it supplied all the illumination anyone could wish on this subject.

Let it be explained now, if possible, otherwise than by the weight of the air why suction pumps lift water less high by one-quarter on the Puy de Dôme in Auvergne than at Dieppe.

[1]See Galileo: *Two New Sciences*, pp. 137-8

Why the same siphon lifts water and transfers it at Dieppe and not at Paris.

Why two polished bodies placed together are more easily pulled apart on a belfry than in the street.

Why a bellows with all its apertures stopped is easier to open on top of a house than in the yard.

Why, when the air is more laden with moisture, the piston of a sealed syringe is harder to draw up.

Finally why all these effects are always proportional to the weight of the air, as effect to cause.

Does nature abhor a vacuum more on mountains than in valleys, more in wet weather than in clear weather? Does she not hate it equally on a belfry, in an attic, and in the yard?

Let all the disciples of Aristotle bring together all the strongest arguments there are in the writings of their master and of his commentators to account for these things by the horror of the vacuum, if they can; if not, let them recognize that experiments are the true masters to follow in physics, that the experiment made on the mountains overturned the universal belief everywhere held that nature abhors a vacuum and opened up this knowledge which can nevermore be forgotten, that nature has no horror of the vacuum, that she does nothing to avoid it, and that the weight of the mass of the air is the true cause of all the effects hitherto attributed to that imaginary cause.

ON GEOMETRICAL DEMONSTRATION

(*On the Geometrical Mind*)

1. We may have three main objects in the study of truth: first, to find it when we are seeking it; second, to demonstrate it after we have found it; third, to distinguish it from error by examining it.

I shall not speak of the first; I shall deal especially with the second, which includes the third. For if we know how to prove the truth, we shall know at the same time how to distinguish it from error, since by examining whether the proof we give conforms to the rules we know we shall find out whether the truth has been exactly demonstrated.

Geometry, which excels in all three of these ways, has expounded the art of finding unknown truths. This art, which is called analysis, would be useless to discuss after all the excellent books that have been written about it.

The art of demonstrating truths already found and of making them so clear that their proofs cannot be refuted is the only art I wish to give. To that end I have only to expound the method used by geometry, which geometry itself teaches perfectly by example without ever putting it into words. And because this art consists of two main parts, the proving of each proposition individually and the arranging of all the propositions in the best order, my treatise will have two sections, of which one will contain the rules of geometrical demonstrations, that is, scientific and perfect demonstrations, and the other will contain the rules of geometrical order, that is, scientific and complete order; so that the two sections taken together will include everything necessary for guiding the reason in proving truths and in distinguishing them from errors. My intention is to give these rules in their entirety.

SECTION 1. *Concerning the method of geometrical demonstrations, that is, scientific and perfect demonstrations*

I can give no clearer idea of the procedure we should follow to make our demonstrations convincing than by expounding the method observed in geometry.

But first I must give the idea of a method still more eminent and complete, but a method to which man could never attain. For what goes beyond geometry goes beyond man. Nevertheless I must say something about it although it is impossible to put it into practice.

This true method, which would produce demonstrations of supreme excellence if it were possible to attain to it, would consist of two main rules: to use no term of which we had not already clearly explained the meaning, and never to put forward any proposition unless demonstrated by truths already known; that is, in a word, to define all the terms and to prove all the propositions. But to follow the very order I am expounding I must state what I understand by definition.

Geometry recognizes only those definitions which logicians call nominal, impositions of a name, that is, on things clearly designated by terms perfectly well known. I speak of such definitions only.

Their usefulness and function is to clarify discourse and to make it more concise by expressing by the name we impose what would otherwise require several terms, in such a way however that the name imposed remains deprived of every other meaning, if it has any, keeping only that one to which it has been uniquely assigned. For example, if we need to distinguish among the numbers those which can be divided into two equal parts from those which cannot, in order to avoid the frequent repetition of this condition we give it a name as follows: I call every number that can be divided into two equal parts an even number.

This is a geometrical definition, because after a thing, in this case every number that can be divided into two equal parts, has been clearly pointed out, it is given a name emptied of all other meaning, if it has any, that it may take the meaning of the thing pointed out.

Whence it is evident that there is great freedom of definition and that definitions are never subject to contradiction, for nothing is more permissible than to give whatever name we please to a thing we have clearly pointed out. Only we must be careful not to take advantage of our freedom to impose names by giving the same name to two different things.

Not that it is inadmissible to do so if we avoid confusion by not extending the consequences of one to the other.

But if we fall into this vice, we can apply to it a most sure and infallible remedy, which is to substitute in the mind the definition in place of the thing defined and always to have such an awareness of the definition that every time we speak, for example, of an even number, we mean precisely a number that can be divided into two equal parts, and that we understand these two things as being so inseparably joined in thought that as soon as one of them occurs in discourse the mind at once attaches the other to it. For geometers and all those who proceed scientifically impose names on things only for concision of discourse and not to impoverish or alter the idea of the subjects of discourse. And they expect the mind always to supplement with the whole definition the short terms, which they use only to avoid the confusion caused by a multitude of words.

Nothing acts more quickly and more effectively against the surprise attacks of captious sophists than this method, which we must always have ready for use, and which alone suffices to banish every kind of difficulty and equivocation.

With these things well understood, I return to my account of the true order, which consists, as I was saying, in defining everything and in proving everything.

Certainly this method would be beautiful, but it is absolutely impossible. For it is evident that the first terms we wished to define would presuppose others for their explication, and that similarly the first propositions we wished to prove would suppose others that preceded them. And thus it is clear we should never arrive at the first propositions.

Accordingly, as we proceed ever further with our investigations, we come of necessity to primitive words which can no longer be defined and to principles so clear that it is no longer possible to find others more clear for their demonstration. Whence it is apparent that men are naturally and inevitably powerless to deal with any science whatsoever in an absolutely perfect order.

But it does not follow that we should abandon every kind of order. For there is one, the order of geometry, which is indeed inferior in that it is less convincing but not in that it is less certain. It does not define everything and does not prove everything, and in this it yields to the perfect order. But it assumes only things clear and invariant by the natural light, and that is why it is perfectly true, nature supporting it in default of discourse. This order, the most perfect possessed by man, does not consist either in defining everything and proving everything or in defining nothing and proving nothing; but it consists in holding to the mean of not defining things clear and understood by all men and defining all the rest, of not proving all the things known by men and proving all the rest. They sin equally against this order who undertake to define everything and prove everything and who fail to define and prove those things which are not self-evident.

This is perfectly illustrated by geometry. It does not define space, time, motion, number, equality, or their like, which are very numerous, because these terms point out so naturally the things they signify to those who understand the language that whatever clarification we might want to give would contribute more obscurity than instruction. For nothing is more ineffectual than the discourse of those who try to define these primitive words. What need is there, for example, to explain what we mean by the word *man*? Are we not sufficiently aware of what the thing is we wish to designate by this term? And what help did Plato think he was giving us by saying that man was a two-legged animal without feathers? As if the idea of man I naturally have and cannot express were not clearer and more certain than that given me by his useless and even ridiculous explanation, since a man by losing his two legs does not lose his humanity and a capon by losing his feathers does not take on humanity.

There are even those who go to the absurdity of explaining a word by the word itself. I know of some who have defined light in this way: "Light is a luminary motion of luminous bodies," as if we could understand the words *luminary* and *luminous* without understanding the word *light* [*lumière*].

We cannot undertake to define being without falling into this absurdity, for we cannot define any word without beginning with these words *it is*, either explicitly or implicitly. Therefore to define being we would have to say *it is*, and thus use the word defined in the definition.

It is sufficiently clear from this that there are words incapable of definition. And if nature had not made up for this defect by giving a like idea to all men, all our expressions would be confused; whereas we make use of them with the same assurance and the same certainty we should have if they had been explained in a perfectly unambiguous way, because nature itself has given us, without words, a clearer understanding of them than we gain through art with all our explanations.

Not that all men have the same idea of the essence of those things I say it is impossible and useless to define.

For, to take an example, time is of this kind. Who can define it? And why try, since all men know what we mean when we speak of time, without further designation? There are nonetheless many different opinions as to the essence of time. Some say that it is the motion of a created thing; others, the measure of motion, etc. Therefore it is not the nature of these things that I say is known by all; it is simply the relation between the name and the thing, so that at the expression *time* everyone considers the same object (which is sufficient to make it unnecessary to define this term) although afterwards, looking into the nature of time, we may come to have different opinions when we have set ourselves to thinking about it. For definitions are made only to point out the things named and not to reveal their nature.

Not that we may not call by the name *time* the motion of a created thing, for, as I was just saying, in nothing is there more freedom than in definitions. But as a result of this definition there will be two things called by the name *time*: one is what everybody naturally understands by this word and what all who speak our language name with this term; the other will be the motion of a created thing, for this too will be called by that name in accordance with the new definition. We shall have, therefore, to avoid ambiguity and to keep the consequences separate. For it will not follow that what we naturally understand by the word *time* is in fact the motion of a created thing. We were free to give these two things the same name, but we shall not therefore be free to make them coincide in nature as well as in name.

Thus if the proposition is put forward: "Time is the motion of a created thing," we must ask what is meant by the word *time*, whether, that is, it keeps its usual and commonly accepted meaning or whether it has been emptied of that meaning to receive for this occasion, as its meaning, the motion of a created thing. If it has been deprived of all other meaning, the statement cannot be contradicted, and it will be an arbitrary definition with the result, as I have said, that there will be two things having the same name. But if it has been allowed to keep its usual meaning and nevertheless it is maintained that what this word means is the motion of a created thing, the statement can be contradicted. It is no longer an arbitrary definition; it is a proposition requiring proof unless it is evident of itself, in which case it will be a principle and an axiom but never a definition, because in this statement it is not understood that the word *time* signifies the same thing as the words, the *motion of a created thing*, but it is understood that what is meant by the term *time* is this supposed motion.

If I had not known how necessary it is that this should be perfectly understood and how, in familiar speech as in that of science, occasions like the one I have given as an example constantly arise, I should not have lingered over it. But it seems to me, from my experience of the confusion of disputes, that it is impossible to go too thoroughly into that exactness of mind for the sake of which I am writing this whole treatise more than for the subject I deal with in it.

For how many people are there who think they have defined time when they have said that it is the measure of motion, leaving it meanwhile its usual meaning!

And yet they have made a proposition and not a definition. How many are there likewise who think they have defined motion when they have said: *Motus nec simpliciter actus nec mera potentia est, sed actus entis in potentia!* And nevertheless if they let the word *motion* keep its usual meaning, as they do, it is not a definition but a proposition; and in this way confounding the definitions they call nominal, which are the true definitions, arbitrary, permissible, and geometrical, with those they call real, which are really propositions by no means arbitrary but subject to contradiction, they take the liberty of making the latter as well as the former; and each defining the same things in his own fashion by a freedom which is as forbidden in this kind of definition as it is permitted in the first, they mix up everything, and losing all order and all light, they lose themselves and wander in a maze of difficulties inexplicable.

We shall never get into such trouble if we follow the order of geometry. That wise science is very far from defining such primitive words as space, time, motion, equality, majority, decrease, all, and those others which the generality of men understand without explanation. But with the exception of these the remaining terms used by geometry are so clarified and defined that we have no need of a dictionary to understand any one of them, so that in a word all these terms are perfectly intelligible either by the natural light or by the definitions given.

This is the way geometry avoids all those vices which may be encountered in connection with the first point, which is to define only those things that need to be defined. It observes the same conduct with respect to the second point, which is to prove those propositions that are not evident. For when geometry has reached the first truths that can be known, it stops there and requires that they be granted since it has nothing clearer to prove them with; so that all the propositions of geometry are perfectly demonstrated either by the natural light or by proofs.

Whence it is that if this science does not define and demonstrate everything, it is only because it is impossible for us to do so. But since nature supplies everything not given by the science, the order of that science, though it does not give a superhuman perfection, has all the perfection men are capable of. It seemed to me fitting at the very beginning of the treatise to give this. . . .

Perhaps it will be thought strange that geometry cannot define any of the things that are its principal objects; for it can define neither motion nor numbers nor space, and yet these are the three things it particularly considers and in accordance with whose investigation it takes the three different names of mechanics, arithmetic, geometry, this last word belonging both to the genus and to the species.

But we shall feel no surprise if we observe that, this admirable science concerning itself only with the simplest things, the very quality which makes them worthy of being its objects makes them incapable of definition; so that the lack of definition is rather a perfection than a defect because it does not come from their obscurity but on the contrary from their extreme evidence, which is such that although it is not so convincing as a demonstration, it is fully as certain. Geometry supposes then that we know what thing is meant by the words: *motion, number, space*; and without stopping uselessly to define them it penetrates their nature and lays bare their marvelous properties.

These three things, which comprise the entire universe, in accordance with the words: *Deus fecit omnia in pondere, in numero et mensura*, are reciprocally and necessarily related. For we cannot imagine a motion without something which moves, and this thing being one, that unity is the origin of all number. Finally, since motion is impossible without space, we see that these three things are contained in the first. Even time is included there too, for motion and time are correlative (fast and slow, which differentiate motion, having a necessary reference to time).

Thus there are properties common to everything, the knowledge of which opens the mind to the greatest marvels of nature.

The most important is constituted by the two infinites which are found everywhere, the infinitely great and the infinitely small.

For however fast a motion may be, we can conceive a faster, and make that still faster, and thus forever to infinity without ever reaching a motion so fast that we can no longer add to it. And on the contrary, however slow a motion may be, we can make it slower, and that still slower, and so to infinity without ever reaching such a degree of slowness that we cannot still descend to an infinity of lower degrees without falling into rest.

Similarly, however great a number may be, we can conceive a greater, and again a greater than that, and so to infinity without ever reaching one which can no longer be increased. And on the contrary, however small a number may be, such as $1/100$ or $1/10,000$, we can still conceive a smaller, and keep on to infinity without reaching zero or nothing.

However great a space may be, we can conceive a greater, and again a still greater, and so to infinity without ever reaching one which can no longer be increased. And on the contrary, however small a space may be, we can still consider a smaller, and keep on to infinity without ever reaching an indivisible space which no longer has any extension.

It is the same with time. We can always conceive a greater without a last, and a lesser without reaching an instant, a pure nothing of duration.

Which is saying, in a word, that whatever motion, whatever number, whatever space, whatever time we take, there is always a greater and a lesser, so that they all keep between nothing and infinity, being always infinitely distant from these extremes.

None of these truths can be demonstrated, and yet they are the foundations and the principles of geometry. But since the cause that makes them incapable of demonstration is not their obscurity but on the contrary their extreme evidence, this lack of proof is not a defect but rather a perfection.

Whence we see that geometry can neither define its objects nor prove its principles, but for the sole and favorable reason that both have by nature an extreme clarity, which is more powerfully convincing to reason than any discourse.

For what is more evident than this truth, that any number whatsoever can be increased? Can it not be doubled? That the speed of a motion can be doubled, and that a space likewise can be doubled? And also who can doubt that any number whatsoever can be divided in half, and its half again divided in half? For could that half be nothing? And how could these two halves, which would be two zeros, make a number? In the same way cannot the speed of a motion, however slow, be cut down by half so that it will traverse the same space in double the time; and how could it be that these two half-speeds, which would be two rests, should together make the first speed? Finally cannot a space, however small, be cut in two, and its halves again cut? And how could it be that these halves should be indivisible without any extension, these halves which joined together made the first extension?

Man has no natural knowledge prior to this knowledge and surpassing it in clarity. Nevertheless, that there may be an example of everything, we find minds excellent in every other respect shocked by these infinites and in no way able to accept them.

I have never known a man who thought a space could not be increased. But I have come across some, and very clever too, who maintained that a space could be divided into two indivisible parts, whatever absurdity might be involved. I tried hard to find the cause of this darkness in them, and I discovered there was only one main cause, which is that they could not conceive an infinitely divisible content, whence they conclude that it is not infinitely divisible.

It is a disease natural to man to believe that he possesses the truth directly, and this is the reason he is always inclined to deny whatever he cannot understand. Whereas in fact he naturally knows nothing but error and should accept as true only those things whose contradictory appears to him to be false. Consequently, whenever a proposition is inconceivable, we must suspend our judgment and not deny it for that reason, but examine its contradictory; and if we find this manifestly false, we may boldly affirm the original statement, however incomprehensible it is. Let us apply this rule to our subject.

There is no geometer who does not believe that space is infinitely divisible. One can no more be a geometer without this principle than one can be a man without a soul. And yet there is no geometer who understands an infinite division. We are sure of that truth only for the reason, certainly sufficient, that we perfectly grasp the falsity of the statement that by dividing a space we can reach an indivisible part, a part, that is, having no extension.

For what is more absurd than to maintain that by continuing to divide a space we finally arrive at a division such that when we divide it in half, each of the halves remains indivisible and without any extension at all, and that thus these two nothings of extension should together make an extension? For I should like to ask those who have this idea whether they distinctly conceive of two indivisibles as touching. If they touch everywhere, they are only one self-same thing; and therefore the two together are indivisible. If they do not touch everywhere, they touch only in part; therefore they have parts; therefore they are not indivisible. But if they confess, as indeed they do when we press them, that their proposition is as inconceivable as the other, let them recognize that it is not by our capacity to conceive these things that we should judge of their truth, since though the two contradictories are both inconceivable, it is nevertheless necessarily certain that one of the two is true.

But to these imaginary difficulties, related only to our weakness, let them oppose these natural insights and solid truths: if it were true that space is composed of a certain finite number of indivisibles, it would follow that of two spaces, each a square (that is to say, having all its sides equal and similar) but one double the other, one would contain a number of these indivisibles double the number of the other. Let them keep this consequence well in mind, and then let them practise making squares out of points until they have found two of which one has double the points of the other, and then I shall make all the geometers in the world give place to them. But if this is naturally impossible, that is, if there is an invincible impossibility in making squares out of points of which one shall have double the points of the other, as I would demonstrate in this very place if it were worth the time, let them draw the conclusion.

And to comfort them in certain difficulties they would find, as in conceiving a space having an infinity of divisibles (in view of its being traversed in so short a time, during which time that infinity of divisibles would have been traversed), we must warn them that they must not compare things so disproportionate to each other as are the infinity of divisibles and the short time in which they are traversed, but that they should compare the whole of space with the whole of time, and the infinite divisibles of space with the infinite instants of time; and thus they will find we traverse an infinity of divisibles in an infinity of instants, and a little space in a little time, and in this there is no longer the disproportion that had overwhelmed them.

Finally, if it seems strange to them that a small space should have as many parts as a large space, let them also understand that they are proportionately smaller, and let them look at the heavens through a little pane of glass that they may grow familiar with this knowledge by seeing each part of the sky in each part of the glass. But if they cannot comprehend that parts so small as to be imperceptible to us can be divided into as many parts as can the heavens, there is no better remedy than to have them look at these delicate points through glasses which magnify each of them into a prodigious mass. Whence they will easily conceive that with the aid of another lens still more skilfully cut these points could be magnified to equal that firmament whose extent they wonder at. And thus these objects now appearing to them as very easily divisible, let them remember that nature is infinitely more powerful that art. For who has told them in fine that these lenses have changed the natural size of the objects or whether they have not on the contrary reëstablished their true size, changed and shrunk by the shape of our eye as by glasses that make smaller?

It is a nuisance to stop for these trifles, but there are times for being childish.

It is enough to say to heads that are clear in this matter that two nothings of extension cannot make an extension. But because there are some who claim to escape from the light of this truth by the wonderful reply that two nothings of extension can just as well make an extension as two units, neither of which is a number, can when brought together make a number, we must reply to them that they could in the same way object that 20,000 men make an army although no one of them is an army, that 1,000 houses make a city though no one of them is a city, or that the parts make the whole though no one of them is the whole, or, to stay within the comparison of numbers, that two dyads make a tetrad and ten decades a century though a dyad is not a tetrad and a decade is not a century. But it is muddleheaded to confuse by comparisons so unequal the unchanging nature of things with their names, which are free, arbitrary, and dependent upon the caprice of those who gave them. For it is clear that to facilitate discourse we have given the name of army to 20,000 men, that of city to several houses, that of decade to ten units, and that from this freedom arise the names *unit*, *dyad*, *tetrad*, *decade*, *century*, different by the dictates of fancy, although the things referred to are actually of the same kind by their invariable nature and are all related to each other in such a way that they differ only by more and less in spite of the fact that, because of their names, a dyad is not a tetrad, nor a house a city any more than a city is a house. But again although a house is not a city, it is not nevertheless a nothing of a city. There is a great difference between not being a thing and being a nothing of it.

For in order that we may understand the matter thoroughly, we must know that the only reason why the unit is not in the class of numbers is that Euclid and the first writers on arithmetic, having several properties to give belonging to all numbers but the unit, in order to avoid repeating that such and such a condition obtains for all numbers but the unit, excluded the unit from the meaning of the word *number* in accordance with the freedom we have already mentioned of making arbitrary definitions. Also if they had wanted to, they would have excluded the dyad and the triad as well, and anything else they pleased (for we are the masters, provided we give warning); as on the other hand the unit takes its place, if we choose, among the numbers, and the fractions too. And in fact in general propositions we are obliged to consider them there to avoid saying each time: "In every number and in the unit and in fractions such and such a property is found." It is in this indefinite sense I have taken number in all my writings about it. But the same Euclid who took away the name of number from the unit, which was his privilege, to make it clear nevertheless that the unit is not nothing but is on the contrary of the same kind, thus defines homogeneous magnitudes: "Magnitudes," he says, "are said to be of the same kind when one by being multiplied can be made to exceed the other." Consequently, since the unit can by being multiplied be made to exceed any number whatsoever, it is of the same kind as numbers precisely by its essence and unchanging nature, according to the same Euclid who would not have it called a number.

An indivisible with respect to an extension is a different matter; for not only does it differ in name, which is arbitrary, but it differs in kind by the above definition, since an indivisible multiplied as many times as we please is so far from being able to exceed an extension that it can never make anything but a single, unique indivisible, which is natural and necessary, as has already been shown. And since this last proof is based on the definition of these two things, indivisible and extension, we shall go on with the demonstration and complete it.

An indivisible is that which is without parts, and extension is that which has distinct separate parts.

On the basis of these definitions I say that two indivisibles when joined do not make an extension. For when they are joined each touches the other in a part; and thus the parts by which they are touching are not separate, since otherwise they would not be touching. However by definition they have no other parts; therefore they have no separate parts; therefore they are not an extension, by the definition which calls for separation of parts. The same thing can be shown by the same argument for all the other indivisibles joined to these. And therefore an indivisible, multiplied as many times as we please, will never make an extension. It is not then of the same kind as extension, by the definition of the same kind.

That is how we demonstrate that indivisibles are not of the same kind as extension. Hence it is that two units can indeed make a number since they are of the same kind, and that two indivisibles do not make an extension since they are not of the same kind. And therefore we see how little reason there is to compare the relation between the unit and numbers to that between indivisibles and extension.

But if we wish to find in numbers a comparison that will justly represent what we are considering in extension, we must take the relation of zero to the numbers, for zero is not of the same kind as numbers because it cannot by being multiplied be made to exceed them; so that zero is a true indivisible of number just as the indivisible is a true zero of extension. And we shall find a like relation between rest and motion, and between an instant and time; for they are all heterogeneous with respect to magnitude because though infinitely multiplied they can never make anything but indivisibles of extension, and for the same reason. And thus we shall find a perfect correspondence between these things; for all these magnitudes are infinitely divisible without ever being reduced to their indivisibles, so that all of them keep the middle ground between infinity and nothing.

Thus wonderfully has nature related these things, and such are the two marvelous infinites she has set before man, not for his mind's grasp but for its wonder; and to close our consideration of them with a last remark, I shall add that these two infinites, although infinitely different, are nevertheless related to each other in such a way that the knowledge of one necessarily leads to the knowledge of the other.

For in numbers, from the fact that they can always be increased, it follows absolutely that they can always be decreased, and that clearly. For if we can multiply a number up to 100,000 times, say, we can also take a hundred thousandth part of it by dividing it by the same number we multiply it with, and thus every term of increase will become a term of division by changing the integer into a fraction. So that infinite increase includes necessarily infinite division.

In space too we find the same relation between these two opposed infinites. That is to say, from the fact that a space can be infinitely extended, it follows that it can be infinitely diminished, as is apparent from the following example: if we watch through a window a ship moving straight away from us, it is clear that the place in the glass where we see any fixed point we please on the ship will keep rising by a continuous motion as the ship moves away. Therefore if the ship continues its course to infinity, the point will continue to rise, and yet it will never reach the foot of the horizontal line drawn from the eye to the glass, so that it will get closer and closer without ever reaching it, incessantly dividing the space which remains under the horizontal point without ever reaching it. Whence we see that from the infinite extent of the vessel's course there follows as a necessary consequence the infinite and infinitely small division of the little space remaining below the horizontal point.

Those who will not be satisfied with these reasons and continue in the belief that space is not infinitely divisible can never aspire to geometrical demonstrations, and although they may be enlightened in other things, they will have very little light in these, for it is easy to be a very clever man though a bad geometer. But those who clearly see these truths can admire the greatness and the power of nature in that double infinity which surrounds us on every side, and learn by the consideration of such marvels to know themselves, seeing themselves placed between an infinity and a nothing of extension, between an infinity and a nothing of number, between an infinity and a nothing of motion, between an infinity and a nothing of time. Whereupon we can learn to assess ourselves at our just value and to make reflections worth more than all the rest of geometry itself.

I felt obliged to consider at such length this double infinity for the sake of those who, though they do not understand it at first, can be persuaded of it. And although there are many who have light enough to do without this treatise, it may nevertheless be that, necessary to some, it will not be entirely useless to the rest.

SECTION II. *Concerning the art of persuasion*

The art of persuasion has a necessary relation to the way in which men agree to what we put before them and to the circumstances of the things we want them to believe.

We all know that opinions are admitted into the soul through two entrances, which are its two chief powers, understanding and will. The more natural entrance is the understanding, for we should never agree to anything but demonstrated truths, but the more usual entrance, although against nature, is the will; for all men whatsoever are almost always led into belief not because a thing is proved but because it is pleasing. This way is low, unworthy, and foreign to our nature. Therefore everybody disavows it. Each of us professes to give his belief and even his love only where he knows it is deserved.

I am not speaking here of divine truths, which I am far from bringing under the art of persuasion, for they are infinitely above nature. God alone can put them into the soul, and in whatever way He pleases. I know He has willed they should enter into the mind from the heart and not into the heart from the mind, that He might make humble that proud power of reason, which claims the right to be judge over the things chosen by the will, and that He might cure the infirmity of that will, which is all corruption from its unclean loves. Whence it comes about that, whereas in speaking of human things we say they must be known before they can be loved (which has passed into a proverb), the saints on the contrary say in speaking of divine things that they must be loved in order to be known, and that we enter into truth only through charity, out of which they have made one of their most useful maxims.

Whereby it is apparent that God established this order above nature and entirely opposed to the order which should be natural to men in natural things. Nevertheless they have corrupted this order by dealing with profane things as they ought to deal with sacred things, because actually we believe almost nothing unless it pleases us. And this is why we are so loath to accept the truths of the Christian religion, which is entirely opposed to our pleasures. "Tell us agreeable things and we will listen to you," the Jews said to Moses; as if agreeableness should govern belief! And it is to punish this disorder by an order conformable to it that God sheds His light into our minds only after having tamed the rebelliousness of the will by a heavenly sweetness which charms and seduces it.

I speak then only of truths within our reach, and it is of them that I say the mind and the heart are the gates, as it were, through which they are received into the soul; but very few enter through the mind, whereas they are brought in in crowds through the rash caprices of the will without the counsel of reason.

These powers have each their principles and prime motives of action.

Those of the mind are natural and universally known truths, such as the whole is greater than the part, besides many particular axioms accepted by some and not by others, which, though false, when once admitted, are as powerful to gain belief as are the truest.

The principles of the will are certain desires natural and common to all men, such as the desire to be happy, which it is impossible for anyone not to have, besides many particular objects which each pursues for the sake of happiness and which, although actually pernicious, because they are capable of pleasing us, are as strong to move the will as if they constituted its true happiness.

So much for the powers which induce our consent.

But as for the qualities of the things we are to persuade men of, they differ widely.

Some are drawn as necessary conclusions from common principles and accepted truths. Of these it is possible to persuade without fail, for by showing their relation to principles that have been granted it is inevitably necessary that we convince, and it is impossible for them not to be received into the soul from the moment we have been able to join them to those truths already admitted there.

There are others which are bound up with the objects of our satisfaction; and these too are received with certainty. For as soon as the soul is made to see that a thing can bring her to what she sovereignly loves, it is inevitable that she embrace it with joy.

But those which have a double bond, with admitted truths and with the heart's desires, are so certain of their effect that there is nothing more certain in nature. As on the other hand whatever is related neither to our beliefs nor to our pleasures is importunate to us, false, and completely foreign.

In all these cases there can be no doubt. But there are others where the things we wish to persuade of are firmly based on known truths, but at the same time are opposed to the pleasures which touch us most nearly. And these are in great danger of illustrating by an experience which is all too common what I said at the beginning: that this imperious soul, whose boast was to act only by reason, follows by a rash and shameful choice the desires of a corrupt will, whatever resistance the too enlightened mind may offer.

It is then that truth and pleasure hang doubtfully in the balance, and the knowledge of one and the feeling of the other engage in a struggle whose outcome is most uncertain since, to judge of it, we should have to know all that takes place in the innermost part of a man, which the man himself almost never knows.

Hence it is apparent that, no matter what we wish to persuade of, we must consider the person concerned, whose mind and heart we must know, what principles he admits, what things he loves, and then observe in the thing in question what relations it has to these admitted principles or to these objects of delight. So that the art of persuasion consists as much in knowing how to please as in knowing how to convince, so much more do men follow caprice than reason.

Now of these two, the art of convincing and the art of pleasing, I shall confine myself here to the rules of the first, and to them only in the case where the principles have been granted and are held to unwaveringly; otherwise I do not know whether there would be an art for adjusting the proofs to the inconstancy of our caprices.

But the art of pleasing is incomparably more difficult, more subtle, more useful, and more wonderful, and therefore if I do not deal with it, it is because I am not able. Indeed I feel myself so unequal to its regulation that I believe it to be a thing impossible.

Not that I do not believe there are as certain rules for pleasing as for demonstrating, and that whoever should be able perfectly to know and to practise them would be as certain to succeed in making himself loved by kings and by every kind of person as in demonstrating the elements of geometry to those who have imagination enough to grasp the hypotheses. But I consider, and it is perhaps my weakness that leads me to think so, that it is impossible to lay hold of the rules. At least I am sure that if anyone can, I know the persons, and that no one else has such clear and abundant light in this matter.

The reason for this extreme difficulty comes from the fact that the principles of pleasure are not firm and stable. They are different in all men, and they vary to such an extent in each individual that there is no man who differs more from another man than from himself at different times. A man has other pleasures than a woman has; a rich man and a poor man have different pleasures; a prince, a warrior, a merchant, a citizen, a peasant, the old, the young, the well, the sick, all vary in this respect; the slightest accidents change them.

However there is an art, the one I am going to expound, showing how truths are related to their principles, both of truth and of pleasure, provided the principles we have once admitted remain constant and are never denied.

But since there are few principles of this kind and since outside of geometry, which considers only very simple figures, there are almost no truths we always agree upon, and still fewer objects of pleasure we do not every hour change our mind about, I do not know whether it is possible to give fixed rules for making discourse conform to the inconstancy of our caprices.

The art which I call the art of persuading, and which is simply the management of perfect scientific proofs, consists of three essential parts: defining by clear definitions the terms to be used; laying down evident principles or axioms to prove the matter in question; always mentally substituting in the demonstration, in place of the things defined, their definitions.

The reason for this method is apparent, since it would be useless to put forward something capable of proof and to undertake its demonstration if we had not first clearly defined all unintelligible terms; and since likewise the demonstration must be preceded by the granting of the evident principles required for the demonstration, for if we do not make sure of the foundation, we can have no assurance of the building; and since finally while demonstrating we must mentally substitute the definition in place of the things defined, for otherwise we could be led astray by the different meanings encountered in the terms. It is easy to see that if we observe this method we are sure to convince, since, with all the terms so defined that they are understood and entirely free from ambiguity and with the principles granted, if in the demonstration we always substitute in thought the definitions in place of the things defined, the invincible force of the conclusions cannot fail of its full effect.

Accordingly no demonstration satisfying these conditions can ever have met with a shadow of doubt, and never can those demonstrations failing to satisfy them have any force.

It is very important, therefore, to understand and to appropriate them, and that is why, that they may be more easily grasped and more accessible, I shall give them all in these few rules which include everything necessary for the perfection of definitions, of axioms, and of demonstrations, and consequently of the entire method of geometrical proofs of the art of persuasion.

Rules for definitions. 1. Do not attempt to define any of those things so well known in themselves that we have no clearer terms to explain them by.

2. Do not leave undefined any terms that are at all obscure or ambiguous.

3. Use in the definition of terms only words perfectly well known or already explained.

Rules for axioms. 1. Do not fail to ask that each of the necessary principles be granted, however clear and evident it may be.

2. Ask only that perfectly self-evident things be granted as axioms.

Rules for demonstrations. 1. Do not attempt to demonstrate any of those things so self-evident that we have nothing clearer to prove them by.

2. Prove all propositions that are at all obscure, and use for their proof only axioms that are perfectly evident or propositions already granted or demonstrated.

3. Always substitute mentally the definitions in place of the things defined, so you will not be led astray by the equivocation of terms whose meanings have been restricted by the definitions.

These are the eight rules which contain the precepts for firm and abiding proofs, three of which are not absolutely necessary and can be neglected without error. It is even difficult and impossible, as it were, always to observe them exactly, although for the sake of perfection we should do so to the best of our ability. These three are those which come first in each of the divisions:

For the definitions. Do not define any of the terms that are perfectly well known.

For the axioms. Do not fail to ask that all the perfectly evident and simple axioms be granted.

For the demonstrations. Do not demonstrate anything very well known in itself.

For it is undoubtedly not a great fault to define and very clearly to explain things which are most clear in themselves, nor to fail to ask in advance that axioms be granted which no one can refuse to grant when the necessity for their use arises, nor finally to prove propositions which would be granted without proof.

But the five other rules are absolutely necessary, and we cannot dispense with them without an essential defect and frequently even error. That is why I shall repeat them here in detail.

Necessary rules for definitions. Do not leave undefined any terms at all obscure or ambiguous. Use in definitions only terms perfectly well known or already explained.

Necessary rule for axioms. Ask only that evident things be granted as axioms.

Necessary rules for demonstrations. Prove all propositions, using for their proof only axioms that are perfectly self-evident or propositions already demonstrated or granted. Never get caught in the ambiguity of terms by failing to substitute in thought the definitions which restrict or explain them.

These five rules comprise everything necessary for making proofs convincing, unchanging, and in a word, geometrical; and the eight together make them still more perfect.

I pass now to the order in which propositions should be arranged if they are to have the right geometrical sequence.

After having established . . .

These are the rules of the art of persuasion, which are contained in these two principles: Define all the names imposed; prove everything, substituting in thought the definitions in place of the things defined.

Whereupon it seems to me in order to anticipate three chief objections that can be made: first, that this method is not at all new; second, that it is very easy to learn without there being any necessity of studying the elements of geometry, since it consists of these two rules that are known as soon as read; and third, that it is pretty useless since its use is almost confined to the objects of geometry alone.

It must then be shown that there is nothing so little known, nothing harder to practise, and nothing more useful and more universal.

As for the first objection, which is that these rules—everything must be defined and everything proved—are common knowledge in the world and that the logicians themselves have included them among the precepts of their art, I only wish it were true and so well known that I should not have had the labor of seeking with such care for the source of all the defects of reasoning, which are really common. But this is so little the case that with the single exception of geometers, who are so few in number as to be unique among a whole people and over a long period of time, we find no one who knows these rules. It will be easy to make this clear to those who have grasped perfectly the little I have said about them; but if they have not perfectly understood that, I admit they will have nothing to learn in this matter. But if these rules have found a way into their minds and have made a strong enough impression to take root and flourish there, they will feel how great a difference there is between what is said in this place and such approximations to it as some logicians may have made by chance here and there in their works.

Discerning minds know how much difference there is between two similar remarks, depending upon the place and accompanying circumstances. Will anyone really believe that two persons who have read and learned by heart the same book know it equally well, if one understands it in such a way that he knows all its principles, the force of its conclusions, the replies to the objections that can be made, and the entire organization of the work, whereas in the other the book is dead words and seeds which, though the same as those that produced such fertile trees, have remained dry and unfruitful in the sterile mind which received them in vain?

Not all those who say the same things possess them in the same way. And that is why the incomparable author of the *Art of Conversation*[1] is at such pains to make it clear that we must not judge a man's capacity by the excellence of an observation we have heard him make. Instead of carrying over to the speaker our admiration of the speech, we should, he says, penetrate the mind it comes from, try and find if he speaks by memory or by a happy chance, listen coldly and scornfully to see if he will resent our not having for what he says the esteem it deserves; we shall find more often than not that he will disavow it on the spot and that, led away from a thought whose worth he does not know, he will fall into another thoroughly common and ridiculous. We must then fathom how that thought is lodged in its author; how, whence, and to what extent he has made it his own; otherwise the judgment, acting in haste, will be judged rash.

I should like to ask fair-minded persons if this principle: "Matter is naturally and invincibly incapable of thought," and this other: "I think, therefore I am," are actually the same in the mind of Descartes and in the mind of St. Augustine, who said the same thing 1200 years before.

Certainly I am very far from saying that Descartes is not its true author, even if he should have learned it only from the reading of that great saint; for I know how much difference there is between making a statement off hand, without considering it more fully and at length, and seeing in that statement an admirable succession of consequences, which proves that matter is distinct from mind, and making out of it a firm and consistently held principle of a whole physics, as it was the intention of Descartes to do. For without examining whether he was

[1]Montaigne, *Essays*, III, 8.

successful in carrying out his intention, I assume that he was, and it is on this assumption that I say the statement in his writings is as different from the same statement in those others who have made it in passing as a man full of life and force is different from a dead man.

One man will say a thing off hand without understanding its excellence where another will see a wonderful succession of consequences which make us say boldly that it is no longer the same observation, and that he no more owes it to him from whom he learned it than a splendid tree belongs to some one who scattered the seed, thoughtlessly and without knowing what it was, in a rich soil which derived this profit from the seed by its own fertility.

The same thoughts sometimes shoot up in another quite otherwise than in their author, unfertile in their native field, abundant when transplanted. But it happens much more often that a good mind itself makes its own thoughts bear all the fruit they are capable of, and that afterwards others, having heard them praised, borrow them and deck themselves out with them, but without knowing their worth; and it is then that the difference of the same observation in different mouths is most apparent.

It is in this fashion that logicians may have borrowed the rules of geometry without understanding their force, and thus it does not follow from their happening to include them among the rules proper to logic that they have entered into the spirit of geometry; and unless they give me other indications of it than the passing mention of these rules, I shall be very far from putting them on the level of that science, which teaches the true method for the conduct of reason. But on the contrary I shall be very much inclined to exclude them, and almost without hope of return. For to have mentioned these rules in passing without noticing that everything is contained in them, and instead of following their light to wander aimlessly in useless investigations, running after what they offer and cannot give, is certainly to show oneself as hardly clearsighted and as having failed to follow the light because one had not seen it.

The method of avoiding error is sought by everyone. The logicians profess to guide us to it, only the geometers reach it, and outside of their science and its imitators there are no true demonstrations. The entire art is contained in these precepts we have given, they alone are sufficient, they alone prove; all other rules are useless or harmful. This is what I have learned from a long experience of all kinds of books and men.

Wherefore I judge those who say that geometers give them nothing new by these rules because they actually had them but mixed up with a lot of others, useless or false, from which they could not separate them out, I judge them, I say, as I do those who, seeking a diamond of great price among many that are false, which they however could not tell from it, should boast, holding them all together, that they possess the diamond as truly as he who, without stopping at the worthless mass, puts his hand on the choice stone they are seeking and for which they did not throw away all the rest.

The defect of false reasoning is a malady which is cured by these two remedies. Another has been compounded of many useless herbs among which the good are mingled but remain without effect because of the bad qualities of the mixture.

To uncover all the sophisms and equivocations of captious arguments they have invented barbarous names which astonish those who hear them; and whereas all the windings of this tangled knot can be straightened out only by pulling one of the ends designated by the geometers, they have noted a monstrous number of others in which these are included, without their knowing which are the right ones.

And thus those who point out to us a number of different roads, which they say will take us where we want to go, although only two of them lead there, must be able to give them a particular mark. It will be said that geometry, which indicates the roads with certainty, only gives what had already been given by the others, because they actually gave the same thing and more, without its being seen that this present lost its value by its very abundance and that by adding they took away.

Nothing is more common than good things; the only question is how to discern them; it is certain that all of them are natural and within our reach and even known by every one. But we do not know how to distinguish them. This is universal. It is not in things extraordinary and strange that excellence of any kind is found. We reach up for it, and we are further away; more often than not we must stoop. The best books are those whose readers think they could have written them. Nature, which alone is good, is familiar and common throughout.

I have no doubt then that these rules, because they are the true ones, should be simple, naive, natural, as they are. It is not *barbara* and *baralipton* which form the reason. We must not force the mind to fly too high. Strained and painful behavior fills it with foolish presumption by giving it an elevation foreign to it and an empty and ridiculous inflation instead of solid and vigorous nourishment. And one of the main reasons which keep those who are beginning these studies out of the true road they ought to follow is the notion they get at the start that the good things are inaccessible because they bear the names: great, high, exalted, sublime. That spoils everything. I should like to call them humble, common, familiar. These names suit them better. I hate those inflated words. . . .

TREATISE ON THE ARITHMETICAL TRIANGLE

Definitions

I call *arithmetical triangle* a figure constructed as follows:

From any point, G, I draw two lines perpendicular to each other, GV, GĞ, in each of which I take as many equal and contiguous parts as I please, beginning with G, which I number 1, 2, 3, 4, etc., and these numbers are the *exponents* of the sections of the lines.

Next I connect the points of the first section in each of the two lines by another line, which is the *base* of the resulting triangle.

In the same way I connect the two points of the second section by another line, making a second triangle of which it is the base.

And in this way connecting all the points of section with the same exponent, I construct as many triangles and bases as there are exponents.

Through each of the points of section and parallel to the sides I draw lines whose intersections make little squares which I call *cells*.

Cells between two parallels drawn from left to right are called *cells of the same parallel row*, as, for example, cells G, σ, π, etc., or φ, ψ, θ, etc.

Those between two lines drawn from top to bottom are called *cells of the same perpendicular row*, as, for example, cells G, φ, A, D, etc., or σ, ψ, B, etc.

447

Those cut diagonally by the same base are called *cells of the same base*, as, for example, D, B, θ, λ, or A, ψ, π.

Cells of the same base equidistant from its extremities are called *reciprocals*, as, for example, E, R and B, θ, because the parallel exponent of one is the same as the perpendicular exponent of the other, as is apparent in the above example, where E is in the second perpendicular row and in the fourth parallel row and its reciprocal, R, is in the second parallel row and in the fourth perpendicular row, reciprocally. It is very easy to demonstrate that cells with exponents reciprocally the same are in the same base and are equidistant from its extremities.

It is also very easy to demonstrate that the perpendicular exponent of any cell when added to its parallel exponent exceeds by unity the exponent of its base.

For example, cell F is in the third perpendicular row and in the fourth parallel row and in the sixth base, and the exponents of rows 3 and 4, added together, exceed by unity the exponent of base 6, a property which follows from the fact that the two sides of the triangle have the same number of parts; but this is understood rather than demonstrated.

Of the same kind is the observation that each base has one more cell than the preceding base, and that each has as many cells as its exponent has units; thus the second base, $\phi\sigma$, has two cells, the third, $A\psi\pi$, has three, etc.

Now the numbers assigned to each cell are found by the following method:

The number of the first cell, which is at the right angle, is arbitrary; but that number having been assigned, all the rest are determined, and for this reason it is called the *generator* of the triangle. Each of the others is specified by a single rule as follows:

The number of each cell is equal to the sum of the numbers of the perpendicular and parallel cells immediately preceding. Thus cell F, that is, the number of cell F, equals the sum of cell C and cell E, and similarly with the rest.

Whence several consequences are drawn. The most important follow, wherein I consider triangles generated by unity, but what is said of them will hold for all others.

First Consequence

In every arithmetical triangle all the cells of the first parallel row and of the first perpendicular row are the same as the generating cell.

For by definition each cell of the triangle is equal to the sum of the immediately preceding perpendicular and parallel cells. But the cells of the first parallel row have no preceding perpendicular cells, and those of the first perpendicular row have no preceding parallel cells; therefore they are all equal to each other and consequently to the generating number.

Thus $\phi = G + 0$, that is, $\phi = G$,

$A = \phi + 0$, that is, ϕ,

$\sigma = G + 0$, $\pi = \sigma + 0$,

And similarly of the rest.

Second Consequence

In every arithmetical triangle each cell is equal to the sum of all the cells of the preceding parallel row from its own perpendicular row to the first, inclusive.

Let any cell, ω, be taken. I say that it is equal to $R+\theta+\psi+\phi$, which are the cells of the next higher parallel row from the perpendicular row of ω to the first perpendicular row.

This is evident if we simply consider a cell as the sum of its component cells.

For ω equals $R+C$

$$\underbrace{\underbrace{\underbrace{\theta+B}_{\psi+A}}_{\phi,}}$$

for A and ϕ are equal to each other by the preceding consequence.

Therefore $\omega = R+\theta+\psi+\phi$.

THIRD CONSEQUENCE

In every arithmetical triangle each cell is equal to the sum of all the cells of the preceding perpendicular row from its own parallel row to the first, inclusive.

Let any cell, C, be taken. I say that it is equal to $B+\psi+\sigma$, which are the cells of the preceding perpendicular row from the parallel row of cell C to the first parallel row.

This is also apparent, as above, simply by the interpretation of cells.

For $C = B+\theta$

$$\underbrace{\underbrace{\psi+\pi}}_{\sigma,}$$

for $\pi = \sigma$ by the first consequence.

Therefore $C = B+\psi+\sigma$.

FOURTH CONSEQUENCE

In every arithmetical triangle each cell exceeds by unity the sum of all the cells within its parallel and perpendicular rows, exclusive.

Let any cell, ξ, be taken. I say that $\xi-G = R+\theta+\psi+\phi+\lambda+\pi+\sigma+G$, which are all the numbers between row $\xi\omega CBA$ and row $\xi S\mu$, exclusive.

This is also apparent by interpretation.

For $\xi = \lambda+R+\omega$

$$\underbrace{\underbrace{\underbrace{\underbrace{\pi+\theta+C}_{\sigma+\psi+B}}_{G+\phi+A}}_{G.}}$$

Therefore $\xi = \lambda+R+\pi+\theta+\sigma+\psi+G+\phi+G$.

N.B. I have written in the enunciation *each cell exceeds by unity* because the generator is unity. If it were some other number, the enunciation should read: *each cell exceeds by the generating number.*

FIFTH CONSEQUENCE

In every arithmetical triangle each cell is equal to its reciprocal.

For in the second base, $\phi\sigma$, it is evident that the two reciprocal cells, ϕ, σ, are equal to each other and to G.

In the third base, A, ψ, π, it is also obvious that the reciprocals, π, A, are equal to each other and to G.

In the fourth base it is obvious that the extremes, D, λ, are again equal to each other and to G.

And those between, B, θ, are obviously equal since $B = A + \psi$ and $\theta = \pi + \psi$. But $\pi + \psi = A + \psi$ by what has just been shown. Therefore, etc.

Similarly it can be shown for all the other bases that reciprocals are equal, because the extremes are always equal to G and the rest can always be considered as the sum of cells in the preceding base which are themselves reciprocals.

SIXTH CONSEQUENCE

In every arithmetical triangle the corresponding cells of parallel and perpendicular rows having the same exponents are equal.

For they are made up of reciprocal cells.

Thus the second perpendicular row, $\sigma\psi BEMQ$, is exactly the same as the second parallel row, $\phi\psi\theta RSN$.

SEVENTH CONSEQUENCE

In every arithmetical triangle the sum of the cells of each base is double that of the preceding base.

Let any base, $DB\theta\lambda$, be taken. I say that the sum of its cells is double the sum of the cells of the preceding base, $A\psi\pi$.

For the extremes................................... $D,$ $\lambda,$

are equal to the extremes............................... $A,$ $\pi,$

and each of the rest................................... $B,$ $\theta,$

is equal to two cells of the other base..................... $A+\psi,$ $\psi+\pi,$

Therefore $D + \lambda + B + \theta = 2A + 2\psi + 2\pi$.

The same thing is demonstrated in the same way of all other bases.

EIGHTH CONSEQUENCE

In every arithmetical triangle the sum of the cells of each base is a number of the double progression beginning with unity whose exponent is the same as that of the base.

For the first base is unity.

The second is double the first; therefore it is 2.

The third is double the second; therefore it is 4.

And so on to infinity.

N.B. If the generator were not unity but some other number, such as 3, the same thing would be true. But we should have to take not the numbers of the double progression beginning with unity, that is, 1, 2, 4, 8, 16, etc., but those of the double progression beginning with the generator 3, that is, 3, 6, 12, 24, 48, etc.

NINTH CONSEQUENCE

In every arithmetical triangle each base exceeds by unity
the sum of all the preceding bases

For this is a property of the double progression.

N.B. If the generator were other than unity, we should have to say: *each base exceeds by the generator.*

TENTH CONSEQUENCE

In every arithmetical triangle the sum of any number of contiguous cells of any base, beginning at an extremity, is equal to the same number of cells of the preceding base together with the same number except one.

Let there be taken the sum of any number of cells of base $D\lambda$, for example the first three, $D+B+\theta$.

I say it is equal to the sum of the first three of the preceding base, $A+\psi+\pi$, together with the first two of the same base, $A+\psi$.

For $\quad\quad D, \quad\quad B, \quad\quad \theta,$

are equal to $A, \quad\quad A+\psi, \quad\quad \psi+\pi,$

Therefore $D+B+\theta = 2A+2\psi+\pi$.

DEFINITION

I call *cells of the bisector* those diagonally cut by the bisector of the right angle, such as cells G, ψ, C, ρ, etc.

ELEVENTH CONSEQUENCE

Each cell of the bisector is double the preceding cell
in its parallel or perpendicular row.

Let any cell of the bisector, C, be taken. I say it is double θ and also double B.
For $C=\theta+B$, and $\theta=B$ by the fifth consequence.

N.B. All the preceding consequences are statements of equalities found in the arithmetical triangle. We now proceed to the statements of proportions, of which the following proposition is the foundation.

TWELFTH CONSEQUENCE

In every arithmetical triangle, of two contiguous cells in the same base the upper is to the lower as the number of cells from the upper to the top of the base is to the number of cells from the lower to the bottom of the base, inclusive.

Let any two contiguous cells of the same base, E, C, be taken. I say that

E	:	C	::	2	:	3
the lower		the upper		because there are two cells from E to the bottom, namely E, H,		because there are three cells from C to the top, namely C, R, μ.

Although this proposition has an infinity of cases, I shall demonstrate it very briefly by supposing two lemmas:

The first, which is self-evident, that this proportion is found in the second base, for it is perfectly obvious that $\phi:\sigma::1:1$;

The second, that if this proportion is found in any base, it will necessarily be found in the following base.

Whence it is apparent that it is necessarily in all the bases. For it is in the second base by the first lemma; therefore by the second lemma it is in the third base, therefore in the fourth, and to infinity.

It is only necessary therefore to demonstrate the second lemma as follows: If this proportion is found in any base, as, for example, in the fourth, $D\lambda$, that is, if $D:B::1:3$, and $B:\theta::2:2$, and $\theta:\lambda::3:1$, etc., I say the same proportion will be found in the following base, $H\mu$, and that, for example, $E:C::2:3$.

For $D:B::1:3$, by hypothesis.

Therefore $\underbrace{D+B:B::1+3:3}$

$$E\quad :B::\quad 4:3$$

Similarly B$:\theta::2:2$, by hypothesis

Therefore $\underbrace{B+\theta:B::2+2:2}$

$$C\quad :B::4:2$$

But $\qquad B\quad :E::3:4$

Therefore, by compounding the ratios, $C:E::3:2$. Q.E.D.

The proof is the same for all other bases, since it requires only that the proportion be found in the preceding base, and that each cell be equal to the cell before it together with the cell above it, which is everywhere the case.

THIRTEENTH CONSEQUENCE

In every arithmetical triangle, of two contiguous cells in the same perpendicular row the lower is to the upper as the exponent of the base of the upper is to the exponent of its parallel row.

Let any two cells in the same perpendicular row, F, C, be taken. I say that

| F | : | C | :: | 5 | : | 3 |

the lower　　the upper　　the exponent of the　　the exponent of the
　　　　　　　　　　　base of C　　　　parallel row of C.

For $E:C::2:3$

Therefore $\underbrace{E+C:C::2+3:3}$

$$F\quad :C::\quad 5\ :3$$

FOURTEENTH CONSEQUENCE

In every arithmetical triangle, of two contiguous cells in the same parallel row the greater is to the lesser as the exponent of the base of the lesser is to the exponent of its perpendicular row.

Let two cells in the same parallel row, F, E, be taken. I say that

| F | : | E | :: | 5 | : | 2 |

The greater　　the lesser　　the exponent of the　　the exponent of the
　　　　　　　　　　　base of E　　　　perpendicular row of E

For $E:C::2:3$

Therefore $\underbrace{E+C:E::2+3:2}$

$$F\quad :E::\quad 5\ :2$$

FIFTEENTH CONSEQUENCE

In every arithmetical triangle the sum of the cells of any parallel row is to the last cell of the row as the exponent of the triangle is to the exponent of the row.

Let any triangle, for example the fourth, $GD\lambda$, be taken. I say that whatever row we take, say the second parallel, the sum of its cells, $\phi+\psi+\theta:\theta::4:2$. For $\varphi+\psi+\theta=C$, and $C:\theta::4:2$, by the thirteenth consequence.

SIXTEENTH CONSEQUENCE

In every arithmetical triangle any parallel row is to the next lower row as the exponent of the lower row is to the number of its cells.

Let any triangle, for example the fifth, μGH, be taken. I say that whatever row we take, say the third, the sum of its cells is to the sum of the cells of the fourth row, that is $A+B+C$ is to $D+E$ as 4, the exponent of the fourth row, is to 2, which is the number of its cells, for it has 2.

For $A+B+C=F$, and $D+E=M$.

But $F:M::4:2$, by the twelfth consequence.

N.B. This proposition could also be enunciated as follows:

Each parallel row is to the next lower row as the exponent of the lower row is to the difference between the exponent of the triangle and the exponent of the upper row.

For the difference between the exponent of a triangle and the exponent of one of its rows is always equal to the number of cells in the next lower row.

SEVENTEENTH CONSEQUENCE

In every arithmetical triangle any cell together with all those of its perpendicular row is to the same cell together with all those of its parallel row as the number of perpendicular cells taken is to the number of parallel cells taken.

Let any cell, B, be taken. I say that $B+\psi+\sigma:B+A::3:2$.

I say 3 because three cells are added together in the antecedent, and 2 because there are two in the consequent.

For $B+\psi+\sigma=C$, by the third consequence, and $B+A=E$, by the second consequence.

But $C:E::3:2$, by the twelfth consequence.

EIGHTEENTH CONSEQUENCE

In every arithmetical triangle two parallel rows equidistant from the extremities are to each other as the number of their cells.

Let there be taken any triangle, $GV\zeta$, and two of its rows equidistant from the extremities, such as the sixth, $P+Q$, and the second, $\phi+\psi+\theta+R+S+N$. I say that the sum of the cells of one is to the sum of the cells of the other as the number of the cells of one is to the number of cells of the other.

For by the sixth consequence the second parallel row, $\phi\psi\theta RSN$, is the same as the second perpendicular row, $\sigma\psi BEMQ$, of which we have just demonstrated this proportion.

N.B. This proposition can be enunciated as follows:

In every arithmetical triangle two parallel rows whose exponents taken together exceed by unity the exponent of the triangle are to each other as their exponents reciprocally.

For this is the same thing as what has just been enunciated.

LAST CONSEQUENCE

In every arithmetical triangle, of two contiguous cells in the bisector the lower is to four times the higher as the exponent of the base of the higher is to a number exceeding it by unity.

Let two cells of the bisector, ρ, C, be taken. I say that $\rho : 4C : : 5$ (the exponent of the base of C) :6.

For $\rho = 2\omega$, and $C = 2\theta$; therefore $4\theta = 2C$.

Therefore $4\theta : C : : 2 : 1$.

But $\rho : 4C : : \omega : 4\theta$, or in the ratio compounded of $\omega : C$ and $C : 4\theta$

by the preceding consequences.................. 5:3   1:2

                                   or 3:6

Therefore $\rho : 4C : : 5 : 6$.

                                         5 : 6   Q.E.D.

N.B. I pass over many other proportions that this triangle could be made to yield, because every one can easily discover them for himself and because those who are willing to devote themselves to the task will perhaps find more admirable ones than any I could give. I end therefore with the following problem, which completes the treatise:

PROBLEM

Given the perpendicular and parallel exponents of a cell, to find its number without making use of the arithmetical triangle.

Let it be proposed, for example, to find the number of cell ξ of the fifth perpendicular and of the third parallel row.

All the numbers which precede the perpendicular exponent, 5, having been taken, namely 1, 2, 3, 4, let there be taken the same number of natural numbers, beginning with the parallel exponent, 3, namely 3, 4, 5, 6.

Let the first numbers be multiplied together and let the product be 24. Let the second numbers be multiplied together and let the product be 360, which, divided by the first product, 24, gives as quotient 15, which is the number sought.

For ξ is to the first cell of its base, V, in the ratio compounded of all the ratios of the cells between, that is to say, $\xi : V$

in the ratio compounded of $\xi : \rho$, $\rho : K$, $K : Q$, $Q : V$

or by the twelfth consequence 3:4   4:3   5:2   6:1

Therefore $\xi : V : : 3 \cdot 4 \cdot 5 \cdot 6 : : 4 \cdot 3 \cdot 2 \cdot 1$.

But V is unity; therefore ξ is the quotient of the division of the product of $3 \cdot 4 \cdot 5 \cdot 6$ by the product of $4 \cdot 3 \cdot 2 \cdot 1$.

N.B. If the generator were not unity, we should have had to multiply the quotient by the generator.

VARIOUS USES OF THE ARITHMETICAL TRIANGLE WHOSE GENERATOR IS UNITY

Having given the proportions obtaining between the cells and the rows of arithmetical triangles, I turn in the following treatises to various uses of those triangles whose generator is unity. But I leave out many more than I include; it is extraordinary how fertile in properties this triangle is. Everyone can try his hand. I only call your attention here to the fact that in everything that follows I am speaking exclusively of arithmetical triangles whose generator is unity.

USE OF THE ARITHMETICAL TRIANGLE
FOR THE ORDERS OF NUMBERS

The numbers of the different progressions have been considered in arithmetic; those of the different powers and of the different degrees have also been considered; but those of which I am speaking have not, it seems to me, been sufficiently investigated, although they are extremely useful. They do not even have a name; therefore I have been obliged to give them one. Because *progression*, *degree*, and *power* are already in use, I adopt the name *order*.

I call therefore *numbers of the first order* the units,

1, 1, 1, 1, 1, etc.

I call *numbers of the second order* the natural numbers which are formed by addition of the units,

1, 2, 3, 4, 5, etc.

I call *numbers of the third order*, known as triangular numbers, those which are formed by addition of the natural numbers,

1, 3, 6, 10, etc.

That is, the second triangular number, 3, is equal to the sum of the first two natural numbers, which are 1, 2; the third triangular number, 6, is equal to the sum of the first three natural numbers, 1, 2, 3, etc.

I call *numbers of the fourth order*, known as pyramidal numbers, those which are formed by addition of the triangular numbers,

1, 4, 10, 20, etc.

I call *numbers of the fifth order* those which are formed by addition of the preceding numbers. Since there is no fixed name for them, they might be called triangulo-triangular numbers:

1, 5, 15, 35, etc.

I call *numbers of the sixth order* those which are formed by addition of the preceding numbers,

1, 6, 21, 56, 126, 252, etc.

And so on to infinity, 1, 7, 28, 84, etc.

1, 8, 36, 120, etc.

Now if we make a table of all the orders of numbers in which we indicate the exponents of the orders at the side and the roots at the top, as follows:

ROOTS

		1	2	3	4	5 etc.
Units..................	Order 1	1	1	1	1	1 etc.
Natural numbers.........	Order 2	1	2	3	4	5 etc.
Triangular numbers.......	Order 3	1	3	6	10	15 etc.
Pyramidal numbers.......	Order 4	1	4	10	20	35 etc.

etc.

we shall find this table equivalent to the arithmetical triangle.

The first order of numbers will be the same as the first parallel row of the triangle.

The second order of numbers will be the same as the second parallel row, and so on to infinity.

For in the arithmetical triangle the first row is wholly made up of units, and the first order of numbers is also made up of units.

Also in the arithmetical triangle each cell, say F, is equal to the cell above together with all the preceding cells in that parallel, that is, $C+B+A$, as was proved in the second consequence of the treatise on this triangle. And we find the same thing in each order of numbers. For example, the third pyramidal number, 10, is equal to the first three triangular numbers, 1, 3, 6, since it is formed by their addition.

Whence it is plainly seen that the parallel rows of the triangle are nothing but the orders of numbers, and that the exponents of the parallel rows are the same as the exponents of the orders, and that the exponents of the perpendicular rows are the same as the roots. Thus, for example, the number 21, which in the arithmetical triangle is in the third parallel row and in the sixth perpendicular row, when considered with respect to the orders of numbers, is of the third order and the sixth of its order, or of the sixth root.

Which makes it clear that everything we have said of the rows and cells of the arithmetical triangle applies exactly to the orders of numbers, and that the same equalities and the same proportions we pointed out in the former will also be found in the latter. We need only change the enunciations by substituting the terms which apply to the orders of numbers, such as root and order, for those which applied to the arithmetical triangle, such as parallel and perpendicular rows. I shall devote a separate little treatise to the subject; a few examples given there will make it easy to see what all the rest would be.

USE OF THE ARITHMETICAL TRIANGLE FOR COMBINATIONS

The word *combination* has been used in several different senses, so that to avoid ambiguity I am obliged to say how I understand it.

When of many things we may choose a certain number, all the ways of taking as many as we are allowed out of all those offered to our choice are here called the *different combinations*.

For example, if of four things expressed by the four letters, A, B, C, D, we are permitted to take, say any two, all the different ways of taking two out of the four put before us are called *combinations*.

Thus we shall find by experience that there are six different ways of choosing two out of four; for we can take A and B, or A and C, or A and D, or B and C, or B and D, or C and D.

I do not count A and A as one of the ways of taking two; for they are not different things, they are only one thing repeated.

Nor do I count A and B and B and A as two different ways; for in both ways we take only the same two things but in a different order, and I am not concerned with the order; so that I could make myself understood at once by those who are used to considering combinations, simply by saying that I speak only of combinations made without changing the order.

We shall also find by experience that there are four ways of taking three things out of four; for we can take ABC or ABD or ACD or BCD.

Finally we shall find that we can take four out of four in one way only, $ABCD$.

I shall speak therefore in the following terms:

1 in 4 can be combined 4 times.
2 in 4 can be combined 6 times.
3 in 4 can be combined 4 times.
4 in 4 can be combined 1 time.

Or:

the number of combinations of 1 in 4 is 4.
the number of combinations of 2 in 4 is 6.
the number of combinations of 3 in 4 is 4.
the number of combinations of 4 in 4 is 1.

But the sum of all the combinations in general that can be made in 4 is 15, because the number of combinations of 1 in 4, of 2 in 4, of 3 in 4, of 4 in 4, when joined together, is 15.

After this explanation I shall give the following consequences in the form of lemmas:

LEMMA 1.

There are no combinations of a number in a smaller number; for example, 4 cannot be combined in 2.

LEMMA 2.

There is 1 combination of 1 in 1.
There is 1 combination of 2 in 2.
There is 1 combination of 3 in 3.
And in general there is only one combination of a number in an equal number.

LEMMA 3.

There is 1 combination of 1 in 1.
There are 2 combinations of 1 in 2.
There are 3 combinations of 1 in 3.
And in general there are as many combinations of 1 in any number as there are units in the number.

LEMMA 4.

If there are four numbers, the first of which is arbitrary, the second exceeding the first by unity, the third any number not smaller than the second, the fourth exceeding the third by unity, the number of combinations of the first in the third together with the number of combinations of the second in the third is equal to the number of combinations of the second in the fourth.

Let there be four numbers as specified:
The first, arbitrary, for example, 1.
The second, exceeding the first by unity, 2.
The third, not smaller than the second, for example, 3.
The fourth, exceeding the third by unity, 4.

I say that the number of combinations of 1 in 3 together with the number of combinations of 2 in 3 is equal to the number of combinations of 2 in 4.

Let there be taken any three letters, B, C, D.
Let there be taken the same three letters together with another, A, B, C, D.

Let us take, in accordance with the proposition, all the combinations of one letter in the three, *B, C, D*. There will be 3, namely, *B, C, D*.

Let us take in the same three letters all the combinations of two. There will be 3, namely, *BC, BD, CD*.

Finally let us take in the four letters, *A, B, C, D*, all the combinations of two. There will be 6, namely, *AB, AC, AD, BC, BD, CD*.

We must demonstrate that the number of combinations of 1 in 3 and of 2 in 3 is equal to the number of combinations of 2 in 4.

The demonstration is easy for the combinations of 2 in 4 are made up of the combinations of 1 in 3 and of 2 in 3.

That this may be seen, it is necessary to observe that among the combinations of 2 in 4, namely, *AB, AC, AD, BC, BD, CD*, some have the letter *A* and some do not.

Those not having it are *BC, BD, CD*, which consequently are made up of two of the three letters, *B, C, D*; therefore they are the combinations of 2 in the three letters, *B, C, D*. Therefore the combinations of 2 in the three letters, *B, C, D*, constitute a part of the combinations of 2 in the four letters, *A, B, C, D*, since they are made up of those not having *A*.

Now if from the combinations of 2 in 4 having *A*, namely, *AB, AC, AD*, we take away *A*, there will remain one letter only of the three, *B, C, D*, namely, *B, C, D*, which are precisely the combinations of one letter in the three letters, *B, C, D*. Therefore if to each of the combinations of one letter in the three letters, *B, C, D*, we add the letter *A*, thus having *AB, AC, AD*, we shall make the combinations of 2 in 4 having *A*. Therefore the combinations of 1 in 3 constitute a part of the combinations of 2 in 4.

Whence it is seen that the combinations of 2 in 4 are made up of the combinations of 2 in 3 and of 1 in 3, and therefore that the number of the combinations of 2 in 4 is equal to that of 2 in 3 and of 1 in 3.

We can show the same thing in all the other examples, as:

The number of combinations of 29 in 40
and the number of combinations of 30 in 40
are equal to the number of combinations of 30 in 41.

Also the number of combinations of 15 in 55
and the number of combinations of 16 in 55
are equal to the number of combinations of 16 in 56
and so on to infinity. Q.E.D.

PROPOSITION 1

In every arithmetical triangle the sum of any parallel row of cells is equal to the number of combinations of the exponent of the row in the exponent of the triangle.

Let any triangle, for example, the fourth, *GD*λ, be taken. I say that the sum of the cells of any row, for example, the second, φ+ψ+θ, is equal to the number of combinations of 2, the exponent of the second row, in 4, the exponent of the triangle.

Similarly the sum of the cells of the fifth row of the eighth triangle is equal to the number of combinations of 5 in 8, etc.

Although there is an infinity of cases, the demonstration can be briefly given by means of the two following lemmas:

The first, which is self-evident, that this equality is found in the first triangle since the sum of the cells of its only row, namely G or unity, is equal to the number of combinations of 1, the exponent of the row, in 1, the exponent of the triangle;

The second, that if an arithmetical triangle is found which has this equality, namely, that whatever row we take, the sum of the cells is equal to the number of combinations of the exponent of the row in the exponent of the triangle, I say that the following triangle will have the same property.

Whence it follows that all the arithmetical triangles have this equality. For the first has it by the first lemma, and it is even still evident in the second; therefore by the second lemma the next triangle will have it too, and consequently the next, and so on to infinity.

All that is necessary then is to demonstrate the second lemma.

Let any triangle be taken, for example, the third, in which we suppose this equality, namely, that the sum of the cells of the first row, $G+\sigma+\pi$, is equal to the number of combinations of 1 in 3, and that the sum of the cells of the second row, $\phi+\psi$, is equal to the combinations of 2 in 3, and that the sum of the cells of the third row, A, is equal to the combinations of 3 in 3; I say that the fourth triangle will have the same equality, and that, for example, the sum of the cells of the second row, $\phi+\psi+\theta$, is equal to the number of combinations of 2 in 4.

For $\phi+\psi+\theta$ $=$ $\underbrace{\phi+\psi}$ $+$ $\underbrace{\theta}$

$\underbrace{G+\sigma+\pi}$

By hypothesis   or the number of + or the number of combinations of   combinations of 2 in 3.   1 in 3.

By the fourth lemma   or the number of combinations of 2 in 4.

The same demonstration applies to all other cases.   Q.E.D.

PROPOSITION 2

The number of any cell is equal to the number of combinations of a number less by unity than its parallel exponent in a number less by unity than the exponent of its base.

Let any cell be taken, say F in the fourth parallel row and in the sixth base. I say that it is equal to the number of combinations of 3 in 5, less by unity than 4 and 6, for it is equal to the cells $A+B+C$. Therefore by the preceding proposition, etc.

PROBLEM 1, PROPOSITION 3

Two numbers having been set out, to find by the arithmetical triangle how many combinations there are of one in the other.

Let the numbers set out be 4, 6. We must find how many combinations there are of 4 in 6.

First way. Take the sum of the cells of the fourth row in the sixth triangle; it will satisfy the problem.

Second way. Take the fifth cell of the seventh base, because the numbers, 5, 7, exceed by unity the given numbers, 4, 6; the number of this cell is the required number.

CONCLUSION

It is easy to see from the relation between the cells and the rows of the arithmetical triangle and combinations that everything proved of the former applies to the latter analogously, as I shall show in few words in a little treatise I have written on combinations.

USE OF THE ARITHMETICAL TRIANGLE

To determine how the stakes should be divided between two players playing for a set of games

To understand the rules of divisions the first thing to consider is that the money staked by the players on the game no longer belongs to them, for they have given up its ownership. But they have received in return the right to expect whatever chance may give them, in accordance with the conditions agreed upon at the beginning.

But since the law by which they are playing is voluntary, they can break it at will; and therefore at any stage of the game they can stop, and reversing their procedure at the beginning, give up their expectations from chance and each return to the ownership of something. In this event the determination of what is to belong to them should be so related to what they had a right to hope from fortune that each of them thinks it comes to exactly the same thing to take what is assigned to him or to continue to run the risks of the game; this just distribution is called the division (of the stakes).

The first principle leading to a knowledge of how divisions should be made is as follows:

If the position of a player is such that whatever happens a certain sum is to belong to him whether he wins or loses and chance cannot take it from him, he should not divide it but take the whole of it as having been assured to him. Since the division should vary as the chances and since there is no chance of losing, he should withdraw the entire sum without division.

The second principle is as follows: If the position of two players is such that if one wins, a certain sum will belong to him, and if he loses, it will belong to the other; if the game is a game of pure chance and if there are as many chances for one as for the other and consequently no more reason why one should win than the other, if they want to separate without playing and take what legitimately belongs to them, they should divide equally the sum ventured and each take his half.

FIRST COROLLARY

If two players are playing a game of pure chance on condition that if the first player wins, a certain sum will be his, and if he loses, a smaller sum will be his, and if they wish to separate without playing and each take what belongs to him, the division is that the first player take what would be his if he lost together with half the difference between that and what would be his if he won.

For example, if two players are playing on condition that if the first wins, he will get 8 pistoles, and if he loses, 2, I say the division is that he take the 2 together with half the difference between 8 and 2, that is, 3, for the difference is 6, half of which is 3.

For by hypothesis if he wins, he gets 8, that is, 6+2, and if he loses, 2; therefore 2 belong to him in either case and consequently by the first principle he should not divide them but take them both. But as for the other 6, they depend on fortune, so that if it favors him, they are his, if not, they belong to his opponent; and by hypothesis there is no more reason for their going to one than to the other. Therefore they should divide them evenly and each take his half, which is what I had proposed.

Therefore, to say the same thing in other words, he gets his share as loser together with half the difference between his shares as loser and as winner.

And consequently if, when he loses, A is his, and when he wins, $A+B$, the division is that he get $A+\frac{1}{2}B$.

SECOND COROLLARY

If two players are playing in the same condition as stated above, I say that the division can be made as follows, which comes to the same thing: that the winner's and the loser's shares be put together and that the first player take half of this sum; that is, that 2 and 8 be added together to make 10, half of which, 5, will belong to the first player.

For half of the sum of two numbers is always the same as the smaller together with half of their difference.

Which is demonstrated as follows:

Let A be the loser's share and $A+B$ the winner's share. I say the division is made by adding these two numbers, which make $A+A+B$, and giving half to the first player, which is $\frac{1}{2}A+\frac{1}{2}A+\frac{1}{2}B$. For this sum is equal to $A+\frac{1}{2}B$, which has been proved to be the just distribution.

These foundations having been laid, we shall proceed with ease to determine the division between two players who are playing for a set of any number of games, whatever their actual status; that is, what the division should be when they are playing for a set of two games with a score of 1 to 0, or for a set of three games with a score of 1 to 0 or 2 to 0 or 2 to 1; and in general whatever the number of games in the set and whatever the score of the players.

The first observation to make is that two players who are playing for a set of two games with a score of 1 to 0 are in the same position as two others who are playing for a set of three games with a score of 2 to 1. For both couples have this in common that in order to win, one player needs only one game and the other, two. And therein consist the odds, which should determine divisions; so that strictly only the number of games left for each to win should be considered and not the number won, since, as we have already said, two players playing for a set of two games with a score of 1 to 0 have the same status as two players playing for a set of twelve games with a score of 11 to 10.

The question must accordingly be put as follows:

Given two players each of whom lacks a certain number of games to complete the set, to make the division.

I shall give the method here, which I shall carry out only in two or three examples, which will be so easy to go on with that there will be no need of more.

For the sake of completeness I shall start with the first example, which it is perhaps inappropriate to mention because it is too clear. I do so, however, to begin with the beginning.

FIRST CASE

If one of the players has the required number of games and the other has not, the whole sum belongs to the first player; for he has won it, since he lacks none of the games in which he was to win it.

SECOND CASE

If one of the players lacks one game and the other one, they should divide the money equally and each take his half, as is evident by the second principle. It is the same if one lacks two games and the other two, and whatever number of games one lacks if the other lacks as many.

THIRD CASE

If one player lacks one game and the other two, the division is determined as follows:
Let us consider what would belong to the first player (who lacks only one game) if he should win the next game, and then what would belong to him if he lost.

It is obvious that if the player who lacks only one game wins the game to be played, he will not lack any; therefore the entire sum will belong to him by the first case. But on the contrary if the player who lacks two games wins the one to be played, he will only lack one; therefore each will be in the position of lacking one game. Therefore they should divide the money equally by the second case.

Therefore if the first wins this game, the entire sum will belong to him, and if he loses it, half will be his; therefore if they wish to separate without playing the game, ¾ will belong to him by the second corollary.

And if we give an example of the sum they are playing for, the matter will be much clearer.

Let us say 8 pistoles; therefore the first player, if he wins, should have it all, that is, 8 pistoles, and if he loses, half, that is 4; therefore in case of division half of $8+4$, that is, 6 pistoles out of 8, belong to him; for $8+4=12$, half of which is 6.

FOURTH CASE

If one of the players lacks one game and the other three, the division will be found similarly by investigating what belongs to the first player if he wins and if he loses.

If he wins, he will have all his games and consequently all the money, which is, for example, 8.

If the first player loses, the second player who lacked three games will now lack only two. Therefore their status will be that the first player lacks one game and the second player two; consequently by the preceding case 6 pistoles will belong to the first.

Therefore if he wins, he should have 8, and if he loses, 6; therefore in case of division half of these two sums belongs to him, that is, 7; for $6+8=14$, half of which is 7.

FIFTH CASE

If one of the players lacks one game and the other four, the method is the same.
The first, if he wins, wins the entire sum, which is, for example, 8; if he loses,

he lacks one game to the other's three; therefore 7 pistoles out of 8 belong to him. Therefore in case of division half of 8 plus half of 7 belong to him, that is, 7½.

SIXTH CASE

Similarly if one player lacks one game and the other five, and so on to infinity.

SEVENTH CASE

The same method applies if the first player lacks two games and the second three, for we must always examine the results of winning and of losing.

If the first player wins, he will lack one game to the second player's three; therefore by the fourth case 7 out of 8 will belong to him.

If he loses, both players will lack two games; therefore by the second case half, that is, 4, belongs to each. Therefore the first player will have 7 if he wins and 4 if he loses; therefore in case of division he will get half of the two together, that is, 5½.

In this way we shall determine the divisions for every kind of situation by always taking what belongs to the first player if he wins and what belongs to him if he loses and assigning to him in case of division half of these two sums.

This is one method of determining divisions.

There are two others, one by the arithmetical triangle and the other by combinations.

METHOD FOR DIVIDING THE STAKES BETWEEN TWO PLAYERS WHO ARE PLAYING FOR A SET OF GAMES BY MEANS OF THE ARITHMETICAL TRIANGLE

Before giving the method we must demonstrate the following lemma:

LEMMA

If two players are playing a game of pure chance on condition that if the first player wins, there will belong to him some part of the sum they are playing for, expressed by a fraction, and that if he loses, there will belong to him a smaller part of the same sum, expressed by another fraction; if they wish to separate without playing, the division will be determined as follows: If the two fractions are not of the same denomination, let them be reduced to a common denominator. Let a fraction be taken whose numerator is the sum of the two numerators and whose denominator is double the common denominator. This fraction expresses the part of the sum at stake belonging to the first player.

For example, let ⅗ of the stakes belong to him if he wins and ⅕ if he loses. I say that what belongs to him in case of division will be found by taking the sum of the numerators, which is 4, and double the denominator, which is 10, and out of them making the fraction ⁴⁄₁₀.

For by what was demonstrated in the second corollary we had to add the cases of winning and losing and take half the sum. Now the sum of the two fractions ⅗ and ⅕ is ⅘, which is obtained by adding the numerators, and half the sum is got by doubling the denominator, and thus we have ⁴⁄₁₀. Q.E.D.

Now these rules are general and without exception, whatever comes from winning or losing; for if, for example, ½ belongs to a player if he wins and nothing if he loses, by reducing the two fractions to the same denominator, we shall have

½ if he wins and %₂ if he loses; therefore in case of division the required fraction is ¼, whose numerator is equal to the sum of the other two and whose denominator is double theirs.

Similarly if the entire sum belongs to a player if he wins and ⅓ if he loses, reducing the fractions to a common denominator, we shall have ⅗ if he wins and ⅓ if he loses; therefore in case of division ⅚ belongs to him.

Similarly if the entire sum belongs to a player if he wins and nothing if he loses, the division will obviously be ½; for winning gives ½ and losing %₁; therefore the division is ½.

And similarly for all possible cases.

PROBLEM 1, PROPOSITION 1

Given two players each of whom lacks a certain number of games to complete the set, to find by the arithmetical triangle what the division should be (if they wish to separate without playing) in the light of the games each lacks.

Let there be taken in the triangle the base which has as many cells as the two players together lack games; then let there be taken in this base as many contiguous cells beginning with the first as the first player lacks games, and let the sum of their numbers be taken. Therefore there remain as many cells as the second player lacks games. Again let the sum of their numbers be taken. These sums are to each other as the odds of the players reciprocally, so that if the sum at stake is equal to the sum of the numbers of all the cells of the base, there will belong to each player that part of it contained in as many cells as the other lacks games. And if they are playing for other stakes, their shares will be proportional.

For example, let there be two players, one of whom lacks two games and the other four, to find the division.

Let there be added together the two numbers, 2 and 4, and let their sum be 6. Let the sixth base of the arithmetical triangle be taken, $P\delta$, in which there are consequently six cells, P, M, F, ω, S, δ. Let there be taken as many cells beginning with the first, P, as the first player lacks games, that is to say, the first two, P, M. Therefore there remain as many cells as the second player lacks games, that is, four, F, ω, S, δ.

I say that the odds of the first player are to the odds of the second player as $F+\omega+S+\delta$ is to $P+M$, which is to say that if the sum at stake is equal to $P+M+F+\omega+S+\delta$, the sum of the four cells, $\delta+S+\omega+F$, belongs to the player who lacks two games, the sum of the two cells, $P+M$, to the player who lacks four games. And if they are playing for other stakes, their shares will be proportional.

And to speak generally, whatever the sum at stake, the share of the first player is expressed by the fraction $\dfrac{F+\omega+S+\delta}{P+M+F+\omega+S+\delta}$, of which the numerator is the sum of the second player's four cells and the denominator the sum of all the cells. And the share of the second player is expressed by the fraction $\dfrac{P+M}{P+M+F+\omega+S+\delta}$, of which the numerator is the sum of the first player's two cells and the denominator again the sum of all the cells.

And if one player lacks one game and the other five, the share of the first player is the sum of the first five cells, $P+M+F+\omega+S$, and the share of the second player is cell δ.

And if one player lacks six games, and the other two, the division will be found in the eighth base, in which the first six cells contain the share of the player who lacks two games and the other two the share of the player who lacks six, and so on to infinity.

Although this proposition has an infinity of cases, I shall nevertheless demonstrate it in a few words by means of two lemmas.

The first lemma is that the second base contains the divisions of the players who lack two games in all.

The second lemma is that if any base contains the divisions of those lacking as many games as the base has cells, the next base will do the same, that is, it too will contain the divisions of the players lacking as many games as the base has cells.

From which I conclude, in a word, that all the bases of the arithmetical triangle have this property; for the second base has it by the first lemma; therefore by the second lemma the third base has it too, and consequently the fourth, and so on to infinity. Q.E.D.

We have then only to demonstrate these 2 lemmas.

The first is self-evident; for if each player lacks one game, it is evident that their positions are to each other as ϕ to σ, that is, as 1 to 1, and that the share of each is expressed by the fraction $\dfrac{\sigma}{\phi+\sigma}$, which is ½.

The second lemma is demonstrated as follows:

If any base, such as the fourth, $D\lambda$, contains the divisions of those lacking four games, that is to say that if the first player lacks one and the second three, the share of the stakes belonging to the first is expressed by the fraction $\dfrac{D+B+\theta}{D+B+\theta+\lambda}$, which has as denominator the sum of the cells of the base and as numerator the first three cells; and that if both players lack two games, the fraction belonging to the first is $\dfrac{D+B}{D+B+\theta+\lambda}$; and that if the first player lacks three games and the second one, the fraction of the first is $\dfrac{D}{D+B+\theta+\lambda}$, etc.

I say that the fifth base also contains the divisions of those lacking five games, and that if, for example, the first player lacks two games and the second player three, the share of the stakes belonging to the first is expressed by the fraction $\dfrac{H+E+C}{H+E+C+R+\mu}$.

For to know what belongs to two players each of whom is lacking in games, we must take the fraction which would belong to the first player if he won and that which would belong to him if he lost, and if they are not of the same denomination, reduce them to a common denominator, then form a fraction of which the numerator is the sum of the two others and the denominator double the other, by the preliminary lemma.

Let us examine then the fraction which would belong to the first player if he won and if he lost.

If the first player, who lacks two games, wins the one to be played, he will lack only one and the second player will still lack three; therefore they will lack four games in all; therefore by hypothesis their division is found in the fourth base, and the share of the first will be the fraction $\dfrac{D+B+\theta}{D+B+\theta+\lambda}$.

If on the contrary the first player loses, he will still lack two games and the second player will also lack only two; therefore by hypothesis the fraction of the first will be $\dfrac{D+B}{D+B+\theta+\lambda}$. Therefore in case of division the fraction of the first player will be $\dfrac{D+B+\theta+D+B}{2D+2B+2\theta+2\lambda}$ that is $\dfrac{H+E+C}{H+E+C+R+\mu}$.   Q.E.D.

This is also demonstrated in the same way of all the other bases, because the foundation of this proof is that a base is always double the preceding base by the seventh consequence and that by the tenth consequence any number of cells of the same base is equal to the same number of cells of the preceding base (which is always the numerator of the player's fraction if he wins) together with the same cells lacking one (which is the numerator of the player's fraction if he loses); which being everywhere true in general, the demonstration is always possible and universal.

PROBLEM 2, PROPOSITION 2

Given two players each of whom stakes the same sum on a given number of games, to find in the arithmetical triangle the part of the loser's money that the last game is worth to the winner.

For example, let two players each stake three pistoles on four games; we want to find what part of the loser's 3 pistoles the last game is worth to the winner.

Let there be taken the fraction of which the numerator is unity and the denominator the sum of the cells of the fourth base, since the set has four games; I say that this fraction is the value of the last game in terms of the loser's money.

For if when two players are playing for a set of four games, one has three games to his credit and thus lacks one game and the other lacks four, it has been demonstrated that the share of the first player for winning his first three games is expressed by the fraction $\dfrac{H+E+C+R}{H+E+C+R+\mu}$, which has as denominator the sum of the cells of the fifth base and as numerator its first four cells; therefore there remains of the entire sum of the two stakes only the fraction $\dfrac{\mu}{H+E+C+R+\mu}$, which would belong to the player who already has the first three games if he won the last; the value of this last in terms of the whole stakes is

$$\dfrac{\mu}{H+E+C+R+\mu} \quad \text{that is} \quad \dfrac{\text{unity}}{2D+2B+2\theta+2\lambda}.$$

But since the entire amount of the stakes is $2D+2B+2\theta+2\lambda$, the amount of each stake is $D+B+\theta+\lambda$; therefore the value of the last game in terms of the loser's stake only is the fraction $\dfrac{\text{I}}{D+B+\theta+\lambda}$, double the preceding fraction, having as numerator unity and as denominator the sum of the cells of the fourth base.   Q.E.D.

PROBLEM 3, PROPOSITION 3

Given two players each of whom stakes the same amount on a given number of games, to find in the arithmetical triangle the part of the loser's money represented by the value of the first game.

For example, let two players each stake 3 pistoles on four games; we want to find what part of the loser's stake the first game is worth to the winner.

Let there be added to the number 4 the number 3, less than it by unity, and let the sum be 7. Let there be taken the fraction which has as denominator the cells of the seventh base and as numerator the cell of the base cut by the bisector, that is, the fraction $\dfrac{\rho}{V+Q+K+\rho+\xi+N+\zeta}$. I say that this fraction satisfies the problem.

For if when two players are playing for a set of four games the first player has one game to his credit, he will have three more to win and the second player will have four. Therefore the first player's share of the whole amount of the stakes is the fraction $\dfrac{V+Q+K+\rho}{V+Q+K+\rho+\xi+N+\zeta}$, which has as denominator all the cells of the seventh base and as numerator its first four cells.

Therefore $V+Q+K+\rho$ belongs to him out of the whole amount of the two stakes, expressed by $V+Q+K+\rho+\xi+N+\zeta$; but since this latter amount is the sum of the two stakes, he had himself staked half of it, namely $V+Q+K+\frac{1}{2}\rho$ (for $V+Q+K=\zeta+N+\xi$).

Therefore he has $\frac{1}{2}\rho$, that is, ω, more than he had at the beginning of the game; therefore he has won a portion of the total amount of the two stakes expressed by the fraction $\dfrac{\omega}{V+Q+K+\rho+\xi+N+\zeta}$. Therefore he has won a portion of the loser's stake double the above, namely, a portion expressed by the fraction $\dfrac{\rho}{V+Q+K+\rho+\xi+N+\zeta}$.

Therefore winning the first game has given the player that fraction, which is accordingly its value.

COROLLARY

Therefore the part of the loser's stake constituting the value of the first game out of two is expressed by the fraction ½.

For to determine this value in accordance with the rule just given we must take the fraction which has as denominator the cells of the third base (because the number of games in the set is 2 and the number less by unity is 1, which taken together make 3), and as numerator the cell in the base cut by the bisector; therefore we shall have the fraction $\dfrac{\psi}{A+\psi+\pi}$.

But the number of cell ψ is 2, and the numbers of cells A, ψ, π are 1, 2, 1; therefore we have the fraction $\dfrac{2}{1+2+1}$, that is, ½.

Therefore winning the first game has given the player that fraction, which is accordingly its value.   Q.E.D.

Problem 4, Proposition 4

Given two players each of whom stakes the same sum on a given number of games, to find by the arithmetical triangle the value of the second game in terms of the loser's stake.

Let the number of games in the set be four; we must find the value of the second game in terms of the loser's stake.

Let the value of the first game be found by the preceding problem. I say that the value of the second game is the same.

For when two players are playing for four games if one of them has two to his credit, the fraction belonging to him is $\dfrac{P+M+F+\omega}{P+M+F+\omega+S+\delta}$, which has as denominator the sum of the cells of the sixth base and as numerator the sum of the first four. But he had staked the fraction $\dfrac{P+F+M}{P+M+F+\omega+S+\delta}$, that is, half of the whole amount. Therefore his winnings are the fraction $\dfrac{\omega}{P+M+F+\omega+S+\delta}$, which is the same as $\dfrac{\rho}{V+Q+K+\rho+\xi+N+\zeta}$; therefore he has won out of half the whole amount, that is, the loser's stake, the fraction $\dfrac{2\rho}{V+Q+K+\rho+\xi+N+\zeta}$, double the preceding fraction.

Therefore winning the first two games gave him this fraction of the loser's money, which is double what the first game gave him by the preceding problem. Therefore the second game gave him as much as the first.

Conclusion

We easily conclude from the relation of the arithmetical triangle to the divisions which should be made between two players that the proportions between cells given in the *Treatise on the Triangle* have consequences extending to the value of divisions, very easy to draw, about which I have written a little treatise dealing with divisions, which explains why and how further extensions can be made.

USE OF THE ARITHMETICAL TRIANGLE TO FIND THE POWERS OF BINOMIALS

If it is proposed to find any power, such as the fourth, of a binomial of which the first term is A and the second unity, that is, if we want to find the fourth power of $A+1$, we must take in the arithmetical triangle the fifth base, that is, the base whose exponent 5 is greater by unity than 4, the exponent of the proposed power. The cells of the fifth base are 1, 4, 6, 4, 1, of which we must take the first number, 1, as the coefficient of A in the proposed power, that is, of A^4; next we must take the second number of the base, that is, 4, as the coefficient of A in the next lower power, that is, of A^3, and take the following number of the base, namely 6, as the coefficient of A in the next lower power, that is, of A^2, and take the following number of the base, that is 4, as the coefficient of A in the next lower power, that is, of A, and take the last number of the base, 1, as it is. Thus we shall have $1A^4+4A^3+6A^2+4A+1$, which will be the fourth power of the binomial $A+1$. So that if A (which represents any number) is unity and therefore the binomial $A+1$ is the dyad, the power $1A^4+4A^3+6A^2+4A+1$ will be $1 \cdot 1^4+4 \cdot 1^3+6 \cdot 1^2+4 \cdot 1+1$, that is,

once the fourth power of unity (A), that is.................. 1

four times the cube of 1, that is........................... 4

six times the square of 1, that is.......................... 6

four times unity, that is................................... 4

plus unity.. 1

which added together make.................................16

And the fourth power of 2 is in fact 16.

If A is another number, such as 4, and consequently the binomial $A+1$ is 5, then its fourth power will still be, in accordance with the above method,

$$1A^4+4A^3+6A^2+4A+1,$$

which now signifies

$$1 \cdot 4^4+4 \cdot 4^3+6 \cdot 4^2+4 \cdot 4+1,$$

that is,

once the fourth power of 4, namely.......................256

four times the cube of 4................................256

six times the square of 4............................... 96

four times the root 4................................... 16

plus unity... 1

the sum of which.......................................625

is the fourth power of 5, as is indeed the case.

And similarly for all other examples.

If we want to find the same power of the binomial $A+2$, we must again take

$$1A^4+4A^3+6A^2+4A+1,$$

and then write the four numbers, 2, 4, 8, 16, which are the first four powers of 2, under the numbers 4, 6, 4, 1, that is, under each of the numbers of the base, beginning with the second, as follows:

$$1A^4+4A^3+6A^2+4A+1$$
$$2\quad 4\quad 8\quad 16$$

and multiply the corresponding numbers by each other

$$1A^4+4A^3+\ 6A^2+\ 4A+\ 1$$
$$\underline{2\quad\ 4\quad\ 8\quad\ 16}$$

as follows $\qquad 1A^4+8A^3+24A^2+32A+16$

Thus we shall have the fourth power of the binomial $A+2$; so that if A is unity, the fourth power will be

once the fourth power of unity (A)........................ 1

eight times the cube of 1 8

$24 \cdot 1^2$..24

$32 \cdot 1$..32

plus...16

of which the sum 81

will be the fourth power of 3, as in fact it is.

And if A is 2, then $A+2$ will be 4, and its fourth power will be

once the fourth power of A, or 2, namely 16

$8 \cdot 2^3$ 64

$24 \cdot 2^2$ 96

$32 \cdot 2$ 64

plus the fourth power of 2 16

whose sum 256

will be the fourth power of 4.

Similarly we shall find the fourth power of $A+3$,
putting down in the same way $A^4+4A^3+6A^2+4A+1$
and underneath, the numbers   3   9   27   81

$$A^4+12A^3+54A^2+108A+81$$

which are the first 4 powers of 3; multiplying the corresponding numbers, we shall find the fourth power of $A+3$.

And so on to infinity. If instead of the fourth power we want the fifth power, we must take the sixth base and proceed as I have indicated in the case of the fifth, and similarly for all the other powers.

We shall find in the same way the powers of the differences $A-1$, $A-2$, etc. The method is exactly the same except for the signs; the signs $+$ and $-$ succeed each other in alternation, the sign $+$ always coming first.

Thus the fourth power of $A-1$ will be found as follows: the fourth power of $A+1$ is by the preceding rule, $A^4+4A^3+6A^2+4A+1$. Therefore changing the signs as indicated, we shall have $A^4-4A^3+6A^2-4A+1$. Also the cube of $A-2$ will be found in the same way. For the cube of $A+2$ by the preceding rule is $A^3+6A^2+12A+8$. Therefore the cube of $A-2$ will be found by changing the signs: $A^3-6A^2+12A-8$. And so on to infinity.

I do not demonstrate these things, because others have already dealt with them, as for example, Herigogne; besides they are evident in themselves.

TREATISE ON THE ORDERS OF NUMBERS

I assume that the reader has read my treatise on the arithmetical triangle and its use for the orders of numbers; if not, I refer to it those who wish to read what follows, which is simply a continuation of it.

I defined what I mean by the orders of numbers there, and I shall not repeat the definition.

I also showed there that the arithmetical triangle is nothing but the table of the orders of numbers; as a result of which it is evident that all the properties given in the arithmetical triangle concerning the relations between cells and between rows have their analogues in the orders of numbers, so that if we possess even a little the art of applying the properties of one to the other, there is no proposition in the treatise on the triangle which does not have its consequence for the different orders. And they can be found with such ease and in such abundance that I am far from wishing to write them all out explicitly. I should prefer leaving everything to the reader since it is all so easy. But to avoid both these extremes I shall just give a few examples which will open the way to finding all the others.

For example, from what was said in one of the consequences of the *Treatise on the Triangle*, namely, that each cell is equal to the immediately preceding parallel and perpendicular cells, I derive the following proposition for the orders of numbers:

PROPOSITION 1

A number of any order whatsoever is equal to the number preceding it in its own order together with the number corresponding to it in the preceding order. Consequently the fourth, for example, of the numbers of the fourth order is equal to the third number of the fourth order together with the fourth number of the third order. Also the fifth number of the fifth order is equal to the fourth number of the fifth order together with the fifth number of the fourth order, etc.

Another example. From its having been shown in the triangle that each cell is equal to the parallel cell preceding it together with all the perpendicular cells preceding this parallel cell, for example, $F = E + B + \psi + \sigma$, I derive the following proposition:

PROPOSITION 2

A number of whatsoever order is equal to the sum of the numbers whose root is less than its own by unity of its own and all preceding orders, and consequently the fourth number of the fourth order, for example, is equal to the third number of the fourth order plus the third number of the third order plus the third natural number plus the third number of the units, that is, unity.

Whence we can now draw other consequences, such as the following, which I give to open the way to other similar ones:

PROPOSITION 3

Every number, whatever its cell, is made up of as many numbers as there are orders from its own to the first, inclusive, each of the numbers representing one of the orders. Thus a number of the fifth order is composed of another number of the fifth order, a number of the fourth order, a number of the third order, a natural number and unity.

If we want to use this proposition for a problem, we can enunciate it as follows:

PROPOSITION 4, PROBLEM

Given a number of any order, to find a number in each order from the first to its own, inclusive, whose sum is equal to the given number.

The solution is easy. We must take in all these orders the numbers whose root is less by unity than that of the given number.

Another example. From the fact that reciprocal cells are equal, it follows:

PROPOSITION 5

That two numbers of different orders are equal if the root of one is the same number as the exponent of the other. Consequently the third number of the fourth order is equal to the fourth number of the third order. The fifth number of the eighth order is the same as the eighth number of the fifth order.

We would never come to an end. For example:

PROPOSITION 6

All the fourth numbers of all the orders are the same as all the numbers of the fourth order, etc.

Because the parallel and perpendicular rows having the same exponent are composed of equivalent cells.

By this method we shall find a wonderful correspondence in everything else, as, for example, the following:

PROPOSITION 7

A number of whatever order is to the next greater in the same order as the root of the lesser is to itself together with the exponent of the order diminished by unity.

Which follows from the fourteenth consequence of the triangle, where it is shown that each cell is to the immediately preceding parallel cell as the exponent of the base of the preceding cell is to the exponent of its perpendicular row.

In order that no part of the method by which these correspondences are found remain hidden, I shall make the relationship explicit. It is a little more difficult here than above, because we see no relationship between the base of the triangles and the orders of numbers. This is the way to find it: For *the exponent of the base* in the fourteenth consequence we must substitute *the exponent of the parallel row together with the exponent of the perpendicular row diminished by unity.* Which gives the same number and with this advantage that we know the relation there is between these exponents and the orders of numbers; for we know that in this new language we must say: *the exponent of the order together with the root diminished by unity.* I say all this that the method of making and facilitating these reductions may be available.

Thus we shall find that:

PROPOSITION 8

A number of whatever order is to the corresponding number of the following order as the exponent of the order of the lesser number is to itself together with the common root diminished by unity.

This is the thirteenth consequence of the triangle. Thus again we shall find that:

PROPOSITION 9

A number of whatever order is to the number of the preceding order whose root is greater than its own by unity as the root of the first number is to the exponent of the order of the second.

This is only the twelfth consequence of the arithmetical triangle.

I omit many other propositions, each of which as well as each of those I have just given can still be greatly increased by different enunciations, for instead of expressing these proportions as I have by saying that *a number is to another as a third is to a fourth,* may we not say that *the rectangle of the extremes is equal to that of the means,* and thus multiply the propositions, and not without utility, for looked at from another side they open up other prospects?

For example, if we wish to express this last proposition in another way, we can enunciate it as follows:

PROPOSITION 10

A number of whatever order when multiplied by the preceding root is equal to the exponent of its order multiplied by the preceding number of the following order.

And because when four numbers are proportional, the rectangle of the extremes or of the means, when divided by one of the other two gives as quotient the remaining number, we can state the proposition as follows:

PROPOSITION 11

A number of whatever order, when multiplied by the preceding root and divided by the exponent of its order, gives as quotient the preceding number of the following order.

The ways of saying the same thing are infinite. I cite an illustrious example and one that does me much honor. This very proposition that I have just been turning about in several of its aspects occurred to our celebrated councilor of Toulouse, M. de Fermat, and the wonderful thing is that without either of us having given the other any slightest hint of what we were doing, he was writing in his province what I was discovering at Paris, and at the very hour, as our letters written and received at the same time bear witness. Happy to have concurred on this occasion as on others in a really extraordinary way with so great and admirable a man, who in all the investigations of the highest reaches of geometry is at the peak of excellence, as his works, which our long prayers have at last obtained from him, will soon make known to all the geometers of Europe, who are waiting for them! His way of taking the proposition is as follows:

In the series of natural numbers beginning with unity the product of any number multiplied by the next higher is double the same number of the third order.

The product of any number multiplied by the next higher number of the third order is triple the same number of the fourth order.

The product of any number multiplied by the next higher number of the fourth order is quadruple the same number of the fifth order; and so on to infinity by a general and uniform method.

See how enunciations can be varied! Since what I show for this proposition is to be understood of the rest, I shall not dwell longer on this convenient method but leave it to each to exercise his genius in these investigations which should claim all the study of mathematicians. For if we cannot turn propositions in every direction and if we make use only of the first glimpse we had, we shall never get very far. It is these different roads that open up new consequences and by enunciations suited to the subject bind together propositions which seemed to be unrelated in the terms in which they were originally conceived. I shall then go on with this subject in the usual geometrical way, and what I say will amount to a new treatise on the orders of numbers. I shall even present it in Latin because I happen to have written it in that language at the time of discovery.

CORRESPONDENCE WITH FERMAT ON THE THEORY OF PROBABILITIES

LETTER FROM FERMAT TO PASCAL

[1654]

Sir,

If I undertake to bring up a given face with a single die in eight throws and if we agree after the money has been staked that I shall not take my first throw, I am entitled by my principle to withdraw from the game $\frac{1}{6}$ of the whole sum as compensation for having given up the said first throw.

But if we again agree after that that I shall not take my second throw, I am entitled to withdraw as indemnity $\frac{1}{6}$ of what is left, which is $\frac{5}{36}$ of the whole.

And if after that we agree that I shall not take my third throw, my indemnity is $\frac{1}{6}$ of what is left, which is $\frac{25}{216}$ of the whole.

And if after that we again agree that I shall not take my fourth throw, I should withdraw $\frac{1}{6}$ of what is left, which is $\frac{125}{1296}$ of the whole, and I agree with you that this is the value of the fourth throw on the assumption that I have already been compensated for the preceding throws. But what you ask me to consider in the last example of your letter is (I use your own words): if I undertake to bring up a six in eight throws and have taken three without doing it, if my fellow player asks me to give up my fourth throw but wants to compensate me for losing my chance, $\frac{125}{1296}$ of the whole stakes will belong to me.

But this, according to my principle, is not so. For in this case since the player got nothing from his first three throws and the whole stakes are still in the game, if he agrees not to take his fourth throw, he should have as indemnity $\frac{1}{6}$ of the whole.

And if he had thrown four times without bringing up the assigned face and it should be agreed he would not take his fifth throw, he should still have as indemnity $\frac{1}{6}$ of the whole. For as long as the stakes remain unchanged, it not only follows from principle but it is also common sense that the odds are the same for every throw.

I beg you then to let me know if we are at one on the principle, as I believe we are, and if we differ only in its application.

I am, etc.

FERMAT

LETTER FROM PASCAL TO FERMAT

July 29, 1654

Sir,

I too am overcome by impatience and, although I am still confined to my bed, I can't resist letting you know that I received yesterday evening from M. de Carcavi your letter on divisions (of stakes), which I admire more than I can tell you. I haven't time to write at length, but in a word your determination of the divisions both for the dice and for the games is perfectly correct; which gives me great satisfaction, for now I can no longer doubt the truth of my results after finding myself in such wonderful agreement with you.

I admire your method for the games much more than for the dice. I had known several persons to discover the method for the dice, such as the Chevalier de Méré, who first brought me these questions, and also M. de Roberval. But M. de Méré had never been able to find the right value of the games nor a way of getting there, so that I found myself alone in the knowledge of this proportion.

Your method is very reliable and is the first that occurred to me in this investigation, but because of the labor involved in using combinations I have found an abridgment of it, or rather a different method much shorter and simpler, which I should like to be able to tell you about here in a few words. For I should like henceforth to open my heart to you if possible, so great is my pleasure in our agreement. I see indeed that truth is the same at Toulouse and at Paris.

This is about the way I find the value of each game when two players are playing, for example, for three games and each has staked 32 pistoles on the play:

Let us suppose one player has two games and the other one. They now play a game of which the necessary consequence is that if the first player wins it, he wins all the money at stake, namely, 64 pistoles, and if the second player wins it, the score is two to two. Consequently if they wish to separate, each should withdraw his own stake, namely, 32 pistoles.

Consider then, Sir, that if the first player wins, 64 pistoles belong to him; if he loses, 32. Therefore if they wish not to venture this game and to separate without playing it, the first player should say: "I am sure of having 32 pistoles, for even if I lose, I get them. But as for the other 32, perhaps they will be mine, perhaps yours; the odds are even. Let us share these 32 pistoles equally therefore, and give me in addition my own 32, which are mine in either case." He will have 48 pistoles then and the second player will have 16.

Let us suppose now that one player has two games and the other player none, and they are beginning a game with the following consequences: if the first player wins it, he takes all the money, 64 pistoles; if the second player wins it, they are back at the preceding case, where one player has two games and the other one.

But we have already shown that in this case 48 pistoles belong to the player who has two games. Therefore if they wish not to play this game, he should say: "If I win, I shall win the entire sum, which is 64; if I lose, 48 will legitimately be mine. Therefore give me the 48 which are mine even if I lose, and let us share equally the other 16, since you have as much chance of winning them as I have." Thus he will have 48 and 8, that is, 56 pistoles.

Finally let us suppose that one player has only one game and the other none. Clearly, Sir, if they begin a new game, it follows that if the first player wins it, he will have two games to his credit, and consequently by the preceding case 56 pistoles will belong to him; if he loses, each has a game, and therefore 32 pistoles belong to him. Therefore he should say: "If you want not to play this game, give me 32 pistoles, which are mine in either case, and let us share the rest of the 56 equally. From 56 take 32 and 24 are left; divide 24 in half, you take 12 and I take 12, which with 32 make 44."

Now in this way you see by simple subtraction that for the first game 12 pistoles of the loser's stake belong to the winner, for the second game another 12, and for the last game 8.

Now, no longer to make a mystery of it, since you see the whole thing perfectly clearly and I was being mysterious about it only to find out if I was not mistaken, the value (I mean value in terms of the loser's money only) of the last game of two is double that of the last game of three and four times that of the last game of four and eight times that of the last game of five, etc.

But the proportion of the first games is not so easy to find. This then is the way it is, for I don't want to hide anything, and here is the problem I was making so much of, for indeed I am very much pleased with it:

Given any number of games, to find the value of the first.

Let the given number of games be, for example, 8. Take the first eight even numbers and the first eight odd numbers, namely: 2, 4, 6, 8, 10, 12, 14, 16, and 1, 3, 5, 7, 9, 11, 13, 15.

Multiply the even numbers as follows: the first by the second, the product by the third, the product by the fourth, the product by the fifth, etc. Multiply the odd numbers in the same way: the first by the second, the product by the third, etc.

The last product of the even numbers is the denominator and the last product of the odd numbers is the numerator of the fraction expressing the value of the first game of eight; that is, if each player stakes the number of pistoles expressed by the product of the even numbers, the number of the loser's pistoles belonging to the winner will be expressed by the product of the odd numbers.

Which is demonstrated, but with much labor, by combinations used in the way you thought of; I have not been able to demonstrate it in that other way I was just telling you about, but only by the method of combinations. Here are the preliminary propositions, which are simply arithmetical propositions about combinations, of which I have found some rather nice properties.

If in any number of letters, for example, 8: A, B, C, D, E, F, G, H, you take all the possible combinations of 4 letters and then all the possible combinations of 5 letters and then of 6, of 7, and of 8, and thus you take all the possible combinations from the number which is half the whole up to the whole, I say that if you add together half the combinations of 4 and all the higher combinations, the sum will be the number of the quaternary progression beginning with the dyad which corresponds to half the number of letters.

For example, and I'll write it in Latin, for French is no good here:

If in as many letters as you please, for example, 8: A, B, C, D, E, F, G, H, all combinations of 4, 5, 6, etc., up to 8 are taken, I say that if you add together half the combinations of 4, namely 35 (half 70), all the combinations of 5, namely 56, all the combinations of 6, namely 28, all the combinations of 7, namely 8, and all the combinations of 8, namely 1, you have the fourth number of the quaternary progression beginning with 2: I say *fourth number* because 4 is half of 8.

For the numbers of the quaternary progression beginning with 2 are: 2, 8, 32, 128, 512, etc., of which 2 is the first, 8 the second, 32 the third, and 128 the fourth, which 128 is equal to 35, half the combinations of 4 letters, +56, the combinations of 5 letters, +28, the combinations of 6 letters, +8, the combinations of 7 letters, +1, the combination of 8 letters.

This is the first proposition, which is purely arithmetical; the second is concerned with the doctrine of divisions and is as follows:

First it must be stated that if one game out of 5 has been won, for example, and therefore 4 are lacking, the set will have to be decided in 8 games, which is double 4.

The value of the first game of 5 in terms of the loser's money is the fraction which has as numerator half the combinations of 4 in 8 (I take 4 because it is equal to the number of games lacking and 8 because it is double 4) and as denominator the numerator together with all the higher combinations.

Thus if I have one game out of 5, $\frac{35}{128}$ of my fellow player's money belongs to me; that is, if he has staked 128 pistoles, I take 35 and leave him the rest, 93.

But the fraction $\frac{35}{128}$ is the same as $\frac{105}{384}$, of which the denominator is the product of the even numbers and the numerator is the product of the odd numbers.

You will undoubtedly see all this very well if you take the trouble to consider it at all. That is why I think there is no use saying anything more about it. However, I am sending you one of my old tables (p. 479); I haven't time to copy it. I shall make another one. You will see there as always that the value of the first game is the same as that of the second, which is easily found by combinations.

You will also see that the numbers of the first line always increase; similarly those of the second line and those of the third line.

But afterwards those of the fourth line decrease, those of the fifth, etc., which is strange.

I haven't time to send you the demonstration of a difficulty which caused M . . . great astonishment, for he is very intelligent, but he is not a geometer (which is, as you know, a great defect); he does not even understand how a mathematical line can be infinitely divisible and thinks he knows very well that it is composed of a finite number of points. I have never been able to get that out of his head; if you could do it, we would make him perfect.

He told me then that he had found something wrong with numbers for the following reason:

If we undertake to throw a six with one die, the odds for succeeding in 4 throws are as 671 to 625.

If we undertake to throw a double six with two dice, the odds are against success in 24 throws.

And yet 24:36 (which is the number of faces of the two dice) ::4:6 (which is the number of faces of one die).

This was so great a scandal to him that he openly proclaimed propositions were doubtful and arithmetic self-contradictory. But with your principles you will easily see the explanation.

I shall put down in order everything I have done with this when I have completed the geometrical treatises on which I have been working for some time now.

I have also written some arithmetical treatises, in connection with which I beg you to send me your opinion on the following demonstration.

I assume the well-known lemma that twice the sum of as many numbers as we please of the continuous progression beginning with unity, such as 1, 2, 3, 4, is equal to the last, 4, multiplied by the next greater, 5, that is, that twice the sum of the numbers contained in A is equal to the product of A and $(A+1)$.

Now I come to my proposition:

The difference of any two successive cubes exceeds by unity six times all the numbers contained in the root of the smaller cube.

Let there be two roots, R, S, differing by unity:

I say R^3-S^3-1 is equal to six times the sum of the numbers contained in S. For let S be called A; therefore R is

$$A+1.$$

Therefore the cube of root R, or $A+1$, is

$$A^3+3A^2+3A+1^3.$$

But the cube of S, or A, is

$$A^3;$$

and their difference is

$$3A^2+3A+1^3,$$

that is

$$R^3-S^3;$$

therefore if we subtract unity,

$$3A^2+3A=R^3-S^3-1.$$

But twice the sum of the numbers contained in A or S is equal by the lemma to

$$A(A+1), \text{ that is, } A^2+A;$$

therefore six times the sum of the numbers contained in A is equal to

$$3A^2+3A.$$

But

$$3A^2+3A=R^3-S^3-1; \text{ therefore}$$

R^3-S^3-1 is equal to six times the sum of the numbers contained in A or S.

Q.E.D.

No one has objected to my demonstration, but I have been told that no objection was made because everyone now is used to this method. But I claim that without any favor to me this demonstration should be accepted as excellent in kind. However I await your opinion with full submission.

All my arithmetical demonstrations are of this kind. Here are two more difficulties.

I have demonstrated a proposition in plane geometry by making use of the cube of a line compared to the cube of another line. I claim that this is purely geometrical and in accordance with the strictest standards.

Also I have solved the problem:

Of four planes, four points, and four spheres, any four (of the twelve) being given, to find a sphere which, touching the given spheres, passes through the given points and leaves on the planes parts of spheres in which given angles can be inscribed, and this problem:

Of three circles, three points, and three lines, any three (of the nine) being given, to find a circle which, touching the circles and the points, leaves on the lines an arc in which a given angle can be inscribed.

I found a complete solution for these problems, using in the construction only circles and straight lines; but in the demonstration I make use of conic sections, of parabolas or hyperbolas. However I claim that since the construction is plane, my solution is plane and should be accepted as such.

It is a poor return for the honor you do me in suffering my letters, to take up so much of your time. I never think I am going to write more than a word or two, and so I don't tell you what I have most at heart, which is that the more I know you, the more I admire and honor you, and that if you knew my feelings in this respect, you would give a place in your friendship to him who is, etc.

PASCAL

TABLE REFERRED TO IN THE PRECEDING LETTER

If each player stakes 256 on

	6 Games	5 Games	4 Games	3 Games	2 Games	1 Game
1st Game	63	70	80	96	128	256
2nd Game	63	70	80	96	128	
3rd Game	56	60	64	64		
4th Game	42	40	32			
5th Game	24	16				
6th Game	8					

Of the 256 pistoles of my fellow player I should have for the

If each player stakes 256 on

	6 Games	5 Games	4 Games	3 Games	2 Games	1 Game
1st Game	63	70	80	96	128	256
1st 2 Games	126	140	160	192	256	
1st 3 Games	182	200	224	256		
1st 4 Games	224	240	256			
1st 5 Games	248	256				
1st 6 Games	256					

Of the 256 pistoles of my fellow player I should have for the

LETTER FROM PASCAL TO FERMAT

August 24, 1654

SIR,

I was not able to put before you in their entirety my views on the subject of divisions among several players by the last mail; I am even somewhat reluctant to do so for fear that that wonderful agreement between us which was so dear to me may begin to fail here, for I am afraid that we have different opinions on this subject. I want to put my whole argument before you, and you will do me the favor of correcting me if I am in error, or of supporting me if I have struck it right. I really ask this in all sincerity for I shall only feel sure of my view when you are on my side.

When there are only two players, your method, which uses combinations, is very reliable; but when there are three players, I think I have proof that it is not accurate, unless you go about it in some other way I do not understand. But the method I explained to you and which I use everywhere is applicable to all imaginable conditions of every kind of division, whereas the method of combinations (which I use only in certain cases where it is shorter than the general method) is good only for those occasions and not for all.

I am sure I shall succeed in making myself understood, but it will take a few words on my part and a little patience on yours.

This is your procedure when there are two players:

If the situation of two players playing for several games is such that the first player lacks two games and the second player three, to find the division we must (you say) see in how many games the play will have to be decided.

It is easy to reckon that it will be in four games, whence you conclude we must see how many combinations there are of four games between two players and see in how many combinations the first player would win and in how many the second, and divide the money in that ratio. I should have had difficulty in following that statement if I hadn't already known what it meant by my own work; and of course you had written it with that in mind. To see how many times four games combine between two players then, we must imagine that they play with a die having two faces (since they are only two), as in heads and tails, and that they throw four of these dice (because they are playing four games); and now we must see in how many different ways these dice can fall. That is easily reckoned: they can fall in sixteen ways, since sixteen is the second power of four, that is the square. For let us imagine one of the faces marked with *a*, favorable to the first player, and the other with *b*, favorable to the second player; therefore the four dice can fall in any one of the sixteen ways indicated: *aaaa ... bbbb*.

And because the first player lacks two games, all the casts with two *a*'s give him the set; therefore there are 11 for him. And because the second player lacks three games, all the casts with three *b*'s can give him the set; therefore there are 5. Therefore they must share the sum in the ratio of 11 to 5.

This is your method when there are two players. Whereupon you say that if there are more, it will not be difficult to determine the divisions by the same method.

Here, dear Sir, I must tell you that this division for two players, based on combinations, is perfectly accurate and satisfactory, but that if there are more than two players, it will not always be accurate; and I shall tell you the reason for this difference.

I communicated your method to our friends, whereupon M. de Roberval raised the following objection:

That it is an error to base the method of determining the division on the supposition that four games would be played, since when one player lacks two games and the other player three, it is not necessarily true that four games would be played, but it is possible that only two or three would be played or to be sure perhaps four;

a	a	a	a	1
a	a	a	b	1
a	a	b	a	1
a	a	b	b	1
a	b	a	a	1
a	b	a	b	1
a	b	b	a	1
a	b	b	b	2
b	a	a	a	1
b	a	a	b	1
b	a	b	a	1
b	a	b	b	2
b	b	a	a	1
b	b	a	b	2
b	b	b	a	2
b	b	b	b	2

And that he did not see therefore why it should be claimed that the just division would be made on the fictitious condition that four games would be played, since the natural condition of play is that the players stop as soon as one of them has won, and that at least if this division was not erroneous, it had not been demonstrated, so that he had some suspicion we were guilty of a paralogism.

I replied that I did not rely so much on the method of combinations, which is really not in its proper place here, as on my other universal method, which deals with all cases and carries its demonstration with it, and which gives exactly the same division as the method of combinations. Moreover I demonstrated for him the correctness of the division between two players by combinations as follows:

Isn't it true that if two players of whom one lacks two games and the other three, in accordance with the hypothesis, now freely agree to play four games, that is, to throw the four dice with two faces all at once, isn't it true, I say, that if they decided to play the four games, the division should be as we said, in accordance with the number of casts favorable to each?

He agreed, and indeed this can be demonstrated; but he denied the case was the same when there was no commitment to play the four games. Thereupon I spoke as follows:

Isn't it evident that the same players, not committed to playing the four games but wishing to stop as soon as one should have reached his number, can without advantage or disadvantage commit themselves to playing all four games, and that this agreement does not change their situation in any respect? For if the first player wins the first two games of the four and therefore has won the set, will he refuse to play two more games in view of the fact that if he wins them, he has not won better, and if he loses them, he has not won less, for these two games that the second player has won are not enough for him since he lacks three, and thus four games are not enough to make it possible for both of them to get the number they lack?

Certainly it is easy to see that it is a matter of perfect indifference to both whether they play on the condition natural to their game, which is to stop as soon as one has his number, or whether they play all four games. Therefore since there is nothing to choose between these two conditions, the division should be exactly the same in both. But it is just when they have to play four games, as I have shown; therefore it is just in the other case as well.

That is how I demonstrated it, and you will notice that the demonstration is based on the equality of the two conditions, actual and fictitious, with respect to two players, and on the fact that the same player will always win in both, and if one player wins or loses in one case, he will win or lose in the other and two will never have the required number of games.

Let us now consider three players in the same way and suppose that the first player lacks one game, the second and third each two. To determine the division, following the same method of combinations, we must first find out how many games will decide the play, as we did when there were two players. It will be three, for they could not play three games without there being necessarily a decision.

We must now see how many combinations there are of 3 games among three players and how many are favorable to the first, second, and third player, respectively, and in accordance with this proportion distribute the money just as before on the hypothesis of two players.

As for seeing how many combinations there are in all, that is easy: it is the third power of 3, that is, its cube, 27. For if we throw three dice together (since three games must be played) each of which has three faces (since there are three players), one marked with an *a*, favorable to the first player, another with a *b* for the second player, and the other with a *c* for the third player, it is obvious that these three dice thrown together can fall in 27 different ways, namely:

But the first player lacks only one game; therefore all the casts with an *a* are for him; therefore he has 19.

The second player lacks two games; therefore all the casts with two *b*'s are for him; therefore he has 7.

The third player lacks two games; therefore all the casts with two *c*'s are for him; therefore he has 7.

If we then concluded that the shares of the players should be proportional to 19, 7, 7, our error would be too gross, and I am far from thinking you capable of it. For some casts are favorable to the first and to the second at the same time, such as *abb*, for the first player finds the *a* he needs there and the second player the two *b*'s he needs; similarly *acc* is for both the first and the third.

Therefore we must not count those casts favorable to two players as worth the whole sum to each, but only half the sum. For if *acc* were thrown, the first and the third would have equal rights to the sum, each having the required number of games; therefore they would share the money equally. But if *aab* is thrown, the first alone wins. The reckoning should therefore be made as follows:

a	a	a	1		
a	a	b	1		
a	a	c	1		
a	b	a	1		
a	b	b	1	2	
a	b	c	1		
a	c	a	1		
a	c	b	1		
a	c	c	1		3
b	a	a	1		
b	a	b	1	2	
b	a	c	1		
b	b	a	1	2	
b	b	b		2	
b	b	c		2	
b	c	a	1		
b	c	b		2	
b	c	c			3
c	a	a	1		
c	a	b	1		
c	a	c	1		3
c	b	a	1		
c	b	b		2	
c	b	c			3
c	c	a	1		3
c	c	b			3
c	c	c			3

There are 13 throws which give the entire sum to the first player, 6 which give him half and 8 which give him nothing. Therefore if the whole sum is a pistole, there are 13 casts which are each worth a pistole to him, 6 which are each worth half a pistole, and 8 worth nothing.

Therefore in case of division we must multiply

13 by one pistole, which makes. 13
6 by half a pistole, which makes. 3
8 by 0, which makes. 0

Sum 27   Sum 16

and divide the sum of the values, 16, by the sum of the casts, 27, which gives the fraction $\frac{16}{27}$, which is what belongs to the first player in case of division, namely 16 pistoles out of 27.

The divisions of the second and third players will be found in the same way:

There are 4 casts worth 1 pistole:

multiply 4

There are 3 casts worth ½ pistole:

multiply 1½

And 20 casts worth nothing 0

Sum 27   Sum 5½

Therefore 5½ pistoles out of 27 belong to the second player, and as many to the third player, and these three sums, 5½, 5½, and 16, added together, make the 27.

This, it seems to me, is the way divisions should be determined by combinations in accordance with your method unless you have a different method here which I must not know. But unless I am mistaken, this is not the right division.

The reason is that a false supposition is made, namely, that three games are necessarily played, whereas the natural condition of that play is that no more games are played as soon as one of the players has reached the required number.

Not that it can't happen that 3 games are played; but it can also happen that only one or two are played. There is nothing necessary about it.

But how is it, someone will ask, that it is not permissible in this case to make the same fictitious supposition as in the case of two players? The reason is:

In the actual condition of these three players there is only one who can win, for the condition is that as soon as one wins, the play stops. But in the fictitious condition two players can both reach the required number of games: namely, if the first player wins the one he lacks and one of the others the two he lacks; for they will have played only three games. Whereas when there were only two players, the fictitious and the actual conditions were the same in all respects so far as the odds of the players were concerned; and that is what makes so great a difference between the two conditions.

But if the players in the situation supposed (that is, one player lacking one game and the other two players each lacking two games) now freely agree to the condition that they will play all three games and that if anyone is alone in winning the required number of games, he will take the entire sum, and that if two win the required number, they will share the stakes equally, in this case the division should be as I just said: the first should have 16, the second 5½, the third 5½, out of the 27 pistoles, and that requires no demonstration if we suppose the condition to be as stated.

But if they play simply on condition not that three games will necessarily be played but that only as many will be played as are needed to give one of them the required number and that then the play stop without giving one of the others a chance to get the required number too, then 17 pistoles of the 27 belong to the first player and 5 to the second and to the third, each.

This is shown by my general method, which also determines that in the preceding situation the first player should have 16, the second and the third 5½ each, without the use of combinations, for this method is universal and always possible.

There you have, Sir, my thoughts on this subject, in which the only advantage I have over you is that I have reflected much more about it. But that is a small matter where you are concerned, since your first insights go deeper than my long efforts.

The reason I expound my views to you is to get a judgment from you on them. I think I must have convinced you that the method of combinations is good for two players accidentally, as it is also sometimes for three players, as when two each lack one game and the other player lacks two, because in this case the number of games in which the set must be completed does not permit its being won by two players. But the method is not general and is generally good only for the case in which the players are committed to a fixed number of games regardless of the score.

So that, since you did not know my method when you set me the problem of dividing the stakes among several players, but only the method of combinations, I am afraid we may have different opinions on this matter.

I beg you to let me know how you go about finding this division. I shall receive your answer with respect and joy, even if your opinion is at variance with mine. I am, etc.

PASCAL

LETTER FROM FERMAT TO PASCAL

Toulouse, *August 29, 1654*

SIR,

Our double thrusts still keep up, and like you I am struck with admiration that our ideas fit so perfectly it seems as if they have taken the same road and covered the same distance. Your recent treatises on the arithmetical triangle and its application are a real proof of it, and if my calculation is right, your twelfth consequence was being carried with the mail from Paris to Toulouse while my proposition on figural numbers, which is actually the same, was on its way from Toulouse to Paris.

I am not afraid of going astray as long as I fall in with you in this way, and I am convinced that the true method of avoiding error is to find oneself in agreement with you. But if I said more, it would smack of compliment, and we have banished that enemy of easy and agreeable conversations.

It is my turn now to tell you some of my discoveries in arithmetic, but I am so busy with the end of Parliament that I venture to hope you will be kind enough to grant me a deserved and as it were necessary respite.

Nevertheless I shall answer your question about the three players who are playing for two games. When the first player has a game and the others do not, your first solution is right, and the shares of the stakes should be to each other as 17, 5, and 5; the reason for which is obvious and comes as always from the same principle, it being clear at once by combinations that 17 of the 27 equal chances are for the first player and only 5 for each of the other two.

As for the rest, there is nothing that I shall not communicate to you in the future in all sincerity. Consider meanwhile, if you find it convenient, the following proposition:

The squares of the powers of 2, increased by unity, are always primes.

The square of 2, increased by unity, is 5, which is a prime.

The square of the square, 16, increased by unity, is 17, a prime.

The square of 16 is 256 which, increased by unity, is 257, a prime.

The square of 256 is 65,536 which, increased by unity, is 65,537, a prime. And so on to infinity.

I will answer to you for the truth of this property, but it is not easy to prove, and I confess that I have not yet been able to find a complete demonstration. I wouldn't ask you to work at it if I had been successful.

With this proposition we can find numbers which are in a given ratio to their aliquot parts, in connection with which I have made some important discoveries. We shall speak of them another time.

I am, etc.

FERMAT

LETTER FROM FERMAT TO PASCAL

[*September* 25, 1654]

SIR,

Do not be afraid that our concordance is at an end. You have yourself confirmed it while thinking to destroy it, and it seems to me that in answering M. de Roberval for yourself you have also answered for me.

I take the example of the three players, of whom the first lacks one game and each of the other two lacks two games, which is the case you urge against me. I find only 17 combinations there for the first player and 5 for each of the others; for when you say that the combination *acc* is favorable to the first player and to the third player, it seems that you are no longer remembering that everything which happens after one of the players has won is of no use. Since this combination has given the set to the first player with the first game, what difference does it make that the third player wins two games afterwards when, if he won thirty, they would all be superfluous?

Which is due to the fact that, as you very well observed, this fiction of extending the play to a certain number of games serves only to facilitate the rule and (in my opinion) to make all the chances equal or, more intelligibly, to reduce all the fractions to a common denominator.

And to remove all possible doubt, if in the case before us you extend the fiction to four games instead of three, there will be not merely 27 combinations but 81, and we must see how many combinations will give the first player one game before either one of the other two players has two games and how many will give each of the others two games before the first player has one. You will find that the combinations favorable to the first player will be 51 and those favorable to each of the other two 15, which comes to the same ratio.

And if you take five games or any other number you please, you always find 3 numbers proportional to 17, 5, 5.

And so I have a right to say that the combination *acc* is only for the first player and not for the third, and that *cca* is only for the third player and not for the first, and that consequently my rule of combinations is the same for three players as for two, and generally for every number.

You could already see by my preceding letter that I did not hesitate over the true solution of the question of three players, for which I sent you the three decisive numbers, 17, 5, 5. But since M. de Roberval will perhaps be very glad to see a solution that makes no use of fiction, and since it can sometimes shorten the labor in many cases, here it is in the example before us:

The first player can win either in a single game or in two or in three.

If he wins in a single game, he must bring up on the first throw the favorable face of a die having three faces. A single die gives 3 chances. This player then has $\frac{1}{3}$ of the chances if only one game is played.

If two games are played, he can win in two ways, either when the second player wins the first game and he wins the second, or when the third player wins the first game and he the second. But two dice give 9 chances. This player then has $\frac{2}{9}$ of the chances when two games are played.

If three games are played he can win in only two ways, either when the second player wins the first game, the third player the second game, and he the third, or when the third player wins the first game, the second the second, and he the third; for if either the second player or the third player won the first two games, he and not the first player would win the set. But three dice give 27 chances. Therefore the first player has $\frac{2}{27}$ of the chances when three games are played.

The sum of the chances which give the set to the first player is consequently $\frac{1}{3}+\frac{2}{9}+\frac{2}{27}$, which makes $\frac{17}{27}$ in all.

The rule works and is general for all cases, so that without recourse to fiction the actual combinations in each number of games give a solution and make clear what I said at the start, that extension to a given number of games is nothing but the reduction of different fractions to a common denominator. There you have in a few words the whole mystery, which will undoubtedly restore our good understanding, since neither of us is looking for anything but reason and truth.

I hope to send you at Martinmas a summary of everything considerable I have discovered about numbers. You will excuse me for being concise and speaking to be understood only by a man who gets everything at a word.

The most important thing you will find there concerns the proposition that every number is composed of one, two, or three triangles, of one, two, three, or four squares, of one, two, three, four, or five pentagons, of one, two, three, four, five, or six hexagons, and so on to infinity.

Before it can be demonstrated, we must first demonstrate that every prime number which exceeds by unity a multiple of four is composed of two squares, such as 5, 13, 17, 29, 37, etc.

Given a prime number of this kind, such as 53, to find by a general rule the two squares composing it.

Every prime number which exceeds by unity a multiple of 3 is composed of a square and the triple of another square, such as 7, 13, 19, 31, 37, etc.

Every prime number which exceeds by 1 or by 3 a multiple of 8 is composed of a square and the double of another square, such as 11, 17, 19, 41, 43, etc.

There is no triangular number whose area is equal to a square number.

This will be followed by the discovery of many propositions which Bachet confesses not to have known and which are not found in Diophantus.

I am convinced that as soon as you are familiar with my method of demonstrating this kind of proposition, you will be delighted with it and will find it the means of making many new discoveries, for it is necessary, as you know, *multi pertranseant ut augeatur scientia*.[1]

If I have time, we shall then talk about magic numbers and I shall recall my old cases on this subject.

I am with all my heart, Sir, your, etc.

FERMAT

[1]Many should go over the ground that science be increased.